Orchid Biology—Reviews and Perspectives, III

Other Books and Reviews by Joseph Arditti

Orchid Biology, Reviews and Perspectives, I (editor)

Orchid Biology, Reviews and Perspectives, II (editor)

Aspects of the Physiology of Orchids (*Advances in Botanical Research* 7, contributor)

Factors Affecting the Germination of Orchid Seeds (*Botanical Review* 33[1])

Experimental Plant Physiology (with A. S. Dunn)

Experimental Physiology: Experiments in Cellular, General, and Plant Physiology (with A. S. Dunn, first author)

Experimental Animal Physiology (with A. S. Dunn, first author)

Orchid Biology

REVIEWS AND PERSPECTIVES, III

EDITED BY

JOSEPH ARDITTI

Department of Developmental and Cell Biology
University of California, Irvine

COMSTOCK PUBLISHING ASSOCIATES a division of
CORNELL UNIVERSITY PRESS | Ithaca and London

Copyright © 1984 by Cornell University Press

First published 1984 by Cornell University Press.
Published in the United Kingdom by Cornell University Press, Ltd., London.

Library of Congress Cataloging in Publication Data
(Revised for volume 3)

Main entry under title:

Orchid biology.

Includes bibliographies and indexes.
1. Orchids—Collected works.   I. Arditti, Joseph.
QK495.064'053   584'.15   76-25648
ISBN 0-8014-1040-1 (v. 1)

Printed in the United States of America

*The paper in this book is acid-free and meets the guidelines for
permanence and durability of the Committee on Production Guidelines
for Book Longevity of the Council on Library Resources.*

Dedicated to Mak Chin On of Singapore by the editor

CONTENTS

ILLUSTRATIONS

BOARD OF EDITORS

AUTHORS

JOSEPH ARDITTI is a Professor in the Department of Developmental and Cell Biology, University of California, Irvine. He joined the department in 1966, one year after receiving his Ph.D. from the University of Southern California. He became interested in orchids as an undergraduate while working part-time as a grower for the late Roy J. Scott, who, at the time, was a well-known orchid amateur in California. Dr. Arditti's research centers on orchid development, physiology, and phytochemistry.

PHILLIP J. CRIBB was educated at Cambridge University, where he received an M.A. in 1971, and the University of Birmingham, where he was awarded his Ph.D. in 1972. Since then he has specialized in orchid taxonomy at the Royal Botanic Gardens, Kew, where he is employed as a senior botanist. His main research centers on the orchids of tropical Africa, and he has also studied particular genera from Southeast Asia and New Guinea. He has traveled widely in the tropics in connection with his work and is the joint author of *The Manual of Cultivated Orchid Species, Orchids from Curtis's Botanical Magazine,* and *Mountain Flowers of Southern Tanzania.* He is also a regular contributor to several orchid journals, notably the *Orchid Review* (England), *Die Orchidee* (Germany), and the *Orchadian* (Australia).

ROBERT ERNST was trained as a chemical engineer and first became interested in orchids as a hobby. Subsequently he combined his interest in orchids and scientific training and became Adjunct Assistant Professor in the Department of Developmental and Cell Biology at the University of California, Irvine, where he earned his Ph.D. in 1979. His research interests are centered on the biological effects of surfactants and the physiology and germination of orchids.

ROBERT M. HAMILTON, formerly Associate Professor at the University of British Columbia School of Librarianship, later the Assistant Librarian for Collections at the University of British Columbia, has compiled several reference books on Canada and recently has produced a number of indexes to orchid illustrations and guides to the care of orchids. He is now retired.

BJÖRN M. HAUSEN is an Assistant Professor in the Department of Dermatology, University Hospital, Hamburg, where he heads the Laboratory of Experimental Allergology. After studying biology at the University of Hamburg he specialized in biologically active low-molecular compounds and received his Ph.D. in 1970 from the Institute of Wood Chemistry, University of Hamburg. Following three years of research on toxic trace metals and compounds in drinking water at the Federal Environmental Bureau in Düsseldorf, he returned to Hamburg. He joined the faculty of medicine at the University Hospital, Hamburg, in 1980. Dr. Hausen is the author of the book *Woods Injurious to Human Health,* which was published in 1981.

HARUYUKI KAMEMOTO, Professor of Horticulture at the University of Hawaii at Manoa in Honolulu, received his B.S. and M.S. from the University of Hawaii and his Ph.D. from Cornell University. His dissertation dealt with chromosomes of the *Cattleya* alliance. Since 1950 he has been actively engaged in research at the University of Hawaii on cytogenetics and the breeding of orchids. He has written numerous articles on orchids and has coauthored with Rapee Sagarik of Thailand the book *Beautiful Thai Orchid Species*. Dr. Kamemoto has been awarded numerous international, national, and local honors for his scientific work.

LEONARD J. LAWLER is a professional officer in the Department of Biochemistry at the University of Sydney. His early background is in hospital biochemistry, and he gained his fellowship in the Australian Institute of Medical Scientists with a thesis on the biochemistry of Australian orchids. He is currently interested in folk medicine and traditional food of the aboriginal Australians.

REBECCA TYSON NORTHEN attended Radcliffe College and received an A.B. from Wayne State University and an M. A. from Mount Holyoke College. She has traveled extensively throughout the world to collect and lecture about orchids and is the author of several books and many articles. In 1979 she was awarded the American Orchid Society's Gold Medal of Achievement.

ELOY RODRIGUEZ received his Ph.D. from the University of Texas at Austin and joined the Department of Developmental and Cell Biology at the University of California, Irvine, after one year as a postdoctoral fellow at the University of British Columbia. His research centers on chemicals that are produced by plants.

CHRISTOPHER J. SETH studied agriculture at Reading University and subsequently took a postgraduate diploma in education. He taught for four years in a grammar/technical school in the United Kingdom before taking a post in teacher training, lecturing in rural science. His interest in controlled environments, conservation, and orchids developed during this period, and he was able to build a collection of *Cymbidium* species—now at the Royal Botanic Gardens, Kew—on which he concentrated his research. He is head of the Science Department at a college of further education and is involved in developing courses for unemployed young people.

ALBERT STOESSL obtained his B.Sc. at Birkbeck College (University of London) in 1955 and a Ph.D. in chemistry from Imperial College in 1960. Since 1961 Dr. Stoessl has been a research scientist with Agriculture Canada at the Research Centre in London, Ontario. His primary research interests have been chemical aspects of plant-pathogen interactions, particularly the chemistry and biosynthesis of phytoalexins and phytotoxins.

RYUSO TANAKA is a Professor at the Botanical Institute, Faculty of Science, Hiroshima University, Japan, where he does research on orchids and other plants. He received his D.Sc. from Hiroshima University. From 1958 to 1959 he worked on the cytogenetics of orchids with Professor Kamemoto at the University of Hawaii.

PREFACE

Publication of a third volume of *Orchid Biology* is an indication that the series continues to meet my original goal—to present a balanced selection of scientific review articles about orchids. To achieve that goal, I invite eminent orchidologists throughout the world to contribute articles. For the prefatory chapters, I invite people who have made major contributions to the field and who usually are past the age of retirement to write on a topic of their choice. By publishing their articles, I hope to provide personal glimpses of some outstanding orchidologists.

Except for the prefatory chapters, all articles are submitted to two members of the *Orchid Biology* Board of Editors for prepublication review. Final acceptance depends on their recommendations. In addition, I read, comment on, and edit the contributions to achieve uniformity of style.

Rebecca Tyson Northen, the author of the prefatory chapter in this volume, made her mark writing articles in many orchid publications and a series of books for both experts and beginners which are erudite, accurate, and a pleasure to read.

The uses of orchids are as varied as their sizes, shapes, fragrances, and distribution. Some of the uses are astounding (for example, in magic); others are prosaic. Information on ethnobotany of orchids is usually not easy to trace or obtain since it is published in a multitude of journals (some very obscure or not the kind one might expect to include such reports). Len Lawler spent many years collecting information for his article, traveled widely in doing it, and consulted all original sources. The result is a chapter that is informative, interesting, and, above all, summarizes previous reports accurately even if they appear fanciful.

Phytoalexins, which are now known to be present in many plants, are a group of substances that may or may not be chemically related. They were first discovered by Noel Bernard in his work with orchids, shortly before his death in 1911. His paper was published posthumously, and research on the subject was renewed about 30 years later. The term phytoalexin was coined around 1940 as a result of work with other plants. Phytoalexins are known to function as defensive substances that inhibit bacteria and fungi. In orchids they may regulate the mycorrhizal fungi. My coauthor for this chapter, Albert Stoessl, is an expert on phytoalexins.

The physiology of orchid seed germination is both unique and fascinating. Much has been learned about it, and more remains to be elucidated. The review in this volume summarizes the available knowledge in the hope of encouraging further research. Robert Ernst is an authority on orchid physiology and biochemistry.

Carbohydrates play numerous and varied roles in the life cycle of orchids. The chapter by Robert Ernst and Eloy Rodriguez discusses orchid carbohydrates in depth and detail.

It may come as a surprise to many that some orchids can be poisonous or allergenic, or both. D. T. McDougal, an American botanist, was an early investigator in this area. Björn Hausen, the current leading authority on the subject, has written an informative chapter.

Cymbidium is an important genus for both hobby and cut-flower growers in the United States and abroad. Unfortunately, its taxonomy is not clear. The article by Christopher Seth and Phillip Cribb, both from Kew Gardens (the cradle of orchidology), is therefore most welcome.

Chromosome numbers of orchids are of considerable importance to breeders, students of evolution, cytologists, taxonomists, and growers because they may explain relationships and determine compatibility. The very best cytogeneticist to study orchid chromosomes is Haruyuki Kamemoto, who has trained a number of excellent students and postdoctoral scholars, including Ryuso Tanaka, his coauthor in this volume. Their joint contribution is instructive, informative, and authoritative.

For simplicity or because of their use in the original literature it is sometimes necessary to employ trade names of chemicals, equipment, apparatus, products, and so forth. Such use does not imply endorsement of the named products, and no such endorsement is intended. Nor is any criticism or lack of endorsement implied or intended for similar items that are not mentioned.

I thank the authors, Board of Editors, and staff of Cornell University Press for their help. In many years of dealing with publishers I have never had the pleasure of working with a more dedicated or competent group of editors. I did some of the preparation for this volume while on sabbatical leave (1981) and on a visit (1982) to the Botany Department of the National University of Singapore. I thank its chairman, Professor A. N. Rao, and my colleagues there, P. N. Avadhani and C. J. Goh, for their hospitality. I also thank Leslie Paul Nyman, my postdoctoral fellow, for his assistance when an emergency forced me to be absent for nearly two months.

JOSEPH ARDITTI

Irvine, California

1

Orchids: Their Innocent Past, Their Promising yet Perilous Future

REBECCA TYSON NORTHEN

Plate 1-1. Rebecca Tyson Northen

It is a delightful honor to have been invited to contribute a little personal history and a few thoughts to this volume. In some ways my story is typical of the growth of an amateur of the 1940s when there were few of us and not much cultural help available. When the first edition of my *Home Orchid Growing* was published in 1950, I heard reverberations to the tune of "What can that woman possibly know about growing orchids, way out there in Wyoming?" And "How can anyone raise orchids in that high, cold country?" Most of the comments came from the East, which itself has anything but an ideal climate, but some came from sun-blessed California. The tune soon changed as people came to realize that orchids can be grown in a greenhouse almost anywhere and that Wyoming, with its bright sun and cool summers, had some good points other areas lacked. In those early days of inexpensive gas heat, Wyoming's lack of humidity was my only growing problem. Today, with the high cost of fuel, the cold climate is a definite disadvantage. For this reason and for my husband's health, we retreated to California. I decided to stay after he passed away. Most of the year here is like a Wyoming summer.

I was born in Detroit and lived in a neighborhood not yet filled with houses. I spent hours exploring the vacant lots, picking violets and other wild flowers, and climbing trees with much more ease than when I finally had a chance to climb those with orchids on them. I graduated from the Liggett School during the Depression and started college at Radcliffe with scholarship aid. When scholarship money ran out, I returned to Detroit to get an A.B. in zoology at Wayne State University. From there I went to Mount Holyoke College with a graduate assistantship in zoology. After receiving an M.A. in 1937, I accepted a job teaching sciences at a private eastern high school. Since the job involved teaching botany, which I was weak in, I looked for a summer school that would fill me in. The brochure from the University of Wyoming Summer Science Camp, with its pictures of snow-capped mountains, glacial lakes, and rustic cabins for students, captivated me. I didn't even know where Wyoming was and had to look at the map several times to memorize its location.

The instructor of the course I enrolled in was Dr. Henry (Hank) T. Northen, an attractive young plant physiologist from the University of California at Berkeley, who had joined the University of Wyoming Botany Department the year before. That was the end of my teaching job. We were married and made our home in Laramie for the next forty years, during which time we acquired a daughter and two sons, while he rose to become professor, then chairman of the department, and finally professor emeritus. I continued to learn botany from him, working in his laboratory when I could, coauthoring a few papers, learning in a thousand ways. At times it was very handy, when I made a botanical mistake, to be able to say: "Well, after all, I'm a zoologist, you know."

Hank gave me Liberty Hyde Bailey's *Standard Cyclopedia of Horticulture,* which had descriptions of orchids on every few pages. It sealed my fate. I began buying seedlings with a complete lack of sanity, first community pots, which I kept on the kitchen window sill, then a flask of cattleya seedlings, which had far more—at least a thousand—than I expected. Incubators were created from tubs and tanks, with water in the bottom and platforms of hardware cloth to hold the pots. They were placed in strategic spots all over the house. Even at that, there were at least two hundred tiny seedlings left over, most of them no more than protocorms. These I put in a glass pie plate in sterilized sand moistened with nutrient solution and covered with a pane of glass propped up on matchsticks. I knew nothing about replating, but pie-plating worked pretty well—half of those seedlings survived to maturity, and some of the best plants came from them. I have held ever since that the smaller seedlings should not be thrown away; I had proof that they could give good things. Waiting for flowers became an impossibility, so we bought mature plants to tide us over. Our home was so swamped that a greenhouse became a necessity. We bought a 12-×-18-foot Orlyt and attached it to the garage. There followed a wild spree of buying flasks and more flasks, cymbidiums and cattleyas. We built storied benches of glass over glass, and the seedlings thrived. Within a year we needed a second greenhouse and got a larger Orlyt. The overflow didn't immediately fill it, so Hank practiced some of the greenhouse culture he had learned during his college years and raised all sorts of other kinds, from strelitzias to bedding plants.

The only modern book on culture I had was E. A. White's *American Orchid Culture* (1942), which was some help. Through interlibrary loan I obtained B. S. and H. Williams's *Orchid Grower's Manual* (1894) and W. Watson's *Orchids: Their Culture and Management* (1890), now available in reprints. In spite of the good old English advice, there was much to be learned by trial and error. During those first four years we did not meet another orchid grower. At the end of two years we met a taxonomist, Louis O. Williams, a University of Wyoming graduate who had returned for a visit and kindly came to see what we were doing. Although he said everything looked pretty good, he also said he could not make any suggestions because he was not a grower. Eventually we met a few amateurs and an occasional greenhouseman. With six others, we organized the Colorado-Wyoming Orchid Society. It had a short life; as soon as the word spread that there were orchid growers around, it was replaced by the Denver Orchid Society.

We tried our hands at a little orchid research—conditions that hindered or accelerated growth of seedlings in flasks, low-temperature tolerances of seed, studies of root habits. After a few years I found that cool nights—for cattleyas 55°F and for cymbidiums 45°F—made cattleya and cymbidium flowers heavier and more long-lasting.

As the seedlings matured, we sold hundreds. The greenhouses became a riot of flowers—we could hardly walk down the aisles—so we entered the Denver wholesale cut-flower market, beating the West Coast growers there by a few years. This brief venture into marketing was exciting, and like all other experiences, instructive. It was just as well that prices dropped at the end of World War II because by that time I had discovered other kinds of orchids and had found my true love, the species. Besides, I couldn't have competed with the West Coast growers, who by that time had discovered Denver.

I also discovered Margaret Ilgenfritz of Michigan, who was pioneering in species as a commercial enterprise, and Harry Dunn, of Panama, who loved the wild plants and collected and exported them. From the lists of each I acquired species in wonderful variety. Harry Dunn used to tuck into each shipment plants not on his list, sometimes a few unknowns. It was a thrill to open a box of plants fresh from the forests and intoxicating to have them grow and flower. I felt a deep bond with them, all so different, each an individual that had started down the evolutionary path perhaps as our own ancestors were developing.

Those were years of innocence in orchid growing. We used osmunda fiber for potting. Such long hours it required, but what wonderful growth it gave. My husband helped with the potting, for he could stay in one spot while I often had to leave to attend to family needs, even do a little cooking. When easier-to-use bark came along, I took over the potting and he went fishing more often. We didn't know what caused sepal wilt, we knew nothing about viruses, and we battled scale with a toothbrush dipped in whatever insecticide we happened to have. We welcomed DDT as a panacea until insects became resistant to it. We adopted Parathion until we learned that it was lethal to human beings, as well as pests. The pesticide story is a long one. Growers still keep trying to find the least toxic but at the same time effective new ones. Chemicals to combat disease are also a long story. I have never used praying mantis or ladybugs, but I do have two frogs, uninvited but beautiful guests.

I had already written a few articles about orchid growing when a friend wrote a piece for the *Denver Post* about my kitchen windowsill beginnings. It brought letters from all over the country, some addressed to "The Orchid Lady, Laramie, Wyoming." The post office put notice after notice in our mailbox asking me to inform my correspondents of my correct address. I couldn't answer them all individually, so I wrote several pages of instructions, had copies made, and sent them to one and all. One recipient wrote that what I'd said was more helpful than anything he'd been able to find, and why didn't I write a book? After a bit, I decided to try, for surely what we had learned was just what beginners needed. Hank encouraged me, and his criticisms and suggestions were a great help. The result was the first edition of *Home Orchid Growing*, published in 1950, subsequently revised in 1962 and 1970, and in the process of revision again. Gordon Dillon asked me to initiate a beginner's series for the *American Orchid Society Bulletin* (I later did two more), and I initiated the Question Box and carried it on for some time.

My husband wrote a college botany text, *Plant Science,* published in 1953, which was considered one of the best and most understandable texts in print. Its third edition, published in 1968, is still in demand. Although writing is a form of sweet torture, seeing our books in print was so stimulating that we went on. In 1954 we coauthored *The Secret of the Green Thumb* and in 1955 *Greenhouse Gardening,* the latter revised in 1973. To interest people in growing orchids indoors, I wrote *Orchids as House Plants,* published in 1955, updated in 1976. The last book we coauthored and the one we enjoyed most was *Ingenious Kingdom: The Remarkable World of Plants* (1970), at the request of Joseph Wood Krutch. My own most recent book is *Miniature Orchids,* 1980.

Soon after *Home Orchid Growing* was published I began to speak at meetings, where I met not only fellow amateurs but also some of the outstanding growers and hybridizers of the time. It was an unexpected honor to be asked to chair the amateur section at the First World Orchid Conference in St. Louis in 1954, Gordon Dillon's brainchild. His dream took hold and there has been one every three years. I have participated in many of them. Wherever I go, I am happy to see an increasing interest in species among amateurs and commercial growers alike. Some of both are specializing in them. Through the years I have been credited with the role of defender of the amateur and helper of the beginner. I am also always learning from the amateurs themselves, those wonderful people who let nothing daunt them, who try everything, even the impossible, and who have discovered new methods and created new hybrid lines.

If life was exciting up to that point, it became more so with the opportunity to collect orchids. In 1963 Hank obtained a grant to take a course in tropical biology in Costa Rica, and I went along for part of the time. I'd read about species-rich Costa Rica but was completely unprepared for the experiences ahead. There we met Charles Lankester, one of the legendary orchidists of the time, who, with his daughter Dorothy welcomed us and more or less adopted me while my husband was busy with his class. The beautiful Lankester Garden was my introduction to orchids in a natural environment. Later, it was my privilege to help implement its purchase by the American Orchid Society and the Stanley Smith Horticultural Trust and its presentation to the University of Costa Rica.

Clarence Horich, who probably knows more about Costa Rican orchids in the wild than anyone else, took me to beautiful spots to collect. The country was a dream world of ridges and valleys clothed with forests; of waterfalls tumbling down cliffs green with plants; of clean, soft, damp air; of sun suddenly obscured by downpours and breaking through to produce rising mists and glistening foliage. I was dazzled by trees covered with damp mosses, lichens, ferns, aroids, vines, and orchids, from eye level to tops that disappeared into the sky. The array of species changed as one progressed from high elevations toward sea level and from very wet to less wet areas. I wondered how so many kinds from so many areas could possibly grow together in a greenhouse; the miracle was that they did. I brought back species in forty genera. I could identify very few myself. The rest went to Charles Schweinfurth at the Orchid Herbarium of Oakes Ames at Harvard. He kindly continued to identify species for me, from Costa Rica and elsewhere, until he retired. Dr. Leslie Garay and other taxonomists, for example, those at the various botanical gardens here and abroad, are usually willing to help amateurs on a personal basis. The American Orchid Society helps support the Orchid Identification Center at the Marie Selby Botanical Gardens in Florida, which charges a fee.

The Costa Rican adventure was an irresistible appetizer; we had to go farther. We visited Peru, where David Bennett and his wife, Aurora, took us collecting up and over the Andes and down to about 6,000 feet elevation on the Amazon side, then beautiful Ecuador, less forbidding than Peru, with José Strobel and Luis Figueroa, and then Colombia and Mexico. There we met Stirling Dickinson and, on other trips, Glenn Pollard, Federico Halbinger, and Eric Hagsater. Later on I visited Adolph Heller in Nicaragua and did a bit of collecting with him. He showed me his orchid notebooks containing the more than 600 species he had collected. This material is now at the Selby Gardens, where Fritz Hamer is working on it.

Other delightful trips took me to Jamacia, with hosts Dr. and Mrs. Aubrey Jacobs, Ancil Gloudon, and Noel Gauntlett, and to South Africa, where my guides were Michael O'Conner and Frieda Duckitt and my hosts were Carmen and Ivan Coll. My last trip before leaving Wyoming was camping in Mexico with William and Micky Thurston of Colorado, who have done so much to build the orchid collection of the Denver Botanical Gardens and to help finance its magnificent orchid greenhouses and display theater.

I cannot be grateful enough to have seen the tropics in all their glory, for the glory is vanishing. Many of the forests I saw are now gone. I have seen the most pathetic landscapes littered with felled trees or scored by gullies. Experts estimate that only about 20% of the tropical forests of the world remain and the percentage is diminishing every year. It is most distressing, and there seems to be no remedy. Forests have disappeared in our country, where some entire states now have only a few acres of native vegetation left. How can such a fate be forestalled in the tropics where there is not enough work for people, where slash-and-burn farming is often the only means of support, and where timber is needed for housing and other purposes? The Brazilian government's effort to turn forests into farmland resulted in many problems and failures. Tropical land that has been deforested does not retain its fertility for long. Trees that are cut down are either stripped and sent to the mill or are burned, and orchids are destroyed in the process. No one will ever know what species are thus lost, including some still unknown to man. The authors of the Convention on International Trade in Endangered Species, subscribed to by sixty-nine nations, did not fully understand the situation. They believed that it was collectors and exporters who were devastating the orchids, whereas it was actually forest destruction that was to blame. No amount of human collecting can possibly equal the estimated two hundred billion orchid plants a year lost to agricultural clearing alone. And no one can estimate the aesthetic and possible medicinal value of those disappearing before we have a chance to get to know them.

None of the measures we might take can solve the problem completely, but we must do what we can. Most urgent is the need to save orchid habitats by setting aside natural areas as national forests and preserves. Even this will save only those species living within their confines, leaving unprotected those in surrounding areas. Costa Rica is to be commended for establishing over twenty national parks representing different types of habitat. I would like to see the Convention include some sort of rescue policy, so that orchid plants could be collected where forests are being leveled.

Seed banks are being developed and should be expanded. Unfortunately, not all species in cultivation can be made to set seed, and those being grown represent only a fraction of those in existence. People tend to preserve those species they think are "valuable," whereas some less beautiful ones might be of greater scientific interest. Goodale Moir is quick to point out that growing species in cultivation does not allow natural evolution to take place,* but neither can it take place where the species no longer exist. We are too rapidly destroying nature's gene pools, robbing future generations of what might come about through further evolution.

We live in an exciting time for science and orchids. If it were possible to divide orchidology into historical and chronological phases, the first would be the exploration and discovery of species, including their classification and naming by the early taxonomists and their illustration by means of drawings and paintings and beautiful lithographic plates in the gardeners' magazines and elegant folios of the late 1800s and early 1900s. Imagine the thrill those people experienced when one after another was seen in flower for the first time. Each one was thought worthy of having its portrait painted. A second phase was the discovery of hybridization and its potential for creating new and unusual, often superior forms. Hybridization continues with that purpose today, but perhaps a more important function has been to elucidate the relationships among genera and species. A third phase is the observation of orchids in nature, includ-

---

*But the seeds produced by such plants will preserve genes. [Ed.]

ing their adaptations to different environments, their relationships with their pollinators, and their methods of maintaining integrity. These pursuits have led to the fourth phase, the study of cytology, morphology, chemistry, and physiology.

The old attitude that orchids were just something to look at has changed. Scientists have discovered that the plants and flowers are much more important research material than they once cared to admit. The discovery of polyploidy apparently awakened the orchid public to the role science could play. Hybridization then took a new turn. Cytological studies explained why some strains of species were superior parents and why some would cross readily and some would not. Various tricks and treatments have since been devised to avoid the barriers of incompatibility and infertility. Morphological studies are elucidating the microscopic details of structure, the accumulation of which in many cases can distinguish one species from another and supply data about evolution.

The physiological workings of orchid plants involve such a myriad of processes that there is no end to the discoveries that will be made. Fragrances, pigments, alkaloids, amino acids, lipids, hormones, enzymes—a whole line of compounds—are being found to differ from one species to another. Some compounds can be related to species of other plant families. Discovering what happens from seed to germination to maturity, even to death, requires all the scientific tools, mechanical and chemical, available. What is found in one experiment leads inevitably to another discovery. You can't get to the end results without going through the intervening steps. We should back the scientists even though we, the amateurs, cannot always see exactly where they are going, for they are the only ones who can do this detective work. Laymen often want something useful right away, forgetting that discoveries more important than those they envision may result if they are only patient.

We are about to come full circle. When it was first learned that orchids could be crossed with each other, it was feared that hybridizers would "drive the botanists mad." What is around the corner *will* drive the botanists mad—that is, the possibility of fusing the nuclear contents of a cell of one species with that of a cell of a totally unrelated one, thereby producing a plant that simply cannot be grown by ordinary pollination. In 1969 Gordon Dillon, in the *American Orchid Society Bulletin*, vol. 38, explained the derivation of hybrid names and invented some totally impossible crosses to illustrate: *Selenipanthes* (*Selenipedium* × *Lepanthes*), *Restesia* (*Restrepia* × *Orleanesia*), *Pattoniheadia* (*Pattonia* × *Bromheadia*), and *Pterocottia* (*Pterostylis* × *Prescottia*). Perhaps seriously, or more probably with tongue in cheek, Garay and Herman Sweet reported these names in Supplement 1 of the *Natural and Artificial Hybrid Generic Names* (Harvard Botanical Museum Leaflets, vol. 22, December 1969). Will we live to see them become a reality? If we do, their new names are already published.

Whatever is done with orchids, or to them, I hope we will have the sense to treasure the species for what they are, evidence of an evolutionary history which, if recklessly destroyed or allowed to disappear will never occur again.

2

Ethnobotany of the Orchidaceae*

LEONARD J. LAWLER

*The literature survey pertaining to this chapter was concluded in August 1981; the chapter was submitted in October 1982, and the revised version was received in February 1982.

I first became interested in the ethnobotany of orchids while I was engaged in a project that concerned the use of orchids in aboriginal Australian medicine. At that time I assembled a modest bibliography of uses of orchids in Australia and nearby areas to the north, so that when I was invited by Joseph Arditti to prepare the present article, I accepted with alacrity. It soon became obvious that, while a survey of the modern literature was not difficult, the sighting of older references, in particular those on which many modern reports rest, and their translation and interpretation were a formidable task. In the nine years during which this article was being prepared, I was fortunate to be able to visit Europe on four occasions and to consult important material in libraries there.

Several short summaries of uses of orchids (most of which tend to be repetitive) have appeared in the literature. Many of the original reports were not quoted and had to be ferreted out by a systematic search in floras, herbals, manuals of economic botany, and similar sources. Whenever possible I have endeavored to trace and consult the original reports and to record them accurately. In many cases several references are given, for two purposes: first, to provide alternatives to abstruse publications, and second, to show how some reports become altered after repeated (mis)quoting.

The accurate citation of botanical names and authors, particularly those from early works, has posed many problems. The great majority of these names can be found in the *Index Kewensis,* however, and in the interest of uniformity a small number have been changed to conform with the taxon recognized there. A very few exceptions, suffixed "non I.K.," have been included in the belief that further investigation will validate their use. Reports based on obviously dubious nomenclature have been ignored. In the interest of brevity, only a few well-recognized synonyms are given.

Names of political areas and natural features are taken, for the most part, from *The Times Atlas* (1972). For convenience I have chosen to present some information grouped according to arbitrarily selected areas that are not intended to denote any definitive geographical or botanical relationship.

Every item in the bibliography has been examined by me, but I have chosen not to include all of the available literature (especially that pertaining to salep and vanilla), as many reports provide no additional information.

I do not pretend that this work is complete[1]—far from it; a task of such magnitude is beyond the scope of this review. Nor can I vouch for the truth of any of the reports quoted herein: many are fanciful, some dubious, and some clearly erroneous; nevertheless, all are of interest.

I have no doubt that many more reports relevant to this review will come to light. I will be grateful to any person who contributes such information, as I hope to prepare an addendum in the not too distant future.

---

[1]But it is the most complete one assembled to date. [Ed.]

1. Introduction

The Orchidaceae, as they are now defined, comprise perhaps the largest family of flowering plants, with more than 20,000 species in some 650 genera. Orchids are found in all continents except Antarctica, and occur from sea level to the snow line. There are epiphytic, lithophytic, terrestrial, saprophytic, and subterranean orchids. Plant dimensions vary greatly: the pseudobulbs of *Bulbophyllum globuliforme* Nicholls scarcely exceed three millimeters in diameter (Rupp, 1969), while the individual canes of *Grammatophyllum speciosum* Bl. may be up to seven meters long and the whole plant thirteen meters or more in circumference, with a mass of three-quarters of a tonne[2] (Ridley, 1896; Soysa, 1934; J. J. Smith, 1939); the climbing species *Galeola kuhlii* Rchb. f. may attain a height of sixteen meters or more (Holttum, 1964). The flowers are equally varied in size, ranging in diameter from less than one millimeter in *Oberonia* to over 300 millimeters in *Sobralia*, with a wide range of colors and an incredible variety of shapes, particularly in the labellum.

It is indeed remarkable that such a large, widespread, and varied family provides but one product of current economic use: vanilla. While orchids make but a minor contribution to the world's economy today, however, this was not always so.

Several accounts of the uses of orchids have been published (including those by Morren, 1846; Puydt, 1880; Linden, 1894; J. J. Smith, 1927; Bulhart, 1927, 1930; Dakkus, 1935; Caius, 1936; Bakhuizen van den Brink, 1937; White, 1938; Cooray, 1940; Hawkes, 1943, 1944a, 1961; M. A. Miller, 1959; Jannese, 1964; Richter, 1965; Arditti, 1966, 1973; Lawler and Slaytor, 1970a; Duggal, 1972; Emboden, 1974; Limartha, 1974; Yearsley, 1976; Lawler, 1981), but they provide only limited information and some of them merely repeat earlier accounts.

It may never be known when a human first used an orchid. We may speculate that our nomadic ancestors, before settling down to agriculture, included orchid tubers in their diet, as aboriginal Australians and southern African Bushmen do today. Our first definite information, however, is from folk medicine, the earliest records of which come from China, Japan, India, and the eastern Mediterranean region, and date from the sixth and fifth centuries B.C.

Orchids have long played a part in the life of the Chinese. Since the time of Confucius (551–479 B.C.), who mentioned *lan* in his writings, orchids have been important in many facets of Chinese life, including literature, painting, horticulture, and, not least, medicine.

The celebrated materia medica *Sheng nung pen ts'ao ching (Shennong bencaojing)* is ascribed by tradition to the legendary emperor Sheng Nung, said to have ruled in the twenty-eighth century B.C. Some authors (Withner, 1959; Reinikka, 1972) have asserted, on the basis of this date, that human association with orchids came much earlier in the East than in the West. Bretschneider (1881, 1895), however, concludes that the work was compiled in the Han period, about 200 B.C.–A.D. 200, presumably from earlier tradi-

---

[2]Tonne (metric ton), 1.1 tons; ton, 2,000 lb. [Ed.]

tions, and Huard and Wong (1958) have arrived at a similar conclusion. Hu (1971a, 1971b), Emboden, (1974), Ho (1978), and Hyatt (1978) are also of the opinion that it is post-Confucian. Wong and Wu (1936) suggest that it is a compilation from various authors which appeared about the time of the western Han dynasty, 206 B.C.–A.D. 25, as it is not mentioned in the ancient records and its existence was not known until the Han period. Kimura and Migo (1936) place this work in the period A.D. 25–220. Needham and Gwei-Djen (1969) and But, Hu, and Kong (1980) refer the work to the first and second centuries of the Christian era. Needham, in his authoritative work on China (1975), makes the point that a great deal of legendary material is a backward reflection of historic practices. Be that as it may, from the time of Confucius, orchids have been mentioned in Chinese literature. The first botanical manuscript was produced between A.D. 290 and 307, and the first extant book (dated 1228) was followed by a large number of books devoted to orchids (for reviews of Chinese orchidology, see Bretschneider, 1880, 1881, and 1895; Watling, 1928; Hsia, 1948; Withner, 1959; Nagano, 1960; Hu, 1971a, 1971b; Reinikka, 1972; Kramer, 1975). Hou (1977) has written a concise summary of ancient and modern Chinese herbal medicine, and Huard and Wong (1958) discuss the evolution of the Chinese materia medica and its relationship to those of other cultures.

In Japan the growing of orchids is an ancient art. It is said that in the olden days their perfumes were transmitted to the clothes of lovers, and that one pot of *Dendrobium* or *Cymbidium* would scent a room or even a whole house. They were esteemed also for their beautiful leaves, which were a popular subject for drawing in black and white. From the early seventeenth to late nineteenth centuries, a curious class system of orchid culture prevailed. The royal peers grew *Dendrobium* species, with which they perfumed their clothes; *D. moniliforme* Sw., regarded as the plant of longevity, was their favorite. The Samurai grew *Angraecum falcatum* Lindl. syn. *Neofinetia falcata* Hu, while *Cymbidium* species (mainly *C. virescens* Lindl.) were grown by merchants and other wealthy people. From comparatively early times there has been a free exchange of information on orchids between Japan and China (Nagano, 1952, 1953, 1960; Withner, 1959; Reinikka, 1972).

On the Indian subcontinent the folk medicine was known as ayurveda, and the earliest records are contained in the Sanskrit writings of the Aryan peoples who moved into the Indus Valley from the west. This movement has been variously dated between 4000 B.C. and 1500 B.C., and the dates of the ancient Sanskrit writings are also obscure. The earliest accounts of the medicinal uses of plants occur in the Rig-Veda and the Atharva-Veda. While these works no doubt have earlier roots, they are generally conceded to have been compiled about 1500 B.C. and 1000 B.C. respectively. The vedic age of medicine (approximately 1500–800 B.C.) saw many plants employed in the treatment of disease, but always in association with charms or incantations. As yet it has not been possible to identify these plants with any precision, but Emboden (1974) refers to shamanistic practices of ayurvedic medicine men who used *Vanda roxburghii* R. Br. and *Ephemerantha macraei* (Lindl.) Hunt *et* Summerh. in medicinal rites involving prophecy and divination.

Ayurvedic medicine reached its peak in the Buddhist, or Brahman, period (approximately 800 B.C.–A.D. 1000). The writings of Charaka and Sushruta date from this era and now form the basis of ayurvedic medicine. Each lists many plants used in medicine, including some that we can now identify as orchids. The dates of these writings are not known with any degree of certainty; indeed, it is not agreed which is the earlier. The compilations known as *Sushruta Samhita* and *Charaka Samhita* have been dated about 600 B.C. and 200 B.C. respectively, but some authors maintain that these dates are too early.

From about the fifth century B.C. there has been a close connection between Indian and Greek materia medica. Indian plants are mentioned by Ctesius of Cnidos, Hippocrates, Theophrastus, and Dioscorides. Suggestions that India was the birthplace of medicine have not been substantiated; it is generally thought that medicine developed independently in several places, and that information was exchanged among them. For a detailed history of Indian medicine and discussion of the dates of vedic literature, see Wise (1867), Jee (1896), Jeliffe (1906), Hoernle (1907), Gupta (1919), Sarma (1931), Zimmer (1948), Gordon (1949), Ghosh (1951), Major (1954), Sigerist (1961), Said (1969), Stutley and Stutley (1977), and Zysk (1979).

Neither the Egyptian Papyrus Ebers (ca. 1550 B.C.) nor Assyrian herbal writings from the period of Ashur-Bani-Pal (668–627 B.C.) make a recognizable reference to orchids (Thompson, 1924, 1949; Ebbell, 1937).

A not inconsiderable aspect of the materia medica of the Assyrians and early Egyptians was the use of offal and excrement of both domestic and wild animals, to which Paullini (1714) has given the name *Dreckapotheke* (*Dreck,* filth; *Apotheke,* pharmacy). The fox is not mentioned in the Egyptian *Dreckapotheke,* but is included in the very large Mesopotamian one (Sigerist, 1951). Budge (1913) and Jastrow (1917) describe the use of "testicles of a fox" for breasts that produce too little (or perhaps too much) milk. It is possible that these reports refer to orchid tubers rather than to animal material. Apart from one reported in the Sinai (Täckholm and Drar, 1969), no orchids occur in Egypt, whereas there are several species in the area of the Assyrian Empire (Williams, Williams, and Arlott, 1978); the English word "salep" derives from an Arabic word meaning "testicles of the fox" (see sec. 14.1), which, in view of the relationship of Arabic to the ancient Assyrian languages, may indicate a common origin; there are many reports of the use of orchids as a lactagogue (Brøndegaard, 1971).

The word "orchid" is derived from the Greek *orchis,* meaning testicle (Liddell and Scott, 1966). Uses mentioned by early Greek and Roman authors are partly medical, partly magical, based on the resemblance of the plant's twinned tubers to testicles, in accordance with the doctrine of signatures.[3]

---

[3]The theory known as the doctrine of signatures was current for a long time. Probably originating in the Orient, it was much in evidence in Greece at the time of Dioscorides, who attributed sexual powers to the bulbs, regarding the old bulb as female and the new as male. (In the early nineteenth century, aboriginal people of western Australia had a similar belief [Nind, 1832]). The theory was revived in Europe in the early sixteenth century by Paracelsus and his followers. Essentially the theory professed to find a resemblance or connection (the signature) between a plant and either a part of the body or a disease; e.g., liverwort, feverwort (Allbutt, 1921; LaWall, 1927; Grieve, 1931; Stone, 1962; Hu, 1971a, 1971b). Orchids have been thought to have the signature of the testicles (didymous tubers), the mammae or hand (palmate tubers), the female pudenda, and, rarely, the penis. For a general discussion of the doctrine in relation to orchids, see Leclerc (1918), Schultes and Pease (1963), Lauer (1968), and Brøndegaard (1971).

Brøndegaard (1971) discusses orchids in relation to the festivals of the gods and fertility rites. The use by the Greeks of the word *satyrion* (from *satyros*, one of Dionysos' mythological followers) for an orchid is directly related to the use of these supposedly aphrodisiac plants in the orgiastic rites of Dionysos (Folkard, 1884; Murr, 1890). It is generally accepted that these rites were practiced by the peoples of Thrace and Phrygia who settled in Greece in the early part of the last millennium B.C. (Seltman, 1952; *Oxford Classical Dictionary*, 1970).

It has been suggested that *cosmosandalon* was an orchid, *Ophrys ferrum-equinum* Desf. (Sprengel, 1826; Morren, 1846; Pickering, 1879; Vacherot, 1954).[4] The word is used by the Greek comic poets Pherecrates (1880) and Cratinus (1880) in the fifth century B.C. In Cratinus' *Malthakoi*, *cosmosandalon* is used as a crown of flowers; if it were indeed an orchid, this could be the earliest recorded "use" of an orchid. In the second century of our era Pausanias (1918) wrote of wreaths woven of the flower *cosmosandalon* worn in the festival at Demeter's sanctuary at Hermione.

The earliest Greek writings dealing with plants are medical in emphasis and imperfectly known. The writings attributed to Hippocrates survive only as fragments in the compilation known as the Hippocratic Collection, dating from the fifth and fourth centuries B.C. They mention some 300 herbal plants (Singer, 1927; *Oxford Classical Dictionary*, 1970). The word *didyme* used therein is suggestive of orchid tubers, and was equated to *orchis* by Galen (1780) in the second century and determined as *Orchis papilionacea* L. by Pickering (1879). The *Rhizotomicon* of Diocles of Carystos (*fl. ca.* 375 B.C.), which is generally accepted to be the first Greek herbal, has not survived. These early writings were influenced by the Alexandrian and Sicilian schools (Wellmann, 1905; Allbutt, 1921; Singer, 1927). The earliest such work extant is the *Peri phyton historias*,[5] ascribed to Theophrastus (ca. 370–285 B.C.). Its use of the word *orchis* is generally considered to be the earliest use of this word in a botanical sense (Billerbeck, 1824; Ames, 1942b; Liddell and Scott, 1966; Täckholm and Drar, 1969).[6] There is doubt as to the authorship of this work, however; it is clearly a compilation and probably dates to about 250 B.C., after the death of its putative author. Book 9, which contains the reference to *orchis*, is almost certainly based on earlier Alexandrian herbals that have not survived (Thorndike, 1924; Singer, 1927). The credit for the first use of *orchis* in a botanical sense may well belong to a person who antedated Theophrastus and whose identity we may never know. The *Materia medica* of Dioscorides (trans. 1959) appeared in about the middle of the first century of the Christian era and has survived in its entirety. Dioscorides was influenced by earlier writers, including Hippocrates, Diocles, Theophrastus, and Crateuas (Allbutt, 1921; Singer, 1927). He described two plants as *orchis*,

[4]This identification is by no means unanimously accepted (Dierbach, 1833). Billerbeck (1824) determined *cosmosandalon* as *Cypripedium calceolus* L.

[5]This work is sometimes referred to as the *History of Plants*. The accepted English translation is by Hort (Theophrastus, 1916), who renders it as *Enquiry into Plants*.

[6]Some confusion has arisen from Hort's translation (Theophrastus, 1916). Whereas *orchis* is listed in the index, the relevant passage (9.18.3) is omitted in both the Greek text and the English translation; a footnote clearly indicates that it has been omitted deliberately. Täckholm and Drar, in stating that they have not been able to locate the word, and that the passage appears to be incomplete, have evidently overlooked this footnote. Gemmill (1973) gives a translation from a Greek text, and I have translated it from a Latin text (Theophrastus, 1818). There is no doubt that the word *orchis* (Latin *testiculus*) was used by Theophrastus.

presumably basing his interpretation on the *orchis* of Theophrastus. These two plants are undoubtedly the *Orchis* of modern botanists (Ames, 1942b; Schweinfurth, 1959; Arditti, 1966; Reinikka, 1972). Schultes and Pease (1963) point out that it was Dioscorides who codified the earlier lore of orchid nomenclature and preserved it for posterity.

Pliny the Elder, in the first century of the Christian era, quoted Theophrastus in his *Naturalis historia* (A.D. 77, trans. 1956) and used the terms *orchis*, *serapias*, and *satyrion*. Some authorities claim that Pliny gave only the information presented by Dioscorides (Brøndegaard, 1971), but others claim that Pliny's publication was earlier: for example, Täckholm and Drar (1969) give the documented date of A.D. 77 for Pliny's *Naturalis historia* and A.D. 78 for Dioscorides' *Materia medica*. It seems most likely that both works owed much to Theophrastus and other earlier writers, but even though they were contemporaneous, they were written independently; see Allbutt (1921), Singer (1927), and Stearn (1976).

Following the publication of *Orchis* as a genus by Linnaeus (1753), various combinations of the word were used to denote the family until the adoption of Orchidaceae, proposed by Lindley (1836). Thus this ancient Greek word has become established in modern botanical nomenclature.

There are no direct references to orchids in the Bible, but the aphrodisiac "dudaim" requested of Leah by Rachel (Genesis 30:14) has been held to be salep and has been identified as *Orchis sancta* L. or *Satyrium maculata* Desf. syn. *Habenaria intacta* Benth. (Chatin, 1868). It has been suggested that the mustard seed of Jesus' parables may have been orchid seed (Moldenke and Moldenke, 1952). The rods of Moses and Aaron (Exodus 4:2, 17, 20; Numbers 17:2–10) have been identified as *Orchis purpurea* Huds. (Teirlinck, 1930).

Shakespeare included an orchid in Ophelia's garland (*Hamlet*, Act 4, scene 7); using the common names "long purples" and "dead men's fingers."[7]

The plant of the gallows, believed to arise from the semen of a hanged person, has been said to be an orchid (Emboden, 1974).

It is astonishing to learn that random searches in the Ames Herbarium yielded no notes on the use of orchids (Altschul, 1973). There are in fact a considerable number of reports in other sources of the uses of orchids, ranging from the mundane to the bizarre. It is clear that plants now recognized as orchids were mentioned in writings during the fifth century B.C. in both the Orient and the Occident. Orchids have figured in legends, magic, and religions and have been used in many societies for food, flavoring, and medicine, as aphrodisiacs and decoration, and in arts and crafts.

Human association with orchids has had many diverse expressions. A late medieval Icelandic saga, *Halfdanar Saga Eysteinssonar*, mentions an orchid, probably *Orchis maculata* L. (O. A. Høeg, personal communication). Orchids were held in high esteem by Aztec royalty; Montezuma and Netzhualcoyotl cultivated orchids in their gardens. *Stanhopea tigrina* Batem. was one of their favorites; the strange beauty of the flower, likened to the

---

[7]Shakespeare's apparent confusion of two common names has caused a controversy as to the identity of this orchid. There is considerable support for both *Orchis maculata* L. and *O. mascula* L. (Folkard, 1884; Fernie, 1914; Grieve, 1931; Ames, 1942b; Grigson, 1958; Duperrex, 1961; Summerhayes, 1968; Reinikka, 1972; Emboden, 1974).

lynx, led to its adoption as the emblem of the learned Lycean Academy of Rome[8] (Bateman, 1837–1843; Morren, 1846; Urbina, 1903a). The royal Aztec gardens were used also for the cultivation of simples so that their properties might be studied; *Vanilla planifolia* G. Jackson in Andr. was one such plant (Tezozomoc, 1878; Gerste, 1910).

In 1913 woman suffragists smashed the glass of the orchid house at Kew and fifty-odd rare and inoffensive specimens were destroyed (Bingham, 1975). An expensive bypass road in Worcestershire has been diverted around a colony of rare orchids (Anonymous, 1975a).

Epipactus helleborine (L.) Crantz. was brought to New York by European immigrants as a cure for gout and has now become an aggressive weed[9] (Hawkes, 1944b; Correll, 1950). An orchid was the crest in the coat-of-arms of Manchukuo (Japanese-occupied Manchuria), where the highest order of chivalry was the Imperial Order of the Orchid (Soysa, 1934; Shimadzu, 1935; Jannese, 1964). The collar of the Grand Order of the Lanhua was the highest decoration granted by the imperial court of Manchukuo (Anonymous, 1939). No fewer than 474 stamps featuring orchids were issued by 94 postal authorities to 1976 (Gibbons, 1976). It is perhaps fitting that work on an orchid, *Phaius tancarvilliae*[10] (Banks) Bl. (under the name *Limodorum tankervillae*), led to the discovery of the nucleus of the cell by Francis Bauer in 1802. Robert Brown (1833) published the first description of this work (*Kew Handlist*, 1904; Curtis, 1950). There was reputed to be a secret league known as the Society of the Golden Orchid in China (Friend, 1884b; Beals, 1917). The "language of flowers," which originated in the Middle Ages or perhaps before, reached its peak in the mid-nineteenth century; orchids in general were equated with beauty or luxury. Specific orchids had their own meanings: bee orchis, industry; butterfly orchis, gaiety; fly orchis, error; spider orchis, adroitness; bee ophrys, error; frog ophrys, disgust (Osgood, 1844; Burke, 1866; Conway, 1973).

The wearing of an orchid buttonhole by Joseph Chamberlain perhaps did most to popularize the orchid cult in England. His granddaughter, daughter of Sir Austen, carried *Odontoglossum* flowers (Joseph's favorite) in her bridal bouquet (Soysa, 1934; Anonymous, 1935; Jannese, 1964).

We must not overlook the popularity of orchid growing as a hobby. Since the first importation of a tropical orchid into England in the early eighteenth century,[11] a large industry has grown up around the supply of various materials and equipment to enable enthusiasts to pursue their hobby. From this amateur orchid growing came the introduction of orchids to horticulture, resulting in the establishment of today's large commercial nurseries in many countries. Much time and effort are spent in producing interspecific

---

[8]This orchid was used only as a supplementary emblem of the academy, in particular by one of its patrons, Federico Cesi (Toni, 1901; Galli, 1910; Gerste, 1910).

[9]See n. 81.

[10]Also spelled *Phajus tankervilliae*. [Ed.]

[11]With the possible exception of *Vanilla* (see sec. 5.1), *Bletia verecunda* R. Br. was the first tropical orchid cultivated in England. A plant received in 1731 from the Bahamas by Peter Collinson was grown by Sir Charles Wager and flowered in 1732 (Curtis, 1950; Arnold, 1958; De Wolf, 1959; Withner, 1959; Stearn, 1960; Hawkes, 1961; *cf.* Castle, 1886). Parkinson (1640) has a drawing and description of "a sort of our Ladyes Slipper brought from the North parts of America." *Brassavola nodosa* Lindl., imported from Curaçao, was in cultivation in Holland before 1698 (Reinikka, 1972).

and indeed intergeneric hybrids for this trade. Hawkes (1952) gives an imaginative account of the use of orchid flowers for decoration in the home.

John Dominy was the first person to experiment successfully with orchid hybridization. He commenced his work with *Cattleya* species in 1852, but *Calanthe* × Dominii Lindl., made in 1854, was the first artificial hybrid to flower (in October 1856). It created a sensation. First described by Lindley and figured by Curtis, it came from the parents *C. furcata* Batem. ex Lindl. and *C. masuca* Lindl. In 1863 Dominy flowered the first intergeneric hybrid, *Laeliocattleya* × exoniensis Rolfe. It was not until the early twentieth century that Knudson's development of the work of Bernard and Burgeff led to asymbiotic germination of orchid seed, which revolutionized the hybridization of orchids (Curtis, 1858; Lindley, 1858; Rolfe, 1893; Anonymous, 1952c; Stearn, 1960; Hawkes, 1961; Reinikka, 1972).

While it is generally held that the singular demand for orchid flowers is due to their undeniable beauty, it may also be due in part to their reputation for having aphrodisiac properties (Uyldert, 1971).

Puydt (1880) wrote eloquently of orchids, pointing out that despite their minor economic importance, they nonetheless serve humankind in their own very special way. I am sure that all admirers of the orchid will heartily endorse Puydt's sentiments.

A detailed history of orchids may be found in Castle (1886), Schweinfurth (1959), Stearn (1960), and Reinikka (1972). It is interesting to compare Castle's nineteenth-century bibliography with the comprehensive bibliographies provided by Curtis (1950), Vacherot (1954), Schweinfurth (1959), Täckholm and Drar (1969), and Reinikka (1972).

2. Religion, Superstition, and Magic

Orchids have long been associated with magic and superstition, usually in connection with their supposed aphrodisiac effects on humans and animals (see secs. 10 and 13). Many superstitions were associated with pre-Christian religions, particularly in Scandinavia, and were later transferred to Christianity (Friend, 1884a; Brøndegaard, 1971; Emboden, 1974).

2.1. Charms

Brøndegaard (1971) has reviewed in detail the use of orchids as love charms. In Nigeria several epiphytic orchids may be used in the preparation of a love charm (Dalziel, 1937). The Chimbu in Papua New Guinea use an orchid to ensure that a girl will become strong and hard-working: the mother rubs her daughter with the leaves on the day she is born (Sterly, 1973).

Ansellia gigantea Rchb. f.: The roots of this species and of *A. humilis* Bull were used by Zulu youths to make unmarried girls temporarily sterile (Watt and Breyer-Brandwijk, 1932, 1962; Schelpe, 1961, 1966).

A. humilis Bull: Zulu youths wear the leaf under an arm bangle when they go courting. As an antidote to bad dreams, Zulus take an infusion of the stem or hold their heads in the smoke of the burning root (Watt and Breyer-Brandwijk, 1962).

Brachycorythis ovata Lindl.: This plant has been used as a charm in southern Africa (Rayner, 1977).

Corycium nigrescens Sond.: In southern Africa an infusion is used to ward off evil (Rayner, 1977).

Cymbidium finlaysonianum Lindl.: See *Dendrobium crumenatum* Sw.

Cypripedium humile Salisb. syn. *C. acaule* Ait.: The root of this species was an ingredient of a love charm used by the Meskawi Indians of North America (H. H. Smith, 1928).

Cytheria bulbosa (L.) House. syn. *Calypso borealis* Salisb.: This plant was sometimes used as a charm by the Indians of British Columbia (Steedman, 1930).

Dendrobium sp.: When the people of southeastern Malaita, in the Solomon Islands, must visit unfriendly areas, they use this orchid to decorate a comb worn to hide a talisman (G. F. C. Dennis, personal communication).

D. acinaciforme Roxb.: The leaves of this plant were used as a love charm in Ambon; lovers sent them to each other to beg forgiveness. In Seram men wore the leaves, stems, and flowers in their armbands when they went plundering or headhunting; they believed that the plant was lucky and made them courageous (Rumphius, 1750).[12]

D. crumenatum Sw.: This is one of several orchids used in Perak, Malaysia, for protective magic. It was used as a besom (broom) to sprinkle water in the house of a recently deceased person to prevent his spirit from haunting the living (Burkill and Haniff, 1930; Gimlette and Thomson, 1971). *Cymbidium finlaysonianum* Lindl. and *Plocoglottis porphyrophylla* Ridl. were used similarly (Burkill and Haniff, 1930).[13]

D. pulchellum Roxb. syn. *D. dalhousieanum* Paxt.: In Indochina the flowers, resembling the head of a dog, were fed to dogs to make them skillful at the hunt (Dournes, 1955).

D. secundum Lindl.: In the Andaman Islands the skin of this species, and perhaps others, is used to decorate strings of bones worn as necklets or belts to prevent or cure illness (Radcliffe-Brown, 1964; see sec. 8.7).

Disa stachyoides Rchb. f. and *D. versicolor* Rchb. f.: Infusions of these orchids have been used in southern Africa to protect against evil (Rayner, 1977).

Eulophia angolensis (Rchb. f.) Summerh. and *E. ensata* Lindl.: These plants have been used by men in southern Africa to ensure success in courting. *E. barbata* Spreng., *E. clavicornis* Lindl., and *E. inaequalis* Schltr. were used in the same area to repel evil (Rayner, 1977).

E. virens Spreng.: In western India the dried roots placed in small bags were said to drive away snakes (Dalgado, 1896).

Grammatophyllum scriptum Bl.: The Ambonese made a secret love philter from seed, called by Rumphius the "yellow flour of the fruit." It was said that a woman must pursue any man who gave her this flour in food or drink (Rumphius, 1750; Morren, 1849; Lindley, 1853; Dragendorff, 1898; Hawkes, 1944b; Burkill, 1966; Wood, 1977).[14]

---

[12]My interpretation of Rumphius' names is that of Merrill (1917); see also Wit (1977).

[13]Burkill and Haniff (1930) are clearly the originators of these reports, which are correctly restated by Gimlette and Thomson (1971). However, in 1935 and 1966, Burkill, although quoting Burkill and Haniff (1930), gives a different interpretation of this use of each of the three orchids. To complicate the issue further, Hawkes (1944b) gives yet another interpretation of the use of *C. finlaysonianum* and quotes Burkill (1935). These differences in interpretation illustrate the difficulties of compiling a review paper and reinforce my policy of quoting the original report exactly whenever possible.

[14]Bateman (1837–1843), reporting the arrival of living plants in England, comments, "We tremble for the consequences if what Rumphius says of its properties is true."

Habenaria dives Rchb. f.: This orchid has been used as a death charm in southern Africa. When the tubers were mixed with food, the victim was expected to waste away (Rayner, 1977).

H. dregeana Lindl. and *H. epipactidea* Rchb. f.: These plants have been used as charms in southern Africa (Rayner, 1977).

H. leucostachys S. Wats.: The Thompson Indians of British Columbia prayed to this plant in the belief that it would bring wealth and possessions. A wash prepared from the plant was used to wash guns to ensure good hunting, and to make the young men lucky, handsome, and sweet smelling (Steedman, 1930).

H. media Niles: The Potawatomi Indians used to rub or paint the plant on the cheek as a love charm; it was said to be efficacious for either sex (H. H. Smith, 1933).

H. saccata Greene: The Kwakiutl Indians of British Columbia used the plant as an ingredient of a love charm (Turner and Bell, 1973).

H. viridis R. Br.: The Ojibwa Indians used this plant as a love charm (H. H. Smith, 1932).

Ipsea speciosa Lindl.: This orchid is much sought after by sorcerers in Sri Lanka to make charms and love potions (Perera, 1940).

Orchis mascula L.: In Scotland the dried tubers of this plant were carried as love talismans (Grigson, 1958).

Plocoglottis porphyrophylla Ridl.: See *Dendrobium crumenatum* Sw.

Satyrium parviflorum Sw.: This plant was used by men in southern Africa to ensure success in courting (Rayner, 1977).

Spiranthes sp.: In Nova Scotia men gave a drink made from the roots of this species to women as a love charm (Bergen, 1899).

S. gracilis Beck: The Ojibwa Indians used the root as an ingredient of a charm to bring game to them during the hunt (H. H. Smith, 1932).

Vanilla planifolia G. Jackson in Andr.: In Mexico the flowers were used in a charm to ensure the protection of travelers (Gates, 1939).

2.2. Magic

In ancient China, orchids were used to ward off evil spirits; the noun *lan*, orchid, is homonymous with the verb *lan*, to ward off (Hu, 1971a, 1971b).

Satyrion erythronion of Dioscorides was considered an antimagic plant, as the root put a protective radiation over those who might be bewitched by evil people (Friend, 1884b; Teirlinck, 1930).

Orchid tubers were long used as magic plants in the folk medicine of Norway. It was held that they were most efficacious when gathered on St. John's Eve (O. A. Høeg, personal communication).[15]

Uses of epiphytic orchids in west tropical Africa were mainly superstitious. In Nigeria they have been used as a potion to prevent slaves from escaping, or given to children being weaned in order to make them forget the breast (Dalziel, 1937).

---

[15]In the Erzgebirge it was believed that the tubers of *Orchis latifolia* L. had five "fingers" when they were dug on St. John's Eve, instead of the more usual four (Brøndegaard, 1971).

In Arnhem Land a sorcerer uses the juice of an orchid pseudobulb in (fanciful) ritual killing. He rubs his arm all over with the juice before placing it inside the victim's body (Warner, 1937).[16]

Aerangis thomsoni Schltr.: A paste made in east Africa from the pounded orchid was said to have magical properties; when placed near a clutch of hen's eggs, it ensured their hatching (Kokwaro, 1976).

Agrostophyllum glumaceum Hook. f.: There was a superstition in Indonesia that ghosts resided in this plant (Clercq, 1909).

Anoectochilus spp.: Dayaks who sought these valuable medicinal plants in western Kalimantan (Borneo) attributed their rarity to the ability of this orchid to walk away when a human approached (Coomans de Ruiter, 1935).[17]

Aplectrum hyemale (Muhl. ex Willd.) Torr.: In the southeastern United States the two joined corms were worn as amulets and used to tell fortunes. In Alabama and Georgia the separated corms were known as Adam and Eve, and were used to forecast success in obtaining work or a lover (Bergen, 1899; Niles, 1904; Correll, 1950; Luer, 1975). The Cherokees used this plant to endow children with eloquence (Hamel and Chiltoskey, 1975).

Bulbophyllum sp.: Sterly (1974/75) reports that at least one species is used in magic and ritual by the Chimbu people of Papua New Guinea.

Cryptostylis sp.: On Guadalcanal the juice from the crushed leaf was placed on the eyelids of a corpse to prevent the dead from returning to haunt the house (M. Tedder, personal communication).

Dendrobium sp.: In the Chimbu region of Papua New Guinea the name *duruagle* is given to both an orchid and a whore. The name refers to charming, fair-skinned female ghosts who stroll naked along the rivers and seduce young men into sexual intercourse. Failure to satisfy the demands of the *duruagle* causes a painful sexual disease on the following night. The use of the orchid is said to repair the disease (Sterly, 1973, 1974–75).

D. dactylodes Rchb. f.: In Samoa this plant was used to combat ear diseases caused by evil spirits (Uhe, 1974).

Eria muscicola Lindl.: In old Sanskrit writings this orchid was used in a preparation said to ward off calamities, avert ill fortune, and promote prosperity (Hoernle, 1893–1912).

Eulophia barteri Summerh.: When a baby cries without cause in Liberia, it is believed that the parents have broken a taboo against intercourse during pregnancy; to counteract the effect, an aqueous extract of the leaves of this orchid is dropped into the baby's eyes (Hawkes, 1944b; M. A. Miller, 1959; Harley, 1970).

Gymnadenia conopsea (L.) R. Br.: In Central Europe this orchid played a part in popular superstition: its roots were dug out by treasure seekers, who made use of it in their secret work (Rosenthal, 1862; *cf. Orchis mascula*). It was sometimes known as the devil's hand (Emboden, 1974).

Habenaria ciliaris R. Br.: The Cherokees used a piece of root on the hook to make fish bite (Hamel and Chiltoskey, 1975).

---

[16]For the determination of these species, see n. 71.

[17]It is indeed unfortunate that this magical power was not possessed by the many endangered orchid species that have suffered human depredation.

Laelia sp.: In Mexico it was said that pregnant women who fail to satisfy a food craving may abort; a decoction containing this plant would prevent the abortion (Redfield, 1928; Ford, 1975).

Lissochilus madagascariensis Kraenzl.: In Madagascar a preparation of this orchid is reputed to protect bullfighters from being gored (Boiteau, 1978a).

Macodes sp.: On Guadalcanal the crushed leaves of this orchid were rubbed inside a baby's cheeks to make it talk, and the crushed roots were used in a mixture to attract river fish (M. Tedder, personal communication).

M. petola Lindl.: In Java this plant is called "letterleaf" because the leaf markings were held to resemble Javanese letter symbols.[18] In earlier times the rubbed leaves were mixed with the liquid from the leaf sheaths of the banana and dropped in the eye on a Friday morning as an introduction to the art of reading (Bulhart, 1930; J. J. Smith, 1930.[19] Dakkus (1935) reports, quoting Smith, that the drops were used in the eyes of "those who wished to master the art of writing." Bakhuizen van den Brink (1937) gives the report as quoted by Dakkus and concludes: "Se non è vero . . . !" Usher (1974) reports that the juice is dropped into the eye "to increase close vision."[20]

Orchis maculata L. and *O. latifolia* L.: Both of these orchids were believed to work against witchcraft in Europe. The roots were used to help men who had been rendered impotent or sterile by witchcraft. The bulbs of the white-flowered *O. maculata* L. were used as a charm against the evil hand, which could not cross the threshold if the bulbs were buried beneath the door on St. John's Eve (Dodoens, 1644; Teirlinck, 1930).[21]

O. mascula L.: In Europe witches were supposed to use the tubers in their philters, the fresh tubers to promote true love and the old to check wrong passion (Grieve, 1931; M. A. Miller, 1959). This is one of the orchids known as cuckoo flowers (see sec. 2.5). In parts of Germany the cuckoo's call was thought to disclose the location of ore bodies; consequently a luxuriant growth of this orchid was believed to indicate rich metal deposits beneath (Friend, 1884a; Beals, 1917).

Spiranthes lucida Ames: Cherokee infants were washed in a warm steep from this plant to ensure fast, healthy growth (Hamel and Chiltoskey, 1975).

Vanda roxburghii R. Br.: Old Sanskrit writings record this orchid as an ingredient in a preparation that was taken to avert calamities and in another that was eaten with food by women who wanted sons (Hoernle, 1893–1912).

2.3. Religion

The use of *cosmosandalon* in the festival of Demeter and the association of orchids with Confucius are discussed in the Introduction.

In Mexico the pre-Conquest tribal chiefs placed great value on the possession of brilliant orchid flowers. After the Spaniards settled in the region, many orchids were

---

[18]Other orchids that have the same local name (but apparently not the magical power) include *Goodyera colorata* Bl., *Anoectochilus reinwardtii* Bl., *A. setaceus* Bl., and *A. geniculata* Ridl. (Ridley, 1896; Bakhuizen van den Brink, 1937).

[19]Smith's report concludes: "At the present time such methods are superfluous."

[20]The magical property of this orchid is an example of the doctrine of signatures; because their markings resembled letters, the leaves would influence reading ability.

[21]This is another example of the doctrine of signatures: because the tubers are shaped like a hand, they were believed to counter the evil hand.

incorporated in Christian rites. They have been used in the celebrations of baptism, marriage, and burial, and to express devotion to God and the saints. Many common names for the flowers are derived from their religious image, such as crucifix orchid, *Epidendrum radicans* Pav. ex Lindl; *flor de Jesús, Laelia rubescens* Lindl.; *flor del Espíritu Santo* (flower of the Holy Ghost), *Peristeria elata* Hook.; *flor de los muertos* (flower of the dead), *Oncidium tigrinum* La Llave *et* Lex., which is used to decorate graves on All Souls' Day; and *flor del paraíso* (flower of paradise), *Sobralia dichotoma* Ruiz *et* Pav. (Bateman, 1837–1843; Spae, 1847; Puydt, 1880; Urbina, 1903a; Dakkus, 1935; Richter, 1965).

In Papua New Guinea the Kukukuku men wore a portion of orchid stem in the nasal septum as part of their puberty rites (Blackwood, 1940). In the Jimmi area a species of *Calanthe* and one of *Spathoglottis* were used in ritual (Rappaport, 1967; Powell, 1976a, 1976b). In the eastern highlands the leaf and stem of a species of *Dendrobium* are a special ornament for boys undergoing initiation (Hays, 1980).

Cattleya skinneri Batem: The Guatemalans call this plant *flor de San Sebastián* and decorate churches with it on the saint's day (Paxton, 1844; Morren, 1845, 1847a).

Coelogyne asperata Lindl.: In parts of Kalimantan this plant has been considered sacred (Hawkes, 1944b; Steenis, 1958; M. A. Miller, 1959). The abundance of the blooms was held to forecast an equally fertile rice harvest (Anonymous, 1890, 1952b; Rifai, 1975).

Cypripedium parviflorum Salisb.: The Menomini Indians made this plant into sacred bundles for the purpose of inducing dreams of the supernatural (H. H. Smith, 1923).

Dendrobium macarthiae Thw.: In Sri Lanka the blooms were used as a temple offering on Buddha's birthday, in May (Soysa, 1934, 1943; Cooray, 1940; Kupper, 1961; Duggal, 1972).

D. moniliforme Sw.: This plant was used in Japan as a beautiful ornament to decorate temples. It was "more or less sacred," but Puydt's statement that "it was venerated" must be discounted (Kaempfer, 1712; Morren, 1847b; Puydt, 1880; Dakkus, 1935).

Macodes petola Lindl.: The Javanese regard this plant as of divine origin and relate the following legend: Long ago a radiantly beautiful goddess, Petola, was sent by the gods to Java to show the uncivilized natives the right and good ways. Her gentleness did not persuade them, and they chased her away to a rocky outcrop in the deep forest. She returned the next day in an angry mood and the people then subjected themselves to her. They pleaded for her beautiful scarf as a sign of her forgiveness, but she could not leave it. She returned to the rocky outcrop and while asleep laid her scarf on the ground. Soon the ground was covered with lovely plants that bore on their leaves the pattern of the heavenly scarf; and so originated the *daun petola* of Java, brought there by a goddess. Soon the news of the divine flowers spread, and people came from far and near to collect them for themselves. All these plants, however, began to die. The goddess magically restored them to the rock, breathed life back into them, and left them in the care of the mountain fairies. The Javanese explain that this is why the plant cannot be grown away from the place of its origin. A detailed account is given by Walterida (1916), and summaries are given by Puydt (1880), Dakkus (1935),[22] Vacherot (1954), and Rifai (1975).

Orchis mascula L.: The spots on the leaves are said to be bloodstains from the body of

---

[22]Bakhuizen van den Brink (1931) writes scathingly of Dakkus' comment that this legend may have been thought up by some joker.

Christ at Calvary, where this species is reported to have grown (Friend, 1884a; Fernie, 1914; Beals, 1917; Grigson, 1958).[23]

Peristeria elata Hook.: The flowers of this orchid were worshiped religiously in Panama (Seeman, 1852–57; Dragendorff, 1898; Guzmán, 1924).

2.4. Legends regarding the Origin of Orchids

Early observers of orchids failed to realize that the "dust" that fell from the dead flowers was in fact seed, and consequently mythical explanations of the origin of orchids were invented, culminating in the theory of abiogenesis, most fully expressed by Bock (1552) and Kircher (1678). According to this theory, orchid plants arose from putrified sperm in the dead bodies of beasts and men as they lay in the fields, and from semen of birds and animals spilled on the ground during copulation. Correspondingly, the plants resembled either the creatures from whose seed they sprang or the insects that were believed to generate spontaneously from the corpses (*e.g.*, bees from cattle and wasps from horses). The origin from semen also accorded with the supposed sexual powers of orchids (Rumphius, 1750; Greene, 1910; Ames, 1942a; Withner, 1959; Brøndegaard, 1971; Arditti, 1972; Reinikka, 1972; Emboden, 1974).

Several twentieth-century authors give slightly varying versions of the mythological origin of the orchid. Orchis was the son of a nymph, Acolasia, and a satyr, Patellanus, and was killed during a feast of Bacchus because he violated a priestess. Following his father's prayer, he was turned into an orchid to serve as a sensually provocative plant. Even the flower was alleged to retain a sensual quality, and to eat the root was to suffer momentary conversion to the satyr state (Beals, 1917; Skinner, 1925; Grieve, 1931; Täckholm and Drar, 1969; Leyel, 1970; Brøndegaard, 1971; Emboden, 1974; Gordon, 1977).[24]

Malay tradition attributes the planting of all trees to the prophet Elias. When the orchid was to be planted, there was no room in the ground, so it was planted on the trees (Skeat, 1900).

There are legends, too, of the origins of several particular species of orchids. Brøndegaard (1971) relates two legends from Bohemia about the origin of orchids with palmate tubers. In the first a virgin wept on her brother's grave until God turned her into a plant; when the tuber is unearthed, one finds the "dead virgin's hand." In the second a woman attempted to steal a church offering but on stretching out her hands fell dead, whereupon the hands turned black and the body withered away. A plant grew from the hands, with the roots black as the "hands of the dead."

Nigritella nigra (L.) Rchb. f.: According to a legend from the Tyrol, a young girl died of grief after her lover was unfaithful, and God turned her into an orchid. The white root represents the faithful girl's hand and the black the hand of her unfaithful lover (Brøndegaard, 1971). Another legend relates that a monk stole an arm from a statue of the Christ child and bore it away. He became lost in the mountains, and buried the arm

---

[23]Another version of the legend records that this orchid grew in the garden of Gethsemane, and that the drops of blood that Christ sweated in his hour of agony fell on the leaves and stained them (Beals, 1917).

[24]A careful search in standard works of classical mythology has failed to find any evidence of this legend.

before he died. The next year an orchid flowered on the spot with roots resembling a child's hand (Duperrex, 1961).

Satyrium spp.: In mythology satyrs were half man and half goat, and in 1800 the name *Satyrium* was given by Olof Swartz to a genus of European terrestrial orchids. Caproic acid has been found in the flowers of *Satyrium hircinum* L. syn. *Himantoglossum hircinum* Spreng., which have a strong hircine smell.[25] Arditti (1972) suggests that here we have modern biochemical evidence for the origin of a myth.

2.5. Other Legends

A legend that orchids were the food of satyrs and induced the sexual excesses attributed to them is suggested as an explanation of the name satyrion, once given to various orchids and the medicaments prepared from them (Grieve, 1931; Täckholm and Drar, 1969; Leyel, 1970). O. P. Brown (1878) describes the disease of satyriasis, characterized by a constant and insatiable desire for coition, so called because the satyrs were greatly addicted to excesses.[26]

Some orchids have been included in the group of plants known as "cuckoo plants," which have been associated in legend with the cuckoo, and some magical powers associated with the bird have been transferred to the plant (see sec. 2.2). Orchids and the cuckoo have been linked because of the supposed origin of orchids from cuckoo sperm (see sec. 2.4), because each had a reputation of influence on human sexuality, and, more understandably, because the plants flowered when the cuckoo's call was first heard, or the spots on the leaves resembled the spots on the wings. *Orchis maculata* L. and *O. mascula* L. are two orchids that have been included in this group (Friend, 1884; Swainson, 1886; Beals, 1917; Brøndegaard, 1971; Emboden, 1974).

The power of the woodpecker to attack wood has been ascribed in legend to a plant that some writers have considered to be an orchid (Laisnel de la Salle, 1875; Teirlinck, 1930).[27]

Cymbidium gyokuchin Makino (non I.K.): A Chinese legend of the Shin dynasty (*ca.* 200 B.C.) relates that the empress Yohki-hi was barren until the emperor obtained a plant of this orchid. The plant flowered and in due course the empress bore a son. This treatment was repeated until the royal couple had thirteen sons. This plant averages thirteen flowers on a spike, and is called "thirteen great treasures" (Nagano, 1960).

Cypripedium calceolus L.: Legend relates that Venus lost a slipper in the woods during a storm; when a mortal tried to touch the slipper, it was changed into the flower known as Venus' shoe or lady's slipper (Duperrex, 1961).

---

[25]Caproic acid, $CH_3(CH_2)_4COOH$; caprylic acid, $CH_3(CH_2)_6COOH$; and capric acid, $CH_3(CH_2)_8COOH$, are known as the goat acids, as their odor is powerfully reminiscent of the goat. They occur in goat fat, milk, and butter, and were named from the Latin *caper*, goat. Capric and caproic acids were isolated and named in 1818 by Chevreul (1823, 1889), caprylic acid by Lerch (1844).

[26]As treatment, Brown prescribes a low diet, frequent shower baths, physical outdoor labor, icebags to the cerebellum, a hard bed, and hop pillows.

[27]The woodpecker plant was said to be placed in the nest by the bird and to be much sought after by men; possession of it gave them the strength of Hercules. Swainson (1886) gives a full English translation of Laisnel de la Salle.

Ipsea speciosa Lindl.: A legend in Sri Lanka tells of the infatuation of a prince for his stepsister and of her rejection of his suit. When he ate the tubers of this orchid, he became crazy and killed her. This orchid sprang up from the ground stained with her blood (Soysa, 1934, 1943; Cooray, 1940; Perera, 1940).

Orchis maculata L.: In Germany and Slovakia it was believed that this plant gave forth a plaintive cry when it was drawn from the ground (Schell, 1901; Delatte, 1938). This is clearly an adaptation of a similar legend surrounding the mandrake, *Mandragora officinarum* L. W. T. Stearn (personal communication) is of the opinion that the mandrake legend was an early attempt to conserve a valuable plant for the privileged classes, and that the legend was transferred to the orchid for a similar purpose. Orchids have been called "mandrake of the north" (Brøndegaard, 1971).

2.6. Funerary Uses

Corymborkis veratrifolia (Reinw.) Bl.: Backer and Bakhuizen van den Brink (1968) record that in Java this orchid, cultivated as an ornamental, is often found on old sacred graves.

Dendrobium spp.: In the upper part of Cape York Peninsula, in northeastern Australia, the bones carried by near relations of the dead are decorated with lashings made from the yellow skin of local species (Roth, 1907).

In the Andaman Islands, bones preserved for relics and made into strings are often ornamented with the dried yellow skin from local species (Radcliffe-Brown, 1964; see sec. 8.7).

D. phalaenopsis Fitzg.: Plants collected in the Tanimbar Islands of Indonesia by Micholitz were growing among skeletons in a tribal cemetry. One plant sold at a London auction was growing in a human skull (Soysa, 1934).

Sobralia spp.: In El Salvador one species has been used to decorate an altar of human sacrifice, and in Guyana another species has been found planted inside a human skull in a burial ground (Guzmán, 1924).

3. Floral Emblems

The adoption of orchids as state or national flowers is yet another example of the diverse use of orchids.

Cattleya skinneri Batem. is the national flower of Costa Rica.

C. trianaei Linden *et* Rchb. f. is the national flower of Colombia.

Cypripedium humile Salisb. syn. *C. acaule* Ait. is the floral emblem of Prince Edward Island.

C. pubescens Willd. is the state flower of Minnesota.

Dendrobium bigibbum Lindl. is the state flower of Queensland.

D. marcarthiae Thw. is the national flower of Sri Lanka.

Lycaste virginalis Linden is the national flower of Guatemala.

Peristeria elata Hook. is the national flower of Panama.

Vanda Miss Joaquim is the national flower of the Republic of Singapore.

4. Food

Reports of uses of orchids as food adjuncts are given in separate sections: vanilla, section 5; flavoring and confectionery, section 6; beverages, section 7; and salep, section 14.

4.1. Africa

Orchid roots have been used as food in Zambia (Irvine, 1952).

Brachycorythis tysoni Bolus: Children in the Transvaal eat the tubers (Phillips, 1917).

Cynorchis flexuosa Lindl.: The tubers were sometimes eaten in eastern Madagascar (Jumelle, 1910; Usher, 1974).

Disa sp.: In Malawi the tubers are sold in the form of a prepared jelly, which is boiled in salted water and served with peanuts as a side dish (Williamson, 1955).

D. barbata Sw., *D. lacera* Sw., and *D. venusta* Bolus: Much sweet nutritious juice is contained in the roots of these species (Pappe, 1857; Watt and Breyer-Brandwijk, 1962).

Eulophia spp.: The roots of two species, either raw or roasted, were used for food by the Bushmen of southern Africa (Story, 1958).

E. flanagani Bolus: The tubers were eaten by children in South Africa (Phillips, 1917).

E. hereroensis Schltr.: The people of the central Kalahari Desert sometimes collected the bulbs as supplementary food (J. Tanaka, 1976).

E. livingstoniana (Rchb. f.) Summerh.: The natives of eastern Madagascar sometimes ate the tubers (Jumelle, 1910; Usher, 1974).

E. plantaginea Rolfe: In eastern Madagascar the natives sometimes ate the tubers (Jumelle, 1910).

Habenaria walleri Rchb. f.: In Malawi the tubers are used in the same way as the *Disa* listed above (Williamson, 1955).

Satyrium sp.: The tubers are used in Malawi in the same way as *Disa* (Williamson, 1955).

S. bicorne Thunb., *S. candidum* Lindl., *S. carneum* R. Br., and *S. erectum* Sw.: The large tuberous roots contain much sweet nutritious juice (Pappe, 1857; Watt and Breyer-Brandwijk, 1962).

4.2. The Americas

Tubers of orchids are listed as emergency foods in eastern North America (Fernald and Kinsey, 1943).[28]

Aplectrum hyemale (Muhl. ex Willd.) Torr.: The baked bulbs are not disagreeable to eat, and many people have professed to be fond of them (Niles, 1904).

Bletia verecunda R. Br.: In the West Indies the bulbs were eaten; the taste is piquant and bitter, leaving a sensation of warmth (Morren, 1846).

Calypso borealis Salisb.: The bulbs were eaten by the Creek people of North America (Uphof, 1959) and by the Indians of the northwestern United States and Alaska (Yanovsky, 1936). Kirk (1975) reports that the tubers are edible raw, roasted, or boiled.

---

[28]Kirk (1975) and McPherson and McPherson (1977) properly discourage the use of these rare and protected plants as wild food.

Epilobium coloratum Muhl. ex Willd.: This plant was used by the Hopis of Arizona to make bread (Hough, 1897; Castetter, 1935).

Goodyera menziesii Lindl.: The exudation of this plant has been used as a chewing gum by the Indians of British Columbia (Yanovsky, 1936).

Habenaria dilatata A. Gray: Kirk (1975) reports that the tuber-like roots, raw or cooked, are edible.

H. sparsiflora S. Wats.: In times of want New Mexico Indians ate the plant (Castetter, 1935; Yanovsky, 1936; Uphof, 1959).

Maxillaria bicolor Ruiz et Pav.: A viscid fluid from the pseudobulbs was sucked with delight by the people of Peru (Morren, 1846).

Stanhopea tigrina Batem.: The flowers were used in the preparation of tortillas in some parts of Mexico (Urbina, 1903a).

4.3. Asia

In northeastern India the local tribes use *Cymbidium* species for food. The new shoots are ground and made into a sauce for cereals and the pseudobulbs are eaten like potatoes with curry or boiled and eaten with salt (Pempahishey, 1974).

Cephalanthera ensifolia Rich.: In India the roots and rhizomes were used as food (Duggal, 1972).

Cremastra variabilis Nakai: The rooty stem has been eaten in Japan (T. Tanaka, 1976).

C. wallichiana Lindl.: The boiled root of this plant was sometimes eaten by the Ainu of Japan (Batchelor and Miyabe, 1893).

Eulophia campestris Wall.: Joret (1904) reports that the bulbs have formed part of the diet of the Indian people from time immemorial.

Gastrodia elata Bl.: In China the raw or steamed tubers were used for food (Stuart, 1911); they were eaten roasted in China, Japan, and Tibet (Henry, 1887; Forbes and Hemsley, 1903; Goeze, 1916; Bulhart, 1927; Hawkes, 1943).

Habenaria acuminata Thw. ex Trim.: The roots have been used as food in India (Duggal, 1972).

H. commelinifolia Wall. ex Lindl.: In the western Himalayas the tuberous roots were used to make a gruel (Usher, 1974).

H. susannae R. Br.: The tubers were relished by jungle tribes in India (*Wealth of India*, 1959; Chopra, Chopra, and Varma, 1969).

Liparis japonica Maxim.: In Korea the young leaves were boiled as a vegetable (T. Tanaka, 1976).

Orchis sp.: Watt (1891) notes a dubious report that the Afghans cooked the leaves with ghee and ate them.

O. coriophora L.: The dried root was cooked and eaten in the Levant (Hedrick, 1919).

O. latifolia L.: In India the tubers are reported to be edible (Maheshwari and Singh, 1965).

Pholidota articulata Lindl.: The stems were used as food in India (Duggal, 1972).

Platanthera delavayi Schltr.: In China the fleshy root was cooked for food (Hu, 1957).

Satyrium spp.: Several species were used for food in India (Duggal, 1972).

Spathoglottis eburnea Gagn.: The bulbs of this orchid have been eaten in Indochina (Gagnepain and Guillaumin, 1933; Pételot, 1954; Douk, 1966).

Spiranthes australis Lindl.: The cooked fleshy root was used for food in China (Hu, 1957).

4.4. Australasia and Oceania

There are many reports of the use of orchids for food in this area, particularly by the aboriginal people of Australia (Campbell, 1905b). While these reports may seem incommensurate with those involving comparable peoples elsewhere, it should be remembered that the aboriginal Australians and Tasmanians were nomadic peoples who practiced virtually no agriculture (Campbell, 1965). In an inhospitable land of largely arid climate, they looked to tuberous plants for a considerable proportion of their vegetable food (Meggitt, 1964). There are some 500 terrestrial species of orchids in Australia, many of which occur in large colonies, and some inhabit areas of low rainfall. It is therefore logical for orchids to have had comparatively intensive use in Australia. Uses of orchids as food in Australia have been reported by many observers, notably Maiden (1888b, 1889); these reports have been summarized by Lawler and Slaytor (1970b) and Lawler (1981).[29]

Orchid tubers have been used for food by the aboriginal peoples of New South Wales (Palmer, 1883), Northern Territory (W. Marika, personal communication), Queensland (Petrie, 1932), South Australia (Campbell, Cleland, and Hossfield, 1946;[30] Cleland, 1957), Tasmania (Anonymous, 1834; Gunn, 1842), Victoria (Smyth, 1876; Dawson, 1881; Morris, 1943; Cleland, 1964; Blainey, 1975), Western Australia (Grey, 1841; Moore, 1842; Anonymous, 1877; Meagher, 1974), and New Zealand (R. Taylor, 1848, 1870). In Tasmania and Western Australia the leaves also have been used for food (Nind, 1832; Roth, 1899; Campbell, 1905a; Noetling, 1911; Meagher, 1974).[31]

The bulbs of some species of orchids were eagerly sought after by the aboriginal people of New South Wales; highly esteemed for food because of their viscous mucilage, they were known as *boyams* (Simmonds, 1854b; 1877; Anonymous, 1977).[32] Hunter (1793), writing of the first settlement at Port Jackson, describes the use of roots for food by the aboriginal Australians. The "yams" that he describes undoubtedly included tubers of terrestrial orchids (Colliver, 1974).

[29]The statement of Ratzel (1896) that the northwestern Australians know how to deprive the orchid bulbs of their poisons is clearly without foundation.

[30] These authors state they are making an inference of aboriginal use of orchids for food from Mueller's list in Smyth (1876). Compare n. 31.

[31]Noetling (1911) and Meagher (1974) very properly draw attention to those published reports that list plants that are "available" as food. Such reports must be read carefully to ascertain whether a plant has in fact been used by the aboriginal people or the later colonists. See n. 30. Compare also Smyth (1876), Campbell *et al.* (1946), Hope and Coutts (1971), and Jones (1971).

[32]New South Wales originally consisted of the whole eastern half of Australia. Early reports do not necessarily refer to the state of New South Wales within its present boundaries. For an exact definition of state boundaries since 1786, see Holmes (1963).

Tubers of terrestrial orchids, notably *Diuris* species, known as "yams" by the present Australian population, have been and still are extensively eaten by both aborigines and people of European origin; they are juicy, with a sweetish taste, and are much relished by children (Hamilton, 1888, 1937; Maiden, 1898; Sulman, 1914; Lawler and Slaytor, 1970b).

Lucas (1912) states that the bulbs of terrestrial orchids and the pseudobulbs of epiphytes were usually roasted before they were eaten. With some definite exceptions, quoted here, reports do not support this statement. Tubers of terrestrial orchids are usually eaten raw; Hope and Coutts (1971) and Meagher (1974), however, suggest that they sometimes were cooked.

The tubers of (unspecified) orchids are recommended as emergency bush foods for travelers in the interior (Anonymous, n.d.).

Acianthus spp.: In Victoria tubers were commonly eaten by the natives (Smyth, 1876).

Caladenia spp.: The tubers have been used for food by Australian aborigines and colonists (Smyth, 1876; Maiden, 1888b, 1889; Hitchcock, 1962). Irvine (1957) implies that they were eaten throughout Australia.[33]

C. carnea R. Br.: Aborigines in South Australia ate the tubers (Boyd, 1966).

C. dilatata R. Br.: The aboriginal people of northwestern Victoria ate the tubers (Morris, 1943).

C. pattersonii R. Br.: The tubers were eaten by Victorian aborigines (Keble, 1917; Morris, 1943).

Cryptostylis erecta R. Br.: The roots of this orchid (one of three locally known as "yams") were a staple food of the aboriginal people of the Beecroft Penninsula, New South Wales (Lampert and Sanders, 1973).

C. leptochila F. Muell. ex Benth. and *C. subulata* (Labill.) Rchb. f.: These two species were eaten by the aboriginal population of Wilsons Promontory, Victoria (Hope and Coutts, 1971).

Cymbidium spp.: Leichhardt (1849) states that the stems of a *Cymbidium* are edible but very glutinous and insipid; the stems may be used for food (Woolls, 1879). The pseudobulbs of *Cymbidium*, particularly *C. canaliculatum* R. Br., were used by the aboriginal people of eastern Australia for food, either chewed raw or made into a form of tapioca or sago (White, 1938).

C. canaliculatum R. Br.: The tubers, which are of a gelatinous sticky consistency, were used as food by northern Queensland aborigines (Palmer, 1883, 1884).[34] Starch has been prepared from the pseudobulbs (Flecker, Stephens, and Stephens, 1948). Aborigines of southeastern Queensland ate the tender parts of the stem and the base of the

---

[33]As Irvine here quoted Maiden (1889), this statement is questionable. Clearly what Maiden wrote was that the genus occurs thoughout Australia. In his preface Maiden makes it clear that the tubers were eaten by the aborigines, but he does not delimit any geographical area.

[34]Irvine (1957) writes, citing Palmer (1883), "Mueller says of *Cymbidium canaliculatum* (Orchideae) that it is the only orchid of Australia which affords mucilaginous food." This is erroneous, as is his further statement, again citing Palmer, that the aborigines dug up the tubers. Neither of these statements is from Palmer; furthermore, *C. canaliculatum* is a pseudobulbous plant, epiphytic on trees.

leaves (Woolls, 1867). The pseudobulbs were eaten by aborigines on the Darling River in New South Wales (Turner, 1903). Mueller (1858) reported that this orchid afforded a mucilaginous food for Gregory's expedition in northern Australia.[35] Hedley (1888) stressed its value as an emergency food, advising that even the raw fruit and pseudobulbs will support life, and that the grated and cooked pseudobulbs were indistinguishable from arrowroot.

C. madidum Lindl.: The aborginal people of Queensland used this orchid for food (Bailey, 1889).[36] The pseudobulbs were used for food by the aboriginal people (Maiden, 1899). Starch can be prepared from the pseudobulbs (Flecker *et al.*, 1948).

C. suave R. Br.: This orchid was eaten by the aboriginal people on the northern coast of New South Wales (Browne, 1894).

Dendrobium spp.: The stems of *Dendrobium* may be used for food (Woolls, 1879).

D. canaliculatum R. Br.: Aboriginal people of northern Queensland used this orchid for food. The pseudobulbs are edible when stripped of the old leaves and baked (Thozet, 1866, 1868; Crawfurd, 1868; Maiden, 1888b).

D. speciosum Sm.: The pseudobulbs have been eaten by the aboriginal Australian people (J. Smith, 1882; Maiden, 1889, 1899).

Dipodium sp. Natives of Victoria commonly ate the tubers (Smyth, 1876).

D. punctatum (Sm.) R. Br.: The tubers of this plant were eaten by the aboriginal people of Wilsons Promontory, Victoria (Hope and Coutts, 1971).

Diuris spp.: The bulbs are edible (Woolls, 1867). They were eaten by the natives of Victoria (Smyth, 1876), New South Wales (Maiden, 1899), and Tasmania (Backhouse, 1843; Hitchcock, 1962).

D. longifolia R. Br. and *D. maculata* Sm.: The tubers were eaten by the aboriginal people of Victoria (Keble, 1917).

D. palustris Lindl.: This orchid was used for food in western Victoria by the aboriginal people (Officer, 1868).

D. pedunculata R. Br.: The aboriginal people of Victoria ate the tubers (Keble, 1917).

Eriochilus cucullatus (Labill.) Rchb. f.: The tubers were eaten in South Australia by the aboriginal people (Boyd, 1966).

Gastrodia cunninghamii Hook. f.: The Maoris of New Zealand ate the tubers (Lindley and Moore, 1866; R. Taylor, 1870; Colenso, 1880/81; Edwards, 1913).

G. sesamoides R. Br.: The roasted roots were eaten by the Tasmanians and were called "native potatoes" by the colonists (Robinson, 1966; Anonymous, 1834; Gunn, 1842; Backhouse, 1843; Bunce, 1857; Bonwick, 1870). The tubers were eaten by the aboriginal

[35]The following statement is attributed to Mueller by several authors, including Woolls (1867) and Maiden (1888b, 1889, 1899): "[It is] the only orchid of the interior of tropical Australia which affords mucilaginous food." The only relevant passage in Mueller's writings that I have been able to find is the following: "The tender parts of the stem, and the base of the leaves of *Cymbidium canaliculatum*, the only orchid of the interior of tropical Australia, afforded a mucilaginous food." If, as seems likely, Woolls and Maiden were referring to this statement, they have misinterpreted it.

[36]Bailey says that according to Hedley (1888), the natives called this plant *dampy-ampy*, whereas in fact Hedley ascribes this name to *C. canaliculatum* R. Br. and does not mention *C. madidum*.

people of Victoria, including Wilsons Promontory (Smyth, 1876; Hope and Coutts, 1971).[37]

Geodorum pictum (R. Br.) Lindl.: The tubers were eaten in central Queensland by the aboriginal people (Hedley, 1888; Maiden, 1899).

Glossodia spp.: The native peoples of Victoria ate the bulbs (Smyth, 1876).

G. major R. Br.: This plant was eaten by the aborigines of Wilsons Promontory, Victoria (Hope and Coutts, 1971).

Liparis disepala Rchb. f.: The cooked tubers are eaten by the natives of New Calendonia (N. Hallé, personal communication).

Lyperanthus spp.: The tubers were eaten in Victoria by the natives (Smyth, 1876).

L. nigricans R. Br.: This orchid was eaten by the aboriginal people of western Victoria (Officer, 1868) and of Wilsons Promontory (Hope and Coutts, 1971).

Microtis spp.: The tubers were eaten by the native peoples of Victoria (Smyth, 1876) and Tasmania (Backhouse, 1843; Hitchcock, 1962).

M. porrifolia R. Br.: This orchid was eaten by the Maoris of New Zealand (R. Taylor, 1870; Uphof, 1959).

M. unifolia (Forst. f.) Rchb. f.: The aboriginal people of South Australia ate the tubers (Boyd, 1966).

Orthoceras strictum R. Br.: The Maoris of New Zealand ate the tubers (R. Taylor, 1870).

Prasophyllum spp.: The tubers were eaten by the natives of Victoria (Smyth, 1876), Western Australia (Meagher, 1974), and Tasmania (Backhouse, 1843; Hitchcock, 1962).

P. fimbria Rchb. f.:[38] The aboriginal people of Western Australia ate the bulbs of this plant (Moore, 1842; Meagher, 1974).

P. patens R. Br.: In western Victoria the aboriginal people used the plants for food (Officer, 1868).

Pterostylis spp.: The tubers were eaten by natives of Victoria (Smyth, 1876) and by the Tasmanians (Backhouse, 1843; Hitchcock, 1962).

P. concinna R. Br., *P. cycnocephala* Fitzg., *P. mutica* R. Br., and *P. rufa* R. Br.: The aboriginal people of the Wimmera and Mallee districts of Victoria ate the tubers of these orchids (Morris, 1943).

Thelymitra spp.: The tubers were eaten by the natives of Victoria (Smyth, 1876) and of Tasmania (Backhouse, 1843; Hitchcock, 1962). In Western Australia the aboriginal people ate the roasted tubers, and also the raw young tubers and leaves, of an orchid they called *tuboc,* which Nind (1832) suggested was a species of *Thelymitra,* but which Meagher (1974) records as *Prasophyllum* (*cf.* Anonymous, 1877; Simmonds, 1877).

---

[37]*Gastrodia sesamoides* is the orchid most often reported to have been used for food in Australia. The references given above include the two earliest yet seen. There is doubt as to the author of the 1834 report, whether Ross, Gunn, or Backhouse; see Jones (1971). Gunn attributes it to Backhouse, but there appears to be no other supporting evidence. The accounts in Ross and Gunn coincide remarkably—e.g., in describing the taste as resembling beetroot—whereas Backhouse's account gives a somewhat different description and says the tubers are watery and insipid. Bunce describes the tubers as "well flavoured."

[38]The determination of this species is doubtful, as Moore's description is inadequate.

T. antennifera (Gunn ex Lindl.) Hook.: The bulbs were eaten by the aboriginal people of Western Australia (Nicholls, 1969).

T. longifolia Forst. *et* Forst. f.: In New Zealand and Maoris ate the tubers (R. Taylor, 1870).

4.5. Europe

The use of orchids for food in Europe has almost exclusively taken the form of salep (see sec. 14.10). There are recipes for salep jelly and salep soup in *Larousse gastronomique* (Froud and Turgeon, 1961).

Orchis mascula L.: The dried root has been cooked and eaten in Greece (Pickering, 1879; Hedrick, 1919).

O. morio L., *O. papilionacea* L., and *O. longicruris* Link: The dried roots were cooked and eaten in Greece (Pickering, 1879).

4.6. Indo-Malaysian Region

Anoectochilus albo-lineatus Par. *et* Rchb. f., *A. geniculata* Ridl., and *A. reinwardtii* Bl.: These orchids, formerly abundant, were sold in the markets of West Malaysia for use as pot herbs (Ridley, 1924; Hawkes, 1944b; Burkill, 1935, 1966).

Ceratostylis latifolia Bl.: The people of western Java still eat the young leaves, either cooked or raw as a salad (Rifai, 1975).

Epiblastus cuneatus J. J. Sm.: The new shoots are used for food by children in Enga Province, Papua New Guinea (Reeve, 1981).

Eulophia sp.: In Ambon the roots were used as a preserve after being well extracted with water (Rumphius, 1750; Heyne, 1922, 1927).

Goodyera rubicunda Lindl.: The Kukukuku of New Guinea eat the fresh leaves with salt (Blackwood, 1940; Powell, 1976a).[39]

Habenaria sp.: The tubers were foraged and eaten as a supplementary food in eastern New Guinea (Massal and Barrau, 1955; Treide, 1967; Powell, 1976a).

H. multipartita Bl. ex Kraenzl.: The tubers were eaten by the native people in Java (Bunnemeijer, 1918; Heyne, 1922, 1927; Bakhuizen van den Brink, 1937).

H. rumphii Lindl.: In Ambon the bulbs were pickled and eaten (Rumphius, 1750; Heyne, 1922, 1927; Smith, 1927; Dakkus, 1935).

Nervilia flabelliformis (Lindl.) Tang *et* Wang: The fresh tubers are chewed in Guam to quench thirst (Safford, 1905; Burkill, 1935, 1966).

Phalaenopsis amabilis Bl.: It has been reported that the tops of the leaves were used as a vegetable in Java (Backer, 1936; Latif, 1960; Rifai, 1975).

Renanthera moluccana Bl.: The young leaves were pickled in salt or vinegar and used by the natives of Ambon for flavoring (Rumphius, 1750; J. J. Smith, 1927; Burkill, 1966).

Thelymitra papuana J. J. Sm.: In the eastern highlands of Papua New Guinea the tubers have been eaten (Hays, 1980).

---

[39]Straatmans (1971) cites Coode (1969) as saying that the juice is used as food, but Coode makes no such statement.

5. Vanilla

Vanilla is the sole product from the Orchidaceae which is of significant economic importance in the world today. It is a product of several species of the genus *Vanilla* Sw. and is extracted from fermented partially ripe capsules.

The active principle vanillin, methylprotocatechuic aldehyde or 3-methoxy-4-hydroxy benzaldehyde (Fig. 2-1, I), was isolated in 1858 by Gobley, who named it vanilline. After Carles (1870, 1872) had purified vanillin and established its formula, Tiemann and Haarmaan (1874) succeeded in preparing vanillin artificially by splitting coniferin, and thereafter the synthetic product supplied an increasing proportion of the demand.[40] As the flavor is not due solely to vanillin, however, the natural product is often held to be superior, and the demand for it is still sufficient to warrant cultivation on a large scale in several countries.[41] The curing process is essentially one of alternate drying and sweating, during which enzymolysis produces vanillin and other compounds (whose function in the flavor is not yet properly understood).[42] Lawler, Slaytor, and Done (1971) have referred to the importance of vanillin in the C_6–C_1 group of chemical constituents of Orchidaceae. For a discussion of the chemistry of vanillin, see Hegnauer (1963).

5.1. History

Vanilla is a product of the New World. It was cultivated in pre-Columbian times and used by the Mayas and Aztecs, but the extent of its antiquity is not known (Roys, 1931; Hill, 1937; Pardal, 1937).

By 1510, Spaniards had carried vanilla to Europe, where it was used as a perfume. The account of Cortés' visit to the court of Montezuma in 1520 mentions the use of the beverage *chocolatl* (chocolate),[43] which reached Europe in the same year. It subsequently became known that the flavoring materials of *chocolatl* included vanilla (called by the Aztecs *tlilxochitl,* literally "black pod" or "black flower"), and Spanish factories were making chocolate flavored with vanilla in the second half of the sixteenth century (Díaz del Castillo, 1632, trans. 1974; Morren, 1839,[44] 1846; Urbina, 1903a; Gates, 1939; Correll, 1953; Täckholm and Drar, 1969; Arditti, 1971; Reinikka, 1972).

It is recorded that Montezuma took no beverage other than *chocolatl,* and that fifty pitchers were prepared for his own daily consumption. The beverage was prepared to a consistency that melted gradually in the mouth and was served in golden goblets with spoons of gold or tortoise shell. He was reputed to drink the beverage before visiting his

[40]Artificial vanillin is prepared from coniferin, eugenol, guiacol, and other sources (Wood, Remington, and Sadtler, 1886; Täckholm and Drar, 1969).

[41]Leyel (1970) states that "French cooking, which is founded on making food nourishing as well as appetizing, discards all synthetic essences of vanilla and only uses the vanilla bean."

[42]The concentration of vanillin in the end product is between 1.70% and 2.75% (Maisch, 1890; Planchon and Collin, 1895).

[43]Díaz' eyewitness account does not support the suggestion that Cortés himself was served chocolate by Montezuma, nor does Cortés (1843) refer to it in his dispatches.

[44]Morren states that vanilla was introduced at the same time as cacao, cochineal, and indigo, some ten years before the introduction of tobacco.

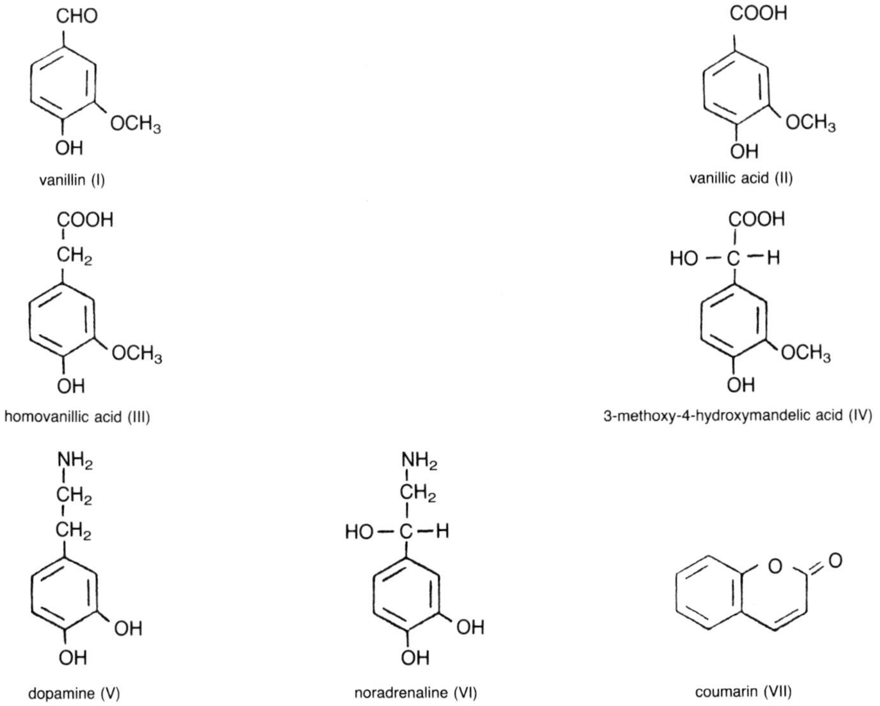

CHO

OCH₃

OH

vanillin (I)

COOH

OCH₃

OH

vanillic acid (II)

COOH

CH₂

OCH₃

OH

homovanillic acid (III)

COOH

HO — C — H

OCH₃

OH

3-methoxy-4-hydroxymandelic acid (IV)

NH₂

CH₂

CH₂

OH

OH

dopamine (V)

NH₂

CH₂

HO — C — H

OH

OH

noradrenaline (VI)

O

O

coumarin (VII)

Fig. 2-1. Vanillin and related compounds

wives (Díaz del Castillo, 1632, trans. 1974; Prescott, 1904). Vanilla was, and still is, used in Yucatan for similar flavoring purposes (Standley, 1930; Gates, 1939).

L'Escluse (1605) published the first botanical notice of a *Vanilla* species based on material obtained from Hugh Morgan, apothecary to Queen Elizabeth I (Rolfe, 1895, 1896a; Correll, 1953).[45] There is some doubt as to when the first living plant was brought to Europe. Rolfe (1895) dates the arrival in England before 1739, in which year P. Miller, in *The Second Volume of the Gardeners Dictionary*, gave an account of the importation of a Mexican plant, which subsequently had produced roots and leaves;[46] Rolfe assumes this plant did not survive. A plant introduced by the Marquis of Blandford in 1800 was cultivated in the Paddington garden of Charles Greville, where it flowered and fruited in, or perhaps before, 1807,[47] in which year a flowering specimen was figured and described by Salisbury under the name of *Myobroma fragrans*. A year later Andrews

[45]Morgan subsequently advocated the use of vanilla as a flavoring apart from its use in chocolate (Correll, 1953; Reinikka, 1972).

[46]Some authors are confused in their citation of Miller's work. The work first appeared in 1731; a second edition was published in 1733 and a third in 1737. Vanilla is not mentioned in these editions or in the appendix that appeared in 1735. In 1739 *The Second Volume of the Gardeners Dictionary: Which Completes the Work*" appeared, which included the above account of vanilla.

[47]There is doubt as to whether this plant did in fact bear fruit. A capsule shown in a drawing by Francis Bauer is reputed to be of this plant, but this is not unanimously accepted (Morren, 1839; Rolfe, 1895, 1896a; Correll, 1953; Childers, Cibes, and Hernández-Medina, 1959).

published another figure as *Vanilla planifolia*. Cuttings from this plant were supplied to Paris and Antwerp (Morren, 1839; Rolfe, 1896a; Correll, 1953; Reinikka, 1972). Vanilla is said to have been the first tropical orchid in the greenhouses of England (Goeze, 1916). Rolfe (1895) gives the history of vanilla in more detail.

5.2. Etymology

The English word *vanilla* is an adaptation of the Spanish *vainilla*, derived from *vaina*, a diminutive of the Latin *vagina*, meaning sheath or (of plants) hull or husk (Pereira, 1850; *Diccionario de la lengua española*, 1956; *Oxford English Dictionary*, 1961). It is clear that the Spaniards followed the Aztecs in naming the plant for the capsule (Urbina, 1903a; Correll, 1953; Schultes and Pease, 1963; Plowden, 1972); a suggestion by Wedeck (1962) that the plant was named from the human vagina because of its reputation as on aphrodisiac should be disregarded. The first use of the word *vaynilla*, from which the generic name is derived, is attributed to William Piso in 1658 (Rolfe, 1895; Correll, 1953).

5.3. Botany

Vanilla Sw. is a genus of the subtribe Vanillinae, which includes the tallest orchids known. The plants are climbing, terrestrial, or epiphytic, and have large fleshy leaves or are apparently leafless.[48] The genus consists of some sixty species, essentially tropical, occurring in Central and South America, Africa, Southeast Asia, and Polynesia. The revision of the genus by Rolfe (1896a) is still very useful.

5.4. Species of Major Economic Importance

Only three species are now important for the production of vanilla, namely, *V. planifolia* G. Jackson in Andr., *V. pompona* Schiede, and *V. tahitensis* J. W. Moore. The first of these species is native to the West Indies, Mexico, Central America, and northern South America; the second to Central America, northern South America, and Trinidad; and the third to Tahiti. Vanilla from *V. planifolia* is the vanilla of commerce, that from *V. tahitensis* is of lesser quality, and that from *V. pompona*, sometimes known as "vanillon," is regarded as of low quality. The latter has been used as an adulterant (Pereira, 1850; Correll, 1953), and, being difficult to dry, was sometimes used uncured by tobacco and perfume manufacturers (Rolfe, 1896a).

There has been some confusion over the nomenclature of the Mexican plant that produces the vanilla of commerce. *V. planifolia* G. Jackson in Andr. is now the accepted name, taking precedence over *Myobroma fragrans* Salisb. *nom. illegit.* and *V. fragrans* (Salisb.) Ames (Ames, 1924; Portères, 1954; Mansfeld, 1959; Täckholm and Drar, 1969; Garay and Sweet, 1974).[49]

---

[48]*V. planifolia* G. Jackson in Andr., together with other orchids, has been shown to exhibit crassulacean acid metabolism, normally an adaptation to arid conditions (Dittrich, 1976; Goh *et al.*, 1977; Avadhani, Goh, and Arditti, 1978).

[49]*V. aromatica* Sw. was long thought to be the species used by the Aztecs to flavor chocolate and to be the source of commercial vanilla; however, it is scentless (Morren, 1846; Pereira, 1850; Mühle, 1923; Bulhart, 1927). The U.S. pharmacopoeia formerly ascribed commercial vanilla to this species (Wood *et al.*, 1886).

5.5. Species of Minor Economic Importance

Several species are reported to have been involved in commercial vanilla production in a minor way:

V. claviculata Sw.: This plant has been grown experimentally in Puerto Rico because of its resistance to disease, but there is no record of its commercial use (Childers and Cibes, 1949).

V. ensifolia Rolfe: As part of a collection of commercial varieties at Kew, this plant was reported to be the probable source of some of the vanilla occasionally imported from South America (Anonymous, 1892b).

V. gardneri Rolfe: The source of "Brazilian vanilla," and perhaps of "South American vanilla," it has been used chiefly as an adulterant of vanilla from *V. planifolia* (Rolfe, 1896a) and has had limited commercial use as a flavoring agent (Uphof, 1959).

V. guianensis Split.: The aromatic fruit of this plant has been used for flavoring (Pereira, 1850; Wood *et al.*, 1886; Cointe, 1934; Uphof, 1959), but its inferior product may be used also as an adulterant (Correll, 1953).

V. palmarum Lindl.: This species has an aromatic fruit (Wood *et al.*, 1886) and is the source of "Rio vanilla," a product of inferior quality (Pereira, 1850) that may be used to adulterate vanilla (Correll, 1953).

V. phaenantha Rchb. f.: Grown experimentally in Puerto Rico because of its resistance to disease, it has been cultivated in the West Indies, but the fruit is said to possess very little perfume (Rolfe, 1896a; Childers and Cibes, 1949; Correll, 1953). The capsules have occasionally been collected and sold as vanilla beans (Uphof, 1959).

V. sylvestris Schiede: This species is the source of the Spanish *vainilla simarona* of commerce. The capsules are reported to have little aroma and to contain no vanillin (Wood *et al.*, 1886).

5.6. Species Used Locally for Flavoring

Local uses for similar purposes are reported for the following:

V. abundiflora J. J. Sm.: This plant has aromatic capsules, but there is no evidence of its having been cultivated (Correll, 1953; Täckholm and Drar, 1969). Although it develops a less strong flavor than the commercially cultivated species, it was used by the natives of Kalimantan, on the island of Borneo, in the manner of *V. planifolia* (Heyne, 1922, 1927; Hawkes, 1943).

V. appendiculata Rolfe: This species has aromatic fruits but is not reported in commerce (Rolfe, 1896a). The fruits are said to retain their aroma for 25 years or more (Correll, 1953).[50]

V. duckei Huber: The fruit has been used for vanilla in Brazil (Cointe, 1934; T. Tanaka, 1976).

V. eggersii Rolfe: The capsules of this species are used in Cuba to flavor tobacco and are sold in drugstores for use as vanilla (Roig y Mesa, 1945).

[50]Correll incorrectly attributes this figure to Rolfe (1896a), who in fact gave 17 years.

V. ensifolia Rolfe: In New Granada the fruits were considered to be similar to vanilla (Dragendorff, 1898).

V. griffithii Rchb. f.: The large, soft fruits, like small bananas, are sweet and edible (Ridley, 1893, 1902, 1924; Anonymous, 1895a; Foxworthy, 1922; Heyne, 1913, 1922; Bulhart, 1930) and were eaten fresh in Malaysia and Indonesia (Hawkes, 1943; Rifai, 1975). It has not the faintest trace of vanillin, or the flavor or perfume of the American plant (Ridley, 1902, 1912). Holttum (1964) reports that the large fruits of the Malaysian species, including *V. griffithii,* are sweet and edible.

V. odorata Presl: This species has aromatic fruits that are not known in commerce (Rolfe, 1896a). It is said that the perfume is retained after 36 years (Presl quoted by Correll, 1953). The fruits were a favorite in Ecuador and much prized as a spice (Ames, 1925; Anonymous, 1925; Bulhart, 1927).

V. parvifolia Rodrig.: The fruit is the source of an aromatic extract used for flavoring confectionery in Brazil (T. Tanaka, 1976).

5.7. Vanillin in Orchids of Other Genera

The following orchids are reputed to contain vanillin: *Cephalanthera pallens* Rich. (Summerhayes, 1968); *Eria pannea* Lindl. (Holttum, 1964); *Gastrodia elata* Bl. (Zhou, Fu, and Lei, 1965; Oliver-Bever, 1968); *Stanhopea tigrina* Batem. (Urbina, 1903a; Goeze, 1916); *Thrixspermum malayanum* J. J. Sm. (Backer and Bakhuizen van den Brink, 1968); *Jumellea fragrans* Schltr. syn. *Angraecum fragrans* Thou.; *Nigritella nigra* (L.) Rchb. f.; *Orchis fusca* Jacq.; *Spiranthes cernua* Rich. (Correll, 1953).

5.8. Substitutes and Adulterants

In addition to the inferior vanillas mentioned above which have been used as diluents or substitutes for first-grade vanilla, several plant products and chemicals are reported to have been used as substitutes or adulterants.

Substitutes. Vanilla chica is prepared from the fruits of *Selenipedium chica* Rchb. f.; these fruits replace vanilla and were highly esteemed by the people of Panama (Rolfe, 1896b; Bulhart, 1927; Hawkes, 1943; Correll, 1953; Uphof, 1959), and were used for all purposes for which vanilla is commonly used (Seeman, 1852–1857). The fruits of *S. isobelianum* Rodrig., *S. liliastrum* Lindl., and *Tetramicra bicolor* Rolfe and the leaves of *Jumellea fragrans* Schltr. have served a similar purpose (Rolfe, 1869b; Pfitzer, 1903; Bulhart, 1927; Cointe, 1934). *Chica vanilla* or *vanilla chica* is also the name given in Panama to the fruit of a species of *Sobralia* (Seeman, 1852–1857; Lindley and Moore, 1866).

Vegetable adulterants. In a sense, vegetable adulterants are chemical adulterants, as the basis of adulteration is usually the presence of coumarin, 1,2-benzopyrone (Fig. 2-1, VII), which has a pleasant and fragrant odor resembling that of vanilla and a burning taste. It is worth noting here that coumarin in high concentration is toxic to humans (Correll, 1953).

The tonka bean or snuff bean (*Dipteryx* species) is the main source of coumarin and has been described as the most notorious adulterant of vanilla (Täckholm and Drar, 1969). *Vanilla trilisa,* prepared from *Trilisa odoratissima* Cass., has been reported to contain coumarin and to have been used at one time as an adulterant mainly for the flavoring of tobacco (Correll, 1953; Uphof, 1959; Täckholm and Drar, 1969).

Vanilla chica, which also contains coumarin, has been reported as an adulterant (Hawkes, 1943; Uphof, 1959; Täckholm and Drar, 1969). Species of *Aceras, Habenaria,* and *Orchis* containing coumarin are reported as adulterants (Täckholm and Drar, 1969).[51]

Tincture of balsam of Peru has been reported as a substitute for tincture of vanilla (Pereira, 1850).

Chemical Adulterants. The main chemical adulterant is, of course, artificial vanillin, but substituted vanillins and related compounds are often used. The most common is benzoic acid (Planchon and Collin, 1895; Correll, 1953; Täckholm and Drar, 1969). Exhausted or inferior capsules have been sprinkled with benzoic acid crystals to make them resemble the original product (Correll, 1953; Täckholm and Drar, 1969). Acetanilide has also been used (Täckholm and Drar, 1969), and even lead silicate (Planchon and Collin, 1895).

5.9 Cultivation

Vanilla cultivation has been introduced to many countries. Vanilla is now harvested chiefly in Madagascar and the adjacent islands, Mexico, tropical Africa, Java, Central and South America, the West Indies, Tahiti, and Fiji (Correll, 1953). It has been introduced with limited success into India, Malaysia, the Philippines, Hawaii, Trinidad, Bolivia, Peru, and Venezuela (Hill, 1937; Correll, 1953). Cultivation in New Caledonia (Guillaumin, 1954) and Australia (Anonymous, 1899; White, 1938) has not been commercially successful.

As the vanilla vine is subject to many diseases, attempts have been made to introduce hybrids to improve yields and combat disease and pests (Childers and Cibes, 1949; Correll, 1953). The first such work was done in 1938 by Knudson (Reinikka, 1972).

Morren (1839) reported the first successful artificial pollination of *Vanilla* species in Liège in 1836. In 1841 Edmond Albius, in Réunion, discovered a practical method of artificial pollination. His technique made possible the large-scale cultivation of the plants in areas where there are no natural pollinators, and has been adopted also in areas where

---

[51]Other orchids contain coumarin, either when fresh or after being dried. Among them are *Aceras anthropophora* R. Br., *Jumellea fragrans* Schltr. syn. *Angraecum fragrans* Thou., *Nigritella nigra* (L.) Rchb. f., *Orchis coriophora* L., *O. galeata* Poir., *O. militaris* L., *O. purpurea* Huds., and *O. simia* Lam. (Dragendorff, 1898; Hérissey and Delauney, 1922; Perrot, 1943a; Summerhayes, 1968); *Gymnadenia conopsea* (L.) R. Br. and *G. odoratissima* (L.) Rich. (Fournier, 1948); and *Bulbophyllum auricomum* Lindl. (Backer and Bakhuizen van den Brink, 1968). Geoffroy (1742) reports the smell of coumarin in the water remaining after the preparation of salep, and also in the fading flowers of the species he used.

In 1919 Bourquelot and Bridel isolated a glucoside, which they named loroglossine, from *Himantoglossum hircinum* Spreng. syn. *Loroglossum hircinum* Rich. Hérissey and Delauney (1922) showed that coumarin is formed from a glucoside, and it is now known that it is produced by hydrolysis of loroglossine (Perrot, 1943a; Fournier, 1948). Delauney (1921) and Wehmer (1929) list several orchid species reported to contain loroglossine. For a comprehensive discussion of coumarin and loroglossine in orchids, see Hegnauer (1963).

the indigenous plants are cultivated (Rolfe, 1895; Correll, 1953; Childers *et al.,* 1959; Arditti, 1971).

5.10. Vanilla Poisoning and Allergic Reactions

Suggestions made from time to time that outbreaks of poisoning after the consumption of vanilla-flavored confectionery were due to vanillin have been questioned, and it has been suggested that bacteria or bacterial toxins have been responsible (Correll, 1953; see also Chapter 6 of this volume).

Vanillism. Vanillism is the name given to a disorder that sometimes occurs among plantation or factory workers who are exposed to the latexlike exudation from the cut stem of the vine (Bouton, 1864) or who handle the capsules (Ridley, 1912; Caius, 1936; Bouriquet, 1954). It is characterized by urticaria, sometimes accompanied by headache and gastric trouble (Correll, 1953). Some authorities have suggested that the condition arises from contact with other materials used in the processing of the capsules (Anonymous, 1907; E. P. Smith, 1920), but there is no doubt that some parts of the vanilla plant contain substances that irritate the skin (Anonymous, 1906; Hiley, 1909).

The leaf of the cultivated vanilla in Réunion is reported to have been used as a blistering agent (Ridley, 1912; Correll, 1953). The sap from *V. griffithii* Rchb. f. has a very irritating action on the skin (Ridley, 1896, 1907), and the juice of *V. claviculata* Sw. brings out blisters on the skin (Anonymous, 1952a; Richter, 1965).

Female workers in vanilla factories may present symptoms of masculinity or anomalies of the menstrual cycle (Boiteau, 1979).

For fuller discussions of vanillism, see Mitchell and Rook (1979) and Chapter 6 of this volume.

5.11. Uses of Vanilla

Following the discovery by the Western world of the use of vanilla as a flavoring, its use has continued and spread to all parts of the world. The first vanilla extract was prepared in 1847 by Joseph Burnett, an American druggist, and replaced the capsule itself for flavoring (Lorant, 1961). It is used extensively to flavor confectionary, beverages, pastries, custards, and other foods, snuff and tobacco, and in perfumes (Browne, 1789; Burnett, 1835; Pereira, 1850; Correll, 1953).

Importation of vanilla beans into the United States has been increasing, as the following figures indicate: in 1935, 413.6 tons (A. F. Hill, 1937); in 1951, 638 tons (Correll, 1953); and in the first four months of 1974, 528 tons (U.S. Department of Commerce, Bureau of the Census, 1974).[52]

In the course of its history, vanilla acquired an incredible reputation, now all but lost, as a medicine and as an aphrodisiac. Belief in its medicinal properties was strong during the sixteenth century, but it waned and disappeared by the end of the nineteenth century (Flückiger and Hanbury, 1874; Puydt, 1880; Täckholm and Drar, 1969). The

---

[52]By comparison, 58 tons of tonka beans were imported during the same period (U.S. Department of Commerce, Bureau of the Census, 1974).

present medicinal use of vanilla is confined to the flavoring of otherwise unpalatable medicaments (Ridley, 1912; Freise, 1933; Correll, 1953).

Medicinal Uses. The following quotation illustrates the imagined powers that were once attributed to vanilla. "They [the capsules] are very cordial, cephalic, stomachic, aperative and carminative, opening all obstructions, attenuating viscous humors, provoking urine and menstrual discharge" (Barham, 1794). Descourtilz (1829), Leclerc (1864), Roques (1941), and Arias-Alzate (1971) are perhaps even more enthusiastic in their praise of its virtues.[53]

Vanilla has been officially listed in the pharmacopoeias of many countries, including Austria, Belgium, Finland, France, Germany, Greece, Japan, Portugal, Switzerland, Turkey, and the United States (Mitlacher, 1912; Youngken, 1914; Caius, 1936). It was administered as a powder (capsules ground with sucrose), syrup, tincture (one part vanilla to six parts rectified spirit), essence, or aqueous infusion. The dose was one dram of powder (equal to about 12 grains of pure vanilla) or 15 ml of 2.5% infusion (Pereira, 1850; Wood *et al.*, 1886; Martínez, 1959).

Vanilla is a stimulant that has some influence on the nervous system. It has been recommended for hysteria and low fevers (Wood *et al.*, 1886; Ridley, 1912; Leyel, 1970). It was considered to have an exhilarating effect on the mental functions, to prevent sleep, and to increase the energy of the muscular system. Its effects were said to resemble those of balsam of Peru (Pereira, 1850). It has also been reported, however, that vanilla is detrimental to hysterics and hypochondriacs (Roques, 1809).

In Europe it has been used to treat cases of hysteria, melancholia, impotence, "asthenic fevers," and rheumatism (Pereira, 1850; Brown, 1878).

The Aztecs used vanilla as a diuretic and to purify the blood (Urbina, 1903a; Gerste, 1910; Pardal, 1937; Pérez de Barradas, 1951). It is included in the Codex Badiano as a medicinal plant (Gates, 1939; Domínguez, 1969).

In Jamaica it was said to move urine and the menses, comfort the brain, expel wind, and concoct crude humors, and was regarded as a cooling cordial, a stomachic, and a nerve tonic (Sloane, 1707; Browne, 1789).

Vanilla was used by Spanish physicians in America as a stomachic and stimulant as well as an antidote to poison and the bite of venomous animals (Correll, 1953). It was used in Mexico as an emmenagogue, to accelerate childbirth, to abort a dead fetus, to stimulate the stomach and dissipate flatus, and as an antidote to poison and snakebite (Urbina, 1903a; Martínez, 1959).

In El Salvador it is said to fortify the muscular and generative potency and to diminish uric acid in gout, chronic rheumatism, hysteria, and fever (Guzmán, 1924).

It has been used in Brazil to treat nervous diseases, uterine diseases, convulsion, metritis, chlorosis, melancholia, hypochondria, atony, sterility, and impotence, and as a tonic and emmenagogue (Penna, 1941; Silva Maia, 1942).

An infusion of the capsule is used in Puerto Rico to stimulate digestion and to flavor medicine (Núñez Meléndez, 1964).

---

[53]It is recommended that Descourtilz (1829, pp. 170–171) be read in the original French.

V. aromatica Sw.: This species was reputed to excite the digestive forces of the stomach and to make digestion easier (Leclerc, 1864), and to have been used for hysteria and hypochondria and as an emmenagogue (Rosenthal, 1862). The old dried stems mixed with syrup are used in Cuba as a vermifuge, and the same decoction and the fresh juice are used to cure ulcers. Also in Cuba an aqueous infusion of the roots is used as an antisyphilitic (Roig y Mesa, 1945). In Brazil it has been used as a stimulant and aromatic (Cointe, 1934).

V. claviculata Sw.: A decoction of the fruit was regarded by the people of Hispaniola as an excellent remedy for syphilis (Lindley, 1838; Morren, 1846; Hogg, 1858; Drag-endroff, 1898; Bulhart, 1927). The expressed juice has been used for recent wounds; because of this practice the French in Santo Domingo called it *liane à blessure* (Lindley, 1838; Morren, 1846; Hogg,1858; Bulhart, 1927; Correll, 1953). In Jamaica the expressed juice was used as a vermifuge and to promote urine flow. It was greatly esteemed by some people for treatment of gonorrhea and syphilis (Wright, 1787; Grime, 1976).

V. crenulata Rolfe: The people of the Ivory Coast use this plant as a treatment for otitis; the leaves are heated over a fire, bruised together with a capsicum, and the juice expressed and dropped into the ear (Adjanohoun and Ake Issi, 1973). It is also used by the Manos of northern Liberia for dysmenorrhea; a mat is laid on the floor and covered with a layer of steaming (boiled) leaves and another mat, and the woman then lies face down on the moist warmth (Harley, 1970).

V. eggersii Rolfe: The juice from the toasted stalk is used as a vermifuge in western Cuba (Roig y Mesa, 1945).

V. griffithii Rchb. f.: In Malaysia the flowers were pulped in water and then rubbed on the body in cases of fever (Ridley, 1907, 1924; Hawkes, 1944b; M. A. Miller, 1959).

V. palmarum Lindl.: The fruits have been used in Brazil for treatment of the nervous system, asthenic fever, torpor of the uterine system, and melancholia (Penna, 1941).

V. planifolia G. Jackson in Andr.: This species has been used as an aromatic stimulant in cases of asthenic fevers, rheumatism, and hysteria (Lindley, 1849); Dujardin-Beaumetz and Egasse, 1889). It is used in the Mascarene Islands as a digestive (Pernet, 1958). In Palau it is used against fever, hysteria, and irregular menstruation (Perry and Metzger, 1980). An aqueous extract of the leaves shows some inhibition of *Micrococcus aureus* Zopf., and of the fruit some inhibition of *Escherichia coli* (Migula) Castellani *et Chalmers* (Masiluñgan *et al.*, 1955).

V. wrightii Rchb. f.: This plant is reported to have been used as a remedy for syphilis (Dragendorff, 1898).

Vanillin is reputed to have aphrodisiac, carminative, antispasmodic, tonic, and stimulative properties (Freise, 1933; Täckholm and Drar, 1969). It is said to act as an anticonvulsive agent (Oliver-Bever, 1968). This property has been demonstrated in experimental epilepsy in guinea pigs, electroshock convulsions in rats, and metrozal convulsions in mice; epileptic discharge in electroencephalography is reduced by vanillin (Zhou *et al.*, 1965). It is reported to assist protein synthesis and muscle regeneration, and to be useful in postoperative and posttraumatic states and in some types of prostatic hypertrophy. Its androgenic properties effect weight increase in the seminal vesicles of young castrated rats (Boiteau, 1979).

Through its oxidation product, vanillic acid (Fig. 2-1, II), vanillin is structurally related to homovanillic acid (Fig. 2-1, III) and 3-methoxy-4-hydroxy-mandelic acid (Fig. 2-1, IV, wrongly called vanillylmandelic acid), the naturally occurring degradation products of the neurotransmitters dopamine (Fig. 2-1, V) and noradrenaline (Fig. 2-1, VI) respectively (McGilvery, 1970).

Aphrodisiac Uses. Vanilla is an aromatic stimulant to which aphrodisiac properties have been attributed (Pereira, 1850; Planchon and Collin, 1895). Vanilla flavoring was once considered by both gourmets and erotologists to be a powerful amatory stimulant (Wedeck, 1962).

In the early eighteenth century young husbands were advised to drink vanilla in order to enable them to satisfy their wives. At the court of Louis XV, chocolate spiced with vanilla and amber was considered to be aphrodisiac; Madame de Pompadour was said to be especially fond of it (Zimmermann, 1764; Lehmann, 1955; Wedeck, 1962; Brøndegaard, 1971).

V. aromatica Sw.: In Réunion this species was said to have very marked aphrodisiac properties (Leclerc, 1864).

V. decaryana H. Perrier: This plant is used in Madagascar as an aphrodisiac (Usher, 1974).

V. madagascariensis Rolfe: Sold in the markets of Madagascar, the fresh stems are made into a decoction regarded as a powerful aphrodisiac (Boiteau, 1974).

V. planifolia G. Jackson in Andr.: Used for male impotence (Lindley, 1849), the infusion from this species is allegedly intensely aphrodisiac (Freise, 1933), and is used as such by the Mascareignes (Pernet, 1958). The capsules are used in local medicine in Yucatan for their supposed excitement and aphrodisiac properties (Standley, 1930).

Miscellaneous Uses. Among the miscellaneous uses of *Vanilla* species are the following:

Adhesive: The Aztecs used *V. planifolia* G. Jackson in Andr. as a source of glue (Urbina, 1903a).

Basketry: Roots of *V. ovalis* Blanco have been used in the Philippines in basketmaking (Burkill, 1966).[54]

Charms: Flowers of *V. planifolia* G. Jackson in Andr. were used by early Mexicans as a component of charms of mixed flowers for the protection of travelers (Gates, 1939).

Cosmetics: In West Malaysia the stem and leaves of *V. griffithii* Rchb. f., which contain a sticky, irritant sap, were mashed and applied to the hair to thicken and strengthen it (Ridley, 1896, 1924; Heyne, 1913, 1922; Caius, 1936; Burkill, 1966).

Dyestuff: It was once thought that the brown color of the vanilla fruit might be useful as a dye, but the fruit has not been used commercially for that purpose (Correll, 1953).

---

[54]Burkill's report is based on W. H. Brown (1919), who says that the stems promise to be of value in basketry; he reiterates this statement in 1920. The *Index Kewensis* lists *V. ovalis* as a synonym of *V. aromatica* Sw., perhaps because Blanco (1879) described it as a variety of Guatemalan vanilla (Rolfe, 1895, 1896a, suggests that the Spaniards carried vanilla from Mexico to the Philippines). *V. ovalis* Blanco is now a valid species (Portères, 1954), however, and I have used this taxon here.

Fishing nets: In Gabon the aerial roots of *V. grandiflora* Lindl. have been used as ropes to make fishing nets (Raponda-Walker and Sillans, 1961).

Guitar strings: The aerial roots of *V. crenulata* Rolfe are used in Ghana as guitar strings (Dalziel, 1937), as are those of *V. africana* Lindl. var. *laurentiana* (Wildem.) R. Portères in Gabon (Raponda-Walker and Sillans, 1961).

Perfume: In the form of a tincture, vanilla is extensively employed in perfumery; Arctander (1960) reviews the technical details. Vanilla oil is used in perfumes as an aromatic aphrodisiac (Wedeck, 1962). The Brazilian species have been used in perfumery (Cointe, 1934). The ancient Peruvians used vanilla to impart a musklike scent to their clothes (Yacovleff and Herrera, 1935).

Poison bait: Vanilla has had widespread use in poison baits for insects, particularly for fruitflies (Correll, 1953).

Veterinary uses: An unnamed species of *Vanilla* is used in Bougainville as a vermifuge for domestic swine (Ona, personal communication).

5.12. Literature

So much has been written on *Vanilla,* the plant, and vanilla, the spice, that a full bibliography is beyond the scope of this work. Pereira (1850) and Sawer (1892) gave excellent contemporary résumés, and Linden (1894) has a concise summary. Urbina (1903a) includes a useful review of vanilla in Mexico. More recent surveys and bibliographies are those by Correll (1953), Childers *et al.* (1959), Täckholm and Drar (1969), and Arditti (1971). The most extensive and comprehensive survey of the subject is that of Bouriquet (1954).

6. Flavoring and Confectionery

The greatest contribution of orchids to flavoring is made by the *Vanilla* species, dealt with in section 5. Other reports relating to flavoring are set out in sections 4 (Food), 7 (Beverages), and 14 (Salep).

In Mexico a gum prepared from the pseudobulbs of several species of orchids (see sec. 9) is used in the preparation of a candy or pastry that is formed into the shapes of animals, puppets, fruit, skulls, and so on and sold on holy days in January and November. Urbina (1903a, 1903b) describes the preparation of the gum and its use to make *alfeñique,*[55] which is then used in the preparation of the sweets. Johnson (1952) describes a quite different preparation of the sweets directly from the pseudobulb, and does not mention *alfeñique.* M. A. Miller (1959) describes separately the sweets, following Johnson, and *alfeñique,* following Urbina. Usher (1974) identifies two species used for this purpose as *Laelia autumnalis* Lindl. and *L. grandiflora* Lindl.

In Turkey tubers of species of *Anacamptis, Ophrys, Orchis, Serapias,* and *Spiranthes* are dug in huge quantities and used to flavor ice cream (Vöth, 1973).

Cymbidium virescens Lindl.: In Japan the flowers were made into a preserve with plum vinegar (Anonymous, 1895b).

[55]*Alfeñique* is a paste of orchid mucilage, sugar, and almond oil.

Dendrobium salaccense Lindl.: This plant has been used to flavor rice in the Indo-Malaysian region (Hawkes, 1944b; Uphof, 1959). Heyne (1913, 1922) reports that the leaves are wrapped in banana leaves and steamed in the rice; the flavor is somewhat like that of licorice.

Orchis latifolia L.: The tubers of this orchid are used in India in sweetmeats and chocolates (Uphof, 1959).

Renanthera moluccana Bl.: The leaves have been used in Ambon for flavoring (Hawkes, 1943; Burkill, 1966). They are said to taste like capers (Rumphius, 1750; Heyne, 1913, 1922; J. J. Smith, 1927).[56]

Spiranthes odorata Lindl.: The root has been used in North America to provide a strong flavor (Duggal, 1972).

Tetramicra bicolor Rolfe syn. *Leptotes bicolor* Lindl.: The fruits have been used to flavor milk, tea, sherbet, and ice cream (Morren, 1846; Bulhart, 1927; Anonymous, 1928). The plant was used in Brazil to flavor a kind of ice cream (Hawkes, 1943).

7. Beverages

There are many reports of the use of orchids in decoctions, infusions, tisanes, and similar preparations. Those prepared solely for medicinal purposes are described in section 12. Beverages prepared with vanilla are dealt with in section 5, and the beverage saloop and others made from salep in section 14.10. The only other such beverage to have been prepared commercially is faham.

In South America the pseudobulbs of some orchid species contain a very popular thirst-quenching juice. (Goeze, 1916).

Angraecum fragrans Thou. syn. *Jumellea fragrans* Schltr.: In Mauritius and the island of Bourbon an infusion prepared from this plant has long served the same purpose as tea, and has been variously known as faham, fahum, faum, faham tea, *thé bourbon,* Bourbon tea, and Madagascar tea. The infusion is prepared by putting 15 grains of dried material[57] into a teacup of cold water, boiling for ten minutes, pouring into a closed vessel, and sweetening to taste (Jackson, 1866; Wood *et al.,* 1886; Planchon and Collin, 1895; M. A. Miller, 1959).

It is said that the addition of milk or spirits serves to strengthen the aroma. It does not have to be used immediately on preparation, but can be drunk later, either cold or reheated. The leaves were also used to flavor custards and ices (Jackson, 1866; M. A. Miller, 1959). When the leaves are mixed with ordinary tea, they impart an agreeable perfume to it; if the leaves are touched, the fingers remain impregnated with the aroma (Anonymous, 1892a).

---

[56]Rumphius says that the plants growing closest to the sea are the tastiest, and that the flavor can be sucked out from the fibrous leaves.

[57]The parts of the plant used are the dried leaves, leaf stalks, and flowers; rarely the fruits and roots (Planchon and Collin, 1895). The dried material has a pungent taste and a strong agreeable odor, shown by Gobley (1850a, 1850b) to be attributable to coumarin, capable of scenting a room (Wood *et al.,* 1886; Terrac, 1947). Perrot (1943a) suggests that the production of coumarin in this species is different from that in European orchids (see Vegetable Adulterants, sec. 5.8).

The beverage enjoyed popularity for a time in Paris and in England as a substitute for tea (Rosenthal, 1862; Linden, 1894; Hawkes, 1944a). George Sand is said to have eulogized it (Jackson, 1866). Reported to be agreeable to the taste, it was valued as a stimulant, pectoral, stomachic, sedative, diaphoretic, expectorant, and antispasmodic (Bouton, 1864; Leclerc, 1864; Cordemoy, 1895; Barbier, 1924).

Medicinal uses of faham include stimulation of digestive functions and sedation in insomnia due to nervous excitement (Jackson, 1866; Dupuis and Réveil, 1887; Planchon and Collin, 1895). It may be used as an infusion or made into a syrup (Dupuis and Réveil, 1887). In Madagascar the infusion is administered as an anodyne, especially in the rigors of malaria and the fevers of bilious hematuria (Boiteau, 1975). Faham has been employed in the French colonies as a vermifuge (Descourtilz, 1828). The alcoholic tincture has been highly recommended to restore full delicacy to the sense of touch; one maintains this effect by applying a sponge soaked with the tincture to the fingertips (Descourtilz, 1828).

The leaves are reported to have been used for lung diseases (Rosenthal, 1862; Dragendorff, 1898), including bronchitis, asthma, whooping cough, and pulmonary tuberculosis (Leclerc, 1864; Dupuis and Réveil, 1887; Linden, 1894; Barbier, 1924). In Mauritius and Réunion the dried flowers were smoked in the manner of tobacco for asthma (Leclerc, 1864; Bouton, 1864).

The dried leaves have been used to flavor cigars (M. A. Miller, 1959; Nair, 1963).[58]

Descourtilz (1828) notes a report of the discovery of *faum* in the *Courrier Français* (no. 108, 17 April 1828, Paris). Comments published there on its medicinal virtues and the advice that it was available from only one pharmacist in Paris give an idea of the value once attributed to this orchid.

Orchids other than *Angraecum fragrans* Thou. which contain coumarin have been used to prepare beverages similar to faham. In Algeria an infusion prepared from the dried flowers of *Aceras anthropophora* R. Br., known as "Algerian faham" or *faham d'Algérie*, was said to be superior in flavor and to have the same therapeutic properties (Simmonds, 1891; Planchon and Collin, 1895; Barbier, 1924; Perrot, 1943a). In France *Orchis militaris* L. has been used similarly and given the name "indigenous faham" (Planchon and Collin, 1895).[59] Infusions of other orchids containing coumarin have been proposed as successors to faham (Fournier, 1948).

Bletia spp.: Teas have been made from the leaves and pseudobulbs of these plants (Kramer, 1975).

Cymbidium virescens Lindl.: In Japan the flowers are preserved in salt and made into a drink with hot water (Anonymous, 1895b).

Dendrobium ceraia Lindl.: In Vietnam this plant is used to prepare a decoction that is both tonic and refreshing; it is also used to treat bone and kidney diseases (Pételot, 1954).

---

[58]Jackson (1866) describes specimens of leaves rolled into cigar shape and covered with tobacco leaf in the museum at Kew, but offers no evidence that these cigars were actually smoked.

[59]In France, *O. militaris* L., *O. maculata* L., and *O. mascula* L. together furnished an infusion similar to faham but with less active properties (Barbier, 1924).

Maxillaria bicolor Ruiz *et* Pav.: The natives of Peru sucked the insipid watery fluid from the pseudobulbs in the dry season (Bateman, 1837–1843).

Orchis spp.: In Greece the crushed tubers of *O. coriophora* L., *O. longicruris* Link., *O. mascula* L., *O. morio* L., and so on, were boiled with water and honey to yield a beverage drunk at breakfast (Fraas, 1845; Rosenthal, 1862; Grieve, 1931). Durrell (1975) invites visitors to Corfu to try the local beverage *salepi*, which is an excellent tea made from the bulbs of the "swamp orchis," *Orchis laxiflora* Lam. (Polunin and Huxley, 1965).

O. anatolica Boiss: Cypriots have used the ground tubers to prepare a milk-custard drink (Withner, 1959).

Renanthera spp.: Teas have been made from the foliage of these species (Kramer, 1975).

Saccolabium papillosum Lindl.: In India this plant is used as a substitute for sarsaparilla, as the roots are considered to be cooling (Kirtikar and Basu, 1918).

Tetramicra bicolor Rolfe syn. *Leptotes bicolor* Lindl.: The fruit of this orchid, when infused in tea, iced cream, or milk, gives a mild agreeable flavor, sweeter and less penetrating than vanilla (Morren, 1846; Lindley and Moore, 1866; Anonymous, 1928).

8. Arts and Crafts

8.1. Agriculture and Fishing

The Tasaday of Mindanao use orchid leaves to make cones to hold tadpoles and crabs (MacLeish, 1972).

Dendrobium spp.: Strings made from the fibers of these plants have been used by the natives of some South Sea islands for fishing purposes (Miethe, 1927; Bulhart, 1930).[60] For the use of *Dendrobium* skin to decorate fishing equipment, see section 8.7.

Mystacidium productum Kraenzl.: In Fernando Poo the long aerial roots are used to tie bundles of sticks, which serve as guides for yam cultivation (Nava, 1952).

Phaius tancarvilliae (Banks) Bl.: The pseudobulbs are said to be used in India to strengthen twine for fishing nets (*Wealth of India*, 1969).

Vanilla grandifolia Lindl.: In Gabon the aerial roots furnish ropes for the manufacture of fishing nets (Raponda-Walker and Sillans, 1961).

8.2. Art

Bletia spp.: Local species supplied an adhesive much used by Aztec painters to fix their colors (Gates, 1939). The tubers of Oriental species, now referred to as *Bletilla*, provide a glue used by the Chinese in the manufacture of cloisonné ware (Bretschneider, 1895; Withner, 1959).

B. hyacinthina R. Br. syn. *Bletilla striata* Rchb. F.: In China the mucilaginous roots were rubbed on inkstones with vermilion to fit them for writing (Williams, 1874; Henry, 1887), and the viscid juice was used in making porcelain (Bretschneider, 1895). Porcelain

---

[60]The origin of this report is not given; it may refer to Berkeley's report from the Andaman Islands, which Portman has shown to be erroneous; see *D. secundum* Lindl., sec. 8.7.

manufacturers in Vietnam use the gummy material from the pseudobulbs to decorate their pieces. The powdered bulb is dissolved in hot water, colored (most often blue), and used for decalcomania (Pételot, 1954).

Cranichis speciosa La Llave *et* Lex. and *C. tubularis* La Llave *et* Lex.: These and other orchids provided a mucilage used as a mordant by Mexican painters (Urbina, 1903a, 1903b; M. A. Miller, 1959).

Cymbidium canaliculatum R. Br. and *Dendrobium dicuphum* F. Muell.: The peoples of Arnhem Land and Groote Eylandt employ the juice from the pseudobulbs of these two plants as a fixative in bark and cave painting and the decoration of ceremonial objects. The juice from the cut and chewed stem may be applied directly to the rock and bark surfaces or over the pigments, or it may be mixed with the color on the grinding stone (Tindale, 1926; Mountford, 1956; Specht, 1958; Mathews, 1979; Levitt, 1981). The crushed stem is used as a brush on Groote Eylandt (Levitt, 1981). In the same manner, juice of an orchid bulb is used to glue feathers and paints to dancers' bodies and to their totemic emblems (Warner, 1937). W. Marika has informed me that in the absence of epiphytes he would use the bulbs of terrestrial species to provide a fixative for bark painting. (I observed him using the sap from cut canes of *Dendrobium nobile* Lindl., which appeared to serve equally well.)

Epidendrum pastoris La Llave *et* Lex.: This orchid provided the mordant most commonly used by Mexican painters (Urbina, 1903a).

Geodorum pictum (R. Br.) Lindl.: On Groote Eylandt the sap from the crushed bulb was used as a fixative in bark painting (Levitt, 1981).

8.3. Basketry and Weaving (see also sec. 8.7)

Orchid stems were used for weaving in Papua New Guinea. The people of the Trans-Fly region wove baskets, mats, and so on, and the Nimai of the eastern highlands wove ornamental armbands (Williams, 1938; Hide *et al.,* 1979).

The peoples of the Nassau Range of Irian Jaya make pouches of plaited orchid stems in which they store their most precious possessions; these pouches are in themselves articles of rare beauty (Ripley, 1970).

Stalks of epiphytic orchids were used in the Solomon Islands as plaiting on weapon handles, producing articles of exquisite workmanship (Bühler, 1948); combs were decorated in a like manner (J. Arditti, personal communication).

Bulbophyllum sp.: In the Chimbu region of Papua New Guinea at least one species is used for the plaiting of armlets and belts, and of rings on arrows and axes (Sterly, 1974/75).

Dendrobium acuminatissimum Lindl. and *D. bifalce* Lindl.: The stems of both these species are used for wickerwork in the Indo-Malayan region (J. J. Smith, 1927; Heyne, 1927, 1950; Hawkes, 1943).

D. crumenatum Sw.: In the Philippines the stems of this orchid, and perhaps of other species, are used for straw plaiting, tying, and making straw hats; fibers from yellowing stems are used as decoration on baskets (H. H. Miller *et al.,* 1912; Parker, 1914; W. H. Brown, 1919, 1920; Burkill, 1966).

D. discolor Lindl.: In 1976 I witnessed aboriginal Australians at the Lockhart River

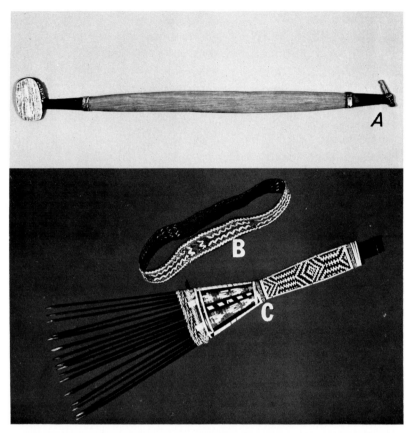

Plate 2-1. Artifacts bound (A) or decorated (B, C) with orchid material. A, womerah (spear-thrower). Cape York peninsula, bound with *Dendrobium discolor* Lindl.; B, comb. Malaita, Solomon Islands; C, arm band. Malaita, Somolon Islands, decorated with *Diplocaulobium solomonensis* Carr. From author's collection, gift of G. F. C. Dennis, Honiara.

Community in northern Queensland crafting weapons using traditional methods and materials; strips of the outer skin of this orchid are used for binding (Plate 2-1, A).

D. faciferum J. J. Sm.: In eastern Indonesia the stalks are used in basketry and mat plaiting (Heyne, 1922, 1927), and in Maluku they are used for weaving (Dakkus, 1935). The stems are used in eastern Malaysia for plaiting (Burkill, 1966).

D. macrophyllum A. Rich.: The stems of this plant have been used for wickerwork in Indonesia (J. J. Smith, 1927; Hawkes, 1943).

D. polytrichum Ames: Canes of this orchid were used in weaving and basketry in the Philippines (Hawkes, 1944b).

D. tetraedre Lindl.: Thin strips of the stems of this orchid, which turn a vivid yellow on drying, were used in hand weaving in the Philippines. They were interwoven with other materials to produce beautiful articles, including small cigar cases and little boxes used to store valuables (Delgado, 1892).

D. utile J. J. Sm.: The dried stems of this plant have been used in Sulawesi and

Kalimantan in basket weaving (Uphof, 1959; Burkill, 1966). The yellowish-green stems are split and wound around a stick to form a smooth ribbon that dries to a beautiful golden yellow (Heyne, 1913, 1922, 1927). As this orchid is scarce, it is used mainly for decorative edging on hats, little baskets, cigar cases, and so on (Heyne, 1913, 1922, 1927; J. J. Smith, 1927; Hawkes, 1943). It is said that its rarity in Sulawesi restricted its use to members of royal and noble households for the weaving of baskets and mats (Heyne, 1913, 1922, 1927). Heyne (1927) suggests that other *Dendrobium* species may be used for similar purposes.

Mystacidium productum Kraenzl.: In Equatorial Guinea and Fernando Poo the long aerial roots are used to make baskets (Nava, 1952).

Trichoglottis wenzelii Ames: The dried stems are used in the Philippines as frames for baskets (Fox, 1950).

Vanda viminea Guill.: In Laos the leaves of this orchid are used to make mats (Gagnepain and Guillaumin, 1933; Vidal, 1960).

Vanilla ovalis Blanco: For the use of this plant in basketry, see Miscellaneous Uses, section 5.11.

8.4. Clothing (see also sec. 8.7)

The tribes in the Baliem Valley and the Nassau Mountains of Irian Jaya use the stems of orchids to make grass skirts (Gardner and Heider, 1969; Ripley, 1970). In the Andaman Islands one of the few articles of male clothing is a belt of rope; used to hold weapons and roots, it is usually decorated with interwoven fiber from *Dendrobium* species (Radcliffe-Brown, 1964). The loin coverings worn by the Tasaday of Mindanao are fashioned from the leaves of a ground orchid (MacLeish, 1972; Nance, 1975).

Dendrobium heterocarpum Wall. ex Lindl.: In the Philippines the dried stem of this plant is woven with rattan to form a belt to support the loincloth (Fox, 1950).

Phreatia sp.: Leaves from this orchid are used for dress in the Chimbu area of Papua New Guinea (Powell, 1976a).

Plocoglottis wenzelii Ames: The Tasaday of Mindanao use the wide leaves to make men's G-strings and women's skirts (Yen and Gutierrez, 1976).

The use of orchids in shoemaking is discussed in section 9.

8.5. Coloring and Pigments

No dyestuffs of commercial interest have been produced from orchids. The presence of indigo derivatives is well recognized (Dragendorff, 1898), however, and some other orchids have had limited use as colors. For investigation of dye from *Vanilla* capsules, see Miscellaneous Uses, section 5.11.

Indigo derivatives have been reported in the following orchids: *Calanthe* species (Burkill, 1966), *Bletia* species, *Calanthe triplicata* (Willem.) Ames, *C. vestita* Lindl., *Epidendrum difforme* Jacq., *Nigritella nigra* (L.) Rchb. f., *Phaius grandifolius* Lour., *P. indigoferus* Hassk., and *P. tancarvilliae* (Banks) Bl. (Rosenthal, 1862; Dragendorff, 1898; Wehmer, 1929; *Wealth of India*, 1969). See Hegnauer (1963) for details of the chemistry of these indigo derivatives.

Cymbidium sp.: This plant has been used in China for coloring (Gordon, 1884).

Dendrobium bigibbum Lindl.: The inner bark of this plant turns bright yellow after it is roasted over a fire, and was used extensively by the natives of northern Queensland for decoration of implements, belts, weapons, and so on (Roth, 1904; *cf.* n. 67). For details of the decorative uses of yellow colors from *Dendrobium* species in southern Asia, see section 8.7.

Nigritella nigra (L.) Rchb. f.: This plant gave a red substance in southern Europe (Rosenthal, 1862; Wehmer, 1929). The flowers have been used in Sweden to color liquor (Pickering, 1879).

Orchis spp.: Some species provide a yellow stain (Rosenthal, 1862; Dragendorff, 1898).[61]

8.6. Decoration, Adornment, and Cosmetics

Some uses of orchids for other specific purposes are related to decoration; see sections 2.3 (Religion), 2.6 (Funerary Uses), 8.2 (Art), 8.3 (Basketry and Weaving), 8.4 (Clothing), and 8.7 (Decoration of Artifacts with Colored Stems). The use of *cosmosandalon* is discussed in the Introduction. Khan (1958) reports the use of orchids for perfume in Pakistan.

Aerides spp.: Flowers of some species were much sought after by the Burmese to adorn their hair (Balfour, 1885a).

Bulbophyllum auricomum Lindl.: Young Karen men of Burma wore the sweet-scented flowers in their ear lobes, and young women wore them in their hair (Mason, 1860; 1883; Balfour, 1871).

Cattleya sp.: In Paris a beauty cream is made from this species, which is specially grown for the purpose in Bengal (Richter, 1965).

C. citrina Lindl.: Indians of Mexico used the flowers to make bouquets and garlands for the head (Altamirano, 1895; Urbina, 1903a).

Coelogyne sp.: The flowers were used for personal ornamentation in the eastern highlands of Papua New Guinea (Hays, 1980).

Cypripedium humile Salisb.: The flowers were held in great esteem by some North American Indians as hair decorations (Pickering, 1879).

C. luteum Rafin.: The women of some North American Indian tribes used to deck their hair with these flowers (Rafinesque, 1828).

Cyrtopodium punctatum (L.) Lindl.: In Cuba an aqueous infusion of the whole plant is drunk to prevent baldness (Roig y Mesa, 1945).

Dendrobium spp.: The Chimbu people of Papua New Guinea used the flowers in their dress (Powell, 1976a); orange-yellow ones were used as a body decoration (Sterly, 1973, 1974/75). In the eastern highlands the flowers of one terrestrial and two epiphytic species are used for personal ornamentation, and the leaf and stem of another epiphytic species serve as ornaments for women at children's parties (Hays, 1980). One species used for personal adornment was sometimes transplanted to settlements and another was transplanted to the roofs of houses to decorate them (Hide *et al.*, 1979).

---

[61]It is said that when cows ate these species they produced saffron-yellow milk with a taste of onion, useless for cheese and butter (Retzius, 1806).

D. acuminatissimum Lindl.: This orchid was used by the Chimbu of Papua New Guinea for body adornment (Sterly, 1974/75).

D. clavatum Wall.: In India the dried plant was used in scent (Irvine, 1848).

D. densiflorum Wall.: Young Naga women of Manipur wore the orange flowers behind their ears (Swinson, 1970).

D. salaccense Lindl.: Because of their pleasant odor when dried, the leaves were worn in the hair by the people of western Sumatra (Heyne, 1913, 1922; J. J. Smith, 1927; Hawkes, 1943).

D. taurinum Lindl.: In the Philippines an aqueous infusion of the mashed plant was employed to wash the head as an effective remedy for falling hair (Delgado, 1892).

Dendrochilum sp.: This orchid is used for body adornment in the Chimbu region of Papua New Guinea (Sterly, 1974/75).

Diplocaulobium sp.: The Nimai of the eastern highlands in Papua New Guinea transplanted this orchid to the roofs of their houses as a decoration (Hide *et al.*, 1979).

Epiblastus sp.: People in the Chimbu area of Papua New Guinea use this plant for adornment (Sterly, 1974/75).

Eria muscicola Lindl.: This orchid was used in an old Sanskrit recipe for a preparation to promote the growth of hair in the old and produce loveliness and grace in women (Hoernle, 1893–1912).

Giulianettia sp.: In Papua New Guinea the Chimbu people used the flowers as part of their dress (Powell, 1976a). Hide *et al.* (1979) report the use of flowers to decorate the arms and backs of dancers.

Grammatophylum scriptum Bl.: In Ternate, Indonesia, it was the custom for highborn women, such as wives, sisters, and daughters of kings, to wear the flowers in their hair, and it was considered a gross affront for ordinary women, let alone slaves, to wear the flowers (Rumphius, 1750; Lindley, 1853; Heyne, 1913, 1922; Wood, 1977).[62]

G. speciosum Bl.: The Balinese used the flowers to decorate their hair (Clercq, 1909).

Liparis sp.: The flowers of this epiphyte are used for personal ornamentation in the eastern highlands of Papua New Guinea (Hays, 1980).

Mediocalcar sp.: This orchid is used for body decoration in the Chimbu region of Papua New Guinea (Sterly, 1974/75).

Mystacidium productum Kraenzl.: The aerial roots of this plant are used by women in Fernando Poo to make bangles (Nava, 1952).

Phaius sp.: In the Chimbu district of Papua New Guinea this orchid was used for personal adornment (Sterly, 1974/75).

Phalaenopsis amabilis Bl.: Reports of the use of the flowers for decoration in Ternate appear to be without foundation.[63]

---

[62]Rumphius explains that this plant was reserved for those of high station because it grew only in high places; this may be considered another example of the doctrine of signatures.

[63]Of his encounter with this plant in Java, Osbeck (1771) writes, "On the Isle of Ternate none but Princesses are allowed to wear this flower, which is but too scarce," and alludes to "Rumph. Herb. Amb. Angraecum alb. majus." Rumphius (1750) makes this statement in relation not to this orchid, but to *Grammatophyllum scriptum* Bl. (*q.v.*). My policy of consulting the original reports is reinforced by Osbeck's apparent misquotation, which has been perpetuated by Sweet (1969), Vaughn and Vaughn (1973), and Yearsley (1976).

Phreatia sp.: This orchid, transplanted from the forest, was used to decorate house roofs by the Nimai of the eastern highlands of Papua New Guinea (Hide *et al.*, 1979).

Rhynchostylis retusa Bl.: Young Hindu women in western India used to wear elegant head garlands made from the flowers of this orchid (Dalgado, 1898).

Spathoglottis grandiflora (non I.K.): In the eastern highlands of Papua New Guinea the flowers are used for ornamentation (Hays, 1980).

S. plicata Bl.: The purple flowers are worn in the hair in the Simbai River area of Papua New Guinea (Clarke, 1971).

Thelymitra papuana J. J. Sm.: In the eastern highlands of Papua New Guinea the flowers are used for personal ornamentation (Hays, 1980).

Vanda coerulea Griff. ex. Lindl.: In the Manipur region of Assam, every woman wore a spray of the flowers in her hair during the autumn Puja festival (Ward, 1928; Anonymous, 1952d).

V. roxburghii R. Br.: The Santal girls in Chutia Nagpur used to split the leaves of this orchid and wear them as anklets (Campbell, 1886; Mehra, Kanodia, and Srivastava, 1975).

Vanilla griffithii Rchb. f.: In West Malaysia the leaves were mashed with oil and used to stimulate the growth of hair and to thicken and strengthen it (Ridley, 1896, 1906b, 1912, 1921; Heyne, 1913, 1922; M. A. Miller, 1959).

8.7. Decoration of Artifacts with Colored Stems

Bulbophyllum sp.: In Papua New Guinea the stems of this orchid provide a red color for plaited leg-, arm-, and waistbands (Powell, 1976a).

Dendrobium spp.: The incorporation into woven articles of the yellow dried stems of *Dendrobium* species is the most frequently reported use of an orchid for decoration.[64] This use is confirmed from Cape York Peninsula, the Torres Strait Islands, Papua New Guinea, the Solomon Islands (Plate 2-1), Irian Jaya (Plate 2-2), the Philippines, Maluku, Kalimantan, Sulawesi, Manipur, and the Andaman Islands.

Several species are involved, not all of them positively identified; some species in New Guinea and one in the Solomons have now been transferred to *Diplocaulobium.*Reports vary as to whether the inner or outer "skin" of the cane is used, but they agree that the yellow color is intensified when the stems are dried, either by the sun or by the heat of a fire. Radcliffe-Brown (1964) suggests that similar use in the Philippines and the Andamans is evidence of a primitive Negrito culture (*cf.* Parker, 1914).[65] Yellow color from a species of *Liparis* has been used for similar purposes (see below).

Andaman Islands: The yellow skin of one or more species of *Dendrobium* was used for the decoration of fishing bows, belts, nets, and various articles of adornment. Great Andaman and Little Andaman have few similarities in ornament; one of the most striking is the use of this orchid (Radcliffe-Brown, 1964).

---

[64]Richter (1965) writes that the practice may have been suggested by the similar habits of the weaverbird, *Amblyornis inornata* Schlegel (see Lawler, 1977).

[65]The Naga of Manipur are said to have strong cultural and physical affinities to the natives of Kalimantan and the Philippines (Swinson, 1966).

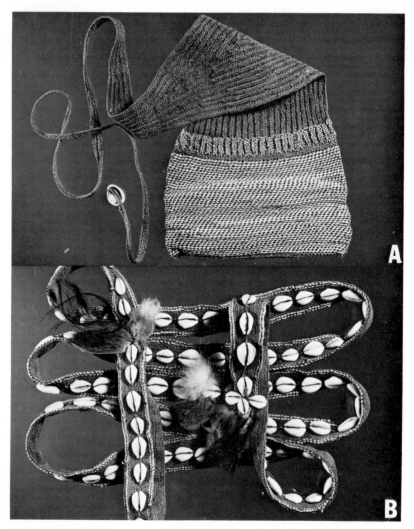

Plate 2-2. Artifacts decorated with yellow fiber from *Dendrobium*. Irian Jaya. A, bag; B, funerary shell string. Courtesy of the Macleay Museum, University of Sydney.

Australia: Thomas (1906) reports that aboriginal Australians use "the yellow strips of a kind of bark" for decorative effect. In the Torres Strait Islands the yellow fiber of an orchid skin was used to bind objects and to decorate armlets, belts, and shoulder belts (Haddon, 1890, 1894, 1912; Quiggin, 1912). The aboriginal people of eastern Cape York Peninsula wore waistbands decorated with the yellow fiber of an orchid (Hale and Tindale, 1934). McConnel (1936) reports that "orchid bark was baked yellow in the fire" by the people on the western side of Cape York Peninsula. For a review, see Lawler (1981).

Manipur: The yellow orchid stalk was used by all tribes as a binding for an ornament or was woven into armlets or leggings or into weapons (Swinson, 1970).

New Guinea: The decorative use of yellow orchid stems has been widespread in Papua New Guinea. There are records of this use by the Kukukuku of eastern New Guinea, the Aiome pygmies of the Ramu River, the Mafulu north of Port Moresby, the Orokaiva of northern Papua, the Buang of eastern New Guinea, the Siuai of southern Bougainville, and the peoples of the eastern highlands, Watut Valley, Jimmi River, Simbai River, Mount Hagen, the Trans-Fly, and eastern New Britain. The orchid material was often bartered between communities and was traded from western Papua to the coast. Generally the yellow material has been used to decorate various artifacts,[66] and occasionally has served as the artifact itself. Blackwood (1950) details the preparation of the material for each type of use.

In the form of yellow strips the orchids were used to decorate articles of clothing and weapons, including headdresses, armlets, bracelets, baldrics, belts, waistbands, women's girdles, grass skirts, lime-gourd stoppers, earrings of cuscus tails, wigs adorned with scarab beetles, spears, clubs, and bows and arrows. The Kukukuku, the Nimai, and the Aiome pygmies threaded the dried stems, cut into short lengths, like beads to make necklaces (Williamson, 1912; Hale and Tindale, 1934; White, 1938; Williams, 1938; Blackwood, 1939, 1940, 1950; Oliver, 1955; Girard, 1959; Panoff, 1970; Clarke, 1971; Strathern and Strathern, 1971; Powell, 1976a, 1976b; Hide *et al.*, 1979; Hays, 1980).

Girard (1959) reports that the Buang people of eastern New Guinea used yellow orchid fiber to decorate bracelets that were finished with black fiber from another orchid; Williams (1930) records a similar color pattern used by the Orokaiva of northern Papua. In southern Bougainville lime-gourd stoppers have been reported to be woven about with black-, red-, and yellow-dyed fibers from an orchid (Oliver, 1955). This characteristic pattern of the Solomons is in fact dyed rattan, with an orchid providing only the yellow element (G. F. C. Dennis, personal communication; M. Tedder, personal communication). Starzecka and Cranstone (1974), perhaps quoting Oliver, report that the foreshafts of spears in the northwestern Solomons were decorated with plaiting of yellow, red, and black orchid stems.

In Irian Jaya natives along the Baliem River carried axheads in string bags (Plate 2-3) ornamented with yellow fiber from orchid stems (Archbold, 1941).

Solomon Islands: The use of *Dendrobium* species to provide a yellow decoration or binding has been widespread. Its use by Melanesian and Polynesian peoples is reported from Malaita, Guadalcanal, San Cristobal, New Georgia, Ulawa, Santa Cruz, and Duff Island. On Malaita the pseudobulbs were soaked in water to detach the outer cortex, which was then sun-dried to a bright yellow. Artifacts decorated or bound with *Dendrobium* material include armbands (Malaita, Guadalcanal, San Cristobal, and Ulawa); spears, bows and arrows, clubs, and ceremonial totems (Malaita); ceremonial spears (Guadalcanal); combs for traditional male hair decoration (Malaita, Plate 2-1, B); decorative armbands for female dance ornamentation (New Georgia and other western Solomon islands); and (in Malaita) ear-lobe ornaments (G. F. C. Dennis, personal communication). Artifacts decorated with orchid fiber are illustrated by Starzecka and Cranstone (1974) and Craven (1977).

[66]See Gilliard (1951), where similar uses are illustrated in two color plates. The set of Papua New Guinea "headdress" stamps issued March 29, 1978, contains three stamps depicting yellow orchid material.

Plate 2-3. Artifacts decorated with yellow fiber from *Dendrobium.* Irian Jaya. A, bag; B, shoulder bag. Courtesy of the Macleay Museum, University of Sydney.

Dendrobium bigibbum Lindl.: The aboriginal people of northern Cape York Peninsula roasted the inner bark of the stems to produce yellow strips and used them to decorate weapons and domestic implements. The women used the strips to make chainwork belts for the men and cross-shoulder bands for themselves (Roth, 1901, 1904, 1909, 1910;[67]

[67]Roth (1909) refers to "the dried (yellow) strips from the outer covering of the 'Rock Lily' (*Dendrobium bigibbum* Lindl.) orchid." *D. speciosum* Sm., the orchid generally known as "rock lily," extends from eastern Victoria to at least the southern part of Cape York Peninsula, where it is known as "king orchid." In north Queensland *D. speciosum* usually grows on rocks, while *D. bigibbum* grows exclusively on trees (except for subvar. *compactum* [C. T. White] Dockr., which does not occur on Cape York Peninsula). *D. ruppianum* A. D. Hawkes is often a lithophyte and can resemble *D. speciosum* (it was once known as *D. speciosum* Sm. var. *fusiforme* F. M. Bail.). It is most likely, however, that the species to which Roth refers is *D. bigibbum*, but see also *D. johannis* Rchb. f.

Bailey, 1902). White (1938) reports that the cortex of this orchid was woven into various articles of decoration on the islands of the Gulf of Carpentaria.[68]

D. crumenatum Sw.: In the Philippines yellow strips from the stem are used in basketry for decorative purposes and as a braiding material for hats (Blanco, 1879; Robinson, 1911; H. H. Miller *et al.*, 1912; Parker, 1913, 1914; W. H. Brown, 1920; Quisumbing, 1951; Burkill, 1966).

D. heterocarpum Wall. ex Lindl.: The dried yellow stems are used to decorate arm-, leg-, and waistbands and baskets in northeastern Luzon (Fox, 1950).

D. johannis Rchb. f.: The aboriginal people of western Cape York Peninsula heat the skin over a fire to accentuate the yellow color and then weave or plait it into a string base. Larger strands are worn by women as girdles or breastlets; the shorter lengths are worn by men as arm-, leg-, or headbands. Strips of the orchid skin are also used to decorate weapons and ceremonial objects. When a newborn child is presented to its father, the umbilical cord is decorated with orchid skin and hung around the baby's neck (McConnel, 1953).

D. lineale Rolfe.: This orchid has been used to provide yellow decoration on Ulawa and San Cristobal (G. F. C. Dennis, personal communication).

D. lobbii Teys. *et* Binn.: In the eastern highlands of Papua New Guinea the long yellow stems are used for ornamentation during festivals or fashioned into necklaces (Hays, 1980).

D. luzonense Lindl.: The Pinatubo Negritos of the Philippines use the dried yellow stems to pattern baskets (Fox, 1952).

D. pulchrum Schltr.: This orchid was transplanted to trees around the settlements of the Nimai people of Papua New Guinea, who used the dried stems to weave armbands (Hide *et al.*, 1979).

D. secundum Lindl.: Berkeley (1893) reported the use in the Andaman Islands of fiber from the stems of this orchid to make string to be tied to fishing arrows. Portman (1899a, 1899b) corrected this report and stated that the yellow orchid fiber was used only for decoration of arrows for shooting fish or swine. The orchid was roasted over embers and the yellow bark stripped off and used on many ornaments in both Little and Great Andaman. Cipriani (1966) reports the use of yellow fibers of *Dendrobium* as a stop on the bow.

D. utile J. J. Sm.: In Kalimantan and Sulawesi the split canes of this scarce orchid are wound around a stick and dried until they are yellow; the strips are used mainly for decorative edging (Clercq, 1909; Heyne, 1913, 1922; Richter, 1965; Rifai, 1975).

Diplocaulobium sp.: The skin of the stem was woven into belts, armbands, and girdles in New Britain, and by the Kukukuku in Papua (Powell, 1976a).

D. regale (Schltr.) A. D. Hawkes: Around the Simbai River in Papua New Guinea the bright-yellow stems, having been dried by heat, were split and used to hold green beetle shells in ceremonial headbands (Clarke, 1971). In Enga Province the dried stems, together with those of *D. centrale* (J. J. Sm.) Hunt *et* Summerhayes and *D. iboense* (Schltr.) A. D. Hawkes, were woven into such articles as armbands and belts (Reeve, 1981).

---

[68]*D. bigibbum* Lindl. does not occur on these islands. It is likely that this report refers to *D. discolor* Lindl.

D. solomonense Carr: In the southwest of Bougainville the yellow stalks were much sought after for use in plaited armlets (Carr, 1934). They are still used for similar purposes on Guadalcanal and Malaita (M. Tedder, personal communication; G. F. C. Dennis, personal communication) (Plate 2-1, C).

Liparis sp.: The yellow stem of this orchid was used in parts of Papua New Guinea to embroider waist-, arm-, and legbands (Powell, 1976a).

8.8. Lubricants

Calanthe sp.: Weavers in Laos used the crushed tuber to work the thread of the weft to render it more resistant (Vidal, 1960).

C. crinita Gagnep.: In Laos the tuber served to wax the weaver's comb (Vidal, 1960).

Cyrtopodium spp.: In Honduras the pseudobulbs of several species are rubbed on guitar strings in place of resin (Bulhart, 1927); the viscous juice is the equivalent of colophony (Morren, 1846). Correll (1950) identifies one species as *C. punctatum* (L.) Lindl.

8.9. Musical Instruments

The aerial roots of *Aerangis biloba* Schltr. are sometimes used in Gabon as guitar strings (Raponda-Walker and Sillans, 1961). The use of the roots of *Vanilla* species as guitar strings is discussed in section 5.11. Children in Honduras used the long hollow stems of *Schomburgkia tibicinis* Batem. as trumpets (Morren, 1846, 1849; Lindley and Moore, 1866; Bulhart, 1927). It is said that they were also used to call children home from the forest (Hawkes, 1943). Other uses of orchids in connection with musical instruments are described in section 9.

8.10. Packaging

The Tasaday of Mindanao cook food by wrapping it in orchid leaves and placing it beside hot coals (MacLeish, 1972).

Acanthephippium papuanum Schltr.: The leaves were used by the Kukukuku in New Guinea to wrap food for cooking in earth ovens (Blackwood, 1940).

Calanthe sp.: Leaves of this plant, and of a species of *Spathoglottis*, were used in the Jimmi area of Papua New Guinea to line ovens and wrap food for cooking (Powell, 1976a).

Dendrobium sp.: In the central parts of Papua New Guinea, the leaves were used to wrap salt prepared from vegetable ash (Powell, 1976a, 1976b).

D. crumenatum Sw.: In the Andaman Islands, the old and partially yellow stalks are cut and used for tying (*Wealth of India*, 1969).

Spathoglottis sp. In the central parts of Papua New Guinea, the leaves are used to wrap salt prepared from vegetable ash (Powell, 1976a, 1976b).

S. plicata Bl.: The leaves were used in Indonesia as a packing material and to wrap parcels (J. J. Smith, 1927; Hawkes, 1943; Burkill, 1966), and in the highlands of Papua New Guinea as a wrapping material (Clarke, 1971). In Ambon they were used to wrap such market products as fish and vegetables (Rumphius, 1750; Heyne, 1913, 1922; Bakhuizen van den Brink, 1937). In Taiwan the leaves were used as a filling (Liu, 1952). The leaves were used in Niue to tie bundles (Yuncker, 1943).

8.11. Miscellaneous Uses

The flattened fleshy stem of an epiphytic orchid from the Simbai River, Papua New Guinea, has been held in the mouth to facilitate the imitation of young birds' distress cries in order to attract adult birds to the hunter (Clarke, 1971).

Coelogyne asperata Lindl.: In central Sumatra the split fresh bulbs are used as black-board erasers (Withner, 1959).

Cymbidium canaliculatum R. Br. and *Dendrobium dicuphum* F. Muell.: Fibers from the crushed pseudobulbs were used in Groote Eylandt as packing for pipe bowls to contain the smoke (Levitt, 1981).

Geodorum pictum (R. Br.) Lindl.: In Groote Eylandt the bulb was heated on a fire and applied to bark and spears to strengthen them (Levitt, 1981).

Schomburgkia thomsoniana Rchb. f.: The hollow bulbs have been used by the islanders of Grand Cayman as pipe bowls (Bulhart, 1927; Hawkes, 1943). Richter (1965) says they are used after being hollowed out by ants (see Lawler, 1979).

Spathoglottis sp.: The Nimai children in Papua New Guinea compete with each other to see who can collect the most flowers (Hide *et al.*, 1979).

9. Adhesives

A tenacious glue obtained from the boiled stems of some Brazilian orchids is employed for many purposes (Loudon, 1872). Salep has been substituted for gum arabic as an agglutinant in technical work (Bulhart, 1927), and is employed as a sizing material in the silk industry in Pakistan (*Wealth of India*, 1966). A few North American species have had miscellaneous household uses as a source of glue and resin (Correll, 1950).

Acanthephippium martinianum L. Lind. *et* Cogn.: See *Geodorum nutans* (Presl) Ames.

Ansellia gigantea Rchb. f.: A gum obtained from the pseudobulbs was used by tribesmen of East Africa to stick feathers to arrows (Stewart and Campbell, 1970).

Aplectrum hyemale (Muhl. ex. Willd.) Torr.: The root of this orchid, known as "putty root," contains a very thick slime that was used in North America as a mastic; when bruised in a little water, the root gives a strong, exceedingly durable cement, which was used to repair glass, china, and earthenware (Griffith, 1847; Rosenthal, 1862; Lindley and Moore, 1866; Niles, 1904; Correll, 1950). Those early colonists who had glazed windows used the juice for putty (Quinn, 1938); it was also used to mend broken crockery (Luer, 1975).

Bletia sp.: This plant supplied an adhesive much used by Aztec painters to fix their colors (Gates, 1939); *cf. Epidendrum pastoris.*

B. hyacinthina R. Br. syn. *Bletilla striata* Rchb. f.: When placed in water, the root forms a thick mucilage, which was used in Peking in the manufacture of wainscoting. The root is called *kiu-ken,* or "mortar root," because it is good for making paste[69] (Hooper, 1929; Roi, 1955). In China and Vietnam a paste made from the bulbs is used to mend broken porcelain and to decorate porcelain during manufacture (Bretschneider, 1895; Pételot, 1954). A glue from the bulb was used in Peking by the manufacturers of cloisonné (Bretschneider, 1895; Withner, 1959). In Japan the roots were used to make paste

[69]Bretschneider (1895) says the name refers to the mortarlike shape of the root.

(Anonymous, 1895b). The mucilage is used in China and Japan also to waterproof fabrics (Usher, 1974). The use of this orchid as an emulsifier in tablet making is discussed in section 12.

B. verecunda R. Br.: In Chiapas, Mexico, the sap from the fresh tuber is used as a glue to repair stringed instruments (Berlin *et al.,* 1974).

Catasetum spp.: Shoemakers in Guyana (Morren, 1846; Josst, 1851) and in Central America (Bulhart, 1927, 1930) applied the viscous sap to the soles of shoes to make them more durable. Brazilian shoemakers used the sap as a glue (Silva Maia, 1942).

C. atratum Lindl., *C. cristatum* Lindl., *C. luridum* Lindl., and others: The juice of these orchids has been used as a glue in South America (Rosenthal, 1862; Dragendorff, 1898).

C. maculatum Kunth: The viscous sap of the pseudobulbs is used in Yucatan as glue to mend the wood of violins (Standley, 1930).

Catasetum and *Cyrtopodium* spp.: Some of the American species contain a viscid substance that was thickened to make glue (Griffith, 1847). It was thickened by boiling and used as an adhesive in Brazil (Burnett, 1835) and Central America (Morren, 1846). It is reported that juices from both *Catasetum* and *Cyrtopodium* species have been used in mixing arrow poison in South America. It is clear that the juices served only as a cement in the mixture, and that they are not in themselves poisonous (Bateman, 1837–1843; Bulhart, 1927; see sec. 11.1). The juice of these orchids is reported to have been used as birdlime (Josst, 1851).[70]

Cattleya citrina Lindl.: See *Epidendrum pastoris*.

Cremastra wallichiana Lindl.: The Ainu pounded the roots of this plant to make a strong glue (Batchelor and Miyabe, 1893).

Cymbidium canaliculatum R. Br. and *Dendrobium dicuphum* F. Muell.: In northern Australia the sap of an orchid bulb is used to glue feathers and paints to dancers' bodies and to stick the same materials onto their totemic emblems (Warner, 1937). The natives of the Northern Territory use the sap from the stems or bulbs of these two tree orchids as a fixative in bark and rock painting (Tindale, 1926; Mountford, 1956) (see also sec. 8.2).[71]

C. crispatum Thunb.: This orchid provided a gum in Brazil (Rosenthal, 1862; Dragendorff, 1898).

C. lancifolium Hook.: In western Java the roasted pseudobulbs produced a sticky substance used as a glue to fasten Sundanese knives to their handles (Rifai, 1975).

Cyrtopodium sp. Some species from tropical America contain a glue in their bulbs which has been used technically (Goeze, 1916; Bulhart, 1927).[72] A paste from the juicy bulbs was used by shoemakers in Guyana, Brazil, and the West Indies (Bateman, 1837–1843; Miethe, 1927; Silva Maia, 1942).

C. andersonii R. Br.: The stem provides a glue used in shoemaking in South America

[70]Josst erroneously attributes this report to Burnett (1835); *cf.* n. 72.

[71]Specht (1958) states that either or both of these orchids are used for the purposes cited here. They are the only common epiphytic orchids in the area (Ewart and Davies, 1917; Chippendale, 1971). Later lists record two further epiphytes, but they are not widespread (Clements, 1978; Simmons, 1979). M. A. Clements (personal communication) confirms Specht's statement.

[72]Bulhart's statement, relying on Goeze, that lime is prepared from the tubers of *Cyrtopodium* species appears to be an error of translation. *Gummileim* translates literally as "rubber glue" (or birdlime). The *Oxford English Dictionary* states that in Old English, "lime" meant "glue."

(Bulhart, 1930; Cointe, 1934); it is said to be used to attach the soles and make them more durable. Other species have been used in the same manner in Guyana (Josst, 1851) and Central America (Bulhart, 1927, 1930).

C. punctatum (L.) Lindl.: In Brazil a useful glue was obtained from the juice (Rosenthal, 1862; Cointe, 1934). A glue for bookbinding and to make the soles of shoes more durable is extracted from the pseudobulbs (Correll, 1950).

C. woodfordii Sims: This species is used by the people of El Salvador as a glue to fill fissures in stringed instruments (Guzmán, 1924).

Epidendrum cochleatum L.: The pseudobulbs were used in Central America as a source of mucilage; *E. vitellinum* Lindl. was probably also used in this way (Uphof, 1959).

E. pastoris La Llave *et* Lex.: People of ancient Mexico used orchid pseudobulbs as a source of an all-purpose glue. They were chopped, dried in the sun, and stored; when they were moistened with water, the mucilage was ready for use. The glue obtained from *E. pastoris* was the best; *Cattleya citrina* Lindl. was used similarly (Altamirano, 1895; Urbina, 1903a, 1903b).[73]

Eulophia sp.: In Malawi the roots are rubbed onto cracked pots to mend them (Williamson, 1955).

E. nuda Lindl.: The tubercules are said to contain a gum (Dalgado, 1898).

E. squalida Lindl.: See *Geodorum nutans* (Presl) Ames.

Geodorum nutans (Presl) Ames: In the Philippines the tuberous roots are the source of a glue of great tenacity, used particularly to cement parts of guitars, mandolins, and other stringed instruments (Wells, 1919; Davis and Steiner, 1952; Uphof, 1959), bolo scabbards (Fox, 1952), and wooden instruments (Valenzuela *et al.*, 1949). The roots are reported to contain 14% of a water-soluble glue (Wells, 1919; Quisumbing, 1951), which is prepared by cooking the rhizomes and grating them finely. Several orchids, including *Acanthephippium martinianum* L. Lind. *et* Cogn. and *Eulophia squalida* Lindl., may be used and are prepared in the same fashion (West and Brown, 1921; Fox, 1952). Other species of *Geodorum* are reported to be used for this purpose; the fresh bulbs are split and applied to the surface to be glued (Hawkes, 1944b).

G. pictum (R. Br.) Lindl.: Sap from the tuber is used on Groote Eylandt as a fixative for pigments used in bark painting (Levitt, 1981).

Govenia liliacea Lindl. and *G. superba* Lindl.: Sap from the fresh tubers is used in Chiapas, Mexico, as a glue to repair stringed musical instruments (Berlin *et al.*, 1974).

Laelia autumnalis Lindl.: The people of northwestern Mexico used the sap from the bulbs as glue in making musical instruments; the skinned bulb was rubbed directly on the surfaces to be joined (Gentry, 1942).

Orchis morio L.: This orchid was used in Europe as a gum (Dragendorff, 1898).

Phragmipedium spp.: In tropical America a glue was obtained from several species (Richter, 1965).

---

[73]Urbina describes the same use for *Arpophyllum spicatum* La Llave *et* Lex., *Bletia campanulata* La Llave *et* Lex., *B. coccinea* La Llave *et* Lex., *Cranichis speciosa* La Llave *et* Lex., *C. tubularis* La Llave *et* Lex., *Epidendrum vitellinum* Lindl., *Govenia liliacea* Lindl., *G. superba* Lindl., *Laelia autumnalis* Lindl., *L. grandiflora* Lindl., and *Stanhopea tigrina* Batem. He also lists *Cypripedium irapeanum* La Llave *et* Lex. and *Vanilla planifolia* G. Jackson in Andr., but gives no details in the text.

10. Animal and Veterinary Uses

10.1. Medicinal Uses

Lactagogical properties were ascribed to orchids with palmate tubers.[74] In Scandinavia and Russia, orchid tubers in the food given to cows and goats ensured against poor milk. In Latvia it was believed that cows would not sicken and would give increased yields of milk if they were fed "light" tubers of *Orchis maculata* L. or *Cypripedium calceolus* L. (Brøndegaard, 1971).

Cymbidium finlaysonianum Lindl.: In Malaysia the roots were an ingredient of a mixture given as medicine to sick elephants (Maxwell, 1906; Ridley, 1906a; Burkill, 1966).

Habenaria hookeriana Torr. ex A. Gray: The leaves of this orchid have been used in Vermont as a poultice to treat lameness in horses (Bergen, 1899).

Orchis and *Platanthera* spp.: During the eighteenth century these orchids were highly esteemed in Norway as a protection against and a remedy for illness in cattle (O. A. Høeg, personal communication).

O. mascula L.: In the Orient dried flour made from the tubers is made into a thick brew with honey and milk and used to restore strength to female animals after difficult labor, and also to treat weakness, sterility, abortion, diarrhea, dysentery, and nervous disorders (Levy, 1963).

Vanilla sp.: This plant is used in Bougainville as a vermifuge for domestic swine (Ona, personal communication).

10.2. Aphrodisiacs

Brøndegaard (1971) has surveyed the use of orchids as aphrodisiacs in veterinary practice. He points out that their fall from favor in human medicine has not been matched in veterinary medicine, in which their use persists to the present day. They have been used in Scandinavia and in northern, central, and southern Europe. Pliny the Elder (1956) wrote in A.D. 77 that satyrion was given to rams, he-goats, and stallions to encourage them to copulate.

Orchis maculata L.: Power to help reluctant cattle was attributed to the bulbs in Sweden (Retzius, 1806). The bulbs were fed in Denmark to "lazy" cows before coition and afterward to "retain the sperm," and were used also to bring cows into heat in Denmark and Norway, and to stimulate bulls in the Faeroes. In Denmark, Germany, Lithuania, and Switzerland, on the other hand, chopped tubers were incorporated in food to prevent cows from coming into heat. In Norway the finely chopped tubers were said to prevent abortion and also to ensure spotted calves (Brøndegaard, 1971).

O. mascula L.: In the Orient the bulbs are prized as an aphrodisiac for animals (Levy, 1963).

10.3. Food

In southwestern Australia it has been reported that cockatoos scratched the ground to a considerable depth to obtain orchid roots for food (Fraser, 1830).

---

[74]This is yet another example of the doctrine of signatures; in Norway these orchids have the common name of cow (or goat) udder (O. A. Høeg, personal communication).

Orchids form a useful food for domestic animals in northeastern India. Sheep, goats, and cattle are driven to pastures where terrestrial orchids are located. *Dendrobium* stems are added to grain as roughage and fed to cows to increase the milk yield. Pseudobulbs of *Cymbidium* are fed to cattle to condition their health (Pempahishey, 1974).

Agrostophyllum sp.: The fruits of this species were said to attract possums and were used for hunting by the Nimai people of the eastern highlands of Papua New Guinea (Hide *et al.*, 1979).

Aplectrum hyemale (Muhl. ex. Willd.) Torr.: The Cherokees added roots of this orchid to the feed of swine to fatten them (Hamel and Chiltoskey, 1975).

Dendrobium speciosum Sm., *D. kingianum* Bidw., and *Liparis:* These orchids are said to have been eaten by bandicoots and kangaroo rats in eastern Australia (Maiden, 1899).

D. speciosum Sw. var. *hillii* F. M. Bail. and *D. gracilicaule* F. Muell.: I have observed that pademelons eat these orchids in New South Wales.

Diuris spp.: Sheep are reported to be especially fond of several species in the Mudgee district of New South Wales (Hamilton, 1886).

Gastrodia sesamoides R. Br.: This plant and species of *Caladenia, Diuris, Microtis, Prasophyllum, Pterostylis,* and *Thelymitra* are reported to have been eaten by cockatoos, bandicoots, and kangaroo rats in Tasmania (Gunn, 1842; Bunce, 1857).

Geodorum pictum (R. Br.) Lindl.: In Groote Eylandt the bulbs are dug out and eaten by wallabies (Levitt, 1981).

Habenaria sp.: The Nimai people in the eastern highlands of Papua New Guinea fed the leaves to pigs to fatten them (Hide *et al.*, 1979).

H. susannae R. Br.: The tubers are eaten by wild pigs in the jungles of India (*Wealth of India*, 1959; Chopra *et al.*, 1969).

Liparis liliifolia A. Rich. ex Lindl.: In North America the bulbs are eaten by rodents (Correll, 1950).

Ophrys spp.: Retzius (1806) reports that these plants were eaten by cattle in Sweden.

Orchis spp.: Several species have been eaten by cattle in France (Chomel, 1804).

O. mascula L.: In the Orient the crushed dried tubers are fed to animals (Levy, 1963).

O. purpurea Huds, and *O. simia* Lam.: Rabbits are fond of the leaves and tender shoots of these plants, and cause depredation to the populations in England (Summerhayes, 1968).

Pholidota pallida Lindl.: The Himalayan squirrel likes to eat the inflorescence (Pradhan, 1977).

Rhizanthella gardneri R. S. Rogers: This subterranean orchid produces an indehiscent capsule containing a small number of relatively large seeds. It has been suggested that the succulent capitula are dug up and eaten by animals and the seeds dispersed on defecation (George, 1980; George and Cooke, 1981).

Spathoglottis rivularis Schltr.: The Kukukuku people of Papua New Guinea feed the leaves and bulbs to pigs (Blackwood, 1940).

10.4. Superstitions

In northern Europe there have been superstitions based on the belief that orchids had magical effects on farm animals. In Norway, orchids, with other magical plants, were fed to cows to prevent milk failure caused by evil powers, whereas in Sweden and Denmark they were buried under the stall doors to provide protection, and in Bohemia their presence in the water trough was assumed to give protection against witchcraft. In East Germany, however, orchid flowers were considered harmful in the cattle stalls and were believed to interrupt lactation (Brøndegaard, 1971).

11. Poisons and Narcotics

11.1. Human Poisons

The Dani of the Baliem Valley in Irian Jaya wind their arrow tips with orchid fiber. This fiber is reported to cause minor wounds to become progressively worse, and often to result in death (Gardner and Heider, 1969).

An orchid from Gabon, where it is known as *ilango,* was said to be a poisonous plant when it was exhibited at the Paris Exhibition of 1878 (Anonymous, 1878).[75]

Catasetum and *Cyrtopodium:* It has been reported that the Indian people of Demerara affixed the mortal arrow poison *wourali* (curare) to their arrows with sap from the stems of species from these genera (Bateman, 1837–1843). Suggestions that the sap of these orchids is poisonous (Morren, 1846; Josst, 1851) should be disregarded; it was clearly serving as a cement (Bulhart, 1927; see sec. 9).

Cymbidium aloifolium Sw.: It has been implied that the Sinhalese name for this orchid (literally "poison dust") refers to irritation of the eye from the fine seed (Cooray, 1940; Soysa, 1943).

Cypripedium spp.: A dermatitis is reported to be caused by contact with the leaves of several species: *C. candidum* Muhl. ex Willd., *C. macranthon* Sw., *C. parviflorum* Salisb., *C. pubescens* Willd., *C. spectabile* Salisb. (Anonymous, 1894; Dragendorff, 1898; Pfitzer, 1903; Coulter, 1905; Harding, 1908; Pammel, 1910; Thomson and Sifton, 1922; Bernhard-Smith, 1923; Bulhart, 1930). Other species may give rise to the trouble under certain conditions (Muenscher, 1940). *C. spectabile* Salisb. and *C. pubescens* Willd. are said to cause a severe dermatitis resembling that caused by poison ivy, *Rhus toxicodendron* L., while *C. candidum* Muhl. ex Willd. is less poisonous (MacDougal, 1894, 1896; Pammel, 1910; Richter, 1965).

Disa chrysostachya Sw.: Rayner (1977) reports the use of this orchid in South Africa as a poison "to get rid of an irritating person."

Eulophia sp.: The fruit and root give a poisonous decoction in the Central African Republic (Vergiat, 1970).

Vanilla spp.: Vanillism is discussed in section 5.10 and in Chapter 6 of this volume.

11.2. Narcotics

There are many reports of the narcotizing effect of exudations from orchid flowers on would-be pollinators, such as bees and flies. Mentioned in these reports are species of *Catasetum, Cycnoches, Gongora,* and *Stanhopea* (Pijl and Dodson, 1969), *Pterostylis recurva* Benth. and *P. sargentii* Andrews (Sargent, 1909), *Diuris pedunculata* R. Br. (Coleman, 1932), and *Dendrobium devonianum* Paxt. (Richter, 1965).

---

[75]The specimen was stolen from the exhibition before it could be identified.

Cypripedium spectabile Salisb., *C. humile* Salisb., and *C. pubescens* Willd.: These orchids have been reported to possess narcotic properties (Wood *et al.*, 1886; Bocquillon-Limousin, 1905; Emboden, 1974).

Epidendrum radiatum Lindl.: This plant is reported to have a narcotic smell (Goeze, 1916).

Oncidium cebolleta Sw.: This alkaloid-containing orchid is an important replacement for peyote among the Tarahumara of Mexico and may be hallucinogenic (Bye, 1979; Schultes and Hofmann, 1980).

Spathoglottis plicata Bl.: The dried leaves have been smoked as a tobacco substitute in the Philippines; this practice began during the Japanese occupation, when tobacco was not available (Fox, 1952).

11.3 Fish, Insect, and Animal Poisons

Bletia verecunda R. Br.: The dried and powdered bulbs have been used as a fish poison in the Bahamas (Miethe, 1927; Bulhart, 1930).[76]

Bletia hyacinthina R. Br. syn. *Bletilla striata* Rchb. f.: This orchid is said to be used in China as an insecticide (Perry and Metzger, 1980). The use of vanilla in insect bait is discussed in section 5.12.

Calanthe discolor Lindl.: In the northern Satsunan Islands this plant is reputed to be poisonous to livestock (Higashi *et al.*, 1975).

Cypripedium spectabile Salisb. and *C. pubescens* Willd.: Greshoff (1900) reports that these plants are avoided by cattle, presumably owing to irritation from the hairs. It has been observed that other species of this genus are avoided by grazing cattle (Richter, 1965).

Dipodium punctatum R. Br.: This orchid has been suspected of poisoning sheep in New South Wales (Maiden, 1897; Greshoff, 1900; Hurst, 1942); Maiden (1897, 1901) states that this report is based on "imperfectly conclusive observations."

Eulophia virens Spreng.: The plants were said to be poisonous to cattle, bringing on madness when eaten (Dalgado, 1896).

Lissochilus buchanani Rchb. f.: In South Africa this plant has been suspected of being poisonous; however, sheep fed on the fresh roots showed no symptoms of poisoning (Steyn, 1950).

Microtis parviflora R. Br.: This plant has been suspected of being poisonous to stock in Queensland (Brünnich, 1914).

Orchis latifolia L. and *O. laxiflora* Lam.: Aitchison (1891) reported from Afghanistan and Iran that browsing sheep and goats avoided these orchids, which survived in large numbers. It must be presumed that the plants were distasteful or toxic to the animals.

Pterostylis sp.: In New South Wales this species has been suspected of poisoning stock, but sheep fed on the plant remained normal (Hurst, 1942).

Thecostele poilanei Gagnep: In Vietnam a decoction made from the whole plant and arsenic is used to poison rice, which is then set out for rats to find. While it may be

---

[76]There appears to be some confusion about the reputed role of this orchid in fish poisoning. Miethe (1927) reports its use to poison fish and is quoted thus by Bulhart (1930). Hawkes (1943), however, while inferring that he is quoting Bulhart, reports its use as an antidote to fish poisoning. Correll (1950), Miller (1959), and Duggal (1972) have all followed Hawkes. (See *Bletia verecunda* R. Br. in secs. 12.2 and 12.3.)

thought that the orchid could be only a vehicle to bind the arsenic to the rice, it may be significant that its vernacular name translates as "rat poison" (Pételot, 1954).

12. Medicine

12.1. Africa

Among some tribes in west tropical Africa a decoction of the pseudobulbs of epiphytic orchids forms part of a medicine for trypanosomiasis (Dalziel, 1937).

Acampe pachyglossa Rchb. f.: The juice of the plant has been used as an antimalarial agent (Haerdi *et al.*, 1964).

Aceras anthropophora R. Br.: This plant has been used in Tunisia as a stomachic (Bocquillon-Limousin, 1894).

Aerangis biloba Schltr.: The leaves are used as an emetic in Gabon (Raponda-Walker and Sillans, 1961).

A. thomsoni Schltr.: The plant is used in East Africa to treat abscess and hernia (Kokwaro, 1976).

Angraecum spp.: In east equatorial Africa a species was used as a remedy for ophthalmia (Pickering, 1879), and in the Central African Republic the crushed roots of another species are used as a poultice on swellings from sprains and strains (Vergiat, 1970).

A. chevalieri Summerh.: In Ghana a decoction of the leaves is used to treat hemoptysis and hematemesis (Dokosi, 1969).

A. dives Rolfe: An infusion of the leaves is used in East Africa as a cure for sores (Kokwaro, 1976).

Ansellia sp.: The stems have been used medicinally in east equatorial Africa (Pickering, 1879).

A. africana Lindl.: In Senegal a decoction of the plant was used to bathe sick children (Sebire, 1899). The juice of the plant is used with an extract of the root as an antimalarial agent (Haerdi, Kerharo, and Adam, 1964; Hoppe, 1975).

A. gigantea Rchb. f.: An infusion of the stem, leaf, or root of this species and of *A. humilis* Bull has been used as an emetic by Zulu herbalists, and the Pedi in Transvaal used an infusion of the roots for children's coughs (Watt and Breyer-Brandwijk, 1932, 1962; Schelpe, 1961; Hoppe, 1975). In East Africa the juice from the heated stem is squeezed into the ear to treat earache (Kokwaro, 1976).

A. humilis Bull: In Zambia an infusion of the leaf and stem was used against madness (Watt and Breyer-Brandwijk, 1932, 1962; Caius, 1936).[77]

Bulbophyllum nutans Thou.: This plant has been used medicinally in Réunion (Chatin, 1868).

Ceratandra grandiflora Lindl.: An infusion of the roots is used in southern Africa to correct the placement of the fetus (Rayner, 1977).

Cheirostylis lepida (non I.K.): A list of plants used in traditional medicine in Nigeria includes this orchid (Odebiyi and Sofowora, 1978).

---

[77]Watt (1967) considers this plant to be potentially useful for mental health.

Corymborkis corymbis Thou.: In Sierra Leone the leaves have been used as a purge and the roots are employed similarly in Tanzania (G. N. Rasmussen, personal communication). A decoction of the boiled root was drunk as a purgative in East Africa (Kokwaro, 1976).

Cynosorchis sp.: In Madagascar a pomade from the plant is applied to burns (Debray, Jacquemin, and Razafindrambaq, 1971).

Cyrtorchis sp.: The plant juice is used as an antimalarial agent (Haerdi *et al.*, 1964).

Disa chrysostachya Sw.: This plant has been used medicinally in southern Africa (Rayner, 1977).

D. polygonoides Lindl.: In southern Africa an infusion of the tubers was believed to restore lost speech (Rayner, 1977).

Eulophia spp.: There are reports from three parts of Africa of the medicinal use of this genus; in each case the species is unidentified. In West Africa the bruised leaves form part of a paste used to treat throat abscesses (Harley, 1970). The Sotho of southeast Africa included the bulb in all medicines given for protracted illnesses (Watt and Breyer-Brandwijk, 1932, 1962). In the Central African Republic cuts on the feet are poulticed with scrapings from the roots (Vergiat, 1970).

E. bacteri Summerh.: In West Africa this plant forms part of an astringent paste used to immobilize a fracture or sprain (Harley, 1970).

E. dilecta Schltr.: The tubers are used medicinally in Gabon for scabies and other skin diseases (Raponda-Walker and Sillans, 1961). In Zaire the crushed tubers have been used against scabies and other skin diseases and against buboes (Staner and Boutique, 1937).

E. ensata Lindl.: In parts of Natal and Swaziland this plant has been used for babies' ailments (Rayner, 1977).

E. flaccida Schltr.: The tuber is said to be astringent. Around northern Lesotho the powdered burned tuber was placed in incisions on sore limbs to relieve pain (Phillips, 1917; Watt and Breyer-Brandwijk, 1932, 1962).

E. galeoloides Kraenzl.: Liquid from the boiled roots is used for infants' stomach troubles in East Africa (Kokwaro, 1976).

E. lindleyana Rchb. f.: The juice from the crushed roots is used against otitis media and the shredded roots are used to treat syphilitic ulcers (Haerdi *et al.*, 1964).

E. petersii Rchb. f.: In East Africa a warm decoction of the roots is drunk as a purgative (Kokwaro, 1976).

Eulophidium sp. aff. *silvaticum* (Schltr.) Summerh.: The salted juice from the crushed stem is used as a lactagogue (Haerdi *et al.*, 1964).

Habenaria cirrhata Rchb. f.: The boiled roots were used for indigestion in East Africa (Kokwaro, 1976).

H. foliosa Rchb. f.: An infusion of the root is used as an emetic by the Zulus (Watt and Breyer-Brandwijk, 1932, 1962).

H. macranda Lindl.: A decoction from the boiled roots is used in East Africa as a purgative (Kokwaro, 1976).

H. steudneri Rchb. f.: In East Africa the roots are crushed to treat myiasis and are made into a decoction that is drunk for stomach disorders and influenza (Kokwaro, 1976).

H. walleri Rchb. f.: The roots are used for stomach diseases in East Africa (Kokwaro, 1976).

Lissochilus arenarius Lind.: The cooked root is used in Malawi as a poultice (Watt and Breyer-Brandwijk, 1962).

L. beravensis (Rchb. f.) H. Perr.: In Madagascar this plant is used against nervous disorders (Terrac, 1947).

L. dilectus Rchb. f.: The root is used in Zaire for scabies and skin lesions (Githens, 1949; Watt and Breyer-Brandwijk, 1962).

L. krebsii Rchb. f.: This plant has been used in southern Africa as a sedative and as a medicine for children (Watt and Breyer-Brandwijk, 1932, 1962).

Manniella gustavi Rchb. f.: In the Congo (Brazzaville) the juice expressed from the entire plant was used as a poison antidote and a purgative. It is prescribed for barren women "to clean the belly" (Bouquet, 1969).

Ophrys lutea Cav.: The plant has been used as a stomachic in Tunisia (Bocquillon-Limousin, 1894).

Orchis lutea Dulac and *O. provincialis* Balb.: The tubers, known as false salep, have been used in Algeria as an analeptic (Chatin, 1868).

Polystachya stauroglossa Kraenzl.: In Kenya a decoction of the leaves is administered to a woman before childbirth (Innamorati, 1973).

Satyrium cordifolium Lindl.: In southern Africa, an infusion of the tubers is mixed with milk as a vermifuge (Rayner, 1977).

Stenoglottis fimbriata Lindl.: The people of Transkei and Natal use the root as an enema and as a cure for flatulence (Rayner, 1977).

12.2. Mexico, Central America, and the West Indies

Arpophyllum spicatum La Llave *et* Lex.: A decoction of the tubers was used in Mexico for dysentery (Maisch, 1885).

Bletia campanulata La Llave *et* Lex. In Mexico this plant was used against dysentery (Maisch, 1885; Dragendorff, 1898); it was listed as a medicinal plant in the Codex Badiano (Domínguez, 1969).

B. coccinea La Llave *et* Lex.: A decoction of the tubers was used in Mexico to treat dysentery (Maisch, 1885).

B. verecunda R. Br.: The dried corms were used as a stomachic and tonic, notably in Jamaica (Burnett, 1835; Lindley, 1838, 1849; Morren, 1846; Griffith, 1847; Dragendorff, 1898; Bulhart, 1927). An aqueous infusion of the dried plant is used in Cuba as a stomachic (Roig y Mesa, 1945). The Bahamians drink a decoction of the boiled tubers as a cure for fish poisoning,[78] and apply the freshly cut bulbs to wounds. In the West Indies the dried bulbs are used as a tonic (Hawkes, 1943).

Brassia caudata Lindl.: In the West Indies an alcoholic tincture of this species was used as an antispasmodic and for epilepsy and nervous disorders (Descourtilz, 1828).

Calanthe mexicana Rchb. f.: The powdered flowers are used in Mexico to arrest nosebleed (Uphof, 1959).

---

[78]See n. 76.

Catasetum maculatum Kunth: The Mayas applied the peeled, salted, and roasted bulbs to boils (Roys, 1931; Steggerda and Korsch, 1943).

Cattleya citrina Lindl.: Mexican Indians used the powdered root to relieve the pain of wounds (Urbina, 1903a).

Cranichis speciosa La Llave *et* Lex. and *C. tubularis* La Llave *et* Lex.: These plants were used by Indian people of Mexico for dysentery, inflammation, fever, hemoptysis, and bone fractures (Urbina, 1903a).

Cyrtopodium punctatum (L.) Lindl.: In Cuba a decoction or syrup from this plant is used for bronchial disease. In eastern Cuba it has been used as an emollient for dislocations and wounds, and in Cienfuegos an aqueous infusion of the whole plant is used for skin disease (Roig y Mesa, 1945). In Chiapas, Mexico, the plant is used to treat a malady that affects the back (Berlin, Breedlove, and Raven, 1974).

C. woodfordii Sims: The mucilage from the pseudobulbs is used as a pectoral in El Salvador (Guzmán, 1924).

Epidendrum bifidum Aubl.: In Martinique and Guadeloupe the juice of this plant has been regarded as purgative, anthelminthic, and diuretic (Morren, 1846; Lanessan, 1886; Emboden, 1974). In Mexico it is used against dysentery (Richter, 1965; Emboden, 1974).

E. pastoris La Llave *et* Lex.: This plant is listed as an Aztec medicinal plant in the Codex Badiano (Domínguez, 1969). Indians of Mexico used a decoction of the root against diarrhea and dysentery (Maisch, 1885; Pardal, 1937), and the dried root as an analgesic and for dysentery, colitis, and other digestive disorders (Urbina, 1903a; Richter, 1965; Emboden, 1974).

E. phonecium Lindl.: In Cuba the pseudobulbs are used for catarrh, and as an emmenagogue and abortifacient (Roig y Mesa, 1945).

Laelia spp.: The bulbs of one species in Mexico contain a fluid that was reputed to cool the system during attacks of fever (Bateman, 1837–1843; Morren, 1846; Bulhart, 1927). Another species was incorporated in a potion used to prevent abortion caused by failure to satisfy a pregnant woman's sudden food craving (Redfield, 1928; Ford, 1975).

L. autumnalis Lindl. and *L. grandiflora* Lindl.: Both of these orchids were used in Mexico for the treatment of coughs (Richter, 1965; Emboden, 1974).

L. digbyana Benth.: In Yucatan this plant is reputed to have medicinal properties (Standley, 1930).

Oncidium cebolleta Sw.: The leaves have been used for fractures and other injuries (Bulhart, 1927). The Mayas used the plant to draw a sliver from the foot (Roys, 1931).

Ponthieva glandulosa R. Br.: In Costa Rica the roots are used as a substitute for ipecacuanha (Duggal, 1972).

Stanhopea tigrina Batem.: Used as a medicinal plant by the Aztecs, this orchid was employed by Mexican Indians against sunstroke and weakness (Urbina, 1903a; Gerste, 1910).

12.3. North America

Moerman (1977) includes Orchidaceae in his bibliography of North American ethnobotany. His reports contain minor inaccuracies, and the list is far from complete.

Aplectrum hyemale (Muhl. ex Willd.) Torr.: The dried root was included in the trade lists of many drug dealers (Henkel, 1906). The plant has been used as an emollient (Dragendorff, 1898; Luer, 1975) and to treat bronchial disease (Krochmal, Walters, and Doughty, 1969, 1971; Krochmal and Krochmal, 1975). It has been used medicinally in New England, and the Catawba Indians used the roots for boils (Taylor, 1940; Correll, 1950). The Cherokees used this plant to make children fleshy and fat (Hamel and Chiltoskey, 1975).

Arethusa bulbosa L.: The tuber has been used as a remedy for toothache, swellings, and maturating boils, and for sluggish tumors (Griffith, 1847; Hogg, 1858; Linden, 1894; Dragendorff, 1898; Bulhart, 1927; Hawkes, 1943; Correll, 1950; Luer, 1975). Poultices have been used to treat cold tumors and similar degenerative diseases (Emboden, 1974).

Bletia verecunda R. Br.: An infusion of the corms is used as a tonic and stomachic and as an antidote to fish poisoning.[79] The fresh corms are used on cuts and skin abrasions (Correll, 1950).

Corallorhiza sp.: This plant is a diaphoretic and is used as a sedative in the eastern United States (Krochmal *et al.*, 1969, 1971), where there is still a limited commercial demand for this genus as a source of botanical drugs (Hardin, 1964).

C. maculata Rafin.: A tea made from the dried stalks was used by Indians in Nevada as a blood tonic in cases of pneumonia, and the roots were used as a sedative, vermifuge, and diaphoretic (Train, Henricks, and Archer, 1957; Krochmal and Krochmal, 1975).

C.'odontorhiza (Willd.) Nutt.: The dried root, now nonofficinal, was included in the trade lists of many drug dealers (Henkel, 1906; Clute, 1919). It was used as a sedative and diaphoretic in fevers and inflammatory infections in the dose of 30 grains of powder every two hours (O. P. Brown, 1878; Wood *et al.*, 1886; Henkel, 1907; Harding, 1908; Grieve, 1924; Hawkes, 1943; Correll, 1950). A tea made from the root was considered efficacious in the treatment of various malignant growths (Emboden, 1974). Kloss (1975) eulogizes this orchid, reporting its value in the treatment of skin diseases, scrofula, scurvy, boils, tumors, cancer, erysipelas, cramps, pleurisy, night sweats, enlarged veins, fevers, typhus, inflammatory diseases, and dysmenorrhea.

Cypripedium spp.: Indians drank a sweetened concoction for headache and chewed the roots as a sedative, especially during menstruation and childbirth (Hawkes, 1944b; Vogel, 1970; Weiner, 1972; Hand, 1976).

At one time official in the United States pharmacopoeia, the drug cypripedium (ladies' slipper) consisted of the rhizome and rootlets of *C. parviflorum* Salisb. and *C. pubescens* Willd. The two species were interchanged indiscriminately, and it is possible that other species were also used. *Calypso borealis* Salisb. (syn. *C. bulbosa* (L.) Oakes and *Cypripedium bulbosum* L.) also has been reported to provide the drug (Bergen, 1898; *Merck Index*, 1960). Rafinesque (1828) remarks that all species are equally nervine, and then gives an order of efficacy. Cypripedium was also included in the *British Pharmaceutical Codex*. It served as a gentle nervous stimulant or antispasmodic used for the same purposes as valerian (Wood *et al.*, 1886; Maisch, 1890; Planchon and Collin, 1895; Heckel, 1897; Anonymous, 1971). Cypripedium has been said to be tonic, stimulant, antispasmodic, and diaphoretic, and to act as a tranquilizer, improving the circulation and the nutrition

[79]See n. 76.

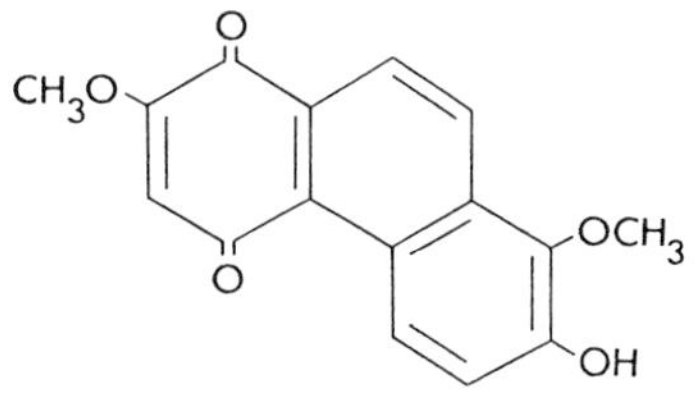

Fig. 2-2. Cypripedin

of the nerve centers. It was used in nervous disease, epilepsy, delirium, hysteria, chorea, nervous headache, insomnia, hypochondria, palpitation, depression from sexual overindulgence, dementia at the climacteric, fever, ague, and rheumatism (Griffith, 1847; Ives, 1850; Hogg, 1858; O. P. Brown, 1878; Millspaugh, 1887; Dujardin-Beaumetz and Egasse, 1889; Linden, 1894; Grieve, 1924; Hawkes, 1943; Clymer, 1963).

The powder produced by precipitating the tincture with water and drying is known as cypripedin (Fig. 2-2).[80] Much used by the eclectics, it was reputed to have exaggerated powers of the root and was given to children instead of opium (Wood *et al.*, 1886; Bocquillon-Limousin, 1905).

The use for similar purposes of these two *Cypripedium* species persisted into the twentieth century in the folk medicine of Indiana (Wright, 1906).

C. calceolus L.: In Appalachia a root extract is used for headache and as a nervine. A sweetened root tea is used as a sedative and analgesic (Krochmal and Krochmal, 1975). The Cherokees used both this species and *C. humile* Salisb. for a variety of medicinal purposes, including the relief of pain and nervous disorders, diabetes, worms, rupture pain, stomach pains, kidney trouble, "female disorders," influenza, and colds (Hamel and Chiltoskey, 1975).

C. humile Salisb. syn. *C. acaule* Ait.: Good (1854) reports the use of this plant in many types of nervous disorders, insomnia, fevers, and consumption. The root was used by Indians as a tonic and nervous stimulant (Hussey, 1974). Women used the plant to relieve difficult menstruation and to facilitate parturition (Vogel, 1970). The Penobscots used the steeped plant for nervousness (Speck, 1915; Vogel, 1970; Hand, 1976). The Menominis used the plant for male disorders (H. H. Smith, 1923).

C. luteum Rafin.: Indians sometimes used this species as a nervine (Hand, 1976).

C. parviflorum Salisb.: The Cherokees used a decoction of the root to treat worms in children (Mooney, 1891, 1932; Vogel, 1970). The Menominis used the plant for "female disorders" (H. H. Smith, 1923), and it was used by Cherokee women for labor pains, hysteria, and insomnia (Hand, 1976). In Appalachia a root tea is used for nervous ailments and headache (Harding, 1908; Krochmal *et al.*, 1969, 1971). The Chippewa Indians used the root for toothache, indigestion, and skin inflammation (Densmore, 1928).

C. pubescens Willd.: This plant was used by Indians as a tonic, sedative, and nervous stimulant. It was used for palpitation and nervous disorders. The Ojibwas used the root

---

[80]Cypripedin (2,8 dimethoxy-7-hydroxy-1,4-phenanthraquinone) is structurally related to the phytoalexin orchinol (Schmalle and Hausen, 1979).

for female troubles of all kinds and the Cherokees employed a decoction of the root as a vermifuge (H. H. Smith, 1932; Taylor, 1940; Hawkes, 1943, 1944b; Correll, 1950; Core, 1967; Vogel, 1970; Weiner, 1972; Hussey, 1974; Hand, 1976).

C. spectabile Salisb.: In western counties of New York State an aqueous decoction of the root was used as an antispasmodic (Rafinesque, 1828). The Pillager Ojibwas used the plant as a nervine (Hand, 1976). Vogel (1970) reports its use by the Indians as a sedative and antispasmodic and in hysteria and chorea.

Epipactis gigantea Dougl. ex Hook.: Indians of California drank a decoction of the roots to combat mania and the most severe cases of illness (Chesnut, 1902; Caius, 1936; M. A. Miller, 1959; Duggal, 1972).

E. helleborine (L.) Crantz.: This orchid is said to have been brought to North America by immigrants from Europe as a treatment of gout (Hawkes, 1944b; Correll, 1950; Emboden, 1974).[81]

Goodyera menziesii Lindl. syn. *G. oblongifolia* Rafin.: This plant was chewed by Thompson Indian women to ease childbirth (Steedman, 1930). Vancouver Island Indians used the boiled leaves as a liniment on sore and stiff muscles. The split leaves were placed, cut side down, on bruises and sores (Turner and Bell, 1971).

G. pubescens (Willd.) R. Br.: Both Indians and European settlers made medicinal use of this plant, the root of which was once officinal (Dragendorff, 1898) and was included in lists issued by drug dealers (Henkel, 1906). The Delawares of Oklahoma used the root as a remedy for pleurisy and rheumatism and gave it to women following childbirth (Tantaquidgeon, 1942). The leaves were made into a mash by the Mohegans to prevent sore mouth in babies (Speck, 1915; Tantaquidgeon, 1928). This species, and the next named, were used medicinally by the Cherokees as appetizers and emetics and for burns, colds, sore eyes, toothache, and kidney disease (Hamel and Chiltoskey, 1975). Indians and Europeans, both empirics and physicians, used the fresh leaves for scrofula, externally as a poultice and internally as a decoction that was also used to wash the sores (Henry, 1814; Rafinesque, 1830; Griffith, 1847; O. P. Brown, 1878). This orchid was once known as "cancer weed" and was used for cancers, lupus, and ulcers; the new leaves and root were bruised and applied to the affected part (Ives, 1850). The plant was reputed to cure rabies and rattlesnake bite (Correll, 1950).[82]

G. repens (L.) R. Br.: Trade lists issued by drug dealers included the dried roots of this orchid (Henkel, 1906). The roots and leaves were used by the Potawatomi Indians for "female disorders" and stomach and bladder diseases. The chewed leaves were applied to the bite of reptiles and at the same time some of the juice was swallowed. European settlers used the leaves for scrofula and diseases of the eye, and as a demulcent (O. P. Brown, 1878; H. H. Smith, 1933; Core, 1967). This plant was favored by the Mohegans, who used the mashed leaves to prevent thrush in infants (Weiner, 1972).

---

[81]I have not found any firm basis for this report. As it is not mentioned by Henkel (1906) in her comprehensive list of United States medicinal plants, it could be an assumption based on similar reports from Europe (see p. 109). It was first reported near Syracuse, New York (Anonymous, 1879), from which it spread rapidly in the United States and into Canada; the precise manner of its introduction may never be known (Greenwood, 1974; Luer, 1975; Sanders, 1978). Several authors (Anonymous, 1879; Gray, 1879; Senghas, 1970) maintain that it is in fact native to North America, but they are not convincing.

[82]Correll points out that the use of this plant against rattlesnake bite is another example of the doctrine of signatures, as the leaves are mottled and striped like the skin of the snake.

Habenaria sp.: The leaves of this orchid were sometimes used to make a salve (Bergen, 1898).

H. ciliaris R. Br.: In Florida the root of this plant was used both internally and externally for snakebite (Pickering, 1879). The Cherokees used a cold infusion of the root for headache and drank a warm tea from the plant for dysentery (Hamel and Chiltoskey, 1975).

H. dilatata A. Gray: The Micmac-Montagnais of Newfoundland used this plant to treat gravel: the juice, expressed from the roots, was drunk with water (Howley, 1915; Speck, 1915).

H. fimbriata R. Br.: The powdered root has been used as a vermifuge, which killed by contact (Rafinesque, 1830).

H. hookeriana Torr. ex A. Gray: This plant was used for a vulnerary known as "heal-all" (Rafinesque, 1830). The Montagnais put the leaves on hands and feet to cure them of blisters (Speck, 1915; Moerman, 1977).

H. leucostachys S. Wats.: The Thompson Indians spread the leaves on hot stones to make a steam bath for treatment of rheumatism (Steedman, 1930).

Liparis loeselii A. Rich.: The root mixed with *Spiranthes lucida* Ames was used by the Cherokees for urinary problems (Hamel and Chiltoskey, 1975).

Microstylis ophioglossoides Nutt.: The Ojibwas used the root in a diuretic mixture (H. H. Smith, 1932).

Orchis fragrans (non I.K.): In New York State the roots were used as a stimulant and nerve tonic (Rafinesque, 1830).

O. macrophylla (non I.K.): This orchid has been used as a vulnerary known as "heal-all" (Rafinesque, 1830).

Spiranthes lucida Ames: See *Liparis loeselii* A. Rich.

12.4. South America

Certain species of South American orchids have been shown to provide some protection against poliomyelitis in mice (Cochran and Lucas, 1958/59).

Catasetum spp. and *Cyrtopodium* spp.: These plants have been used in the interior of Brazil as a cataplasm on suppurating abscesses and tumors, and in Rio de Janeiro State a decoction was employed as a pectoral remedy (Silva Maia, 1942).

C. fimbriatum Lindl. ex Paxt.: The women of northeastern Paraguay use the pseudobulbs of this orchid as one of the ingredients of a sterilizing potion (Moreno and Schvartzman, 1975; Arenas and Moreno, 1977).

Chloraea leucantha Peopp. *et* Endl.: In Chile this plant has been used on wounds and ulcers (Gusinde, 1936).

C. disoides Lindl.: The juice has been used as a lactagogue in Chile (Griffith, 1847; Hogg, 1858; Dragendorff, 1898).

Cymbidium crispatum Thbg.: This plant was used in Brazil as a demulcent (Dragendorff, 1898).

Cyrtopodium punctatum (L.) Lindl.: In Bahia, Brazil, this plant is used as an emollient and a purgative, and as a cough remedy (Mello *et al.*, 1971).

C. woodfordii Sims: A cataplasm made from the stem was used in Brazil against tumors (Hartwell, 1970).

Epidendrum bifidum Aubl.: The juice was used in Guyana and Tortola as a purgative, anthelminthic, and diuretic (Lindley, 1838; Griffith, 1847; Lannessan, 1886; Dujardin-Beaumetz and Egasse, 1889; Heckel, 1897; Dragendorff, 1898; Bulhart, 1927; Hawkes, 1943).

Maxillaria bicolor Ruiz *et* Pav.: In the north of South America this plant has been used as a cure for fever (Richter, 1965; Emboden, 1974).

Oncidium cebolleta Sw.: The viscous sap from the pseudobulbs was used as a vulnerary in Venezuela (Pittier, 1926).

Ophrys argentea Vell.: In Brazil a paste from the pounded tubers is used medicinally (Penna, 1941).

O. tuberculosa (non I.K.): This plant has had extensive medicinal use in Rio de Janeiro State, Brazil (Penna, 1941).

Rodriguezia secunda H. B. *et* K.: The Indians of central Brazil attribute contraceptive properties to this orchid; the crushed pseudobulbs are rubbed over the woman's body (Turner, 1965).

Spiranthes diuretica Lindl.: This plant was a diuretic in Chile, and was administerd in cases of ischuria (Griffith, 1847; Hogg, 1858; Lindley and Moore, 1866; Linden, 1894; Dragendorff, 1898; Bulhart, 1927; Gusinde, 1936; Hawkes, 1943).

12.5. Eastern Asia

Orchids were used in China in the treatment of scabies and as a hemostatic (Wong, 1968).

Acampe multiflora Lindl.: This orchid is listed as a medicinal plant of Hong Kong (Arthur and Cheung, 1960).

Aerides falcatum Lindl. *et* Paxt.: In Indochina a decoction of this plant is used for infantile debility (Gagnepain and Guillaumin, 1933; Pételot, 1954). Dournes (1955) reports the use on infected wounds and skin disease of "a sort of yellow powder from within the fruit (the sulphonamide of the country)."

A. odoratum Lour.: The ground fruit was used in Indochina to treat wounds (Dournes, 1955).

Anaphora liparioides Gagn.: The tubers are applied to burns in Laos (Vidal, 1960).

Anoectochilus formosanus Hay.: In Taiwan an aqueous extract of the whole plant is taken for chest and abdominal pains (Liu, 1952; Hu, 1971a, 1971b).

Bletia hyacinthina R. Br. syn. *Bletilla striata* Rchb. f.: This orchid has been used as a drug in China, Mongolia, Tibet, and Japan (Tsudsioka and Murai, 1883; Read and Lui, 1927; Read, 1936; Hübotter, 1913, 1957). It is said to produce a sense of euphoria, to purify the blood, to strengthen and consolidate the lungs, and to be useful against pus, boils, abscesses, bad ulcers, malignant swellings, and breast cancer (Hübotter, 1909, 1913, 1957; Kariyone and Kimura, 1940; Mosig and Schramm, 1955; Schramm, 1956). The tubers have been employed as a demulcent and for flatulence, gastrointestinal disorders, hemorrhoids, hemoptysis, anthrax, malaria, eye disease, burns, skin disease, tinea, ring-worm, abscess, tumors, and necrosis (Pei, 1955; Schramm, 1960; Wong, 1968). The tuber is steamed or boiled then dried to produce the crude drug. It is used as a hemostatic in hematemasis, hemoptysis, and epistaxis; grated and kneaded with water, it is applied to wounds and boils (Kariyone and Kimura, 1940; Kariyone and Koiso, 1971; Hu, 1971a, 1971b). The dried tubers are used to treat silicosis and traumatic injuries and for cough, chest pain, hemoptysis, gastrorrhagia, enterorrhagia, internal bleeding, wounds, abscess, inflammation, and chapped skin (Anonymous, 1974, 1975b). The powdered root is mixed with oil as an emollient for burns and skin disease (Roi, 1955; Hu, 1971a, 1971b). A preparation of the whole plant is taken as a tonic and for leucorrhea, hemoptysis, and purulent cough (Cheo, 1947; Hu, 1971a, 1971b). The leaves collected in the autumn are said to cure lung disease (Hübotter, 1909, 1913, 1957). In Taiwan it was used as a hemostatic and for skin disease (Liu, 1952).

The plant has been recommended as an emulsifier and binding agent for tablet manufacture in place of gum arabic (Schramm, 1957, 1960; Hoppe, 1975).

In Indochina a decoction of the bulbs has been used against fever, pulmonary disease, dysentery, wounds, and burns (Pételot, 1954).

Bulbophyllum inconspicuum Maxim.: The whole plant is used in China for treatment of pulmonary tuberculosis and cancer of the stomach (Anonymous, 1974).

Calanthe lancifolia (non I.K.): In Szechwan the roots soaked in rice wine give a tincture used to treat internal bleeding and mechanical injury (Cheo, 1947; Hu, 1971a, 1971b).

C. latifolia (non I.K.): Dournes (1955) reports the use of this orchid in Indochina as a hemostatic; "a kind of grey powder from the capsule is very effective in causing leeches to drop off."

C. triplicata (Willem.) Ames: The pseudobulbs are used in Laos as a masticatory (Vidal, 1960).

C. vestita Lindl.: In Vietnam the crushed bulbs are rubbed over aching bones (Gagnepain and Guillaumin, 1933; Pételot, 1954).

Cirrhopetalum sp.: This plant was used in Indochina as a bath to treat splenomegaly (Dournes, 1955).

Coelogyne fimbriata Lindl.: This orchid has been used as a medicinal plant in Hong Kong (Arthur, 1954).

C. henryi Schltr.: In Hupei the pseudobulbs were taken as a cure for tuberculosis and asthma (Wilson, 1913).

C. pogonioides Rolfe: The pseudobulbs are used in Hupei against asthma and tuberculosis (Henry, 1887; Forbes and Hemsley, 1903; Wilson, 1913; Usher, 1974).

Cremastra sp.: In China the bulbs were used against tumors (Hartwell, 1970).

C. wallichiana Lindl. syn. *C. appendiculata* Makino: The roots are used for toothache by the Ainu of Japan; they are chewed and expectorated and the sticky material then clings to the teeth. The root paste is also used as an emollient (Batchelor and Miyabe, 1893; Dragendroff, 1898; Uphof, 1929; Kariyone and Kimura, 1940). In China a paste from the ground tubers is applied to abscesses, scrofula, and freckles, and used as an antidote to snakebite (Hu, 1971a, 1971b).

Cymbidium sp.: The mucilaginous root was used in China against rheumatism and neuralgia (Gordon, 1884; Simmonds, 1892).

C. aloifolium Sw.: In Indochina this plant is used to bathe debilitated infants and to combat menstrual irregularity (Gagnepain and Guillaumin, 1933; Pételot, 1954), and to treat burns and sores (Vidal, 1960).

C. ensifolium Sw.: The flowers are used in Indochina as an eyewash and as a diuretic, and the roots form part of a pectoral medicine (Pételot, 1954). In China an aqueous decoction of the root of the cultivated orchid is used for gonorrhea and syphilis and, in a mixture, for stomachache (Hu, 1971a, 1971b).

Dendrobium spp.: In Indochina the seed of one species was used against gravel (Regnault, 1902) and a wash from another species against unspecified disease (Dournes, 1955).

D. ceraia Lindl.: This orchid was used in Indochina as a tonic and against rheumatic pain and phobias (Regnault, 1902), for disease of the vertebral column, bones, and kidneys, and in the treatment of epilepsy, nervous maladies, and debility (Pételot, 1954; Hu, 1971a, 1971b). The drug *shih-hu* (see *D. nobile*) is said to come from this species in southern China, where it grows on rocks and was used as a tonic medicine (Williams, 1874).

D. crumenatum Sw.: This orchid has been used in Vietnam to purify the blood (Pételot, 1954).

D. gratiosissimum Rchb. f. and *D. pulchellum* Lodd. syn. *D. dalhousieanum* Paxt.: In Indochina these plants are much sought after by the Chinese for medicinal purposes (Pételot, 1954).

D. hancockii Rolfe.: The dried stems are used in Chinese medicine against fever, thirst, and cough (Anonymous, 1975b).

D. moniliforme Sw.: This orchid served in Japan as a stomachic (Kariyone and Kimura, 1940). In Taiwan it was used for night sweats, to fortify the person, and to reinforce the kidneys (Liu, 1952). The entire plant has been used in Korea as an antipyretic, tonic, and peptic (Ishidoya, 1925; Chung, 1964). In Szechwan the source of the drug *shih-hu* (see *D. nobile* and *D. ceraia*) was once thought to be this species (Tu, 1933; Chen and Chen, 1935a).

D. nobile Lindl.: This is the Chinese drug *shih-hu*, which has been regarded as a precious drug in Chinese materia medica at least since the Han dynasty (200 B.C.–A.D. 200) (Bretschneider, 1895; Kimura and Migo, 1936; King-Li-Pin and Li-Teng-Pang, 1936; Kariyone and Koiso, 1971). *Shih-hu* has also been used in Japan, Korea, Taiwan, and Tibet (Suzuki, Keimatsu, and Ito, 1932; Hübotter, 1957). The drug consists of the dried or, rarely, fresh stems of several species of *Dendrobium*, mostly lithophytes, the commonest by far of which is *D. nobile* Lindl.[83] Several species have been cultivated extensively in southern China for export in quantity to eastern China and overseas Chinese communities. On the other hand, some species have been cultivated in northern Vietnam for export to China via Hong Kong.[84] In addition, two Japanese species, *D. moniliforme* Sw. and *D. reptans* Franch. *et* Sav., are imported into eastern China for use as *shih-hu* (Henry, 1887; Forbes and Hemsley, 1903; Braun, 1909; Hooper, 1929; Chen and Chen, 1935a; Kimura and Migo, 1936; Pételot, 1954; Hu, 1970). The preparation of

[83]As a prescription may call for fresh material, retail drug shops often keep some potted plants (Hu, 1971a, 1971b, 1971c). Arditti (personal communication) reports that the plant is still used in China but is now difficult to find in shops.

[84]Chukanso is a trade name assigned to *shih-hu* on the Hong Kong market; the species involved are *D. lohohense* Tang *et* Wang, *D. nobile* Lindl., and *D. plicatile* Lindl. (Inubushi *et al.,* 1968; Takahashi, Namba, and Hayashi, 1965).

both the dried and fresh drug, with a key to differentiate the various types, is described by Hu (1970). Other associated species that provide the drug *shih-hu* include *D. aduncum* Lindl., *D. aggregatum* Roxb., *D. bellatulum* Rolfe, *D. ceraia* Lindl., *D. crispulum* Kimura *et* Migo, *D. chrysanthum* Wall., *D. flaviflorum* Hay., *D. hancockii* Rolfe, *D. hercoglossum* Rchb. f., *D. kwantungense* Tso, *D. linawianum* Rchb. f., *D. loddigesii* Rolfe syn. *D. pulchellum* Lodd., *D. lohohense* Tang *et* Wang, *D. officinale* Kimura *et* Migo, *D. plicatile* Lindl., *D. tosaense* Makino, and *D. wangii* Tso (Simmonds, 1892; Suzuki *et al.,* 1932, 1934b; Kimura and Migo, 1936; Hu, 1970; Chow, 1977).

The orchids *Bulbophyllum japonicum* Makino and *Eria japonica* Maxim. have also been used as *shih-hu;* in Korea a species of *Bulbophyllum* has been used also (Suzuki *et al.,* 1932).

Chen (1925) reproduces a prescription containing *D. nobile,* dated 1908, written for the emperor Kwang Hsu.

The virtues attributed to *shih-hu* (or to one or another of the plants used in the drug) have been reported in detail. It is traditionally used as a tonic and strengthening medicine.[85] It nourishes the yin system of the body and is a drug of longevity and an aphrodisiac. It has been credited with stomachic, pectoral, antiphlogistic, expectorant, analgesic, antipyretic, and antiepileptic properties, and has been used to increase appetite and to treat rheumatism, weakness from thirst, excessive perspiration, impotence, entropion, insects in the ear, leucorrhea, and menstrual pain. The dose is 5–10 gm of the dried preparation (F. P. Smith, 1871; Soubeiran and Thiersant, 1874; Gordon, 1884; Dragendorff, 1898; Braun, 1909; Stuart, 1911; Read and Liu, 1927; Hooper, 1929; King Li-Pin and Li-Teng-Pang, 1936; Read, 1936; Pei, 1951; Pételot, 1954; Roi, 1955; Hübotter, 1957; Wong, 1970; Hu, 1970, 1971a, 1971b; Kariyone and Koiso, 1971; Anonymous, 1974). In Szechwan an aqueous decoction from the stem is used as a stomachic and sialagogue (Cheo, 1947; Perry and Metzger, 1980).

D. nobile Lindl. contains several alkaloids, the most important of which is dendrobine (Suzuki and Keimatsu, 1932; Suzuki *et al.,* 1932, 1934a; Chen and Chen, 1935a). The occurrence alkaloids in this and related species has been reviewed by Luning (1974) and Slaytor (1976). The pharmacodynamics of dendrobine have been investigated by Chen and Chen (1935b), King Li-Pin and Li-Teng-Pang (1936), and Roi (1955). Their findings show that dendrobine provokes violent uterine contraction, progressively paralyzes peristalsis, lowers blood pressure, has a feeble analgesic action, produces a mild hyperglycemia, and augments the secretion of saliva. It does not appear to affect the vasomotors and has no antipyretic properties. The lethal dose for mice is 20 mg/kg, for guinea pigs 22 mg/kg, and for rabbits 17 mg/kg; the action is rapid, leading to convulsions and paralysis. Amytal is an antidote.

Epipactis mairei Schltr.: A paste of the whole plant has been used in Szechwan for burns (Cheo, 1947; Hu, 1971a, 1971b), and a decoction of the fruit is tonic and stimulates hormone secretion (Perry and Metzger, 1980).[86]

Galeola septentrionalis Rchb. f.: In Japan the capsule of this orchid, known as *tsuchiakebi,*

---

[85]*Shih-hu* means "rock living." As such a plant must be hardy, it follows, in accord with the doctrine of signatures, that it must provide a strengthening medicine (Hu, 1970).

[86]This report is dubious, as Perry and Metzger claim to cite Kariyone and Kimura, who do not mention *Epipactis mairei.* It is unfortunate that the section on Orchidaceae in Perry and Metzger's comprehensive work is marred by several errors.

has been used in medicine (*Encyclopedia Japonica,* 1970). It was used to treat diseases of the bladder and urinary tract (Anonymous, 1885a, 1885b) and gonorrhea (Dragendorff, 1898).[87] The ashed plant was incorporated in a hair tonic to treat scalp disease (Kariyone and Kimura, 1940).

Gastrodia elata Bl.: The tuber and, to a lesser extent, the stem have been used as a drug in China and Japan (Tsudioka and Murai, 1883; Anonymous, 1895b; Read and Lui, 1927; Read, 1936). The Ainu of Japan used the boiled tuber (Batchelor and Miyabe, 1893). In China the drug was considered very beneficial, expelling poisonous effluvia, giving strength and virility, improving circulation, and improving the memory. It has been used for rheumatism, neuralgia, paralysis, lumbago, fever, numbness, headache, and other neuralgic and nervous afflictions, to expel wind, and as a tonic and a longeval (Stuart, 1911; Roi, 1955; Hübotter, 1957; Wong, 1968; Hu, 1971a, 1971b; Anonymous, 1974, 1975b; Hyatt, 1978). In Chinese medicine the dried young stalks were used as a tonic and longeval, and were part of a mixture taken for headache and dizziness (Kariyone and Koiso, 1971; Hu, 1971a, 1971b). In Korea the tubers were used to prevent the common cold and as a tonic (Chung, 1964) and for nervous disorders (Perry and Metzger, 1980). In Taiwan this orchid was used as a fortifier and for headache, dizziness, and weakness of the nervous system (Liu, 1952). In Japan the dried plant was used for vertigo, headache, and nervous diseases, particularly in children (Kariyone and Kimura, 1940). Zhou and his colleagues (1965) have identified vanillin as the anticonvulsive agent in this plant.

Goodyera nantoensis Hay.: In Taiwan an aqueous extract was used as a febrifuge by the aboriginal mountain people (Liu, 1952; Hu, 1971a, 1971b).

G. schlechtendaliana Rchb. f.: A tincture of the plant in rice wine is used in Szechwan as a tonic, for internal injuries, and to improve circulation (Cheo, 1947; Hu, 1971a, 1971b).

Habenaria sp.: The powdered tuber is used in Indochina on infected wounds (Dournes, 1955).

H. ciliolaris Kraenzl.: In Szechwan a tincture of the whole plant is used for internal injuries (Cheo, 1947; Hu, 1971a, 1971b).

H. japonica A. Gray: An aqueous decoction of the plant is used as a vulnerary in western China (Cheo, 1947; Hu, 1971a, 1971b).

H. miersiana Champ. ex Benth.: The pounded root was used by the aboriginal mountain people of Taiwan to dress wounds and swellings, and in Szechwan a decoction of the root is taken for colic (Cheo, 1949; Liu, 1952; Hu, 1971a, 1971b).

Haemaria discolor Lindl.: This orchid was much sought after in Hong Kong for its medicinal value (Walden, 1977).

Liparis bicallosa Schltr.: In the northern Satsunan Islands a decoction of this plant is used for stomach trouble (Higashi *et al.,* 1975).

L. keitaoënsis Hay.: An aqueous extract of the root is taken in Taiwan for stomach pains (Liu, 1952; Hu, 1971a, 1971b).

L. plicata Franch. *et* Sav.: In Szechwan a decoction of this plant was used as a diaphoretic; it is said to be good for coughs and colds (Cheo, 1947; Hu, 1971a, 1971b).

---

[87]Dragendorff confuses *tsuchiakebi* with *ilango,* an unidentified species from Gabon (see sec. 11.1). Wehmer (1929), who quotes Dragendorff, is also confused. Both cite the two anonymous references cited above, which are quite clear!

Listera grandiflora Rolfe: The whole plant cooked with pork is used in Szechwan as a tonic (Cheo, 1947; Perry and Metzger, 1980).

Luisia teres Bl.: This plant has been used medicinally in China (Read and Liu, 1927; Read, 1936). It was used as a counterpoison, against infection, cancer, and malaria, and to counteract medicinal poisons (Stuart, 1911; Pételot, 1954; Roi, 1955). In Indochina a bitter decoction prepared from the roots is used on sores and ulcers, and to provoke vomiting or diarrhea in cases of poisoning; Chinese and Vietnamese pharmacists regard it as specific against gout (Pételot, 1954). Matsui and his colleagues (1967) have shown that it does not affect fertility in mice.

Microstylis muscifera Ridl.: In Szechwan a decoction of the root is used as a tonic to strengthen the kidneys (Cheo, 1947; Hu, 1971a, 1971b).

Nephelaphyllum chowii (non I.K.): A broth made in Szechwan from the rhizome is used as a diuretic, and a paste made from the pounded rhizome is used on itching sores (Cheo, 1947; Hu, 1971a, 1971b).

Oberonia longibracteata Lindl.: This plant has been used against scorpion bites in Kampuchea (Gagnepain and Guillaumin, 1932; Pételot, 1954).

Orchis spp.: These plants are used as emollients in Tibet (Gusseva-Badmaeva, Hammermann, and Sokolov, 1972).

Phaius somai Hay.: The pseudobulbs have been used in Chinese medicine (Chow, 1977).

Pholidota chinensis Lindl.: This species is reported as a medicinal plant in Hong Kong (Arthur and Cheung, 1960); an aqueous extract of the pseudobulbs is taken for scrofula, feverish stomach, and toothache, and a tincture is used for internal bleeding, hemorrhage, asthmatic cough, and tuberculosis, and in the treatment of rheumatism and dysentery (Hu, 1971a, 1971b).

P. yunnanensis Rolfe: In Szechwan a broth from the whole plant cooked with pork is used as an expectorant for cough and asthma (Cheo, 1947; Hu, 1971a, 1971b).

Pleione bulbocodioides Rolfe: In China an application of this orchid is used for boils and snakebite (Perry and Metzger, 1980).

Sarcanthus ophioglossa Guill.: This plant is used in Laos to treat orchitis (Vidal, 1960).

Spathoglottis lobbii Rchb. f.: In Indochina this plant is used on infected wounds; it once had a reputation for treatment of war wounds (Dournes, 1955).

S. plicata Bl.: The pseudobulbs of this plant have been used in Chinese medicine (Chow, 1977).

Spiranthes australis Lindl.: This orchid has had an unspecified medicinal use in Indochina (Pételot, 1954). In Szechwan the whole plant is made into a broth taken as a tonic for hematemasis and kidney disease (Hu, 1971a, 1971b).

Uncifera maxilla-leonis Guill.: This orchid has had an unspecified use in Indochinese medicine (Gagnepain and Guillaumin, 1933; Pételot, 1954).

12.6. Western Asia

In Afghanistan and Iran orchid tubers have been used as medicines (Royle, 1839; Aitchison, 1891). Bulbs are sold in Turkish markets for the household preparation of a drink said to cure colds; the drink is sometimes sold by street vendors. The bulbs come from species of *Anacamptis, Ophrys, Orchis, Serapias,* and *Spiranthes* (Vöth, 1973).

Aceras anthropophora R. Br.: This plant has been used in Arabia as a stimulant and diaphoretic (Dragendorff, 1898).

Acampe papillosa Lindl.: In India a decoction of the root is used in acute rheumatism, sciatica, and neuralgia, and also for secondary syphilis and uterine disease (Dey, 1896). The roots are used to treat rheumatism both internally and externally and have cooling properties. The plant is a substitute for sarsaparilla in Darjeeling and the Sikkim Himalayas (Dymock, 1885; Kirtikar and Basu, 1918; Caius, 1936; Biswas, 1950, 1956; Chopra, Nayar and Chopra, 1956). The root is employed under the name *rasna* for rheumatism, sciatica, and neuralgia (Dymock, Warden, and Hooper, 1893; Caius, 1936; Nadkarni, 1954).[88] It is used in Sri Lanka for rheumatism (Attygalle, 1917).

A. wrightiana Lindl.: This orchid is a bitter tonic used in India for rheumatism (Caius, 1936; Chopra, Nayar, and Chopra, 1956).[89] It promotes perspiration and is used for fevers. The fresh juice of the leaves mixed with honey relaxes the bowels (Rhede tot Drakestein, 1703; Dalgado, 1896, 1898).

Anoectochilus intermedius Hort. ex Loud.: This plant has appeared in a treatise on Sinhalese medicinal herbs (Cooray, 1940).

A. regalis Bl.: In Sri Lanka this orchid was an ingredient in certain medicinal oils (Cooray, 1940; Soysa, 1943).

A. setaceus Bl.: Noted in Sanskrit works as a secret medicine for certain diseases, this plant was regarded as medicinal in Sri Lanka (Attygalle, 1917; Chopra, Nayar, and Chopra, 1956).

Calanthe masuca Lindl.: The flowers are used in Nepal to stop nosebleed (Singh *et al.*, 1979).

Cephalanthera ensifolia Rich.: In India the roots and rhizomes have been used as a tonic (Duggal, 1972).

Cirrhopetalum maculosum Lindl.: This plant was used in ayurvedic medicine in India (Duggal, 1972).

Coelogyne cristata Lindl.: The pseudobulbs are used medicinally in Nepal; they are cooling and soothing (Anonymous, 1970).

C. ovalis Lindl.: Known in ayurvedic medicine as *jivanti*, this orchid was part of a large number of preparations used to treat an equally large number of ailments (*Sushruta Samhita*, 1907–1911; *Charaka Samhita*, 1888–1903; Hoernle, 1893–1912).

Cymbidium aloifolium Sw.: In India a decoction made by powdering the plant with ginger and extracting the mixture with water was said to excite vomiting and diarrhea, and to cure chronic illness, weakness of the eyes, vertigo, and paralysis (Rhede tot Drakestein, 1703; Dymock *et al.*, 1893; Dalgado, 1896, 1898; Dragendorff, 1898; Greshoff, 1900; Caius, 1936; *Wealth of India*, 1950; Chopra, Nayar, and Chopra, 1956). In Sri Lanka this plant has been used in ayurvedic medicine (Cooray, 1940), and was a constituent of oils that were applied to tumors, both benign and malignant (Soysa, 1943).

C. macrorrhizum Lindl.: This orchid has been used in India as a diaphoretic and febrifuge, and to treat boils (Duggal, 1972).

C. tenuifolium Willd.: In Malabar the plant was said to be antifebrile, to dissipate

---

[88]See *Vanda roxburghii* R. Br., below.
[89]See *Vanda roxburghii* R. Br., below.

tympanitis, purge blood, dissolve stones, and correct the menstrual flow (Rhede tot Drakestein, 1703). It was used in western India as an emollient, against dysuria and blood dyscrasias, and externally against swellings (Dymock *et al.*, 1893; Dragendorff, 1898). In India the plant formed a poultice for tumors; when powdered with vinegar, it was used for hemorrhoids, leucorrhea, and gonorrhea (Griffith, 1847).

Cypripedium elegans Rchb. f.: In India this and several other species are used in nerve disorders and rheumatism (Duggal, 1972).

C. guttatum Sw. The root and leaf have been used in eastern Russia and Siberia against epilepsy (Gmelin, 1747; Dragendorff, 1898; Hawkes, 1944b).

Dendrobium alpestre Royle: This and other *Dendrobium* species are used in India as an emollient to treat pimples, boils, and skin eruptions (Duggal, 1972).

D. chlorops Lindl.: This orchid has been used in India as an emollient. The fresh juice of the whole plant was used for colic and stomach ills; it was said to move the bile and relax the bowels (Rhede tot Drakestein, 1703; Dymock *et al.*, 1893; Dalgado, 1896, 1898; Dragendorff, 1898; Kirtikar and Basu, 1918; Caius, 1936; *Wealth of India*, 1952; Chopra, Nayar, and Chopra, 1956).

D. moschatum (Willd.) Sw.: The juice from the leaf is used in the Indian state of Meghalaya as drops for earache (Rao, 1981).

Ephemerantha macraei (Lindl.) Hunt *et* Summerh.[90] In India this plant is considered tonic, astringent, and expectorant, and has been used for disorders of the bile, blood, and phlegm and to treat asthma, bronchitis, consumption, fevers, diseases of the eye, and throat trouble (Dymock *et al.*, 1893; Dalgado, 1898; Dragendorff, 1898; Kirtikar and Basu, 1918; Kirtikar, Basu, and An I. C. S., 1975). It has been used as a stimulant and a tonic in cases of debility due to seminal loss, and also following snakebite and scorpion sting (Caius, 1936;[91] Nadkarni, 1954; Chopra, Nayar, and Chopra, 1956; Chopra *et al.*, 1958). It has been used as a stimulant and demulcent in Nepal (Anonymous, 1970), and as a restorative and an external application for rheumatism in Sri Lanka (Attygalle, 1917; Cooray, 1940; Soysa, 1943). Ray and Majumdar (1976) have not been able to demonstrate any antimicrobial activity of this plant. A chemical fraction obtained from the plant has been found to lower blood pressure (Satyavati, Raina, and Sharma, 1976).

Epidendrum sterile Lindl.: The plant was used in eastern India against catarrh, herpes, and scabies, and the juice was dropped into the ear to treat deafness. The fruit was used as a diuretic (Dragendorff, 1898).

Eria muscicola Lindl.: Known in early Sanskrit works as *jivanti,* this orchid was an ingredient in numerous medications said to be useful for diseases of the chest, heart, lungs, eye, ear, and nervous system, for facial tumors, ranula, lockjaw, fever, and erysipelas, and in tonic, strengthening, and longeval medicines (Hoernle, 1893–1912). The formulas often included *rasna* (see *Vanda roxburghii* R. Br., below).

Eulophia campestris Wall.: In India the rhizome was used in folk medicine as a tonic, stomachic, and astringent. It was given for stomatitis, purulent cough, paralysis, and

---

[90] I have found it difficult to interpret these reports, as the nomenclature is confused and the synonymy in the *Index Kewensis* is by no means clear. Some reports cited under this taxon may well refer also to *E. fimbriata* (Bl.) Hunt *et* Summerh. and perhaps other taxa.

[91] Caius has shown that it is of no benefit in snakebite or scorpion sting.

cardiac conditions, and to stimulate the appetite (*Charaka Samhita*, 1976; Caius, 1936; Biswas, 1950; Chopra, Nayar, and Chopra, 1956; Chopra *et al.*, 1958). The tubers are reputed to be nutritive, astringent, blood purifying, and anthelminthic; they resemble scrofulous glands and are used both internally and externally to treat glands in the neck (Nadkarni, 1954).[92] In Nepal the tubers are used as a tonic and to treat stomatitis, purulent cough, and heart troubles (Anonymous, 1970). The tubers were used in Iranian medicine (Joret, 1904).

E. nuda Lindl.: The tubers have been used in India to treat tumors, scrofulous glands, blood disorders, bronchitis, and tuberculosis, and as a vermifuge (Dymock *et al.*, 1893; Dalgado, 1896; Nadkarni, 1954; Chopra, Nayar, and Chopra, 1956; Chopra *et al.*, 1958; Merchant, Shah, and Hirwe, 1962).

E. pratensis Lindl.: The tubers are used in India to treat neck glands and as an anthelminthic (Chopra, Nayar, and Chopra, 1956).

E. virens Spreng.: In Goa the dried and powdered roots were used for rabies and as a vulnerary. The roasted bulbs were reputed to cure all abscesses, and the juice of the bulbs, the leaves, and the whole plant to have various medicinal properties (Dalgado, 1896). In India the tubers were used as a purgative and vermifuge and the whole plant externally for burns, swellings, and tumors (Dragendorff, 1898; Greshoff, 1900; Chopra, Nayar, and Chopra, 1956; Burkill, 1966).

Geodorum purpureum R. Br.: In western India a liniment prepared from the bulb and rice water was used for skin inflammation, tumors, and abscesses (Rhede tot Drakestein, 1692; Dalgado, 1896).

Habenaria acuminata Thw. ex Trim.: The roots are used as a tonic in India (Duggal, 1972).

H. susannae (L.) R. Br.: In India the bulbs were used as a cure for blebs or bullae, especially on the palm of the hand (*Wealth of India*, 1959; Chopra *et al.*, 1969).

Ipsea speciosa Lindl.: An extract distilled in Sri Lanka from the pseudobulb was considered efficacious as a stimulant to the nervous system (Cooray, 1940).

Liparis odorata Lindl.: In India the juice was used for burns, cancerous ulcers, and gangrene, and internally for fever and dropsy (Rosenthal, 1862; Dragendorff, 1898). In Malabar the juice of the leaves was considered antifebrile and was used against edema and St. Thomas' foot, and the juice from the crushed root was used for burns, inflammation, tumors, and gangrene (Dalgado, 1896, 1898).

L. rostrata Rchb. f.: The tubers are used in India for stomach troubles (Duggal, 1972).

Lissochilus arabicus Lindl.: The mucilaginous juice is used by Arabs for treatment of wounds, especially for the painless extraction of thorns (Richter, 1965; Emboden, 1974).

Luisa tenuifolia Bl.: In Malabar the whole plant was used as a poultice to draw abscesses painlessly. The powder mixed with vinegar was used for kidney disease, scalding, gonorrhea, and leucorrhea (Dalgado, 1896; 1898). The plant was considered emollient and applied as a poultice to boils, abscesses, and tumors (Chopra, Nayar, and Chopra, 1956).

L. teretifolia Gaud.: Ayurvedic practitioners in Sri Lanka have long used a preparation of oils from this plant to treat fractures (Cooray, 1940; Soysa, 1943).

Microstylis versicolor Lindl.: In Malabar a potion prepared from this plant was used to

---

[92]This is another example of the doctrine of signatures.

purge bile, for infantile epilepsy, and as a diaphoretic and antifebrile (Dalgado, 1896, 1898; Dragendorff, 1898).

M. wallichi Lindl.: This orchid forms part of a mixture used in India as a tonic (Bhatnagar, Handa, and Duggal, 1971; Duggal, 1972).

Orchis incarnata L.: The tubers are used as a tonic in Nepal (Anonymous, 1970).

O. latifolia L.: In India the tuber is regarded as expectorant and astringent (Caius, 1936; Chopra, Nayar, and Chopra, 1956; Kirtikar *et al.*, 1975). In the Indian Himalayas the tubers are used as a tonic (Uniyal, 1968). In Pakistan the plant is fed in milk to diabetics and used as a convalescent food and nerve tonic. It and other *Orchis* species were used in Unani medicine (Hocking, 1962). This species and *O. laxiflora* Lam. have been used in Iranian medicine (Joret, 1904).

O. laxiflora Lam.: The tuber is considered astringent, nutritious, and expectorant in India (Chopra, Nayar, and Chopra, 1956).

O. longicornu Poir.: In India the roots of this plant, imported from Iran, were used as an astringent and diuretic (Irvine, 1848).

O. mascula L.: The tuber is considered astringent, expectorant, and nutritious in India (Chopra, Nayar, and Chopra, 1956). It is used as a tonic, and for gout and gonorrhea (Said, 1969). In Iraq the tuber is used as a demulcent, tonic, astringent, nervine, and nutrient, especially in infantile diarrhea (Ali-Al-Rawi and Chakravarty, 1964).

Pholidota pallida Lindl.: In Malabar the crushed roots were placed on the head of a person with fever, and the whole plant was applied to the soles of the feet to cure intermittent fevers. The fruit was used to purge chronic and malignant ulcers, stop earache and headache, induce sleep, and drive out bilious evaporations. The whole plant was used as a poultice to the loins to assist childbirth and to promote the menses and urine. It is reported that some of its properties come from the trees on which it grows (Dalgado, 1896; 1898). Dragendorff (1898) reports that the pseudobulb was used on ulcers.

Pleione spp.: An Indian folk-medicine remedy is prepared from bulbs of some species (Miethe, 1927).

Rhynchostylis retusa Bl.: In Malabar various preparations of this plant have been used against asthma and tuberculosis and for nervous twitchings, cramps, infantile epilepsy, vertigo, palpitation, kidney stone, and menstrual disorders (Rhede tot Drakestein, 1703; Dalgado, 1896, 1898). The fresh plant has been used as an emollient in India (Dymock *et al.*, 1893; Caius, 1936; Chopra, Nayar, and Chopra, 1956). In Nepal it has been used as an emollient (Anonymous, 1970). Under the name *rasna*, the root is used for rheumatism throughout the Indian subcontinent (Dymock *et al.*, 1893; Nadkarni, 1954).[93]

Sarcanthus peninsularis Dalz.: The whole plant was used in Malabar in a cataplasm and for kidney disease, leucorrhea, gonorrhea, and scalding (Rhede tot Drakestein, 1703).

Satyrium nepalense D. Don: The pseudobulbs have been used as a tonic in the Indian Himalayan region (Gupta, 1960; Chopra *et al.*, 1969).

Tropidia curculigoides Lindl.: In India a decoction of the root is drunk for diarrhea, and a decoction of the whole plant forms part of a mixture given in the cold stage of malaria (Chopra *et al.*, 1969).

[93]See *Vanda roxburghii* R. Br., below.

Vanda coerulea Griff. ex Lindl.: The flowers were used in India as a pectoral, and the juice from the leaves for diarrhea and dysentery and externally for skin diseases (Nadkarni, 1954).

V. cristata Lindl.: In India the leaves have been used as a tonic and expectorant (Duggal, 1972).

V. roxburghii R. Br. syn. *V. tessellata* Hook. ex G. Don: This orchid has long been known throughout the Indian subcontinent as *rasna*, which is recorded in early Sanskrit works as an ingredient of numerous medicaments said to be efficacious against rheumatism (see below) and an extremely wide range of human disease[94] (*Sushruta Samhita*, 1907–1911; *Charaka Samhita*, 1888–1903; Hoernle, 1893–1912). *Rasna* still has widespread use in most systems of Indian folk medicine (Dymock *et al.*, 1893; Bulhart, 1930; Caius, 1936; Biswas, 1950; Chopra, Nayar, and Chopra, 1956; Said, 1969). Its use has been reported in Bengal (Dymock, 1885), Lower Bengal, and Chutia Nagpur (Griessen, 1899), Malabar (Dalgado, 1898), Orissa (Bal, 1942), Tripura (Deb, 1968), eastern India by the Santal (Bodding, 1927; Jain and Tarafder, 1970), Burma (Nair, 1963), and Sri Lanka (Attygalle, 1917; Cooray, 1940; Soysa, 1943; Richter, 1965). Chopra, Handa, and Sobti (1956) have suggested that it should be cultivated because of its medicinal virtues.

Rasna is regarded as a specific for rheumatism in India (Dymock, 1885; Dymock *et al.*, 1893; Dalgado, 1898; Dragendorff, 1898; Bal, 1942; Chopra *et al.*, 1958) and in Burma (Nair, 1963) and Sri Lanka (Attygalle, 1917). It is usually incorporated in medicated oils for external use (Griessen, 1899; Caius, 1936; Chopra *et al.*, 1958). *Rasna* has been used also for sciatica, neuralgia, lumbago, nervous disorders, dyspepsia, bronchitis, abdominal diseases, hemorrhoids, dropsy, asthma, secondary syphilis, hiccough, toothache, and tremor, and to heal fractures (Dymock *et al.*, 1893; Griessen, 1899; Dutt, 1900; Caius, 1936; Bal, 1942; Nadkarni 1954; Chopra *et al.*, 1958; Kirtikar *et al.*, 1975). The root has been used as an antidote to snakebite and scorpion bite but has been shown to be ineffective (Caius, 1936; Nadkarni, 1954; Chopra *et al.*, 1958). The leaves also are used medicinally, the juice being dropped into the ear for infections (Campbell, 1886; Bodding, 1927; Caius, 1936; Chopra *et al.*, 1958; Jain and Tarafder, 1970). A decoction of the leaves has been used in Orissa to treat bilious complaints (Bal, 1942). A paste made from the crushed leaves is applied to the body in febrile conditions (Campbell, 1886; Griessen, 1899; Caius, 1936; Chopra *et al.*, 1958). The leaves were used also by the Santal for eye complaints and infected sores, etc., and in a mixture of plants as a dust for carbuncles, and as an ingredient of a medicine for urticaria and dyspepsia. The juice formed part of a Santal medicine for rabies (Bodding, 1927; Jain and Tarafder, 1970).

Other orchids have been used indiscriminately as *rasna*, including *Acampe papillosa* Lindl., *A. wrightiana* Lindl., *A. praemorsum* Hook. f. syn. *Rhynchostylis retusa* Bl. and *Vanda spathulata* Spreng. (Dymock, 1885; Dymock *et al.*, 1893; Dutt, 1900; Caius, 1936; Soysa, 1943; Nadkarni, 1954).

Gupta, Roy, and Sen Gupta (1946) have isolated a glucoside from *V. roxburghii* which lowers blood pressure and has a stimulant action on organs that have autonomic cholinergic nerve supply.

---

[94]The Bower Manuscript, pt. 2, fasc. 1, pp. 97–98 (Hoernle, 1893–1912), describes a preparation containing *rasna* and reports: "It cures . . . , in fact, all diseases, if it is properly administered."

V. spathulata Spreng.: In India the crushed leaves and stems were used in an ointment for skin diseases and scabies, and the powdered leaves were taken for diarrhea (Lindley and Moore, 1866; Dragendorff, 1898). In Malabar the whole plant formed part of a cure for leprosy and was used for dysentery, diarrhea, and madness (Rhede tot Drakestein, 1703; Dalgado, 1896). The powdered flowers were used against asthma, tuberculosis, and madness (Rhede tot Drakestein, 1703; Dymock *et al.*, 1893; Dalgado, 1896; Kirtikar and Basu, 1918; Caius, 1936; Chopra, Nayar, and Chopra, 1956; Chopra *et al.*, 1958). The powdered leaves and flowers are reported to be used as a substitute for *Vanda roxburghii* R. Br. (Nadkarni, 1954).

Zeuxine regia Trimen: This plant is mentioned in Sanskrit works as being a secret medicinal plant in Sri Lanka (Attygalle, 1917; Cooray, 1940; Soysa, 1943).

12.7. Australasia

Bailey (1881) stated that no important medicinal properties had been detected in Australian orchids, and Maiden (1888a) reported that there was a paucity of information on the use of plants in the medicine of the aboriginal Australians.

The juice of epiphytic orchids is mixed with chalk and used in Arnhem Land as a poultice on wounds (W. Marika, personal communication). In eastern Arnhem Land the chewed stem is applied to burns when the skin is still intact, and a dressing of the orchid is applied to the head of an embedded spear to loosen it from a wound (Webb, 1933).[95]

Cymbidium spp.: The pseudobulbs are used successfully by bushmen to check diarrhea (Bancroft, 1889). Maiden is reported to have advised that all Australian *Cymbidium* species were used for dysentery, either chewed or as an arrowroot (Roth, 1903).

C. canaliculatum R. Br.: The tubers were used in northern Queensland for dysentery and such complaints (Palmer, 1884; Webb, 1959). The pseudobulbs were chewed by the aboriginal people to cure dysentery (White, 1938).

C. madidum Lindl.: In northern Queensland the bulb was chewed for dysentery by the aborigines (Roth, 1903), and they used the seed as an oral contraceptive (Webb, 1959), but no antifertility activity has been found (Barnes, Price, and Hughes, 1975).

C. suave R. Br.: This plant has been used by shepherds in Queensland for dysentery (Browne, 1894).

Dendrobium discolor Lindl.: In Queensland a paste from the young canes was used by Chinese herbalists to draw boils, and a spirit extract of the crushed mature canes was used as a liniment cum cure-all, especially for ringworm (E. Brennan, personal communication).

Oberonia muellerana Schltr.: This orchid has been reported as having antifertility activity, but laboratory tests did not confirm it (Chaudhury, 1966).

12.8. Europe

Medicinal uses of orchids given in the first century of the Christian era by Dioscorides (1st century A.D.) and Pliny the Elder (A.D. 77) have been incorporated in later writings with numerous additions. Anglo-Saxon leechbooks and English herbals of the sixteenth, seventeenth, and eighteenth centuries include many medicinal uses of orchids. Orchids

---

[95]For the determination of these orchids, see n. 71.

were recommended to nourish and strengthen the body in cases of consumption and hectic fever; to dissipate tumors and swellings; to cleanse fistulas, ulcers, tetters, and sores (particularly of the mouth); as a purge and for bellyache and dysentery; as a vermifuge for children; to treat gout, sciatica, bowing of the neck, scrofula, malaria, and retention of urine (Turner, 1551; Dodoens, 1578; Gerarde, 1597; Langham, 1633; Parkinson, 1640; Culpeper, 1649, 1656; J. Miller, 1722; Sheldrake, 1759; Payne, 1904; Kroeber, 1947).

Orchids were used medicinally as nutritives, emollients, tonics, pectorals, febrifuges, nervines, sudorifics, and diuretics (Argenta, 1864).

In Belgium orchid flowers were believed to be vulnerary. Those with a sweet and agreeable odor were used as balsamics and cordials, while those with a hircine or fetid odour were used as antihysterics (Heurck and Guibert, 1864).

In southern Norway orchids were used against the wasting disease known as *svek* and against eye complaints (O. A. Høeg, personal communication).

Corallorhiza innata R. Br.: The tubers were used as an emollient in Eastern Europe (Dragendorff, 1898).

Cypripedium calceolus L.: This plant was used as a vulnerary (Brøndegaard, 1971) and for the treatment of epilepsy (Burnett, 1835; Griffith, 1847).

C. guttatum Sw.: In eastern Russia and Siberia the leaf and root were used against epilepsy (Gmelin, 1747);[96] Dragendorff, 1898; Hawkes, 1944b).

Epipactis helleborine (L.) Crantz.: The flowers were regarded as cleansing and vulnerary (Heurck and Guibert, 1864; Planchon and Collin, 1895). The plant has been used as a remedy for gout (Linden, 1894; Dragendorff, 1898; Bulhart, 1927; Hawkes, 1943) and arthritic pains (Le Maout and Decaisne, 1876).

Gymnadenia conopsea (L.) R. Br.: This orchid has been employed against nervous disorders and epilepsy (Rosenthal, 1862; Planchon and Collin, 1895; Dragendorff, 1898) and as an astringent (Linden, 1894; Bulhart, 1927; Hawkes, 1943). The flowers and roots were used against dysentery (Le Maout and Decaisne, 1876; Castle, 1886).

Listera ovata R. Br.: An infusion of this species has been used for hemorrhoids (Hill, 1789; Brook, 1868), and the plant has been used as a vulnerary (Dragendorff, 1898).

Neottia nidus-avis (L.) Rich.: This plant was said to be good for wounds, ruptures, and burning (Dodoens, 1578). The root was used as a resolvent, vulnerary, and anthelminthic (Hogg, 1858; Heurck and Guibert, 1864; Dragendorff, 1898; Greshoff, 1900).

Orchis maculata L.: In the early twentieth century an extract of this orchid was the basis of an injection known as angiolymph, which was extensively used in Europe for the treatment of all forms of tuberculosis (Barbier, 1924).

O. mascula L.: The bruised roots were applied to the scalp to cure scrofula (Culpeper, 1656; Grieve, 1931). When warmed they served as a poultice to accelerate the suppuration of tumors, especially venereal buboes; the juice of the bulbs was considered coolant and resolvent (Waller, 1822). The root was recommended in Scotland as a demulcent (Woodville, 1792). Tubers, together with those of other species of *Orchis* and of *Ophrys*, are ingredients of some pediatric remedies (Schauenberg and Paris, 1977).

---

[96]Gmelin reports that for this purpose the Russians collect, one by one, those plants of which the flower is turned in its anterior part to the east.

O. morio L.: The root has been used to treat dysentery and ulcers of the bladder (Whitlaw, 1829).

Platanthera bifolia (L.) Rich.: The root has been used to treat tabes, sterility, and dysentery (Whitlaw, 1829).

12.9. Indo-Malaysian Region

New Guineans used the flowers of certain orchids to treat some contagious diseases (Cochran and Lucas, 1958/59). The fresh juice of an orchid forms part of a medicine used by the Chimbu to treat respiratory disease (Sterly, 1973).

Acriopsis javanica Reinw. ex Bl.: A decoction made from the boiled roots and leaves is drunk in Malacca for fever (Ridley, 1896, 1907; Heyne, 1922, 1927; Burkill, 1966). In Indonesia the juice from the pseudobulbs is dropped in the ear for tinnitus and earache, and the powdered pseudobulbs are applied to the head or stomach for fever or hypertension. In Malacca the orchid is a remedy for headache (Bakhuizen van den Brink, 1937).

Anoectochilus spp.: One species brought from the mountains has been used as a medicine by the Chinese in northern Perak (Berkhout, 1910; Burkill, 1966). In western Kalimantan the rhizomes of more than one species were collected by the Dyaks for sale to the Chinese, who used them as a medicine against tuberculosis (Coomans de Ruiter, 1935;[97] Steenis, 1958).

Bletia hyacinthina R. Br.: In West Malaysia this orchid was used as a demulcent for children of dyspeptic tendency, and against dysentery, hemorrhoids, and ague (Hooper, 1929).

Bromheadia palustris Lindl.: A decoction of the boiled roots was drunk for rheumatism in Malacca (Hawkes, 1944b; Burkill, 1966).

Bulbophyllum spp.: In the Philippines the juice from the heated leaves is used on wounds; the powdered and salted leaves from other species are plastered on the head for headache (Fox, 1950).

Calanthe rubens Ridl.: The bulbs have been used in medicine in Indonesia (Clercq, 1909; Heyne, 1913, 1922).

C. triplicata (Willem.) Ames syn. *C. veratrifolia* R. Br.: In Ambon the roots formed part of a medicine used for external treatment of swollen hands. With other ingredients the roots were chewed for diarrhea (Rumphius, 1750; Dragendorff, 1898; Heyne, 1913, 1922; Bakhuizen van den Brink, 1937). The flowers have been used in Sumatra as a pain killer in caries (Heyne, 1922, 1927).

Cirrhopetalum vaginatum Lindl.: In Malacca the hot juice from the roasted fruit was dropped into the ear to cure earache (Hawkes, 1944b; Burkill, 1966).

Corymborkis veratrifolia (Reinw.) Bl.: This plant is cultivated in Kelantan, where the juice of the fresh leaves is given as an emetic to break fever, especially in children (Ridley, 1906b; Foxworthy, 1922; Burkill, 1966).

Cymbidium ensifolium Sw.: In Indonesia a decoction of the flowers is used to treat sore eyes and the leaves are used as a diuretic (Usher, 1974).

Dendrobium sp.: The leaves of this orchid are used by the people of central Papua to

[97]Coomans de Ruiter (1935) writes, "In the good times the price was 6 guilders per thail" (37.8 gm).

relieve severe cough (Holdsworth, 1974; 1977; Holdsworth and Farnsworth, 1974; Powell, 1976a).

Dendrobium sp. sec. *Monanthos:* The stem and leaf of this plant are used to treat internal bleeding in Bougainville (F. McKillop, personal communication).

D. bifarium Lindl.: In Maluku the juice from the stem was used as a medicine for whitlow (Dragendorff, 1898).

D. crumenatum Sw.: The sap from the pseudobulbs has been used as drops for earache in Indonesia (Dongen, 1913; Bakhuizen van den Brink, 1937; Steenis-Kruseman, 1953). In West Malaysia the juice was squeezed from the heated pseudobulbs for relief of pain from ear infection; the ear was also poulticed with the plant (Anonymous, 1886; Holmes, 1892; Ridley, 1896; 1906b; Steenis-Kruseman, 1953; Burkill, 1966; Gimlette and Thomson, 1971).[98] The boiled pseudobulbs were used in Malacca for earache (Ridley, 1896); a similar use has been reported in Java (Heyne, 1922, 1927; Pételot, 1954; Burkill, 1966). In West Malaysia and Java the pounded canes make a poultice for boils and pimples (Quisumbing, 1951; *Wealth of India,* 1952; Chopra, Nayar, and Chopra, 1956; Burkill, 1966). The pounded leaves were applied to swellings by the Chinese in Malaysia (Hu, 1971a, 1971b). The plant has also been used for ailments of the brain and nerves, and a conserve of the flowers and leaves is used for cholera (Hawkes, 1944b; Chopra, Nayar, and Chopra, 1956).

D. nobile Lindl. (also *D. ceraia* Lindl., *D. moniliforme* Sw., and *D. reptans* Franch. *et* Sav.): These plants were imported and sold by Chinese herbalists in West Malaysia as the same drug, credited with tonic, stomachic, pectoral, and antiphlogistic properties (Hooper, 1929).[99]

D. planibulbe Lindl.: A poultice from the pounded leaves and pseudobulbs was used for itch on the neck in Pahang (Burkill and Haniff, 1930; Burkill, 1966).

D. pumilum Roxb.: A decoction of the boiled root has been used in West Malaysia for dropsy (Ridley, 1896, 1924; Heyne, 1922, 1927; Burkill, 1966).

D. purpureum Roxb.: In Ambon the crushed heated canes were used to treat boils and whitlows (Rumphius, 1750). A warm ointment made from the stalks has been used in Indonesia to heal infected cuticles and to break the swelling (Heyne, 1913, 1922). In East Malaysia the plant is used as a poultice (Uphof, 1959; Burkill, 1966).

D. quadrangulare Par. ex Hook. f.: This plant was used in cases of dropsy in West Malaysia (Ridley, 1907; Foxworthy, 1922).

D. subulatum Lindl.: In Perak a poultice of the pounded leaves of this *Dendrobium* (and perhaps other species) was used for headache (Burkill and Haniff, 1903; Burkill, 1966).

Dendrochilum sp.: The Chimbu of Papua New Guinea used this plant for medicine (Sterly, 1974–75).

Diplocaulobium sp.: This orchid is used to treat infected wounds in eastern New Guinea (A. Millar, personal communication).

---

[98]Gimlette and Thompson report that another Malay remedy for earache is to stuff the stem of any large epiphytic orchid with herbs and bury it in hot ashes. The hot juice is then squeezed into the ear and the residue used as an external poultice.

[99]See *Dendrobium nobile* Lindl., sec. 12.5.

Dipodium pandanum F. M. Bail.: An aqueous infusion of the leaf is drunk in Bougainville for respiratory infections (Ona, personal communcation).

Eria pannea Lindl.: The aborigines of Malacca boiled the roots and leaves and used the decoction for bathing in cases of ague (Ridley, 1896; Chopra, Nayar, and Chopra, 1956; Burkill, 1966).

Eulophia sp.: In Ternate the warmed, crushed root was used as a poultice on suppurating abscesses (Rumphius, 1750; Heyne, 1922, 1927; Burkill, 1966).

Geodorum nutans (Presl) Ames: In the Philippines this orchid is used as a poultice on running sores. The tuberous base is regarded as an emollient when used as a poultice to ripen boils and has been used as a disinfectant in Luzon (Guerrero, 1921a, 1921b; Hawkes, 1944b; Valenzuela, Concha, and Santos, 1949; Davis and Steiner, 1952).

Grammatophyllum scriptum Bl.: Pith from the pseudobulb was an ingredient of a whitlow treatment in Ambon. The ground pseudobulb was part of a mixture rubbed on the abdomen to kill worms, to expel bad humors from the bowels, and to dissolve a swollen spleen; when bound around swollen legs, it reduced edema. The juice from the chewed pseudobulb was used as a mouthwash for sprue, and a potion made from the seeds was used for dysentery (Rumphius, 1750; Dalgado, 1896; Dragendorff, 1898; Heyne, 1913, 1922; Burkill, 1935, 1966).[100] In Bougainville the seeds are mixed with coconut milk to treat infants' skin disease (Doinau, personal communcation).

Hetaeria obliqua Bl.: The leaves were used in Malacca to poultice sore legs (Ridley, 1896, 1907, 1924; Burkill, 1966).

Hippeophyllum scortechinii Schltr.: In Pahang hot juice from the heated leaves is dropped into the ear for earache (Gimlette and Thomson, 1971).

Liparis treubii J. J. Sm.: In Sulawesi the hot leaves were rubbed on the abdomen and the smaller bulbs chewed for distended abdomen, costiveness, and constipation (Rumphius, 1750; Heyne, 1913, 1922; Hawkes, 1944b).

Nervilia discolor Schltr.: In the Philippines the chewed leaves are rubbed on the stomach for pain, and women drink an aqueous extract to facilitate childbirth (Fox, 1950).

N. flabelliformis (Lindl.) Tang *et* Wang: A decoction of the boiled leaves was used in Perak as a postparturition prophylactic (Burkill and Haniff, 1930; Burkill, 1966).

N. fordii Schltr.: The leaves were used in Singapore in Chinese medicine (Hooper, 1929; Burkill, 1966).

Oberonia anceps Lindl.: This plant was used in Malacca for poulticing boils (Ridley, 1896, 1907, 1924; Caius, 1936; Burkill, 1966).

Phaius callosus Lindl.: In Indonesia the root was said to be a sternutatory (Dragendorff, 1898; Greshoff, 1900; Burkill, 1966).

P. tancarvilliae (Banks) Bl.: The pseudobulbs are used as a poultice in western Java to soothe the pain of abscess (Rifai, 1975).

Phalaenopsis aphrodite Rchb. f.: In the Philippines the Tagalog pound and salt the

---

[100]Reports of the use of this orchid against tumors are dubious. Burkill (1935, 1966) quotes Rumphius faithfully, but Quisumbing (1951) renders "humours" as "tumours," citing Burkill (1935). Hartwell (1970) follows Quisumbing. As this orchid is not found in India, the report by Griffith (1847) that it was used there as a maturating poultice on phlegmonous tumors is suspect.

leaves for use as a poultice for headache, and as a plaster on the back and chest (Fox, 1950).

P. schilleriana Rchb. f.: In southern Luzon a decoction of the leaf was used for tuberculosis, chest pains, stomach trouble, and headache, and the heated leaf was applied to centipede bite (Sulit, 1934; Fox, 1950; Masiluñgen *et al.*, 1959).

Plocoglottis javanica Bl.: In Johore the warm juice of the fruit was dropped into the ear for earache (Anonymous, 1886; Holmes, 1892; Burkill, 1966).

Spathoglottis plicata Bl.: A decoction of the boiled plant was used in Perak for rheumatism; it was used hot, as a foment, and a little of it drunk (Burkill and Haniff, 1930; Burkill, 1966). In Indonesia a salve for children was made from the seeds (Bakhuizen van den Brink, 1937).

Thrixspermum pardale (Ridl.) Schltr.: This species is used in West Malaysia as a poultice for ulcers of the nose (Hawkes, 1944b; M. A. Miller, 1959).

Tropidia curculigoides Lindl.: In Pahang a decoction of the plant is given in the cold stage of malaria (Burkill, 1966; Gimlette and Thomson, 1971). In Perak a decoction from the boiled roots is given for diarrhea (Burkill and Haniff, 1930; Gimlette and Thomson, 1971).

Vanda hookeriana Rchb. f.: A decoction from the boiled leaves has been used in Perak as a fomentation for pains in the bones and joints and for rheumatism (Burkill, 1966; Gimlette and Thomson, 1971).

12.10. Oceania

The Tahitians have tried various indigenous orchids as antisyphilitics, without result (Lanessan, 1886).

Calanthe sp.: In Fiji this plant has been used after an illness, as it is believed to have tonic properties (Parham, 1941).

C. triplicata (Willem.) Ames: This plant has been used in New Caledonia against gastrointestinal disorders (Rageau, 1973).

Corymborkis veratrifolia (Reinw.) Bl.: This species has been used for the preparation of a medicine on New Georgia, Solomon Islands (G. N. Rasmussen, personal communication).

Dendrobium teretifolium R. Br.: The bruised leaves were used externally for headache or other acute pains in Tahiti (Bennett, 1860).

D. tokai Rchb. f.: In Samoa this plant is used to increase children's appetites (Zepernick, 1972). The grated pseudobulbs mixed with hibiscus leaves are used in Fiji as an oral contraceptive or abortifacient (Arditti, 1973).

Galeola rigida Benth. *et* Hook. f.: The leaves are used in New Caledonia against colic and headache (Guillaumin, 1951; Sterly, 1970; Rageau, 1973).

Liparis clypeolum Lindl.: In the Marquesa Islands an aqueous extract of the plant was used externally for burns or inflammation, and the sap from the flowers and stem was diluted with water and used as a remedy for indigestion. The juice was diluted with water and used in Rapa as an internal remedy for sore throat (F. B. H. Brown, 1931).

Macodes spp.: On Guadalcanal the young leaves made an aqueous infusion for treatment of coughs and the heated, crushed leaves were used for skin disease; the juice of another species was drunk for fever (M. Tedder, personal communication).

Microstylis rheedi Lindl.: In Tahiti this plant was used in a plaster to cure sores (Parkinson, 1784) and prevent inflammation of the skin (Zepernick, 1972).

Nervilia flabelliformis (Lindl.) Tang *et* Wang: The tubers are chewed in Guam to allay thirst (Safford, 1905; Burkill, 1966).

Oberonia glandulosa Lindl.: This plant was reputed to be useful in Fiji for alleviating back and chest pains (Parham, 1940; Sterly, 1970).

Taeniophyllum parhamiae L. O. Williams: In Fiji this plant is thought to have great medicinal value. It is used for pains in the lungs and back, the crushed leaves being rubbed on the affected part.[101] A drink made from the plant is used for abdominal pain (Parham, 1943).

13. Aphrodisiacs

"Orchideae sunt aphrodisiacae. Aphrodisiaca inter primaria sunt *Vanilla* americanorum, *Salep* orientalium, *Satyrium* Europaeorum [Orchids are aphrodisiac. Among the primary aphrodisiacs are *Vanilla* of the Americans, *Salep* of the Orientals, *Satyrium* of the Europeans]," wrote Linnaeus in 1751.

The majority of reports of the uses of orchids as aphrodisiacs are related to vanilla or salep, and are discussed in sections 5 and 14. Brøndegaard (1971) gives a review with an extensive bibliography.

Angraecum, Ansellia, Bulbophyllum, Listrostachys, and *Polystachya* spp.: In West Africa the pseudobulbs of some of these epiphytic orchids are ingredients in aphrodisiac prescriptions (Dalziel, 1937).

Ansellia gigantea Rchb. f.: The stem is used in an aphrodisiac in Transvaal, and Zulu men sometimes administer a decoction of the stem to women as an aphrodisiac (Watt and Breyer-Brandwijk, 1962).

Coelogyne ovalis Lindl.: Preparations including this orchid were used as aphrodisiacs in ayurvedic medicine (*Sushruta Samhita,* ca. 600 B.C.; *Charaka Samhita,* ca. 200 B.C.).

Cynorchis purpurascens Lindl.: In Madagascar aphrodisiac properties are attributed to the bulbs (Boiteau, 1978b).

Cypripedium pubescens Willd.: This North American plant is reported to have been used as an aphrodisiac (Emboden, 1974; Yearsley, 1976).[102]

Dendrobium sp.: This orchid is regarded as an aphrodisiac in the Chimbu region of Papua New Guinea (Sterly, 1973).

D. acinaciforme Roxb.: Rumphius (1750) reports that this orchid was used in Ambon to indicate amorous intent; to indicate his ardor, a man sent a woman the leaves when they were stiffest.[103]

D. clavatum Wall.: The dried plant was used as an aphrodisiac in Patna (Irvine, 1848).

D. moniliforme Sw.: In Korea and Taiwan the plant was said to prevent impotence (Liu, 1952; Chung, 1964).

[101]As plants of this genus are leafless, it must be assumed that this report refers to the chlorophyll-containing green roots.

[102]This report is dubious; Yearsley quotes O. P. Brown (1878) and Castle (1886), neither of whom makes this statement.

[103]This is another example of the doctrine of signatures.

D. nobile Lindl.: This plant is believed in China to have an aphrodisiac effect (Kariyone and Koiso, 1971).

Disa aconitoides Sond.: An infusion of the root has been used in southern Africa to promote fertility (Rayner, 1977).

Ephemerantha fimbriata (Bl.) Hunt *et* Summerh.: This plant and the capsule have been used in India as aphrodisiacs (Caius, 1936; Kirtikar *et al.*, 1975).

Eria muscicola Lindl.: This orchid was an ingredient in several preparations used in ayurvedic medicine as aphrodisiacs (Hoernle, 1893–1912; see *Vanda roxburghii* R. Br., below).

Eulophia campestris Wall.: The rhizome was esteemed as an aphrodisiac in India (Charaka Samhita, 1976; Caius, 1936; Chopra, Nayar, and Chopra, 1956; Kirtikar *et al.*, 1975) and Nepal (Anonymous, 1970).

E. cucullata Lindl.: In southern Africa an infusion of the root has been used to promote fertility (Rayner, 1977).

E. hians Spreng. and *E. flaccida* Schltr.: An aqueous infusion of the tubers of one or both of these orchids is drunk daily by barren women in Lesotho; after drinking the infusion for four months, they become pregnant (Phillips, 1917).[104]

E. lindleyana (Rchb. f.) Schltr.: The root juice is drunk in Africa as an aphrodisiac (Haerdi *et al.*, 1964).

Eulophidium sp. aff. *silvaticum* (Schltr.) Summerh.: A plant extract is drunk in Africa as an aphrodisiac (Haerdi *et al.*, 1964).

Gastrodia elata Bl.: In China the stalk of the plant is considered to be aphrodisiac (Stuart, 1911; Hu, 1971a, 1971b).

Habenaria sp.: An infusion of the whole plant has been used in southern Africa to promote fertility (Rayner, 1977).

H. dilatata A. Gray: In North America this orchid was added to women's food to stimulate them sexually (Brøndegaard, 1971).

H. viridis R. Br.: The Ojibwa Indians of North America used this plant in food as an aphrodisiac (H. H. Smith, 1932).

Himantoglossum hircinum (L.) Spreng.: This plant has been used as an aphrodisiac (Rosenthal, 1862; Linden, 1894).

Ipsea speciosa Lindl.: In Sri Lanka the tubers of this orchid have been reputed to possess powerful aphrodisiac powers (Perera, 1940; Soysa, 1943).

Lissochilus sp.: The stem of this species is chewed by Lobedu men in Transvaal; the resulting juice, when swallowed, is said to cause a powerful erection of the penis (Watt and Breyer-Brandwijk, 1962).

L. arenarius Lindl.: The Zulus used an aqueous infusion of the roots as a remedy for impotence or barrenness due to a lack of nervous or muscular power (Bryant, 1909; Watt and Breyer-Brandwijk, 1932, 1962; Githens, 1949; Bryant, 1966).

---

[104]Phillips' report does not make clear whether other species that have the same local name also have the same use. Watt and Breyer-Brandwijk (1932, 1962) state that *E. robusta* Rolfe was used similarly, but go on to say that the infusion is drunk for 4 months after conception. M. A. Miller (1959) follows Watt and Breyer-Brandwijk.

L. madagascariensis Kraenzl.: In Madagascar the roots of this orchid were considered to have great aphrodisiac powers (Boiteau, 1978a).

Microstylis wallachii Lindl.: The pseudobulbs have been used in India as an aphrodisiac (Duggal, 1972).

Ophrys linifolia L.: In the Mediterranean region the bulb was considered a powerful aphrodisiac (Billerbeck, 1824).[105]

O. lutea Cav.: The tubers have been used as an aphrodisiac in Algeria (Chatin, 1868).

Orchis spp.: Wedeck (1962) notes the use of these plants for aphrodisiac purposes, chiefly in the form of satyrion, which possessed a widespread but undeserved reputation. Satyrion was much used by the ancient Greeks as an aphrodisiac (Licht, 1932), and its reputation can be traced back to the first-century Greek herbal of Dioscorides (1st century A.D.; see sec. 1). For the use of satyrion in England, see Turner (1551), Gerarde (1597), and Culpeper (1649); in France, see Venette (1762), Goulin and Labeyrie (1794), Roques (1809), and Morren (1846); and in the Netherlands, see Teirlinck (1930). In Romania sterile gypsy women who wished to become pregnant carried the phallus-shaped root; for maximum effectiveness it should have been pulled from the ground by a black dog (Brøndegaard, 1971; *cf. O. maculata* L., sec. 2.5). It was said that the properties were lost when the root dried. The fresh bulbs may be taken in conserve or aqueous infusion (Waller, 1822). The fresh tubers are sold in the bazaars of the Orient and are used as aphrodisiacs (Meyerhof, 1940). In India the fresh roots of several species have an odor resembling that of semen and are thought to have a powerful aphrodisiac effect when held in the hand (Dymock, 1881, 1885; Watt, 1893).[106]

Orchis, Gymnadenia, and *Platanthera* spp.: These plants have long been regarded as aphrodisiacs in northern Norway (O. A. Høeg, personal communication).

Orchis maculata L.: This plant was used as an aphrodisiac in Iceland (O. A. Høeg, personal communication). In the Netherlands this species along with *O. latifolia* L. and others with twinned tubers, was considered to counteract sterility and impotence caused by witchcraft (Dodoens, 1644; Teirlinck, 1930).

O. mascula L.: The tubers of this orchid have had widespread use as an aphrodisiac. Such use is reported from Patna (Irvine, 1848), India (Said, 1969), Ireland (Moloney, 1919), England (Grigson, 1958), North Africa (Bouquet, 1921), and Iraq (Ali-Al-Rawi and Chakravarty, 1964).

O. provincialis Balb.: The tubers have been used as an aphrodisiac in Algeria (Chatin, 1868).

Phaius tancarvilliae (Banks) Bl.: In the southern highlands of Papua women take the smoked flowers with their food as an aid to conception (Holdsworth and Longley, 1973; Holdsworth, 1974, 1977; Powell, 1976a).

Platanthera bifolia (L.) Rich.: This plant has been used as an aphrodisiac (Rosenthal, 1862; Le Maout and Decaisne, 1876).

Spiranthes autumnalis Rich.: This orchid has been used as an aphrodisiac in Europe

[105]As the *Index Kewensis* lists this as a synonym of *Liparis liliifolia* A. Rich., which is a North American species, Billerbeck's report is questionable. It may well refer to *L. loeselii* (L.) Rich.; see Luer (1975).

[106]This is another instance of the doctrine of signatures.

(Gerarde, 1597; Rosenthal, 1862; Lindley and Moore, 1866; Linden, 1894; Dragendorff, 1898).

S. spiralis (L.) Chevall.: This orchid "provokes venery" (Gerarde, 1597; Grigson, 1958).

Vanda roxburghii R. Br.: Several ayurvedic preparations containing this plant were used as aphrodisiacs and given for impotence and barrenness, and to ensure the birth of a son. It was said that a barren woman who bathed in an oil after menstruation was sure to conceive, and that a clarified butter that also contained *Eria muscicola* Lindl. powerfully excited the venereal appetite (Hoernle, 1893–1912).

14. Salep

The *Oxford English Dictionary* (1961) defines "salep" as "a nutritive meal starch or jelly made from the dried tubers of various orchidaceous plants, chiefly those of the genus *Orchis;* formerly also used as a drug." The orchid product that we now call salep has long been known in Asia Minor and the eastern Mediterranean region. Generally accepted as having been used in western Asia from time immemorial, it was in use by the Greeks in the third century B.C. (Theophrastus, ca. 300 B.C.). The older Sanskrit medical works do not appear to mention salep (Dymock, 1881), but Small (1919) suggests that it served as an aphrodisiac in very early Indian medicine.

The words "orchis," "satyrion," and "serapias," used by Theophrastus, Dioscorides, and Pliny, occur in many important herbals up to the early seventeenth century, including those of Ibn Wáfid in the eleventh century (Saint-Germain, 1943); Apuleius Barbarus, about 1100[107] (Gunther, 1925); Al-Ghâfiqî, about 1164 (Meyerhof and Sobhy, 1937); Maimonides, about 1200 (Meyerhof, 1940); Rufinus, about 1287 (Thorndike, 1946); Otto Brunsfels, 1530–1536 (Sprague, 1928); Leonhart Fuchs, 1542 (Sprague and Nelmes, 1928); Valerius Cordus, 1561 (Sprague and Sprague, 1939), and Mattioli (1571).

Renowned English herbals of the late sixteenth and early seventeenth centuries follow the same pattern (Turner, 1548). Turner (1551), Gerarde (1597), Langham (1633), and Parkinson (1640) describe the sexual powers of orchids in almost the same words as Dioscorides. From the middle of the seventeenth century, however, new ideas and names were introduced (Culpeper, 1649, 1656; How, 1650; J. Miller, 1722).

In 1722, Miller recognized that salep was "the dried root of some species of orchis," an observation confirmed by Buxbaum in 1733 (Bergius, 1771; Woodville, 1792; Thornton, 1810). Thereafter "satyrion" and "salep" were used interchangeably, and after the production of salep from orchid species native to Europe, the word "salep" predominated (Woodville, 1792).

Use of salep spread from Asia Minor both eastward to India and China, where it was regarded as an aphrodisiac, tonic, and restorative, and westward to Europe and North America. It became popular in Europe in the Middle Ages. The independent discovery by Geoffroy, Moult, Retzius, and others that salep could be made from local European orchids led to an enormous increase in its popularity. Following the introduction of salep

---

[107]This is believed to be the earliest herbal written and illustrated in Britain.

into European medicine, it was soon included in many pharmacopoeias and enjoyed widespread use for many purposes. Not until the twentieth century did its reputation decline; it now provides only a pediatric medicine and a substitute for arrowroot.

Reports conflict as to whether orchids have been cultivated for the production of salep. Their assiduous and extensive cultivation was reported by Percival (1773) and Brook (1868), while Richter (1965) states that attempts at commercial cultivation have not been successful. Drar (1943) states that all salep is prepared from wild plants. Leyel (1970) and Kordel (1974) report the cultivation of *Orchis mascula* L. and *O. latifolia* L. for their nutrient and medicinal properties. Singh and his colleagues (1979) describe herb farms in Nepal where medicinal plants, including *O. latifolia* L., are under cultivation.

Landerer (1850) reports from Epirus that while the plants are not actually cultivated, the annual digging of the crop disperses the small tubers, which provide the subsequent crop; Vöth (1973) comments similarly on the small tubers in Turkey.

Figures given for the export of salep from Turkey are astounding. In 1892, 19,000 kg were exported from Istanbul, with reserves estimated at 10,000 kg. In 1879, Izmir exported approximately 6,400 kg, and exports for 1905–1908 totaled 10,500 kg. It is estimated that the bulk of the harvest was used in Turkey, only one-fifth being exported (Tschirch, 1912). Vöth (1973) estimates that in the last quarter of the nineteenth century, 125 tonnes of orchid bulbs were dug out each year. A plate in Vöth's paper gives an idea of the scale of collection of orchid tubers.

Singh and his colleagues (1979) estimate that some five tonnes per annum of tubers of *Orchis latifolia* L. are available in Nepal for export at a price of approximately U.S. $900 per tonne.

Today Europe obtains salep from Anatolia, Asia Minor, and southern Europe (Täckholm and Drar, 1969; Vöth, 1973; H. Lua, personal communication). M. A. Miller (1959) stated that salep could be purchased in Boston at that time.

For the detailed history and bibliography of salep, see Lund (1771), Morren, (1846), Flückiger and Hanbury (1874), Dragendorff (1898), Tschirch (1912), Lauer (1968), Täckholm and Drar (1969), Brøndegaard (1971), and Font Quer (1973).

14.1. Nomenclature

The English word "salep" was formed by transliteration from earlier forms of the Arabic *sahlab,* now the accepted term in the Arab world.[108] The *Oxford English Dictionary* (1961) cites Centlivre (1760), in 1712, as the earliest known use in English. Terms applied to salep in Europe, or to the tubers that provide it, are given by Gerarde (1597), Parkinson (1640), Fernie (1914), Steinmetz (1957), Leyel (1970), and Brøndegaard (1971). Nomenclature on the Indian subcontinent is listed by Dymock *et al.,* (1893) and Watt (1893), and in the Arab world by Leclerc (1877, 1883), Ducros (1930), Renaud and Colin (1934), Meyerhof and Sobhy (1937), and Meyerhof (1940). The relationship of the nomenclatures in the various parts of Asia and Europe from classical times was discussed

[108]The origin and variations of the Arabic word are discussed in detail by Flückiger (1891), Lauer (1968), and Täckholm and Drar (1969).

in the fourth century by Pseudo-Apuleius (1927) and by Royle (1839), Langkavel (1866), Dragendorff (1898), Höfler (1911), and Tschirch (1912).

Apart from the Indo-European language equivalents of early Arabic, Greek, and Latin words, a huge number of expressions are used as synonyms for "salep" or for the tubers from which the preparation is made. These common names reflect the supposed magical, religious, or aphrodisiac properties of orchids and often include vulgar, sometimes coarse, vernacular terms of male and female sex organs. A long list is given by Brøndegaard (1971).

Five varieties named for the area of origin are listed by Täckholm and Drar (1969)—Anatolian, German, Indian, Levant, and Persian salep. Varieties in the markets of the Indian subcontinent are listed by Balfour (1873b), Dymock (1885), and Dymock et al. (1893).

14.2. Preparation

Tubers are collected after fruiting, when the stalk begins to fall. The new full tubers are used, malodorous and older shrunken ones being discarded. The process is described somewhat differently by various authors but essentially consists of three basic steps. First the tubers are washed; then the outer skin is removed, either by brushing or steeping in boiling water; and finally the tubers are dried to a horny consistency either in the sun or in an oven. General descriptions are given by Retzius (1806), Roques (1809), Hooper (1839), Heurck and Guibert (1864), Grieve (1927, 1931), Fournier (1948), Cassone (1952), Christophersen (1960), and Font Quer (1973). The yield is 2 kg from 5 kg fresh tubers (Fournier, 1948).

The method of preparation in Turkey is described by Hill (1789),[109] in Iran by Balfour (1873a, 1885b), and in Macedonia by Landerer 1850).

Following the realization in the early eighteenth century that salep came from orchid tubers, methods describing its preparation from orchid species that occur in Western Europe were soon published. France led the way in 1740 (Geoffroy, 1742; Goulin and Labeyrie, 1794), followed by Sweden (Retzius, 1764) and England (Moult, 1769). Percival (1773) made Moult's method widely known and it was used extensively (Woodville, 1792; Pereira, 1850; Hogg, 1858).[110]

14.3. Description

Fresh tubers are white and succulent, with a bitter taste. Some tubers are described as having a hircine or disagreeable odor, while other authors describe the odor as "sperm-like" (Dymock, 1881; Dujardin-Beaumetz and Egasse, 1889; Martindale and Westcott, 1924; Fournier, 1948; Täckholm and Drar, 1969). The tubers become hard on drying, taking on a horny, semitransparent appearance and a yellowish to yellowish-gray color, and have a feeble odor resembling that of clover and a mild mucilaginous or salty taste (Dierbach, 1817; Dymock, 1885; Wood et al., 1886; Barbier, 1924; Täckholm and Drar,

---

[109]The method used today in Turkey (Vöth, 1973) and Nepal (Singh et al., 1979) is much the same.
[110]Hill wrote in 1751, and again in 1789, that Turkish salep was used in England because the English methods of drying were not successful.

1969). Dried tubers of *Eulophia* are brown with a sweetish taste (Anonymous, 1871). The hard dried tubers may be pulverized by maceration in cold water and rapid drying (Wood *et al.*, 1886). The powder is white to yellowish, odorless and rather tasteless; when made into a jelly with water, it has a faint, peculiar flavor (Dymock, 1885; Vöth, 1973).

14.4. Chemical Composition

After it was shown that salep could be prepared from species of orchids native to western and northern Europe, its use in this area increased greatly, and by the middle of the nineteenth century histologists and chemists had turned their attention to salep and the plants from which it was produced.

Early work sought to establish the chemical constituents. The analysis published by Dragendorff (1865a) is still much quoted:

Mucilage[111]	48.1%
Starch	27.3
Sugar	1.2
Cellulose	2.4
Protein	5.0
Fat	0.4
Acetic acid	trace
Water	8.5
Ash	2.1

The ash consists of chlorides and phosphates of potassium and calcium. Other analyses include a volatile oil yielding coumarin, and give a somewhat different content of mucilage and widely differing amounts of starch. It was noted that the starch content varied with age, perhaps being nil in the tuber bearing the flowering stem (Dymock *et al.*, 1893; Planchon and Collin, 1895; Fournier, 1948). The significance of this variation was not to become apparent until the work of Jaretzky and Bereck in 1938.

Histological work showed that the mucilage was intracellular and often accompanied by bundles of crystals, which were found to be calcium oxalate. Several theories of the origin of the mucilage were advanced; it is now generally accepted that it comes from the protoplasts. Because of variable results of chemical tests, some authors believed that the mucilage was similar to gum arabic, but it has been shown that it is similar to cellulose (Lindley, 1841, 1844; Kuetzing, 1852; Wigand, 1863; Frank, 1866/67; Kohl, 1899; Planchon and Collin, 1895; Dupuis and Réveil, 1887; Fournier, 1948). E. L. Smith (1923) gives a review of orchid histology to that date.

When chemists turned their attention to the carbohydrate content of salep, the presence of mannose was established. Gans is generally credited with this discovery (Fischer and Hirschberger, 1889; Hérissey, 1902; Hilger, 1903). Notwithstanding the report by Gans and Tollens (1888) that both mannose and glucose were present in salep mannan, several workers reported that mannose was the sole constituent monosaccharide (Hilger, 1903; Pringsheim and Genin, 1924; Pringsheim and Liss, 1928). Klages (1934) estab-

---

[111]Dragendorff had difficulty separating arabin and dextrin from mucilage, and all three are included in this figure.

lished the $1 \rightarrow 4$ linkage, and Klages and Niemann (1936) and Klages and Mauren-brecher (1938) confirmed the β $1 \rightarrow 4$ linkage of the constituent units of the polysac-charide now called salep mannan (see Smith and Montgomery, 1959, for a summary to that date). In a series of three papers in 1963, Daloul, Courtois, and Petek showed that the polysaccharide was in fact a glucomannan consisting of mannose and glucose units in a ratio of 3:1. Buchala, Franz, and Meier (1974) demonstrated that *Orchis morio* L. contains a glucomannan that incorporates mannose and glucose in the ratio of 3.3:1 in a branched chain (see also Chapter 5).

Jaretzky and Bereck (1938) showed that in spring the tubers contained only starch, which was changed in summer into readily mobilized glucomannan. Franz and Meier (1971), using glucose and sucrose labeled with ^{14}C, showed that glucomannan is de-graded in spring to yield mannose, which is converted to sucrose. The sucrose is trans-ported to the young tubers and used for synthesis of glucomannan. Franz (1973) has demonstrated that an enzyme system is present in *Orchis morio* L. which can catalyze synthesis of the reserve glucomannan.

Investigation of orchids used as salep in Japan show that "cremastramannan" and "bletillamannan" consist of mannose and glucose in the ratio of 3:1 and 4:1 respectively (Ohtsuki, 1937a, 1937b).

Seen under the microscope, the fresh tuber consists of a thin cortex and a par-enchyma. The latter contains numerous polygonal cells containing discrete starch gran-ules and some large round cells that contain mucilage, with groups of calcium oxalate crystals and fibrous bundles interspaced irregularly. On drying the cell walls distort and the starch becomes agglomerated. Details are to be found in Flückiger and Hanbury (1874), Planchon and Collin (1895), Greenish and Collin (1904), Tschirch (1912), and Karsten and Weber (1946).

14.5. Orchids that Provide Salep

Europe and the Mediterranean. The traditional salep of European commerce has been obtained from southern Europe, the Levant, Asia Minor, and Anatolia. While the bulk of species used for salep production in this area is of the genus *Orchis*, other genera have been used, including *Aceras, Anacamptis, Cephalanthera, Dactylorchis, Epipactis, Gymnadenia, Himantoglossum, Limodorum, Ophrys, Nigritella, Platanthera, Serapias,* and *Spiranthes* (Mitlacher, 1912; Brandt and Wasicky, 1929; Vöth, 1973; Howes, 1974).

Candolle (1816) states that all species of orchids in Europe and the Orient may be used to prepare salep, and Watt (1893) and Drar (1943) report that most *Orchis* species are capable of yielding salep.

The species most commonly used are the following, listed in the order of their importance:

Orchis mascula L.	*Orchis militaris* L.
Orchis morio L.	*Gymnadenia conopsea* (L.) R. Br.
Anacamptis pyramidalis (L.) Rich.	*Orchis ustulata* L.
Orchis italica Poir.	*Orchis purpurea* Huds.
Orchis coriophora L.	*Orchis latifolia* L.
Orchis maculata L.	*Platanthera bifolia* (L.) Rich.

Orchis incarnata L.

Orchis papilionacea L.

Aceras anthropomorpha R. Br.

Barlia longibracteata (Biv.) Parl.

Orchis munbyana Boiss. *et* Reut.

Ophrys apifera Huds.

Ophrys aranifera Huds.

Orchis simia Lam.

Orchis tridentata Scop.

Many other species have had minor use. Comprehensive lists are given by Schumacher (1826), Lindley (1838), Rosenthal (1862), Watt (1893), Planchon and Collin (1895), Mitlacher (1912), Tschirch (1912), Brandt and Wasicky (1929), and Drar (1943).

Those species that give the best salep are said to be *Orchis latifolia* L., *O. mascula* L., *O. militaris* L., *O. morio* L., and *Platanthera bifolia* (L.) Rich. (Wagner, 1828; Royle, 1839, 1853; Anonymous, 1871; Hawkes, 1944).

Species used locally for salep have been reported for the following areas: Algeria (Simmonds, 1891; Dragendorff, 1898; Tschirch, 1912; Täckholm and Drar, 1969), Asia Minor (Tchihatcheff, 1860; Tschirch, 1912), Belgium (Heurck and Guibert, 1864), England[112] (Lindley, 1849; Pereira, 1850; Grieve, 1931), France (Dupuis and Réveil, 1887; Perrot, 1943b), Greece (Pereira, 1850; Tschirch, 1912; Täckholm and Drar, 1969), Italy (Scardavi, 1963, for Pavia; Dragendorff, 1898, for Sicily), Serbia (Tucakov, Krstić, and Gorunović, 1962), and Spain and Portugal (Puerta, 1891; Font Quer, 1973).

Central Asia and the Indian Subcontinent. The so-called Persian salep of central Asia is prepared almost exclusively from *Orchis latifolia* L. and *O. laxiflora* Lam. (Dymock *et al.,* 1893; Tschirch, 1912; Hooper, 1937; Howes, 1974).

Salep from Iran and Afghanistan has been exported to Azerbaydzhan (Hammermann, Damirov, and Sokolov, 1971), and has long been imported into India and Pakistan in large amounts (Powell, 1868; Aitchison, 1891; Dymock *et al.,* 1893; Tschirch, 1912; Hocking, 1962). It has been reported that *Orchis* species from western Pakistan and *O. latifolia* L. from northern Pakistan have been used to prepare salep (Hocking, 1952; Chaudhri, 1959). *O. latifolia* L., *O. laxiflora* Lam., and *O. mascula* L. are reported to provide salep in India (Fleming, 1810; Chopra, Nayar, and Chopra, 1956),[113] and several species of *Orchis* were used in southern India to prepare a salep sold locally (Dymock *et al.,* 1893).

Salep of Lahore is the name given to a preparation of the tubers of *Eulophia campestris* Wall., collected in the Punjab (Aitchison, 1891; Dymock *et al.,* 1893). In northern India and northern Pakistan salep is prepared also from the tubers of *E. herbacea* Lindl., *E. nuda* Lindl., and *E. virens* Spreng. (Royle, 1839; Powell, 1868; Dymock, 1881, 1885; Watt, 1890; Kirtikar and Basu, 1918; T. Tanaka, 1976).

In India salep has been prepared from *Habenaria commelinifolia* Wall. ex Lindl. (Chopra, Nayar, and Chopra, 1956; Kirtikar *et al.,* 1975; T. Tanaka, 1976), *H. pectinata* D. Don (Rosenthal, 1862; Dragendorff, 1898; Tschirch, 1912), and other species (Täckholm and Drar, 1969).

Chopra, Nayar, and Chopra (1956) and Kirtikar *et al.* (1975) report the use of *Cym-*

---

[112]The best English salep is said to come from Oxfordshire (Henslow, 1905).

[113]Fleming (1812) states that salep from *O. mascula* was imported into Hindustan.

bidium aloifolium Sw. in India to provide salep. *Zeuxine strateumatica* Schltr. has been used locally in southern India as salep (Nadkarni, 1954; Chopra, Nayar, and Chopra, 1956; Kirtikar *et al.*, 1975).

Other Areas.

Africa: Pappe (1857) noted that the roots of many common orchids of South Africa (*e.g.*, species of *Disa* and *Satyrium*) might provide salep. Rosenthal (1862) reported that *Satyrium bicorne* Thunb. might provide salep, and Dragendorff (1898) reported its use in the Cape and the Mascarene Islands.

Australia: It has been suggested that the roots of many Victorian orchids might provide salep (British Parliamentary Papers, 1854; Simmonds, 1854a; Anonymous, 1855/56).

Brazil: Powdered bulbs of *Ophrys argentea* Vell., known as *salepo de terre*, have been used like salep (Penna, 1914).

Burma: The tubers of *Habenaria commelinifolia* Wall. ex Lindl. were used to provide salep (Nair, 1963).

China: Soubeiran and Thiersant (1874) report the use of salep in China but could not establish if it was indigenous or imported from central Asia.

Jamaica: Browne (1789) gives the name Jamaica salop to a type of *Satyrium* and describes its preparation.

Japan: The tubers of *Cremastra variabilis* Nakai provided the salep of the Japanese pharmacopoeia; the tubers of this orchid and of *Bletia hyacinthina* R. Br. syn. *Bletilla striata* Rchb. f. were used in Japanese folk medicine for the same purposes as salep (Ohtsuki, 1937a, 1937b). Kariyone and Kimura (1940) report the use of *Cremastra wallichiana* Lindl. syn. *C. appendiculata* Makino as a substitute for salep.

Mexico: The bulbs of *Arpophyllum spicatum* La Llave *et* Lex., *Bletia campanulata* La Llave *et* Lex., *B. coccinea* La Llave *et* Lex., *B. verecunda* R. Br., and *Epidendrum pastoris* La Llave *et* Lex. are reported to have been used like salep (Anonymous, 1885a, 1885c; Dragendorff, 1898; Tschirch, 1912).[114]

New Zealand: Tubers of orchids eaten by the Maoris were reported to contain salep (R. Taylor, 1870).

North America: A species of *Habenaria* was used to provide salep (Hogg, 1858; Yearsley, 1976).

Sri Lanka: Species of orchids yielding salep have been reported by Powell (1868).

14.6. Substitutes and Adulterants

Dried rhizomes, bulbs, and tubers, or powders prepared from them, have been reported as substitutes or cheap imitations of salep. In some cases these materials have been used to adulterate salep.

Watt (1889) states that in India the dried roots of *Curculigo orchioides* Gaertn. are called *musli* and notes that there is confusion between *musli* and salep. Kirtikar and Basu (1918) give the name "black musali" to these roots and the name "white musali" to the roots of

---

[114]All these reports are based on Maisch (1885), who states only that decoctions of these plants were used to treat dysentery (see sec. 12.2). It is unlikely that salep was ever prepared from these orchids.

Asparagus adscendens Roxb. and *A. racemosus* Willd., and report the use of all three as substitutes for salep in India.

In India certain species of *Habenaria* are used as substitutes for salep (Kirtikar and Basu, 1918).

Chaudhri (1959) reports that the rhizomes of *Polygonatum verticillatum* All. are used as a substitute for salep in northern Pakistan. The tubers of *Eulophia campestris* Wall. are used locally in northern India as a substitute for true salep (Dymock *et al.*, 1893; Nadkarni, 1954).

The root of *Asphodelus kotschyi* Pharm. ex Wehmer, *nomen—Quid?* has been used in the Levant as a substitute for salep (Dragendorff, 1865a, 1865b; Tschirch, 1912).

Royal salep (see sec. 14.7) may have been used as a substitute for true salep (Aitchison, 1891).

Salep has been adulterated with bulbs of *Arum maculatum* L. (Brandt and Wasicky, 1929), *Colchicum autumnale* L. (Täckholm and Drar, 1969; Tschirch, 1912), *Crocus* (Hohmann, 1968), rhizomes of *Cyperus esculentus* L. (Brandt and Wasicky, 1929; Planchon, Bretin, and Manceau, 1947), and the bulbs of *Tulipa montana* Lindl. (Aitchison, 1891). In India a product known as *banawati* was prepared from a gum and potatoes and used as a substitute for or adulterant of salep (Dymock *et al.*, 1893; Kirtikar and Basu, 1918; Tschirch 1912; Caius, 1936). The most common adulterant of salep powder is starch (Tschirch, 1912; Brandt and Wasicky, 1929).

Starch from one or more species of the genera *Arum, Caladium, Jatropha, Maranta,* and *Ocimum* has been called salep (Crawfurd, 1866).

Tests for identification of salep are given by Brandt and Wasicky (1929).

14.7. Other Saleps

In some parts of the world preparations from the roots of plants have been given local names that include the word "salep."

Padshah salep of northwestern India was prepared from the pseudobulbs of *Pholidota pallida* Lindl. Of a disagreeable mucilaginous taste, it was supposed to have the same properties as salep (Dymock, 1885; Dymock *et al.*, 1893).

Royal salep (*bajah* or *badsha*) of Afghanistan and Iran has been reported to be prepared from the bulbs of *Allium macleanii* Baker and other *Allium* species (Aitchison, 1891; Caius, 1936; Uphof, 1959), *A. sunorowi* Regel (Holmes, 1896), *Tulipa occulus—solis* St. Amans (Dupuis and Réveil, 1887), and *Ungernia trisphaera* Bunge (Watt, 1890).

Tahiti (Otaheite) salep was prepared from *Tacca pinnatifida* Forst. (Archer, 1853; Simmonds, 1854; Balfour, 1871).

West Indian salep was prepared from *Maranta arundinacea* L. (Benzon, 1822; Schumacher, 1826; Heraud, 1927).

14.8. Medicinal Uses

Salep has been official in most of the pharmacopoeias of Europe as well as those of the United States, Japan, and several South American countries (Mitlacher, 1912; Martindale and Westcott, 1924; Brandt and Wasicky, 1929; Caius, 1936; Høeg, 1958; Christophersen, 1960). Imbesi (1964) gives a very detailed list. A typical entry is that in the third edition of the *Pharmacopoeia Germanica* (1890), which lists species commonly used, the treatment of the tubers, and preparation of the extract.

As a medicine salep was used as an electuary, known as diasatyrion, in the dose of 1–2 drams (Culpeper, 1649; J. Miller, 1722; Sheldrake, 1759; Chomel, 1804), and as a mucilage or powder in the dose of 1–2 grams dry weight (Geoffroy, 1736; Pereira, 1850; Heurck and Guibert, 1864; Grieve, 1931).[115] Salep as a mucilage or jelly was usually prepared with water, milk, or both (Bergius, 1778; Retzius, 1806; Royle, 1853; Dey, 1896; Grieve, 1931), but sometimes with meat broth, soup, or wine (Hill, 1751; Rosenthal, 1862; Flückiger and Hanbury, 1874; Dupuis and Réveil, 1887; Fernie, 1914). Salep was also made into a chocolate or cocoa (Threlkeld, 1727; Dujardin-Beaumetz, and Egasse, 1889; Tschirch, 1912; Fournier, 1948) and taken with rose honey (Levey and Al-Khaledy, 1967). The preparation was sometimes flavored with sugar and such things as amber, cloves, ginger, cinnamon, lemon peel, and sassafras chips (Roques, 1809; Flückiger and Hanbury, 1874; Murray, 1881; Fernie, 1914; Grieve, 1931). The salep root has also been candied (Bryant, 1783).

In the past the extensive use of salep to treat various diseases in many countries was based on its supposed value as a demulcent, emollient, nervine, restorative, and vulnerary (Schumacher, 1826; Pereira, 1850; Hogg, 1858; Heurck and Guibert, 1864; Anonymous, 1871; Dymock, 1881; Maisch, 1890; Watt, 1893; Hooper, 1937; Steinmetz, 1957; Hocking, 1962; Levey and Al-Khaledy, 1967).

The use of salep for treatment of all forms of diarrhea and dysentery has been much recorded (Vogel, 1760; Bergius, 1771, 1778; Percival, 1773; Retzius, 1806; Roques, 1809; Argenta, 1864; Heurck and Guibert, 1864; Heurck, 1876; Dey, 1896; Barbier, 1924; Fournier, 1948). It has been used also for various stomach and intestinal disorders (Schumacher, 1826; Landerer, 1850; Argenta, 1864; Dupius and Réveil, 1887; Dujardin-Beaumetz and Egasse, 1889), intestinal catarrh (Tschirch, 1912; Hoppe, 1951, 1975), heartburn (Lund, 1771), and bilious colic (Vogel, 1760; Lund, 1771; Bryant, 1783).

Salep has been used for coughs, colds, and irritation or inflammation of the chest (Retzius, 1806; Argenta, 1864; Heurck and Guibert, 1864; Heurck, 1876; Dupius and Réveil, 1887; Barbier, 1924; Fournier, 1948) and for tuberculosis (Vogel, 1760; Lund, 1771; Lamark, 1778; Bryant, 1783; Roques, 1809; Schumacher, 1826; Johnson, 1865; Barbier, 1924; Kroeber, 1947).

Various conditions of the urinary tract, including dysury, nephritis, stranguary, stone, gravel, and cystitis, have been treated with salep (Vogel, 1760; Lund, 1771; Percival, 1773; Bergius, 1778; Retzius, 1806; Schumacher, 1826; Hooper, 1839; Cassone, 1852; Argenta, 1864; Fournier, 1948).

Fevers, including enteric and typhoid fever, hectic fever, bilious fevers, and chronic fever from infection, have been treated with salep (Vogel, 1760; Percival, 1773; Retzius, 1806; Hooper, 1839; Argenta, 1864; Heurck and Guibert, 1864; Heurck, 1876; Johnson, 1865; Dey, 1896; Grieve, 1924, 1931; Fournier, 1948).

It is reported that salep has been used in cases of hemorrhage, particularly hemoptysis

---

[115]Irvine (1848) gives the dose of salep as 5 grains to 1 scruple and of the root 2 drams to 2 ounces.

(Lund, 1771; Argenta, 1864; Heurck and Guibert, 1864; Heurck, 1876; Fournier, 1948).

Salep has been used to treat sterility and to facilitate childbirth (Threlkeld, 1727; Saint-Germain, 1943), to prevent abortion (Geoffroy, 1736; Pereira, 1850), to strengthen the uterus, to dispose to conception, and to treat venereal disorders (James, 1745) and abuse of venereal pleasure (Argenta, 1864).

Its use has been reported in cases of diabetes (Hocking, 1962), scurvy (Percival, 1773; Hooper, 1839), heart trouble (Cassone, 1852), rheumatic pains, arthritis, gout, and articular affections (Vogel, 1760; Leclerc, 1877; Saint-Germain, 1943; Levey and Al-Khaledy, 1967), paralytic affections (Dymock 1881, 1885; Watt, 1893), epilepsy (Vogel, 1760), nervous exhaustion (Barbier, 1924), hoarseness (Hooper, 1937), scrofula (Kroeber, 1947), and poisoning (Christophersen, 1960).

Because of its reputed restorative properties, salep has been recommended for those wasted after a long illness and in marasmus (Vogel, 1760; Hill, 1789; Heurck and Guibert, 1864; Heurck, 1876; Dupuis and Réveil, 1887).

Salep has been considered a nutritive and as such has had medicinal use as an aliment rather than as a drug (Hooper, 1839; Griffith, 1847; Dujardin-Beaumetz and Egasse, 1889; Fernie, 1914; Grieve, 1924, 1931; Hooper, 1937; Wren, n.d.). It has been a much-used article of diet for invalids, convalescents, and children, being used in the preparation of castillon powders (Griffith, 1847; Royle, 1853; Heurck and Guibert, 1864; Heurck, 1876; Murray, 1881; Dujardin-Beaumetz and Egasse, 1889; Barbier, 1924).

In recent times the medicinal role of salep has been based solely on its demulcent and nutritive properties, and it is used for infantile diarrhea and in enemas (Tschirch, 1912; Grieve, 1924, 1931; Brandt and Wasicky, 1929; Kroeber, 1947; Hoppe, 1951, 1975; Steinmetz, 1957; Font Quer, 1973; H. Lua, personal communication).

14.9. Aphrodisiac Uses (see also sec. 13)

Orchid tubers and preparations made from them have been used from ancient times to stimulate sexual activity. The terms "cynosorchis," "orchis," "serapias," "satyrion," and "salep" can be considered more or less equivalent, and aphrodisiac virtues have been attributed to these preparations through the ages (Dioscorides, 1st century A.D.; Pliny the Elder, 77 A.D.; Turner, 1551; Dodoens, 1578; Gerarde, 1597; Parkinson, 1640; Miller, 1722; Venette, 1762; Thornton, 1810; Candolle, 1816; Leclerc, 1877; Meyerhof and Sobhy, 1937).

Salep has been used as an aphrodisiac in the Orient (Buxbaum, 1729; Watt, 1890; Meyerhof, 1940), India (Irvine, 1848; Watt, 1893; Dey, 1896; Kirtikar et al., 1975), Turkey (Geoffroy, 1736; Hill, 1789), Syria and Iran (Wedeck, 1962), and Algeria (Chatin, 1868), and this use spread to Europe (Lamark, 1778; Heurck and Guibert, 1864; Dujardin-Beaumetz and Egasse, 1889). Parkinson (1640) stated that "our apothecaries take all sorts of orchis roots for aphrodisiacs."

Salep's reputation as an aphrodisiac was based on the "doctrine of signatures"[116] (Goulin and Labeyrie, 1794; Hooper, 1839; Heurck and Guibert, 1864; Dujardin-Beau-

[116]See n. 3.

metz and Egasse, 1889; Watt, 1890), and is now considered to be unwarranted (Wood *et al.*, 1886; Perrot, 1943a; Wedeck, 1962). It has been suggested that any aphrodisiac effect attributed to salep comes from other substances mixed with it, such as ginger, vanilla, or cinnamon (Bergius, 1771; Hill, 1789; Goulin and Labeyrie, 1794; Chomel, 1804; Roques, 1809; Cassone, 1852; Heurck and Guibert, 1864; Barbier, 1924).

14.10 Food and Beverages (see also secs. 4.5 and 7)

Reports of the use of salep as a food or beverage often are concerned with its tonic or restorative properties. Such nonmedical reports are dealt with here.

Wealthy Persians were said to add the salep root to their dishes to show their opulence (Vogel, 1760).

Salep has long formed part of the diet of people in Iran, Turkey, Syria, and Greece; in particular it has been used, flavored with honey, as a breakfast food (Percival, 1773; Hooper, 1839; Flückiger and Hanbury, 1874; Planchon and Collin, 1895; Howes, 1974). In parts of Greece it was used similarly, with cypress root added to flavor the drink (Fraas, 1845; Landerer, 1850). Vöth (1973) describes its use in the preparation of ice cream in Turkey. Hill (1939) reported that a thin gruel was hawked through the streets in Albania to the cry of "Salee-eep!" Landerer (1850) reports that tubers collected in northern Greece had a disagreeable smell and an unpleasant taste and were used for food only by the poorest classes; *saleptsides* was the name given to those who made the decoction, sold it at night from large vessels kept hot by coals underneath, and advertised it by the cry "Salep!" In Iran and Turkey salep had a great reputation for recruiting the exhausted vitality of aged and ennervated persons (Fernie, 1914).

In India salep was considered a very nourishing article of diet taken with milk and flavored with spices and sugar (Watt, 1893). It was considered to be a restorative and strengthener of the weakened constitution and was prescribed by native practitioners for people who needed tonics (Ainslie, 1813; Aitchison, 1891; Fournier, 1948). In Sind it was regarded as a nutritious diet for the sick and convalescent and for children: it was boiled with water or milk and flavored as sago (Murray, 1881). It is used as a food for convalescents in Pakistan (Hocking, 1962).

In Western Europe salep was at one time regarded as highly nutritious and restorative (Hill, 1751; Woodville, 1792; Chomel, 1804; Morren, 1846; Lindley, 1849; Heurck, 1876; Scardavi, 1963). Morren (1846) reports that salep soup, properly seasoned, is an excellent dish; *Larousse gastronomique* (Froud and Turgeon, 1961) contains recipes for salep soup and salep jelly.

Argenta (1864) describes salep as a useful food either as a broth with water or milk, or with chocolate, or prepared in pastries. A hot drink made from salep was said to be strengthening and agreeable for invalids: the decoction was flavored with sugar and wine, spices (amber, cloves, cinnamon, and ginger), or sassafras (J. Miller, 1722; Flückiger and Hanbury, 1874; Fernie, 1901, 1914). Good salep, properly prepared, was said to be one of the best articles of diet for a convalescent; 2 drams were sufficient for an invalid's meal (Royle, 1839; Hogg, 1858).

Salep was regarded as highly nutritive and was considered equal to tapioca, sago, and arrowroot (Hogg, 1858; Wood *et al.,* 1886) and superior to rice (Percival, 1773; Hooper, 1839).[117] Extravagant comments on the nutritive value of salep have been made by many authors on the premise that salep provided the greatest nutrient in the smallest bulk of any known food (Percival, 1773; Woodville, 1792; Burnett, 1835; Brook, 1868; Anonymous, 1871; Planchon and Collin, 1895). The statement by Percival (1773) that one ounce of salep and one ounce of soup in two quarts of boiling water would sustain a man for a day has been much quoted (Woodville, 1792; Brook, 1868;[118] J. Smith, 1882; Fernie, 1914). Burnett (1835) and Johnson (1865) say that one ounce of salep can sustain a man for a day, and Ward (1937) says it can sustain a navvy. Salep has been recommended as part of the provisions of every ship's company (Percival, 1773; Hooper, 1839; Fernie, 1914), of travelers in wild and uninhabited countries, and of soldiers (Burnett, 1835; Brook, 1868; Fernie, 1914). Chinese and Persians were said to take it on long journeys (Vogel, 1760; Lund, 1771). Percival (1773) reported that bread baked with one ounce of salep to two pounds of flour gave a superior loaf.

The supposed high nutritive value of salep is no longer accepted; it is considered much inferior to sago and tapioca and equal to potato or corn flour (Flückiger and Hanbury, 1874; Hill, 1939; Fournier, 1948; Harris, 1972; Font Quer, 1973).

Salep was used in southern India to make sweetmeats and congee (Dymock, 1893).

Saloop was the name given in England to a beverage prepared from salep and once sold in London and the large towns.[119] E. Smith (1729) gives a method of preparation and insists that it be drunk in china cups. Charles Lamb (1822)[120] alludes to saloop, but his description clearly does not refer to salep—"There is a composition, the groundwork of which I have understood to be the sweet wood 'yclept sassafras." Before the advent of coffee, saloop was sold in London on street corners and later in shops known as salopian houses, and was a favorite breakfast drink for working people. The competition of cheap tea and coffee[121] finally drove saloop out of use. The last saloop vendor, with his tin apparatus for keeping it hot, disappeared about 1865, although saloop balls for preparation of the beverage were still sold in London in 1889. Saloop was a favorite drink of the young bloods and was a sovereign cure for drunkenness (Burnett, 1835; Main, 1845; Archer, 1853; Timbs, 1861; Brook, 1868; Tuer, 1885; S., 1889; Fernie, 1901; Henslow, 1905; Hamilton, 1937).

[117]Hooper in the same article says that the nutritive powers are overrated.

[118]Brook comments, "The commissioners of the new poor law should look at this."

[119]Hibberd (1889) states that this beverage was known as salep "in the language of the people" and as saloop by "good society." Pereira (1850) reports that the name saloop is sometimes applied to sassafras tea.

[120]Lamb is often misquoted as referring to salep from orchids: see Fernie, 1901; Grieve, 1931; and M. A. Miller, 1959; and compare Balfour, 1888, and Hibberd, 1889.

[121]Coffee was introduced into England in the early seventeenth century. The first coffeehouse in England was opened in 1650 at the Angel, in the parish of St. Peter in the East at Oxford, and the first in London was in St. Michael's-alley in Cornhill in 1652. Saloop, prepared from orchids and later from sassafras, was the beverage supplied from houses and stalls to late and early wayfarers in London until reductions in duty, in 1824 and 1842, increased coffee consumption. The old Salopian Coffee House was at 41 Charing Cross during 1841–42. After 1842 coffee stalls became common (Timbs, 1861, 1868, 1872; Mayhew, 1864; Syrett, 1889; Yule and Burnell, 1903; McMichael, 1904).

14.11. Miscellaneous Uses

The following sundry uses of salep have been recorded:

(*a*) To render saltwater potable by concealing the saline taste (Percival, 1773; Hooper, 1839; Dymock, *et al.*, 1893).

(*b*) As a fattener by sultans and women of the East (Morren, 1846; Dymock, 1881, 1885; Meyerhof and Sobhy, 1937).

(*c*) As an adulterant of opium (Landerer, 1851).

(*d*) To replace gum arabic as an agglutinant for technical work (Bulhart, 1927).

(*e*) To cover varnish and as a sizing for dress fabrics and in the silk industry (Brandt and Wasicky, 1929; Kroeber, 1947; *Wealth of India,* 1966).

(*f*) To enrich media used in the asymbiotic germination of orchid seed (Bernard, 1909; Weiss, 1917; Thomale, 1957; Arditti, 1967).

Acknowledgments

I thank Jack L. Still, emeritus professor of biochemistry at the University of Sydney, for his support at the start of this project, and Keith W. Taylor, professor of biochemistry and head of the department, for his encouragement as it was brought to completion; also the many colleagues at the University of Sydney who have assisted with translation from many languages, and Debbie Manning, who with great care typed my complicated and often amended manuscript.

I am also grateful for the invaluable assistance given by the librarians and staffs of the following institutions: Fisher Library, University of Sydney, in particular the interlibrary loan section; National Herbarium of New South Wales, Sydney; Royal Botanic Gardens and National Herbarium, Melbourne; State Library of New South Wales, Sydney; Mitchell Library, Sydney; National Library of Australia, Canberra; Royal Botanic Gardens, Kew; British Library, Bloomsbury and Colindale; British Museum of Natural History, South Kensington; British Medical Association, London; School of Oriental and African Studies, University of London; British Pharmaceutical Society, London; Wellcome Medical Library, London; Royal Anthropological Society of Great Britain and Ireland, London; Musée National d'Histoire Naturelle, Paris; Berenice P. Bishop Museum, Honolulu; and Singapore Botanic Gardens.

Finally I thank my wife, Catherine, who translated the Greek and Latin and edited the manuscript, and without whose patience and encouragement this project would not have been possible.

Literature Cited

Adjanohoun, E., and L. Ake Issi. 1973. Plantes pharmaceutiques de Côte d'Ivoire. Ministère du plan, République de Côte d'Ivoire. Convention 701437.
Ainslie, W. 1813. Materia medica of Hindoostan. Government Press, Madras.
Aitchison, J. E. T. 1891. Notes to assist in a further knowledge of the products of western Afghanistan and of north-eastern Persia. Trans. Bot. Soc. Edin. 18:1–228.
Ali-Al-Rawi and H. L. Chakravarty. 1964. Medicinal plants of Iraq. Ministry of Agriculture, Tech. Bull. no. 15. Government Press, Baghdad.

Allbutt, T. C. 1921. Greek medicine in Rome. Macmillan, London.

Altamirano, D. F. 1895. Historia natural aplicada de los antiguos mexicanos. Proc. 11th Inter. Cong. Americanists:303–378.

Altschul, S. von R. 1973. Drugs and foods from little-known plants. Harvard University Press, Cambridge.

Ames, O. 1924. Additions to the orchid flora of tropical America. Schedulae Orchidianae 7:1–36.

———. 1925. New or noteworthy orchids. Schedulae Orchidianae 9:1–59.

———. 1942a. Orchids in retrospect. Amer. Orchid Soc. Bull. 11:103–106.

———. 1942b. The origin of the term Orchis. Amer. Orchid Soc. Bull. 11:146–147.

Anonymous. 1834. Some remarks on the roots and other indigenous esculents of Van Diemen's Land, pp. 129–134. In Van Diemen's Land annual and Hobart Town almanack for the year 1834. James Ross, Hobart Town.

———. 1855/56. Australian medicinal plants. Pharm. J. 15:114–116.

———. 1871. Salep. Gardeners' Chronicle, ser. 1, 31:642.

———. 1877. The native vegetable food of the colonies (Australia). The Colonies and India, no. 261 (March 31), p. 6 (London).

———. 1878. The Paris exhibition. Pharm. J., ser. 3, 9:41–46.

———. 1879. An orchid new to America. Bull. Torrey Bot. Club. 6:329–330.

———. 1885a. Orchidaceae. Jahresb. Pharm. 20:124–125.

———. 1885b. Tsuchiakabi. Pharm. Rundsch. Prag. 11:637.

———. 1885c. Mexicanische Drogen. Pharmaceut. Zeitung 30, no. 96:927.

———. 1886. Colonial and Indian exhibition at South Kensington, "The Straits Settlements." Pharm. J. 17:4–7.

———. 1890. A sacred orchid. Gardeners' Chronicle, ser. 2, 8:566.

———. 1892a. Faham tea. Kew Bull. 67–68:181–183.

———. 1892b. Vanilla. Pharm. J., 3d ser., 22:614.

———. 1894. Cypripedium spectabile and C. pubescens as poisonous plants. Orchid Rev. 2:141.

———. 1895a. Notes. Orchid Rev. 3:34.

———. 1895b. Useful plants of Japan, described and illustrated. Agricultural Society of Japan, Tokyo.

———. 1899. Vanilla. Q'land Agric. J. 4:477–483.

———. 1906. A Skin eruption due to Vanilla. Lancet 2:478.

———. 1907. Eruption in a worker in Vanilla. Lancet 1:469.

———. 1925. New or noteworthy orchids. Orchid Rev. 33:276.

———. 1928. Fruit of Leptotes bicolor. Orchid Rev. 36:240.

———. 1935. Notes. Orchidol. Zeylan. 2:47.

———. 1939. The Japanese-Manchoukuo year book. Japan-Manchoukuo Year Book Co., Tokyo.

———. 1952a. Poisonous orchids. Orchid J. 1:26.

———. 1952b. A sacred orchid. Orchid J. 1:217.

———. 1952c. The first orchid hybrid. Orchid J. 1:223.

———. 1952d. Orchids of the Manipur region of India. Orchid J. 1:506.

———. 1970. Medicinal plants of Nepal. Ministry of Forests. H.M.G. Press, Katmandu.

———. 1971. British herbal pharmacopoeia. British Herbal Medicine Association, London.

———. 1974. A barefoot doctor's manual. Translation of ch'ih chiao i sheng shou ts'e. U.S. Dept. of Health, Education, and Welfare, pub. (NIH) 75-695, Bethesda, Md.

———. 1975a. By-pass is moved to protect rare orchid. Daily Telegraph, London. May 17, 30.

———. 1975b. Herbal pharmacology in the People's Republic of China. National Academy of Sciences, Washington, D.C.

———. N.d. (available 1969). Northern Territory tour guide. Distributed by Northern Territory Tourist Bureau, Darwin.

Archbold, R. 1941. Unknown New Guinea. National Geog. Mag. 79:315–344.

Archer, T. C. 1853. Popular economic botany. Reeve, London.

Arctander, S. 1960. Perfume and flavor materials of natural origin. S. Arctander, Elizabeth, N.J.

Arditti, J. 1966. Orchids. Sci. Amer. 214:70–78.

———. 1967. Factors affecting the germination of orchid seeds. Bot. Rev. 33:1–97.

———. 1971. Vanilla: an historical vignette. Amer. Orchid. Soc. Bull. 40:610–613.

———. 1972. Caproic acid in Satyrium flowers: biochemical origins of a myth. Amer. Orchid Soc. Bull. 41:298–300.

——. 1973. Use of orchids as contraceptives. Orchid Rev. 81:156–158.

Arenas, P., and R. Moreno. 1977. Plants used as means of abortion, contraception, sterilization, and fecundation by Paraguayan indigenous people. Econ. Bot. 31:302–306.

Argenta, V. M. de. 1864. Album de la flora. Vol. 3. Martínez & Bogo, Madrid.

Arias-Alzate, E. 1971. Plantas medicinales. 8th ed. Salesiana, Medellín, Colombia.

Arnold, R. E. 1958. Bletia verecunda. Orchid Rev. 66:135–136.

Arthur, H. R. 1954. Chemical aspects of the medicinal plants of Hong Kong. Proc. 8th Pacific Sci. Cong. 4A:52–55.

Arthur, H. R., and H. T. Cheung. 1960. A phytochemical survey of the Hong Kong medicinal plants. J. Pharm. Pharmacol. 12:507–570.

Attygalle, J. 1917. Sinhalese materia medica. Rpt. 1952. Gudasenka, Colombo, Ceylon.

Avadhani, P. N., C. J. Goh, and J. Arditti. 1978. Stomatal and acidity rhythms in orchids: practical implications. Amer. Orchid Soc. Bull. 47:131–134.

Backer, C. A. 1936. Verklarend woordenboek. P. Noordhoff, Groningen, Netherlands.

Backer, C. A., and R. C. Bakhuizen van den Brink, Jr. 1968. Flora of Java. Vol. 3. Walters-Noordhoff, Groningen, Netherlands.

Backhouse, J. 1843. A narrative of a visit to the Australian colonies. Hamilton Adams, London.

Bailey, F. M. 1881. Medicinal plants of Queensland. Proc. Linn. Soc. N.S.W. 5:1–28.

——. 1889. Botany of the Bellenden-Ker expedition, pp. 29–80. In A. Meston, Report of the government scientific expedition to Bellenden-Ker Range. Government Printer, Brisbane.

——. 1902. The Queensland flora. Pt. 5. H. J. Diddams, Brisbane.

Bakhuizen van den Brink, R. C. 1931. P. M. W. Dakkus. Trop. Natuur. 20:236.

——. 1937. Synopsis of the vernacular names and the economic use of the indigenous orchids of Java. Blumea, suppl. 1 (J. J. Smith jubilee vol.), 29:38–51.

Bal, S. N. 1942. Useful plants of Mayurbhanj State in Orissa. Rec. Bot. Surv. India 6:1–119.

Balfour, E. 1871. The cyclopaedia of India. 2d ed. Vol. 1. Scottish and Adelphi Presses, Madras.

——. 1873a. The cyclopaedia of India. 2d ed. Vol. 4. Scottish and Adelphi Presses, Madras.

——. 1873b. The cyclopaedia of India. 2d ed. Vol. 5. Scottish and Adelphi Presses, Madras.

——. 1885a. The cyclopaedia of India. 3d ed. Vol. 1. B. Quaritch, London.

——. 1885b. The cyclopaedia of India. 3d ed. Vol. 3. B. Quaritch, London.

Balfour, I. B. 1888. Saloop. Notes and Queries, 7th ser., 6:468.

Bancroft, T. L. 1889. On the materia medica and pharmacology of Queensland plants. Trans. Intercol. Med. Cong. A/sia, 2d sess., pp. 927–931.

Barbier, P. 1924. Étude clinique et expérimentale des orchidées-iridées dans le traitement de la tuberculose. Liège Méd. 17:967–986.

Barham, H. 1794. Hortus americanus. N.P., Kingston, Jamaica.

Barnes, C. S., J. R. Price, and R. L. Hughes. 1975. An examination of some reputed antifertility plants. Lloydia 38:135–140.

Batchelor, J., and K. Miyabe. 1893. Ainu economic plants. Trans. Asiat. Soc. Japan 21:198–240.

Bateman, J. 1837–1843. The Orchidaceae of Mexico and Guatemala. J. Bateman, London.

Beals, K. M. 1917. Flower lore and legend. Rpt. 1973. Gale Research, Detroit.

Bennett, G. 1860. Gatherings of a naturalist in Australia. J. van Voorst, London.

Benzon, P. E. 1822. Om den vestindiske salop. Tidssk. for Naturvidenskaberne 2:158–172.

Bergen, F. D. 1898. Popular American plant-names. J. Amer. Folk-lore, 11:273–283.

——. 1899. Animal and plant lore. Memoirs of the American Folk-lore Society, vol. 7. Rpt. 1969. Kraus, New York.

Bergius, P. J. 1771. Ytterligare anmarkningar om den Osterlandska och Svenska Salep. Kung. Vetensk. Akad. Handl. 32:319–333.

——. 1778. Materia medica. Vol. 2. P. Hesselberg, Stockholm.

Berkeley, E. S. 1893. Notes on orchids in the jungle. Orchid Rev. 1:82–88.

Berkhout, A. H. 1910. Nach den Kautschurlanden. Tropenpflanzer 14:459–467.

Berlin, B., D. E. Breedlove, P. H. Raven. 1974. Principles of Tzeltal plant classification. Academic Press, New York.

Bernard, N. 1909. L'évolution dans la symbiose, les orchidées et leurs champignons commensaux. Ann. Sci. Nat. Bot., ser. 9, no. 9, pp. 1–196.

Bernhard-Smith, A. 1923. Poisonous plants of all countries. Baillière, Tindall & Cox, London.

Bhatnagar, J. K., S. S. Handa, and S. C. Duggal. 1971. Chemical investigations on Microstylis wallachi. Planta Med. 20:156–161.

Billerbeck, J. 1824. Flora classica. J. C. Hinrichssche, Leipzig.

Bingham, M. 1975. The making of Kew. Michael Joseph, London.

Biswas, K. P. 1950. Indian medicinal plants. Pt. 1. University of Calcutta Press, Calcutta.

——. 1956. Common medicinal plants of Darjeeling and the Sikkim Himalayas. West Bengal Government Press, Alipore.

Blackwood, B. 1939. Life on the upper Watut, New Guinea. Geog. J. 94:11–28.

——. 1940. Use of plants among the Kukukuku of southeast-central New Guinea. Proc. 6th Pacific Sci. Cong. 4:111–126.

——. 1950. The technology of modern Stone Age people in New Guinea. Pitt Rivers Museum Occasional Papers on Technology, no. 3. Oxford University Press, Oxford.

Blainey, G. 1975. Triumph of the nomads. Macmillan, South Melbourne.

Blanco, M. 1879. Flora de Filipinas. Vol. 3. Plana, Manila.

Bock, H. 1552. Hieronymi Tragi, De stirpium, maxime earum, in Germania etc. V. Rihelius, Strasbourg.

Bocquillon-Limousin, H. 1894. Les plantes utiles de la Tunisie. Monde de Plantes 4:305–312.

——. 1905. Manuel des plantes médicinales coloniales et exotiques. J.-B. Baillière, Paris.

Bodding, P. O. 1927. Studies in Santal medicine and connected folklore. Pt. 2: Santal medicine. Mem. Asiat. Soc. Bengal 10:133–426.

Boiteau, P. 1974. Dictionnaire des noms malgaches de végétaux. Fitoterapia 45:135–179.

——. 1975. Dictionnaire des noms malgaches de végétaux. Fitoterapia 46:111–134.

——. 1978a. Dictionnaire des noms malgaches de végétaux. Fitoterapia 49:111–144.

——. 1978b. Dictionnaire des noms malgaches de végétaux. Fitoterapia 49:231–240.

——. 1979. Dictionnaire des noms malgaches de végétaux. Fitoterapia 50:207–240.

Bonwick, J. 1870. Daily life and origin of the Tasmanians. Sampson, Low & Marston, London.

Bouquet, A. 1969. Féticheurs et médecines traditionelles du Congo (Brazzaville). Mem. O.R.S.T.O.M. 36:7–282.

Bouquet, J. 1921. Documents sur la matière médicale indigène dans l'Afrique du Nord. Bull. Sc. Pharm. 28:22–36.

Bouriquet, G. 1954. Le vanillier et la vanille dans le monde. Encyclopédie Biologique 46. P. Lechevalier, Paris.

Bourquelot, E., and M. Bridel. 1919. Application de la méthode biochimique à l'étude de plusieurs espèces d'orchidées indigènes. J. Pharm. Chim., ser. 7, 20:21–85, 118–121.

Bouton, L. 1864. Plantes médicinales de Maurice. 2d ed. E. Dupy & P. Dubois, Port Louis, Mauritius.

Boyd, N. 1966. Other uses for orchids. North Shore Orchid Bull. (Sydney), no. 184, p. 4.

Brandt, W., and R. Wasicky. 1929. Erkennung und Charakterisierung der im arzneigebrauchbefindlichen pflanzlichen Inland- und Auslanddrogen. In H. Thoms (ed.), Handbuch der praktischen und wissenschaftlichen Pharmazie, vol. 5, pp. 306–980. Urban & Schwarzenberg, Vienna.

Braun, R. 1909. List of medicines exported from Hankow and other Yangtze ports. Pt. 2. Spec. ser. no. 8. Inspector General of Customs, Shanghai.

Bretschneider, E. 1880. Early European research into the flora of China. J. Roy. Asiatic Soc. No. China Br. 15:1–194.

——. 1881. Botanicon sinicum. Pt. 1. J. Roy. Asiatic Soc. No. China Br. 16:18–230.

——. 1895. Botanicon sinicum. Pt. 3. J. Roy. Asiatic Soc. No. China Br. 29:1–623.

British Parliamentary Papers. 1854. Report of the Government Botanist of the Colony of Victoria, September 1853. Vol. 38, pp. 95–98.

Brøndegaard, V. J. 1971. Orchideen als Aphrodisiaca. Sudhoffs Arch. 55:22–57.

Brook, R. 1868. The cyclopaedia of botany. N.P., Huddersfield.

Brown, F. B. H. 1931. Flora of southeastern Polynesia. Pt. 1. Monocotyledons. Bayard Domick Expedition Pub. no. 20. Berenice P. Bishop. Mus. Bull. no. 84 (Honolulu).

Brown, O. P. 1878. The complete herbalist. O. P. Brown, London.

Brown, R. 1833. On the organs and mode of fecundation in Orchideae and Asclepiadeae. Trans. Linn. Soc. Lond. 16:685–745.

Brown, W. H. 1919. Philippine fiber plants. Bull. no. 19. Department of Agriculture and Natural Resources, Bureau of Forestry, Manila.

——. 1920. Philippine fiber plants. In W. H. Brown (ed.), Minor products of Philippine forests. Bull. no. 22, vol. 1: pp. 311–412. Department of Agriculture and Natural Resources, Bureau of Forestry, Manila.

Browne, G. R. 1894. Additional notes of native plants from the Port Macquarie District. Ag. Gaz. N.S.W. 5:692.

Browne, P. 1789. The civil and natural history of Jamaica. B. White, London.

Brünnich, J. C. 1914. Annual report of the Department of Agriculture and Stock for the year 1913–1914. Government Printer, Brisbane.

Bryant, A. T. 1909. Zulu medicine and medicine-men. Ann. Natal Mus. 2:1–103.

——. 1966. Zulu medicine and medicine-men. C. Struick, Cape Town.

Bryant, C. 1783. Flora diaetetica. B. White, London.

Buchala, A. J., G. Franz, and H. Meier. 1974. A glucomannan from the tubers of *Orchis morio*. Phytochem. 13:163–166.

Budge, E. A. W. 1913. The Syriac book of medicines. 2 vols. Oxford University Press, London. Rpt. 1976, Apa-philo Press, Amsterdam.

Bühler, K. 1948. Plaiting with stretched thread, a first step toward weaving. Ciba Rev. 63:2306–2314.

Bulhart, V. 1927. Orchids of utility. Orchid Rev. 34:234–236.

——. 1930. Orchids of utility. Orchid Rev. 38:85–86.

Bunce, D. 1857. Australasiatic reminiscences of 23 years: wanderings in Tasmania and the Australias. J. T. Hendy, Melbourne.

Bunnemeijer, H. A. B. 1918. Een tucht naar het Diëngplateau. Trop. Natuur 7:101–104.

Burke, C. (ed.). 1866). The illustrated language of flowers. G. Routledge, London.

Burkill, I. H. 1935. A dictionary of the economic products of the Malay Peninsula. 2 vols. Crown Agents for the Colonies, London.

——. 1966. A dictionary of the economic products of the Malay Peninsula. 2d ed. Government Printer, Kuala Lumpur.

Burkill, I. H., and M. Haniff. 1930. Malay village medicine. Gard. Bull. Straits Settlements 6:165–321.

Burnett, G. T. 1835. Outlines of botany. Henry Renshaw, London.

But, P. P-H., Hu, S.-Y., and Kong, Y. C. 1980. Vascular plants used in Chinese medicine. Fitoterapia 61:245–264.

Buxbaum, J. C. 1729. Plantarum minus cognitarum, cent. 3. Typographia Academiae, Leningrad.

Bye, R. 1979. Hallucinogenic plants of the Tarahumara. J. Ethnopharmacol. 1:23–48.

Caius, J. F. 1936. The medicinal and poisonous orchids of India. J. Bomb. Nat. Hist. Soc. 38:791–799.

Campbell, A. 1886. A descriptive catalogue of the economic plants of Chutia Nagpur sent to the Colonial and Indian Exhibition held in London in 1886, annotated by G. Watt. Superintendent of Government Printing, Calcutta.

Campbell, A. H. 1965. Elementary food production by the Australian aborigines. Mankind 6:206–211.

Campbell, H. 1905a. The diet of the precibiculturists. Pt. 1. Brit. Med. J. 2:40–41.

——. 1905b. The diet of the precibiculturists. Pt. 3. Brit. Med. J. 2:350–352.

Campbell, T. D., J. B. Cleland, and P. S. Hossfield. 1946. Aborigines of the lower south-east of south Australia. Rec. Sth. Aust. Mus. 8:445–502.

Candolle, A.-P. de. 1816. Essai sur les propriétés médicales des plantes. Crochard, Paris.

Carles, P. 1870. Étude chimique du givre de vanille. J. Pharm. Chim. 12:254–257.

——. 1872. Étude chimique du givre de vanille. Bull. Soc. Chim. Fr. 17:12–16.

Carr, C. E. 1934. On a collection of orchids from the Solomon Islands. Kew Bull. no. 9, pp. 375–383.

Cassone, F, 1852. Flora medico-farmaceutica. Vol. 6. G. Cassone, Turin.

Castetter, E. F. 1935. Ethnobiological studies in the American Southwest. Pt. 1. Uncultivated native plants used as sources of food. Univ. New Mex. Bull. no. 206, Biol. ser. 4, pp. 3–59.

Castle, L. 1886. Orchids: their structure. history, and culture. Journal of Horticulture Office, London.

Centlivre, S. 1712. Perplex'd lovers. *Rpr.* 1760 *in* Works of the Celebrated Mrs. Centlivre. N.p., London.

Charaka Samhita. ca. 200 B.C. Trans 1888–1903 by A. C. Kaviratna. Calcutta.

——. Vol. 1. Trans. 1976. by R. K. Sharma and V. B. Dash. Chowkhamba Sanskrit Series Office, Baranas.

Chatin, A. 1868. L'histoire naturelle médicale à l'Exposition Universelle. *In* Exposition de 1867 à Paris: Rapports au Jury International, vol. 6, pp. 295–368. P. Dupont, Paris.

Chaudhri, I. I. 1959. Observations on the medicinal plants of Kaghan Valley. Pak. J. Forest. 9:16–28.

Chaudhury, R. R. 1966. Plants with possible antifertility activity. Indian Council of Medical Research, Spec. Report ser. no. 55, pp. 1–19.

Chen, K. K. 1925. Chinese drug stores. Ann. Hist. Med. 7:103–109.

Chen, K. K., and A. L. Chen. 1935a. The alkaloid of chin-shih-hu. J. Biol. Chem. 111:653–658.

——. 1935b. The pharmacological action of dendrobine, the alkaloid of chin-shih-hu. J. Pharmacol. Exper. Therap. 55:319–325.

Cheo, T.-Y. 1947. Medicinal plants of Omei-shan. Bot. Bull. Academia Sinica 1:298–308.

——. 1949. Additional notes on the medicinal plants of Szechwan. Bot. Bull. Academia Sinica 3:135–140.

Chesnut, V. K. 1902. Plants used by the Indians of Mendocino County, California. Contrib. U.S. Nat. Herb. 7:295–408.

Chevreul, M. E. 1823. Sur les causes des différences que l'on observe dans les savons, sous le rapport de leur degré de dureté ou de mollesse et sous celui de leur odeur, et sur un nouveau groupe d'acides organiques. Ann. Chim. Phys. 23:16–32.

——. 1889. Recherches cliniques sur les corps gras d'origine animale. Imprimerie Nationale, Paris.

Childers, N. F., and H. R. Cibes. 1949. Le vanillier et la vanille à Porto-Rico. Rev. Inter. Bot. Appl. Ag. Trop. 29:180–186.

Childers, N. F., H. R. Cibes, and E. Hernández-Medina. 1959. Vanilla—the orchid of commerce, pp. 477–508. In C. L. Withner (ed.), The orchids: a scientific survey. Ronald Press, New York.

Chippendale, G. M. 1971. Checklist of Northern Territory plants. Proc. Linn. Soc. N.S.W. 96:207–267.

Chomel, P.-J. B. 1804. Histoire abregée des plantes usuelles. Vol. 1. L. Duprat-Duverger, Paris.

Chopra, I. C., K. L. Handa, and S. N. Sobti. 1956. Need for the cultivation of vegetable drugs used in Ayurvedic and Unani medicines. Ind. J. Pharm. 18:364–367.

Chopra, R. N., I. C. Chopra, K. L. Handa, and I. D. Kapur. 1958. Indigenous drugs of India. 2d ed. U. N. Dhur, Calcutta.

Chopra, R. N., I. C. Chopra, and B. S. Varma. 1969. Supplement to glossary of Indian medicinal plants. Council for Scientific and Industrial Research, New Delhi.

Chopra, R. N., S. L. Nayar, and I. C. Chopra. 1956. Glossary of Indian medicinal plants. Council for Scientific and Industrial Research, New Delhi.

Chow, C. 1977. Formosan orchids. Chow Cheng Orchids, Taichung.

Christophersen, E. 1960. Norske medisinplanter. H. Aschehoug, Oslo.

Chung, T. H. 1964. Economic plants wild-grown in Korea. J. Nat. Acad. Sci. R.O.K., Natural Sciences ser. no. 5, pp. 57–105.

Cipriani, L. 1966. The Andaman islanders. Weidenfeld & Nicolson, London.

Clarke, W. C. 1971. Place and people. Australian National University Press, Canberra.

Cleland, J. B. 1957. Our natives and the vegetation of Southern Australia. Mankind 4:149–162.

——. 1964. Letter to the editor. Vic. Nat. 80:273.

Clements, M. A. 1978. Report on field trip to Elcho Island and Northern Territory. National Botanic Gardens, Canberra.

Clercq, F. S. A. de. 1909. Nieuw plantkundig wordenbock voor Nederlansch Indië. J. H. de Bussy, Amsterdam.

Clute, W. N. 1919. Medicinal drugs of the United States. Amer. Bot. 25:47–50.

Clymer, R. S. 1963. Nature's heating agents. Dorrance, Philadelphia.

Cochran, K. W., and E. H. Lucas. 1958/59. Chemoprophylaxis of poliomyelitis in mice through the administration of plant extracts. Antibiot. Ann. 1958/59:104–109.

Cointe, P. Le. 1934. Amazonia brazileira. Pt. 3. Arvonnes e plantes uteis. Livraria Classica, Belem and Pará.

Coleman, E. 1932. Pollination of Diuris pedunculata R. Br. Vic. Nat. 49:179–186.

Colenso, W. 1880/81. On the vegetable food of the ancient New Zealanders before Cook's visit. Trans. Proc. N.Z. Inst. 13:1–38.

Colliver, F. S. 1974. Some plant foods of the Queensland aborigine. Q'land Nat. 21:22–31.

Conway, D. 1973. The magic of herbs. E. P. Dutton, New York.

Coode, M. J. E. 1969. A dictionary of the generic and family names of flowering plants for the New Guinea and Southwest Pacific region. Botany Bull. no. 3. Division of Botany, Lae.

Coomans de Ruiter, L. 1935. Op zoek naar de bekerplant met de "Maria-Stuart Kraag." Trop. Natuur 24:195–201.

Cooray, D. A. 1940. Orchids in Oriental literature. Orchidol. Zeylan. 7:73–80.

Cordemoy, E. J. de. 1895. Flore de l'île de la Réunion. Paul Klinksuch, Paris.

Core, E. L. 1967. Ethnobotany of the southern Appalachian aborigines. Econ. Bot. 21:199–214.

Correll, D. S. 1950. Native orchids of North America north of Mexico. Chronica Botanica, Waltham, Mass.

——. 1953. Vanilla—its botany, history, cultivation, and economic import. Econ. Bot. 7:291–358.

Cortés, H., 1520. The despatches of Hernando Cortés. Trans. by G. Folsom, 1843. Wiley & Putnam, New York.

Coulter, S. 1905. The poisonous plants of Indiana. Proc. Indiana Acad. Sci. 14:51–63.

Courtois, J. E., M. Daloul, and F. Petek. 1963. Étude des glucomannanes de quatre espèces d'orchidées françaises. Bull. Soc. Chim. Biol. 45(12):1255–1260.

Cratinus. 5th century B.C.. *In* T. Kock (ed.), Comicorum atticorum fragmenta, 1880, vol. 1, 98.2 p. 43. B. G. Teubner, Leipzig.

Craven, A. 1977. The crafts of the Solomon Islands. Craft Australia 4:10–19.

Crawfurd, J. 1866. On the migration of cultivated plants in reference to ethnology: articles of food. Trans. Ethnol. Soc. 5:178–192.

———. 1868. On the vegetable and animal food of the natives of Australia. Trans. Ethnol. Soc. 6:112–122.

Culpeper, N. 1649. A physicall directory. Peter Cole, London.

———. 1656. The English physitian enlarged. Peter Cole, London.

Curtis, C. H. 1950. Orchids, their description and cultivation. Putnam, London.

Curtis, W. 1858. Calanthe X Dominii. Bot. Mag. 84:5042.

Dakkus, P. M. W. 1935. Orchideën welke in Ned-Indië gekweet kunnen worden. 3d ed. A. C. Nix, Bandoeng.

Dalgado, D. G. 1896. Vires plantarum malabaricum. Rangel Quinta de Bõa Vista, Bastora, Goa.

———. 1898. Flora de Goa e Savantadi. Imprensa Nacional, Lisbon.

Daloul, M., F. Petek, and J. E. Courtois. 1963. Étude des glucomannanes du salep de Syrie. Bull. Soc. Chim. Biol. 45:1247–1254.

Dalziel, J. M. 1937. The useful plants of west tropical Africa. Appendix to T. Hutchinson and J. M. Dalziel, Flora of west tropical Africa. Crown Agents for Overseas Governments and Administrations, London.

Davis, R. S., and M. L. Steiner. 1952. Philippine orchids. William-Frederick Press, New York.

Dawson, J. 1881. Australian aborigines. G. Robertson, Melbourne.

Deb, D. B. 1968. Medicinal plants of Tripura State. Indian Forest. 94:753–765.

Debray, M., H. Jacquemin, and R. Razafindrambaq. 1971. Contribution à l'inventaire des plantes médicinales de Madagascar. Trav. et Doc. de l'O.R.S.T.O.M. 8 (Paris).

Delatte, A. 1938. Herbarius. 2d ed. Faculté de Philosophie et Lettres, Liège.

Delauney, P. 1921. Présence de la loroglossine dans plusieurs espèces d'Orchidées indigènes (1). J. Pharm. Chim., ser. 7, 23:265–272.

Delgado, J. J. 1892. Historia general sacro-profana, política y natural de las islas del Poniente llamadas Filipinas. Juan Atayde, Manila.

Densmore, F. 1928. Uses of plants by the Chippewa Indians. 44th Annual Report, Bureau of American Ethnology, Smithsonian Institution (1926/27), pp. 275–397.

Descourtilz, M. E. 1828. Flora pittoresque et médicale des Antilles. Vol. 6. V. Renard, Paris.

———. 1829. Flore pittoresque et médicale des Antilles. Vol. 8. V. Renard, Paris.

De Wolf, G. R. 1959. Kew and orchidology. Amer. Orchid Soc. Bull. 28:877–880.

Dey, K. L. 1896. The indigenous drugs of India. 2d ed. Thacker, Spink, Calcutta.

Díaz del Castillo, B. 1632. The conquest of New Spain. Trans. by J. M. Cohen, 1974. Folio Society, London.

Diccionario de la lengua española. 1956. 18th ed. Real Academia Española, Madrid.

Dierbach, J. H. 1817. Handbuch der medicinisch-pharmaceutischen Botanik. K. Groos, Heidelberg.

———. 1833. Flora mythologica. J. D. Sauerländer, Frankfurt.

Dioscorides. 1st century A.D., trans. 1959. De materia medica. Trans. by J. Goodyer. Ed. by R. T. Gunther. Hafner, New York.

Dittrich, P. 1976. Nicotinamide adenine dinucleotide—specific "malic" enzyme in *Kalanchoë daigremontiana* and other plants exhibiting crassulacean acid metabolism. Plant Physiol. 57:310–314.

Dodoens, R. 1578. A niewe herball. Gerard Dewes, London.

———. 1644. Cruydt-Boeck Remberti Dodonaei. B. Marteus, Antwerp.

Dokosi, O. B. 1969. Some herbs used in the traditional systems of healing disease in Ghana. Pt. 1. Ghana J. Sci. 9:119–130.

Domínguez, X. A. 1969. Algunos aspectos químicos y farmacológicos de sustancias aisladas de las plantas descritas en el Códice Badiano. Rev. Soc. Quím. Méx. 13:85B–89B.

Dongen, J. 1913. Beknopt overzicht der meest gebruikte geneesmiddelen in Nederlandsch Oost-Indie. Koloniaal Instituut Amsterdam. Druk van Opwijrda, Dieren.

Douk, P. 1966. Contributions à l'étude des plantes médicales du Camboge. Thesis, Université de Paris, Faculté de pharmacie, ser. U, no. 424.

Dournes, J. 1955. Deuxième contribution à l'ethnobotanique indochinoise. J. Agric. Trop. Bot. Appl. 14:64–86.

Dragendorff, G. 1865a. Chemische Untersuchung der Radix corniolae und Radix salep. Pharm. Z. f. Russl. 4:145–159.

——. 1865b. Pharmacognostische Miscellen. Jahresb. Pharm. 15:87–88.

——. 1898. Die Heilpflanzen der verschiedenen Volker und Zeiten. Ferdinand Enke, Stuttgart.

Drar, M. 1943. The salep. Hort. Rev. Cairo 32:14–15.

Ducros, A. H. 1930. Essai sur la drogue populaire arabe de l'Inspectorat des Pharmacies du Caire. Mém. de l'Inst. d'Égypte 15:1–165.

Duggal, S. C. 1972. Orchids in human affairs. Acta Phytotherap. 19:163–173.

Dujardin-Beaumetz, G., and E. Egasse. 1889. Les plantes médicinales indigènes et exotiques. Octave Doin, Paris.

Duperrex, A. 1961. Orchids of Europe. Trans. by A. J. Huxley. Blandford Press, London.

Dupuis, A., and D. Réveil. 1887. Flore médicale. Vol. 2. A. le Vasseur, Paris.

Durrell, L. 1975. Prospero's Cell. Faber & Faber, London.

Dutt, U. C. 1900. The materia medica of the Hindus. Rev. ed. D. Mukerjee, Calcutta.

Dymock, W. 1881. Notes on Indian drugs. Pharm. J., ser. 3, 10:993–994.

——. 1885. The vegetable materia medica of western India. Education Society's Press, Bombay.

Dymock, W., C. J. H. Warden, and D. Hooper. 1893. Pharmacographia indica. Vol. 3. Education Society's Press, Bombay.

Ebbell, B. 1937. The Papyrus Ebers: the greatest Egyptian medical document. Levin & Munksgaard, Copenhagen.

Edwards, H. C. 1913. Orchids at Palmerston North, New Zealand. Orchid World 3:80–81.

Emboden, W. A. 1974. Bizarre plants—magical, monstrous, mythical. Studio Vista, London.

Encyclopedia Japonica. 1970. Shogakukan, Tokyo.

Ewart, A. J., and Davies, O. B. 1917. The flora of the Northern Territory. Minister for Home and Territories, Melbourne.

Fernald, M. L., and A. C. Kinsey. 1943. Edible wild plants of eastern North America. Idlewild Press, Cornwall-on-Hudson, N.Y.

Fernie, W. T. 1901. Kitchen physic. J. Wright, Bristol.

——. 1914. Herbal simples. 3d ed. J. Wright, Bristol.

Fischer, E., and J. Hirschberger. 1889. Ueber Mannose. Pt. 2. Ber. Deut. Chem. Ges. 22:365–376.

Flecker, H., G. B. Stephens, and S. E. Stephens. 1948. Edible plants in North Queensland. North Queensland Naturalists' Club Pub. no. 4., Cairns, Queensland.

Fleming, J. 1810. A catalogue of Indian medicinal plants and drugs. Hindustani Press, Calcutta.

——. 1812. A catalogue of Indian medicinal plants and drugs. Asiatic Researches 11:153–196.

Flückiger, F. A. 1891. Pharmakognosie des Pflanzenreiches. Gaertner, Berlin.

Flückiger, F. A., and D. Hanbury. 1874. Pharmacographia. Macmillan, London.

Folkard, R., Jr. 1884. Plant lore, legends, and lyrics. Sampson Low, Marston, Searle & Rivington, London.

Font Quer, P. 1973. Plantas medicinales. 2d ed. Editorial Labor, Barcelona.

Forbes, F. B., and W. B. Hemsley. 1903. An enumeration of all the plants known from China proper, etc. J. Linn. Soc. Lond. Bot. 36:1–72. Orchidaceae by R. A. Rolfe, pp. 5–67.

Ford, K. C. 1975. Las yerbas de la gente: a study of Hispano-American medicinal plants. University of Michigan Anthropological Papers, no. 60. Ann Arbor.

Fournier, P. 1948. Le livre des plantes médicinales et vénéneuses de France. Vol. 3. Encyclopédie Biologique 32. P. Lechevalier, Paris.

Fox, R. B. 1950. Notes on the orchids and people of northeast Polillo Island, Quezon Province. Philipp. Orchid Rev. 3:16–21.

——. 1952. The Pinatubo Negritos, their useful plants and material culture. Philipp. J. Sci. 81:173–391.

Foxworthy, F. W. 1922. Minor forest products of the Malay Peninsula. Malay. For. Rec. 2:186–204.

Fraas, C. 1845. Synopsis plantarum florae classicae. E. A. Fleischmann, Munich.

Frank, A. B. 1866/67. Über die anatomische Bedeutung und die Entstehung der vegetalischen Schleime. Jb. Wiss. Bot. 5:161–198.

Franz, G. 1973. Biosynthesis of salep mannan. Phytochem. 12:2369–2373.

Franz, G., and N. Meier. 1971. Bildung und Abbau des Schleimpolysaccharids (Salepmannan) von Orchideenknollen. Planta Med. 19:326–332.

Fraser, C. 1830. Remarks on the botany &c. of the banks of Swan River, Isle of Buache, Baie Geographe, and Cape Naturaliste. In W. J. Hooker (ed.), Botanical miscellany, vol. 1, pp. 221–236. John Murray, London.

Freise, F. W. 1933. Plantas medicinales brasileiras. Bol. Agric. S. Paulo 34A252–494.

Friend, H. 1884a. Flowers and flower lore. Vol. 1. W. Swan Sonnerschein, London.

———. 1884b. Flowers and flower lore. Vol. 2. W. Swan Sonnerschein, London.

Froud, N., and C. Turgeon (eds.). 1961. Larousse gastronomique. Hamlyn, Feltham.

Gagnepain, F., and A. Guillaumin. 1932–1934. Orchidées. *In* H. Lecompte (ed.), Flore générale de l'Indo-chine, vol. 6, pt. 2, pp. 142–288 (1932); pt. 3, pp. 289–432 (1933); pt. 4, pp. 433–567 (1933); pt. 5, pp. 577–647 (1934).

Galen. 2nd century A.D. Galeni explanatio vocum Hippocratis. *In* J. G. F. Franz (ed.), Erotiani, Galeni et Herodoti glossaria in Hippocratem . . . , pp. 400–600. J. F. Junius, Leipzig (1780).

Galli, D. I. 1910. Comunicazioni. Atti Accad. Pontif. Nuovi Lincei 63:36–38.

Gans, R., and B. Tollens. 1888. Mannose oder Isomannitose aus Salepschleim. Ber. Deut. Chem. Ges. 21:2148–2152.

Garay, L. A., and H. R. Sweet. 1974. Flora of the Lesser Antilles: Orchidaceae. Arnold Arboretum, Harvard University, Cambridge.

Gardner, R., and K. G. Heider. 1969. Gardens of war. André Deutsch, London.

Gates, W. E. 1939. The De la Cruz–Badiano Aztec herbal of 1552. Pub. no. 23. Maya Society, Baltimore.

Gemmill, C. L. 1973. The missing passage in Hort's translation of Theophrastus. Bull. N.Y. Acad. Med. 49:127–129.

Gentry, H. S. 1942. Rio Mayo plants. Pub. no. 527. Carnegie Institution, Washington, D.C.

Geoffroy, Le Cadet. 1742. Moyen de préparer quelques racines à la manière des orientaux. Mém. Acad. Roy. des Sciences, pp. 96–108.

Geoffroy, S. F. 1736. A treatise of the fossil, vegetable, and animal substances that are made use of in physick. W. Innys & R. Manby, London.

George, A. S. 1980. *Rhizanthella gardneri* R. S. Rogers—the underground orchid of western Australia. Amer. Orchid Soc. Bull. 49:631–646.

George, A. S., and J. Cooke. 1981. *Rhizanthella:* the underground orchid of western Australia. Proc. XIII Inter. Bot. Cong. Orchid Symp. Orchid Society of New South Wales, Sydney.

Gerarde, J. 1597. The herball or generall historie of plants. J. Norton, London.

Gerste, A. 1910. Notes sur la médecine et la botanique des anciens méxicains. 2d ed. Imprimerie Polyglotte Vaticane, Rome.

Ghosh, B. K. 1951. Vedic literature—general view. *In* R. C. Majumdar (ed.), History and culture of the Indian people, vol. 1, pp. 225–240. George Allen & Unwin, London.

Gibbons, Stanley. 1976. Catalogue of stamps of the world. 41st ed. Stanley Gibbons, London.

Gilliard, E. T. 1951. New Guinea's paradise of birds. National Geog. Mag. 100:661–688.

Gimlette, J. D., and H. W. Thomson. 1971. A dictionary of Malayan medicine. Oxford University Press, Kuala Lumpur.

Girard, M. B. F. 1959. Quelques plantes utilisées dans diverses techniques par les Buang. J. Agric. Trop. Bot. Appl. 6:59–67.

Githens, T. S. 1949. Drug plants of Africa. University of Pennsylvania African Handbooks, vol. 8. University of Pennsylvania Press, Philadelphia.

Gmelin, J. G. 1747. Flora sibirica sine histora plantarum sibiriae. Vol. 1. Typographia Academiae Scientiarum, St. Petersburg.

Gobley, T. 1850a. Sur le principe odorant des feuilles de faham. J. Pharm. Chim., ser. 3, 17:348–351.

———. 1850b. On the odoriferous principle of the leaves of Angraecum fragrans. Chem. Gaz. 8:307–309.

———. 1858. Recherches sur le principe odorant de la vanille. J. Pharm. Chim., ser. 3, 34:401–405.

Goeze, E. 1916. Bei den Orchideen. Orchis 10:190–201.

Goh, C. J., P. N. Avadhani, C. S. Loh, C. Hanegraaf, and J. Arditti. 1977. Diurnal stomatal and acidity rhythms in orchid leaves. New Phytol. 78:365–372.

Good, P. P. 1854. The family flora. Vol. 1. Peter P. Good, Jr., Cambridge, Mass.

Gordon, B. L. 1949. Medicine throughout antiquity. F. A. Davis, Philadelphia.

Gordon, C. A. 1884. An epitome of the reports of the medical officers to the Chinese Imperial Maritime Customs Service, from 1871 to 1882. Baillière, Tindall & Cox, London.

Gordon, L. 1977. Green magic. Webb & Bower, Exeter, Eng.

Goulin, J., and Labeyrie. 1794. Dictionnaire des plantes usuelles. Vol. 5. Lamy, Paris.

Gray, A. 1879. Epipactis helleborine, var. viridens (*E. viridiflora*, Reichenbach), a North American plant. Bot. Gaz. 4:206.

Greene, E. L. 1910. Landmarks in botanical history. Pt. 1. Smithson. Misc. Coll. Pub. 1870, 54:1–329.

Greenish, H. G., and E. Collin. 1904. An anatomical atlas of vegetable powders. J. & A. Churchill, London.

Greenwood, E. S. 1974. Broad-leaved helleborine now present in Manitoulin district, Ontario. Canadian Field-Naturalist 88:87–88.

Greshoff, M. 1900. Tweede gedeele van de beschrijuing der giftige en bedwelmende planten bij de vischvangst in gebruik. Meded. Lds. Pltuin. 29:1–253.

Grey, G. 1841. Journals of two expeditions of discovery in north-west and western Australia during the years 1837, 1838, and 1839. Vol. 2. T. & W. Boone, London.

Griessen, A. 1899. Vanda roxburghii at home. Orchid Rev. 7:202–203.

Grieve, M. 1924. Bulbs and tubers used in medicine and commerce. M. Grieve, Chalfont St. Peter.

———. 1931. A modern herbal. Jonathan Cape, London.

Griffith, R. E. 1847. Medical botany. Lea & Blanchard, Philadelphia.

Grigson, G. 1958. The Englishman's flora. Readers Union, London.

Grime, W. E. 1976. Botany of the black Americans. Scholarly Press, St. Clair Shores, Mich.

Guerrero, L. M. 1921a (1918). Medicinal plants. *In* Census of the Philippine Islands, vol. 3, pp. 747–787. Bureau of Printing, Manila.

———. 1921b. Medicinal uses of Philippine plants. *In* W. H. Brown (ed.), Minor products of Philippine forests. Bull. 22, vol. 3, pp. 149–246. Department of Agriculture and Natural Resources, Bureau of Forestry, Manila.

Guillaumin, A. 1951. Données complémentaires sur les plantes médicinales de la Nouvelle-Calédonie. An. Pharm. Fr. 9:676–678.

———. 1954. Les plantes cultivées en Nouvelle Calédonie. Proc. 8th Pacific Sci. Cong. 4:253–268.

Gunn, R. C. 1842. Remarks on indigenous vegetable productions of Tasmania available as food for man. Tas. J. 1:35–52.

Gunther, R. T. 1925. The herbal of Apuleius Barbarus. Oxford University Press, Oxford.

Gupta, J. C., P. K. Roy, and K. K. Sen Gupta. 1946. Pharmacological action of an active constituent isolated from *Vanda Roxburghii* R. Br. Ind. J. Med. Res. 34:253–255.

Gupta, R. 1960. Some useful and medicinal plants of the Naini Tal in the Kumaon Himalayas. J. Bomb. Nat. Hist. Soc. 57(2):309–324.

Gupta, S. N. 1919. The medicine and pharmacy of ancient India. Pacific Pharmacist 13:64–70, 92–97.

Gusinde, M. 1936. Plantas medicinales que los indios araucanos recomiendan. Anthropos 31:850–873.

Gusseva-Badmaeva, A. P., A. F. Hammermann, and W. S. Sokolov. 1972. Heilmittel der Tibetischen Medizin. Planta Med. 21:161–172.

Guzmán, D. J. 1924. Especies útiles de la flora salvadoreña. Imprenta Nacional, San Salvador.

Haddon, A. C. 1890. The ethnography of the western tribe of Torres Straits. J. Anthrop. Inst. Gt. Brit. Ireland 19:297–440.

———. 1894. The decorative art of British New Guinea. Cunningham Memoir 10. Royal Irish Academy, Dublin.

———. 1912. Personal ornaments and clothing, pp. 33–62. *In* Arts and crafts, vol. 4 of Reports of the Cambridge Anthropological Expedition to Torres Straits. Cambridge University Press, Cambridge.

Haerdi, F., J. Kerharo, and J. G. Adam. 1964. Plantes médicinales africaines. Acta Tropica, suppl. 8. Verlag für Recht und Gesellschaft, Basel.

Hale, H. R., and N. B. Tindale. 1934. Aborigines of Princess Charlotte Bay, North Queensland. Pt. 2. Rec. So. Aust. Mus. 5:117–172.

Hamel, P. B., and M. U. Chiltoskey. 1975. Cherokee plants and their uses—a 400-year history. Herald, Sylva, N.C.

Hamilton, A. G. 1886. List of the Orchideae of the Mudgee district. Proc. Linn. Soc. N.S.W. 11:865–878.

———. 1888. Over the hills—a spring ramble. Pt. 1. Sydney Quart. Mag. 5:349–360.

———. 1937. Bush rambles. Angus & Robertson, Sydney.

Hammermann, A. F., J. A. Damirov, and W. S. Sokolov. 1971. Einige aussichtsreiche Pflanzen der Volksmedizin von Azerbajdschan. Planta Med. 20:374–380.

Hand, W. D. (ed.). 1976. American folk medicine. University of California Center for Study of Comparative Folklore and Mythology, Pub. no. 4. University of California Press, Los Angeles.

Hardin, J. W. 1964. North Carolina drug plants of commercial value. N.C. Agric. Expt. Stat. Bull. no. 418, pp. 2–34.

Harding, A. R. 1908. Ginseng and other medicinal plants. Rev. ed. A. R. Harding, Columbus, O.

Harley, G. W. 1970. Native African medicine. Frank Cass, London.

Harris, B. C. 1972. The compleat herbal. Barre Publishers, Barre, Mass.

Hartwell, J. L. 1970. Plants used against cancer: a survey. Pt. 2. Lloydia 33:288–392.

Hawkes, A. D. 1943. Economic importance of the Orchidaceae. Amer. Orchid Soc. Bull. 12:412–415.

——. 1944a. Orchid tea. Orchid Digest 8:146–147.

——. 1944b. Economic importance of the Orchidaceae. Pt. 2. Amer. Orchid Soc. Bull. 13:56–58.

——. 1952. Orchids—what they are and how to use them. Orchid J. 1:29.

——. 1961. Orchids: their botany and culture. Harper & Row, New York.

Hays, T. E. 1980. Uses of plants in Ndumba, Eastern Highlands Province. Sci. in New Guinea 7:118–131.

Heckel, E. 1897. Les plantes médicinales et toxiques de la Guyane Français. Ann. Inst. Col. Marseille 4:70–159.

Hedley, C. 1888. Uses of some Queensland plants. Proc. Roy. Soc. Q'land 5:10–13.

Hedrick, U. P. (ed.) 1919. Sturtevant's notes on edible plants. J. B. Lyon, Albany, N.Y.

Hegnauer, R. 1963. Chemotaxonomie der Planzen. Vol. 2. Birkhäuser, Basle.

Henkel, A. 1906. Wild medicinal plants of the United States. U.S. Department of Agriculture, Bureau of Plant Bull. no. 89, pp. 7–76.

——. 1907. American root drugs. U.S. Department of Agriculture, Bureau of Plant Bull. no. 107, pp. 1–80.

Henry, A. 1887. Chinese names of plants, pt. 1. J. Roy. Asiat. Soc. No. China Br. 22:233–283.

Henry, S. 1814. A new American medicall family herbal. S. Henry, New York.

Henslow, G. 1905. The uses of British plants. Lovell Reeve, London.

Héraud, A. 1927. Nouveau dictionnaire des plantes médicinales. 6th ed. J.-B. Baillière, Paris.

Hérissey, H. 1902. Sur la digestion de la mannane des tubercules d'orchidées. Compt. rend. 134:721–723.

Hérissey, H., and P. Delauney. 1922. Présence dans plusieurs orchidées indigènes de glucosides fournissant de la coumarine par hydrolyse. J. Pharm. Chim., ser. 7, 25:298–305.

Heurck, H. F. 1876. Drogues simples. E. Ramlot, Brussels.

Heurck, H. F., and V. Guibert. 1864. Flore médicale belge. C.-J. Fonteyne, Louvain.

Heyne, K. 1913. De nuttige planten van Nederlandsch-Indië. Ruygrok, Batavia.

——. 1922. De nuttige planten van Nederlandsch-Indië. 2d ed. Vol. 1. Ruygrok, Batavia.

——. 1927. De nuttige planten van Nederlandsch-Indië. 2d rev. and enl. ed. Vol. 1. Nijverheld & Handel, Buitenzorg.

——. 1950. De nuttige planten van Indonesië. 3d ed. Vol. 1. Van Hoeve, The Hague.*

Hibberd, S. 1889. Salep. Notes and Queries, 7th ser., 7:35.

Hide, R., M. Kimin, A. Kora, G. Kua, and K. Kua. 1979. A checklist of some plants in the territory of the Sinasina Nimai (Simbu Province, Papua New Guinea), with notes on their uses. Working paper no. 54, Department of Anthropology, University of Auckland.

Higashi, S., M. Abe, S. Ogata, H. Tobita, and K. Yokota. 1975. Traditional medicinal and poisonous plants in the Satsuman Islands. Pt. 1. Kagoshima Daigaku, Fac. Sc. Repts. Earth Sci. Biol. 8:93–113.

Hiley, R. F. 1909. Dermatitis due to vanilla. Letter to the editor. Lancet 1:1433.

Hilger, A. 1903. Zur Kenntnis der Pflanzenschleime. Ber. Deut. Chem. Ges. 36:3197–3203.

Hill, A. F. 1937. Economic botany. McGraw-Hill, New York.

Hill, J. 1751. A history of the materia medica. T. Longman, C. Hatch & L. Hawes, London.

——. 1789. The useful family herbal. A. Millar, M. Law & R. Cater, London.

Hill, J. 1939. Wild food of Britain. Adam & Charles Black, London.

Hitchcock, M. 1962. Kepeginneh. Skyline 12:21–27 (Launceston).

Ho, P.-y. 1978. Ancient Chinese medicine. Hemisphere 22:36–41.

---

*There have been four separate printings of Heyne's most useful book, originally published in 1913. The second edition, which was considerably larger than the first, appeared in 1922. (In vol. 1 of this edition in the library at Kew, a note signed I.H.B. reads: "This is the second edition of volume one. After it has [sic] been printed the size of the page was altered and this reprinted in quarto in the edition of 1927.") The 1927 edition, however, is clearly designated a "revised and enlarged impression," and, as I have had occasion to discover, references to pagination in the "second edition" may in fact refer to the edition of 1927. The third edition, titled *De Nuttige Planten van Indonesië* and published in 1950, is little changed from the 1927 edition, apart from modernization of the spelling.

Hocking, G. M. 1952. A study of the medicinal plants of West Pakistan. Pub. no. 3862. F.A.O., Rome.
——. 1962. Pakistan medical plants. Pt. 4. Qualitas Plantarum et Mat. Veget. 9:103–119.
Høeg, O. A. 1958. Norske legeplanter. Blyttia 16:145–169.
Hoernle, A. F. R. (ed.). 1893–1912. The Bower manuscript. Archaeological Survey of India, new imp. ser., vol. 22. Superintendent of Government Printing, Calcutta.
——. 1907. Studies in the medicine of ancient India. Clarendon Press, Oxford.
Höfler, M. 1911. Volksmedizinische Botanik der Kelten. Sudhoffs Arch. 5:241–279.
Hogg, R. 1858. The vegetable kingdom and its products. W. Kent, London.
Hohmann, B. 1968. Crocus-knollen als Verfalschung von Tubera Salep. Planta Med. 16:277–281.
Holdsworth, D. K. 1974. Phytochemical survey of medicinal plants in Papua New Guinea. Sci. in New Guinea 2:142–154.
——. 1977. Medicinal plants of Papua New Guinea. Technical paper no. 175, South Pacific Commission, Noumea.
Holdsworth, D. K., and E. R. Farnworth. 1974. A phytochemical survey of medicinal and poisonous plants of the central district of Papua. Sci. in New Guinea 2:155–163.
Holdsworth, D. K., and R. P. Longley. 1973. Some medicinal and poisonous plants from the southern highlands district of Papua. Proc. Papua-New Guinea Scient. Soc. 24:21–24.
Holmes, E. M. 1892. Malay materia medica. Bull. Pharm. Detroit 6:108–117.
——. 1896. Catalogue of the medicinal plants in the Museum of the Pharmaceutical Society of Great Britain. London.
Holmes, J. M. 1963. Australia's open north. Rpt. 1966. Angus & Robertson, Sydney.
Holttum, R. E. 1964. Orchids of Malaya, vol. 1 of Flora of Malaya. 3d ed. Government Printing Office, Singapore.
Hooper, D. 1929. On Chinese medicine: drugs of Chinese pharmacies in Malaya. Gard. Bull. Straits Settlements 6:1–163.
——. 1937. Useful plants and drugs of Iran and Iraq. Pub. no. 275. Field Mus. Bot. Ser. 9:75–241.
Hooper, R. 1839. Lexicon medicum. 7th ed. Rev. by K. Grant. Longman, Orme, London.
Hope, G. S., and P. J. F. Coutts. 1971. Past and present aboriginal food resources at Wilsons Promontory, Victoria. Mankind 8:104–114.
Hoppe, H. A. 1951. Europäische Drogen. Vol. 2. Cram, de Gruyter, Hamburg.
——. 1975. Drogenkunde. 8th ed. Vol. 1. W. de Gruyter, Berlin.
Hou, J. P. 1977. The development of Chinese herbal medicine and the Pen-ts'ao. Comp. Med. East West 5:117–122.
Hough, W. 1897. The Hopi in relation to their plant environment. Am. Anthrop. 10:33–44.
How, W. 1650. Phytologica Britannica. Cited in R. T. Gunther, Early British botanists and their gardens (Oxford: Oxford University Press, 1922).
Howes, F. N. 1974. A dictionary of useful and everyday plants and their common names. Cambridge University Press, London.
Howley, J. P. 1915. The Beothucks or Red Indians. Cambridge University Press, Cambridge.
Hsia, E. 1948. Orchids of the "Middle" or "Flowery Kingdom." Orchid Digest 12:168–170.
Hu, S.-y. 1957. An enumeration of the food plants of China. Arnold Arboretum, Harvard University, Cambridge.
——. 1970. Dendrobium in Chinese medicine. Econ. Bot. 24:165–170.
——. 1971a. Orchids in the life and culture of the Chinese people. Chung Chi J. 10:1–26.
——. 1971b. The Orchidaceae of China. Pt. 1. Quart. J. Taiwan Mus. 24:67–103.
——. 1971c. The Orchidaceae of China. Pt. 5. Quart. J. Taiwan Mus. 26:131–165.
Huard, P., and M. Wong. 1958. Évolution de la matière médicale chinoise. E. J. Brill, Leiden.
Hübotter, F. 1909. Die chinesische Medizin zu Beginn des XX. Jahrhunderts und ihr historische Entwicklungsgang. B. Schindler, Leipzig.
——. 1913. Beiträge zur Kenntnis chinesischen sowie der tibetisch-mongolischen Pharmakologie. Urban & Schwarzenberg, Berlin.
——. 1957. Chinesisch-tibetische Pharmakologie und Rezeptur. K. F. Haug, Ulm and Danau.
Hunter, J. 1793. An historical journal of the transactions of Port Jackson and Norfolk Island. J. Stockdale, London.
Hurst, E. 1942. The poison plants of New South Wales. New South Wales Poison Plants Committee, Sydney.
Hussey, J. S. 1974. Some useful plants of early New England. Econ. Bot. 28:311–337.

Hyatt, R. 1978. Chinese herbal medicine. Wildwood House, London.

Imbesi, A. 1964. Indice delle piante. N.p., Messina.

Innamorati, T. F. 1973. Notizie di medicina popolare africana nell'erbario tropicale di Firenze. Webbia 28:81–134.

Inubushi, Y., Y. Tsuda, T. Konita, and S. Matsumoto, 1968. The structure of shihunine, a new phthalide-pyrolidine alkaloid. Chem. Pharm. Bull. 16:1014–1018.

Irvine, F. R. 1952. Supplementary and emergency food plants of West Africa. Econ. Bot. 6:23–40.

——. 1957. Wild and emergency foods of Australian and Tasmanian aborigines. Oceania 28:113–142.

Irvine, R. H. 1848. A short account of the materia medica of Patna. W. Ridsdale, Calcutta.

Ishidoya, T. 1925. On the medicinal plants in Chosen (Korea). J. Chosen Nat. Hist. Soc. 3:1–10.

Ives, E. 1850. Experience on the virtues of certain plants. Trans. Amer. Med. Assoc. 3:311–316.

Jackson, J. R. 1866. Orchid tea. Gardeners' Chronicle, ser. 1, 26:315.

Jain, S. K., and C. R. Tarafder. 1970. Medicinal plant-lore of the Santals: a revival of P. O. Bodding's work. Econ. Bot. 24:241–278.

James, R. 1745. A medicinal dictionary. Vol. 3. T. Osborne, London.

Jannese, J. A. 1964. "The Greeks had a name for them." Aust. Orchid Rev. 29:137–139.

Jaretsky, R., and E. Bereck. 1938. Der Schleim in der Knollen von Orchis purpureus Huds. und Platanthera bifolia (L.) Rchb. Arch. Pharm. 276:17–27.

Jastrow, M., Jr. 1917. Babylonian-Assyrian medicine. Ann. Med. Hist. 1:231–257.

Jee, B. S. 1896. A short history of Aryan medical science. Macmillan, London.

Jeliffe, S. E. 1906. Charaka and his times. Proc. Charaka Club 2:21–29.

Johnson, C. P. 1865. The useful plants of Great Britain. R. Hardwicke, London.

Johnson, F. B. 1952. Orchid pseudobulbs for candy. Orchid J. 1:468–470.

Jones, R. M. 1971. Rocky Cape and the problem of the Tasmanians. Ph.D. thesis, University of Sydney.

Joret, C. 1904. Les plantes dans l'antiquité et au moyen âge. Vol. 2. E. Bouillon, Paris.

Josst, F. 1851. Orchideen. D. von Rath, Prague.

Jumelle, H. 1910. Les plantes à tubercules alimentaires des climats tempérés et des pays chauds. Octave Doin, Paris.

Kaempfer, E. 1712. Amoenitatum exoticarum politico-physico-medicarum. H. W. Meyer, Lemgo.

Kariyone, T., and Y. Kimura. 1940. Japanese-Chinese medicinal plants: their constituents and medicinal uses. 4th enl. ed. Nihon Yakuho Sha, Tokyo.

Kariyone, T., and R. Koiso. 1971. Atlas of medicinal plants. Takeda Chemical Industries, Osaka.

Karsten, G., and U. Weber. 1946. Lehrbuch der Pharmakognosie für Hochschulen. G. Fischer, Jena.

Keble, R. A. 1917. Aboriginal plant names: their etymology. Vic. Nat. 34:61–76.

Kew Handlist. 1904. Handlist of orchids cultivated in the Royal Botanic Gardens. 2d ed. H.M.S.O., London.

Khan, A. H. 1958. The essential oil-bearing plants of Pakistan. Pt. 2. Pak. J. Forest. 8:342–373.

Kimura, K., and H. Migo. 1936. New species of Dendrobium from the Chinese drug shih-hu. J. Shanghai Sci. Instit. Sec. III 3:121–124.

King Li-Pin and Li-Teng-Pang. 1936. Contribution à l'étude de l'action pharmacodynamique de Dendrobium nobile Lind. Cont. Inst. Physiol. Nat. Acad. Peiping 4:1–18.

Kircher, A. 1678. Mundus subterraneus. J. Jansson & Waesberge, Amsterdam.

Kirk, D. R. 1975. Wild edible plants of the western United States. Naturegraph Publishers, Happy Camp, Calif.

Kirtikar, K. R., and B. D. Basu. 1918. Indian medicinal plants. Pt. 2. S. N. Basu, Allahabad.

Kirtikar, K. R., B. D. Basu, and An I. C. S. 1975. Indian medicinal plants. 2d ed. Vol. 4. Ed., rev., enl., and mostly rewritten by E. Blatter, J. F. Caius, and K. S. Mhaskar. M/S. Bishen Singh Mahendra Pal Singh, Dehra Dun.

Klages, F. 1934. Zur Kenntnis der Steinnuss-mannane. Pt. 1. Ann. Chem. 509:159–181.

Klages, F., and R. Maurenbrecher. 1938. Die Konfiguration des Steinnuss- und Salep-mannans and über den Gültigkeitsbereich der Hudsonschen Superpositionsregeln bei Mannose-derivaten. Ann. Chem. 535:175–204.

Klages, F., and R. Niemann. 1936. Über die Konstitution des Salep-mannans und die übrigen Kohlenhydrate aus Tubera Salep. Ann. Chem. 523:224–234.

Kloss, J. 1975. Back to Eden. 5th ed. Lifeline Books, Santa Barbara, Calif.

Kohl, F. G. 1899. Untersuchungen über die Raphidenzellen. Bot. Zbl. 79:273–282.

Kokwaro, J. O. 1976. Medicinal plants of East Africa. East African Literature Bureau, Nairobi.

Kordel, L. 1974. Natural folk remedies. W. H. Allen, London.

Kramer, J. 1975. Orchids, flowers of romance and mystery. Harry N. Abrams, New York.

Krochmal, A., and C. Krochmal. 1975. A guide to the medicinal plants of the United States. New York Times Book Co., New York.

Krochmal, A., R. S. Walters, and R. M. Doughty, 1969. A guide to the medicinal plants of Appalachia. U.S. Forestry Service Research Paper N.E., no. 138, pp. 1–291.

———. 1971. A guide to the medicinal plants of Appalachia. U.S. Department of Agriculture, Forestry Service, Agricultural Handbook no. 400.

Kroeber, L. 1947. Das neuzeitliche Kräuterbuch. Vol. 2. Hippokrates-Verlag, Marquardt, Stuttgart.

Kuetzing, F. T. 1852. Grundzüge der philosophischen Botanik. F. A. Brockhaus, Leipzig.

Kupper, W. 1961. Orchids. Trans. by J. W. Little. Thomas Nelson, London.

Laisnel de la Salle, G. 1875. Croyances et légendes du centre de la France. Vol. 1. A. Chaix, Paris.

Lamark, J. B. 1778. Flore française. Vol. 3. Imprimerie Royale, Paris.

Lamb, C. 1822. The praise of chimney-sweepers: a May-day effusion. Lond. Mag. 5:405–408.

Lampert, R. J., and F. Sanders. 1973. Plants and men on the Beecroft Peninsula, New South Wales. Mankind 9:96–108.

Landerer, X. 1850. On salep. Pharm. J. 9:435–436.

———. 1851. Adulteration of opium with salep powder. Pharm. J. 10:475.

Lanessan, J. L. de. 1886. Les plantes utiles des colonies françaises. Imprimerie Nationale, Paris.

Langham, W. 1633. The garden of health. 2d ed. T. Harper, London.

Langkavel, B. 1866. Botanik der spätern Griechen. F. Berggold, Berlin.

Latif, S. M. 1960. Bunga anggerik permata belantara Indonesia. Vorkink-van Hoeve, Bandung.

Lauer, H. H. 1968. Zur Überlieferungsgeschichte der Salep-wurzel, pp. 395–420. In G. Keil, R. Rudolf, W. Schmitt, and H. J. Vermeer (eds.), Fachliteratur des Mittelalters: Festschrift für Gerhard Eis. J. B. Metzler, Stuttgart.

LaWall, C. H. 1927. 4000 years of pharmacy. J. B. Lippincott, Philadelphia.

Lawler, L. J. 1977. A new role for Dendrobium luteocilium Rupp. Aust. Orchid Rev. 42:147.

———. 1979. Orchids as ant plants. Aust. Orchid. Rev. 44:209–211.

———. 1981. Ethnobotany of Australian orchids. In Proc. XIII Inter. Bot. Cong. Orchid Symp. Orchid Society of New South Wales, Sydney.

Lawler, L. J., and M. Slaytor. 1970a. The distribution of alkaloids in orchids from the territory of Papua and New Guinea. Proc. Linn. Soc. N.S.W. 94:237–241.

———. 1970b. Uses of Australian orchids by aborigines and early settlers. Med. J. Aust. 2:1259–1261.

Lawler, L. J., M. Slaytor, and J. Done. 1971. Biochemical investigations of Australian Orchidaceae. Proc. 6th World Orchid Conf., Sydney (1969), pp. 51–54.

Leclerc, H. 1918. La médecine des signatures magiques. Janus 23:5–28.

Leclerc, J. 1864. Les plantes médicinales de l'île de la Réunion et leur application à la thérapeutique. La Malle, St. Denis.

Leclerc, L. 1877. Traité des simples par Ibn el Beitar. Notices et extraits des manuscrits de la Bibliothèque Nationale et autres bibliothèques publiés par l'Institut National de France 23:1–478.

———. 1883. Traité des simples par Ibn el Beitar. Notices et extraits des manuscrits de la Bibliothèque Nationale et autres bibliothèques publiés par l'Institut National de France 26:1–486.

Lehmann, F. R. 1955. Kulturgeschichte und Rezepte der Liebesmittel. E. Hoffmann, Heidenheim.

Leichhardt, L. 1849. Notes on the geology, botany, natural history, and capabilities of the country between Moreton Bay and Port Essington. Tas. J. 3:81–113.

Le Maout, E., and J. Decaisne. 1876. A general system of botany. Trans. by Mrs. Hooker. Longmans, Green, London.

Lerch, J. U. 1844. Über die flüchtigen Säuren der Butter. Ann. Chem. Pharm. 49:212–231.

L'Escluse, C. de. 1605. Exoticorum libri decem. Raphelengius, Leiden.

Levey, M., and N. Al-Khaledy. 1967. The medical formulary of Al-Samarqandi. University of Pennsylvania Press, Philadelphia.

Levitt, D. 1981. Plants and people. Australian Institute of Aboriginal Studies, Canberra.

Levy, J. der B. 1963. Herbal handbook for farm and stable. Faber & Faber, London.

Leyel, C. F. 1970. Elixirs of life. Stuart & Watkins, London.

Licht, H. 1932. Sexual life in ancient Greece. G. Routledge, London.

Liddell, H. G., and R. Scott. 1966. Greek-English lexicon. 9th rev. ed. Clarendon Press, Oxford.

Limartha, I. P. 1974. Yang aneh-aneh dari dunia Anggerik. Ideal, no. 60, pp. 22–23 (Jakarta).

Linden, L. 1894. Orchidées exotiques. Octave Doin, Paris.

Lindley, J. 1836. A natural system of botany. 2d ed. Longman, Rees, Orme, Brown, Green & Longman, London.

——. 1838. Flora medica. Longman, Orme, Brown, Green & Longman, London.

——. 1841. A note upon the anatomy of the roots of *Ophrydeae*. Trans. Linn. Soc. Lond. 18:423–428.

——. 1844. Bemerkungen über die Anatomie der Ophryden-wurzeln. Arch. Pharm. 39:178–180.

——. 1849. Medical and oeconomical botany. Bradbury & Evans, London.

——. 1853. Paxton's flower garden. Bradbury & Evans, London.

——. 1858. Note. Gardeners' Chronicle, ser. 1, 18:4.

Lindley, J., and T. Moore. 1866. The treasury of botany. 2 vols. Longmans, Green, London.

Linnaeus, C. 1751. Philosophia botanica Caroli Linnaei. G. Kiesewetter, Stockholm.

——. 1753. Species plantarum. Vol. 2. L. Salvii, Stockholm.

Liu, T.-S. 1952. List of economic plants in Taiwan. Chen-Chung, Taipei.

Lorant, M. 1961. The story of vanilla. Orchid Rev. 69:342–344.

Loudon, J. W. (ed.). 1872. Encyclopaedia of plants. Longmans, Green, London.

Lucas, A. H. S. 1912. Flora and fauna. *In* A. W. Jose, T. G. Taylor, and W. G. Woolnough, New South Wales, pp. 204–230. Whitcombe & Tombs, Melbourne.

Luer, C. A. 1975. The native orchids of the United States and Canada. New York Botanical Garden, New York.

Lund, G. 1771. Forsok med Orchis morio, eller Svensk salep, anstalde och ingisne. Kung. Vetensk. Akad. Handl. 32:310–319.

Luning, B. 1974. Alkaloids of the Orchidaceae, pp. 349–382. *In* C. L. Withner (ed.), The orchids: scientific studies. John Wiley, New York.

McConnel, U. H. 1936. Cape York Peninsula. Walkabout 2:11–15.

——. 1953. Native arts and industries on the Archer, Kendall, and Holroyd rivers, Cape York Peninsula, North Queensland. Rec. So. Aust. Mus. 11:1–42.

MacDougal, D. T. 1894. On the poisonous influence of Cypripedium spectabile and Cypripedium pubescens. Minn. Bot. Studs. 1:32–36; Geol. Nat. Hist. Surv. Bull. no. 9, Bot. ser. 2 (1894–1898).

——. 1896. Poisonous influence of various species of Cypripedium. Minn. Bot. Studs. 1:450–451; Geol. Nat. Hist. Surv. Bull. no. 9, Bot. ser. 2 (1894–1898).

McGilvery, R. W. 1970. Biochemistry: a functional approach. W. B. Saunders, Philadelphia.

MacLeish, K. 1972. The Tasadays: Stone Age cavemen of Mindanao. National Geog. Mag. 142:219–249.

MacMichael, J. H. 1904. Salep or salop. Notes and Queries, ser. 10, 1:97–98, 233.

McPherson, A., and S. McPherson. 1977. Wild food plants of Indiana and adjacent states. Indiana University Press, Bloomington.

Maheshwari, P., and U. Singh. 1965. Dictionary of economic plants in India. Indian Council of Agricultural Research, New Delhi.

Maiden, J. H. 1888a. Some reputed medicinal plants of New South Wales. Proc. Linn. Soc. N.S.W. 13:355–393.

——. 1888b. Australian indigenous plants providing human foods and food adjuncts. Proc. Linn. Soc. N.S.W. 13:481–556.

——. 1889. The useful native plants of Australia (including Tasmania). Turner & Henderson, Sydney.

——. 1897. Plants reported to be poisonous to stock. Ag. Gaz. N.S.W. 8:1–22.

——. 1898. Some plant-foods of the aborigines. Ag. Gaz. N.S.W. 9:349–354.

——. 1899. Native food plants. Pt. 4. Ag. Gaz. N.S.W. 10:730–740.

——. 1901. Plants reported to be poisonous to stock in Australia. Ag. Gaz. N.S.W. 12:637–666.

Main, J. 1845. Hortus dietetica. M. S. Orr, London.

Maisch, J. M. 1885. Materia medica of the New Mexican pharmacopoeia. Amer. J. Pharm. 57:506–507.

——. 1890. A manual of the organic materia medica. 4th ed. Lea, Philadelphia.

Major, R. H. 1954. A history of medicine. Blackwell Scientific Publications, Oxford.

Mansfeld, R. 1959. Vorzäufiges Verzeichnis landwirtschaftlich- oder gärtnerischkultivierter Pflanzenwarten. Die Kulturpflanze, suppl. 2. Institut für Kulturpflanzen Forschung, Deutsche Akademie der Wissenschaften, Berlin.

Martindale, W. H., and W. W. Westcott. 1924. The extra pharmacopoeia. H. K. Lewis, London.

Martínez, M. 1959. Las plantas medicinales de México. 4th ed. Ediciones Botas, Mexico City.

Masiluñgan, V. A., N. C. Diokno, and V. B. Quisumbing. 1959. Screening of Philippine medicinal plants used in the treatment of tuberculosis for substances inhibitory to Mycobacterium tuberculosis 607. Philipp. J. Sci. 88:245–251.

Masiluñgan, V. A., J. Marañon, V. V. Valencia, N. C. Diokno, and P. de Leon. 1955. Screening of Philippine higher plants for antibacterial substances. Philipp. J. Sci. 84:275–301.

Mason, F. 1860. Burmah, its people and natural productions. T. Stowe Ranney, Rangoon.

——. 1883. Botony, vol. 2 of Burma, its people and productions. 3d ed. Rewritten by W. Theobald. Stephen Austin, Hertford.

Massal, E., and J. Barrau. 1955. Pacific subsistence crops: cassava. So. Pac. Comm. Quart. Bull. 5:15–18.

Mathews, J. 1979. Totem and taboo. Collins, Sydney.

Matsui, A. S., J. Rogers, Yen-kong Woo, and W. C. Cutting. 1967. Effects of some natural products on fertility in mice. Med. Pharmacol. Exp. 16:414–424.

Mattioli, P. A. 1571. Compendium de plantis omnibus. Officina Valgrisiana, Venice.

Maxwell, W. G. 1906. Mantra gajah. J. Roy. Asiatic Soc. Straits. Br. 45:1–46.

Mayhew, H. 1864. London labour and the London poor. Vol. 1. Charles Griffin, London.

Meagher, S. J. 1974. The food resources of the aborigines of the south-west of western Australia. Rec. West. Aust. Mus. 3:14–63.

Meggitt, M. J. 1964. Aboriginal food-gatherers of tropical Australia, pp. 30–37. *In* The Ecology of man in the tropical environment. International Union for the Conservation of Nature and Natural Resources, 9th Technical Meeting, Nairobi (1963).

Mehra, K. L., K. C. Kanodia, and R. N. Srivastava. 1975. Folk uses of plants for adornment in India. Econ. Bot. 29:39–46.

Mello, M. O. de A., C. F. da Costa, M. M. da S. Barbosa, and E. L. P. G. de Oliveira. 1971. Catálogo das plantas tóxicas e medicinais do estado da Bahia. Bol. Inst. Biol. Mar. Rio Grande Nor. 10:39–66.

Merchant, J. R., R. J. Shah, and S. N. Hirwe. 1962. Chemical investigation of *Eulophia nuda* Lindl. Current Sc. (India) 31:95.

Merck Index. 1960. The Merck index of chemicals and drugs. 7th ed. Ed. by A. G. Stecher, M. J. Finkel, and O. H. Siegmund. Merck & Co., Rahway, N.J.

Merrill, E. D. 1917. An interpretation of Rumphius' Herbarium amboinense. Department of Agriculture and Natural Resources, Bureau of Sciece, Manila, Pub. no. 9.

Meyerhof, M. 1940. Une glossaire de matière médicale du Maimonide. Mém. de l'Inst. d'Egypte 41:1–258.

Meyerhof, M., and G. P. Sobhy. 1937. The abridged version of "the book of simple drugs" of Ahmad ibn Muhammad al Ghâfiqê. Vol. 2. Faculty of Medicine, Egyptian University, Cairo.

Miethe, E. 1927. Die Einfuhr and Kultur, pp. 613–743. *In* R. Schlechter (ed.), Die Orchideen, 2d ed. P. Parey, Berlin.

Miller, H. H., J. F. Minier, H. E. Cutler, L. P. Willis, U. S. Andes, T. Muller, *et al.* 1912. Philippine baskets. Philipp. Craftsman 1:1–47.

Miller, J. 1722. Botanicum officinale. E. Bell, London.

Miller, M. A. 1959. Orchids of economic use. Amer. Orchid. Soc. Bull. 28:157–162, 269–271, 351–354.

Miller, P. 1739. The second volume of the Gardeners dictionary: which completes the work. P. Miller, London.

Millspaugh, C. F. 1887. American medicinal plants. Vol. 3. Boericke & Tofel, Philadelphia.

Mitchell, J., and A. Rook. 1979. Botanical dermatology. Greengrass, Vancouver.

Mitlacher, W. 1912. Die offizinellen Pflanzen und Drogen. C. Fromme, Vienna.

Moerman, D. E. 1977. American medical ethnobotany. Garland, New York.

Moldenke, H. N., and A. L. Moldenke. 1952. Plants of the Bible. Chronica Botanica, Waltham, Mass.

Moloney, M. F. 1919. Irish ethno-botany. M. H. Gill, Dublin.

Mooney, J. 1891. The sacred formulas of the Cherokees. 7th Annual Report, Bureau of American Ethnology, Smithsonian Institution (1885/86), pp. 301–397.

——. 1932. The Swimmer manuscript. Rev., compl., and ed. by F. M. Olbrechts. Bureau of American Ethnology, Smithsonian Institution, Bull. no. 99.

Moore, G. F. 1842. A descriptive vocabulary of the language in common use among the aborigines of western Australia. Suppl. to Diary of an early settler in western Australia, 1830–1841. W. S. Orr, London.

Moreno, R., and B. Schvartzman. 1975. 268 plantas medicinales utilizadas para regular la fecundidad en algunos paises de Sudamérica. Reproducción 2:163–183.

Morren, C. 1839. On the production of vanilla in Europe. Ann. Nat. Hist. 3:1–9.

——. 1845. Plantes nouvelles dont les descriptions sont publiées à l'étranger. Pt. 1. Ann. Soc. Roy. Agric. Bot. Gand 1:23–24.

——. 1846. Aperçu sur les orchidées et leur culture. Ann. Soc. Roy. Agric. Bot. Gand 2:238–344.

——. 1847a. Plantes nouvelles. Ann. Soc. Roy. Agric. Bot. Gand 3:19–20.

——. 1847b. Dendrobium moniliforme. Swartz. Ann. Soc. Roy. Agric. Bot. Gand 3:215–216.

——. 1849. Schomburgkia tibicinis. Batem. var. Grandifl. Lindl. Ann. Soc. Roy. Agric. Bot. Gand 5:413–414.

Morris, P. F. 1943. Vegetable foods of the Wimmera and Mallee. Vic. Nat. 59:167–170.

Mosig, A., and Schramm. G. 1955. Der Arzneipflanzen- und Drogenschatz Chinas und die Bedeutung des Pên-ts'ao kang-mu. Veb Verlag Volk und Gesundheit, Berlin.

Moult, J. 1769. A letter from Mr. J. Moult to Dr. Percival of Manchester, F.R.S., containing a new manner of preparing salep. Phil. Trans. Roy. Soc. Lond. 59:1–3.

Mountford, C. P. 1956. Art, myth, and symbolism, vol. 1 of Record of the American-Australian Scientific expedition to Arnhem Land. Melbourne University Press, Melbourne.

Mueller, F. 1858. Botanical report of the north-Australian expedition under the command of A. C. Gregory, Esq. J. Linn. Soc. Lond. Bot. 2:137–163.

Muenscher, W. C. 1940. Poisonous plants of the United States. Macmillan, New York.

Mühle, A. 1923. Orchideen. Gartenschönheit 4:1–4.

Murr, J. 1890. Die Pflanzenwelt in der griecheschen Mythologie. Wagner'scher Universitätsbuchhandlung, Innsbruck.

Murray, J. A. 1881. The plants and drugs of Sind. Richardson, London.

Nadkarni, A. K. 1954. Indian materia medica. 3d ed. Vol. 1. Popular Book Depot, Bombay.

Nagano, Y. 1952. Three main species of orchids in Japan. Amer. Orchid Soc. Bull. 21:787–789.

——. 1953. History of orchid growing in Japan. Amer. Orchid Soc. Bull. 22:331–333.

——. 1960. Orchids in Japan. Proc. 3d World Orchid Conf., London, 3:50–55.

Nair, D. M. N. 1963. The families of Burmese flowering plants. Vol. 2. Rangoon University Press, Rangoon.

Nance, J. 1975. The gentle Tasaday. Harcourt Brace Jovanovitch, New York.

Nava, J. N. 1952. Las plantas espontáneas útiles y perjudiciales de Guinea Española. Pt. 3. Farmacognosia Anales 12:191–240.

Needham, J. 1975. Science and civilization in China. Vol. 1. Cambridge University Press, Cambridge.

Needham, J., and L. Gwei-Djen. 1969. Chinese medicine, pp. 255–284. In F. N. L. Poynter (ed.), Medicine and culture. Wellcome Institute of the History of Medicine, London.

Nicholls, W. H. 1969. Orchids of Australia. Nelson, Melbourne.

Niles, G. G. 1904. Bog-trotting for orchids. Putnam, New York.

Nind, S. 1832. Description of the natives of King George Sound (Swan River Colony) and adjoining country. Geog. J. 1:21–51.

Noetling, F. 1911. The food of the Tasmanian aborigines. Papers Proc. Roy. Soc. Tas. for 1910, pp. 279–305.

Núñez Meléndez, E. 1964. Plantas medicinales de Puerto Rico. Estación Experimental Agrícola de Puerto Rico, Bull. no. 176.

Odebiyi, O. O., and E. A. Sofowora. 1978. Phytochemical screening of Nigerian medicinal plants. Pt. 2. Lloydia 41:234–246.

Officer, E. M. 1868. Vegetables used for food by the aborigines. Official Record of the Intercolonial Exhibition in Australasia, Melbourne, 1866–67, pp. 258–259.

Ohtsuki, T. 1937a. Studien über "Cremastramannan," das Mannan des japanischen Saleps. Acta Phytochim. 10:1–28.

——. 1937b. Untersuchungen über das Bletillamannan, ein Mannan aus den Knollen von Bletilla striata. Acta Phytochim. 10:29–41.

Oliver, D. L. 1955. A Solomon Island society. Harvard University Press, Cambridge.

Oliver-Bever, B. 1968. Drug plants in ancient and modern Mexico. Quart. J. Crude Drug Res. 8:1957–1972.

Osbeck, P. 1771. A voyage to China and the East Indies. Trans. by J. R. Foster. Benjamin White, London.

Osgood, F. S. (ed.). 1844. The poetry of flowers and flowers of poetry. J. C. Riker, New York.

Oxford classical dictionary. 1970. 2d ed. Ed. by N. G. L. Hammond and H. H. Scullard. Clarendon Press, Oxford.

Oxford English Dictionary. 1961. Corr. ed. Ed. by J. A. H. Murray, H. Bradley, W. A. Craigie, and C. T. Onions. Clarendon Press, Oxford.

Palmer E. 1883. On the plants used by the natives of North Queensland, Flinders, and Mitchell rivers, for food, medicine, etc. Proc. Roy. Soc. N.S.W. 17:93–113.

———. 1884. Notes on some Australian tribes. J. Anthrop. Inst. Gt. Brit. Irel. 13:276–347.

Pammel, L. H. 1910. Manual of poisonous plants. Torch Press, Cedar Rapids, Ia.

Panoff, F. 1970. A feminine costume in New Britain. J. Polynes. Soc. 79:99–106.

Pappe, L. 1857. Florae capensis medicae prodromus. 2d ed. W. Brittain, Cape Town.

Pardal, R. 1937. Medicina aborígena americana. J. Anesi, Buenos Aires.

Parham, H. B. R. 1940. Fiji plants, their names and uses. Memoir 16, installment 4. J. Polynes. Soc. 49:49–64 (suppl.).

———. 1941. Fiji plants, their names and uses. Memoir 16, installment 7. J. Polynes. Soc. 50:97–112 (suppl.).

———. 1943. Fiji native plants. Polynesian Society, Wellington.

Parker, L. 1913. Primitive Philippine basketry. Philipp. Craftsman 2:71–83.

———. 1914. Some common baskets of the Philippines. Philipp. Craftsman 3:1–25.

Parkinson, J. 1640. Theatrum botanicum. N.p., London.

Parkinson, S. 1784. A journal of a voyage to the South Seas in H.M. ship *Endeavour*. C. Dilly & J. Phillips, London.

Paullini, C. F. 1714. Dreck-Apotheke. Friedrich Knochen, Frankfurt.

Pausanias. 1918 (ca. A.D. 150). Description of Greece. Trans. by W. H. S. Jones. William Heinemann, London.

Paxton, J. 1844. Cattleya skinneri. Paxton's Mag. Bot. 11:193.

Payne, J. F. 1904. English medicine in the Anglo-Saxon times. Clarendon Press, Oxford.

Pei, C. 1951. Chinese medicinal plants. Vol. 1. Science Publications, Shanghai.

———. 1955. Chinese medicinal plants. Vol. 2. Science Publications, Shanghai.

Pempahishey, K. T. 1974. Orchid eaters of "Shangri-la." Amer. Orchid Soc. Bull 43:716–725.

Penna, M. 1941. Diccionario brasileiro de plantas medicinais. E. Eichner, Rio de Janeiro.

Percival, T. 1773. On the preparation, culture, and use of the Orchis root. *In* Essays medical and experimental, 2d ed., vol. 2, pp. 37–50. J. Johnson, London.

Pereira, J. 1850. The elements of materia medica and therapeutics. 3d ed. Vol. 2, pt. 1. Longman, Brown, Green & Longman, London.

Perera, S. J. 1940. The legend of the "daffodil orchid." Orchidol. Zeylan. 7:90–92.

Pérez de Barradas, J. 1951. Plantas mágicas americanas. Instituto Bernardino de Sahagún, Madrid.

Pernet, R. 1958. Les plantes médicinales Malgache. Mémoirs de l'Institut Scientifique de Madagascar, ser. B (Biologie végétale), 8:1–143, with suppls. 1–10.

Perrot, E. 1943a. Matières premières usuelles du règne végétal. Vol. 1. Masson, Paris.

———. 1943b. Plantes médicinales de France. Vol. 4. Presses Universitaires de France, Paris.

Perry, L. M., and J. Metzger. 1980. Medicinal plants of east and southeast Asia. M.I.T. Press, Cambridge, Mass.

Petek, F., J. E. Courtois, and M. Daloul. 1963. Identification de trois oligosaccharides isolés après hydrolyse acide partielle du salep de Syrie. Bull. Soc. Chim. Biol. 45:1261–1266.

Pételot, P. A. 1954. Les plantes médicinales du Cambodge, du Laos, et du Vietnam. Pt. 3. Arch. Rech. Agron. Pastorales Vietnam 22:1–347.

Petrie, C. C. 1932. Tom Petrie's reminiscences of early Queensland. 2d ed. Queensland Book Depot, Brisbane.

Pfitzer, E. 1903. Orchidaceae—Pleonandrae. *In* H. G. A. Engler (ed.), Das Pflanzenreich, vol. 12. W. Engleman, Leipzig.

Pharmacopoea Germanica. 1890. 3d ed. R. V. Deder, Berlin.

Pherecrates. 1880 (5th century B.C.). *In* T. Kock (ed.), Comicorum atticorum fragmenta, vol. 1, 131.4, p. 183. B. G. Teubner, Leipzig.

Phillips, E. P. 1917. A contribution to the flora of the Leribe Plateau and environs. Ann. So. Afric. Mus. 16:1–379.

Pickering, C. 1879. Chronological history of plants. Little, Brown, Boston.

Pijl, L. van der, and C. H. Dodson. 1969. Orchid flowers, their pollination and evolution. University of Miami Press, Coral Gables, Fla.

Pittier, H. 1926. Manual de las plantas usuales de Venezuela. Litografía del Comercio, Caracas.

Planchon, G., and E. Collin. 1895. Les drogues simples d'origine végétale. Octave Doin, Paris.

Planchon, L., P. Bretin, and P. Manceau. 1947. Précis de matière médicale. 15th ed. Vol. 1. Librairie Maloine, Paris.

Pliny the Elder. A.D. 77, trans. 1956. Naturalis historia. Vol. 7, bk. 26, 62.95–96. Trans. by W. H. S. Jones. Loeb Classical Library. William Heinemann, London; Harvard University Press, Cambridge.

Plowden, C. C. 1972. A manual of plant names. 3d (corr.) ed. George Allen & Unwin, London.

Polunin, O., and A. Huxley. 1965. Flowers of the Mediterranean. Chatto & Windus, London.

Portères, R. 1954. Le genre Vanilla et ses espèces. In G. Bouriquet (ed.), Le vanillier et la vanille dans le monde, vol. 46 of Encyclopédie biologique, pp. 94–290. P. Lechevalier, Paris.

Portman, M. V. 1899a. Use of orchid-bark for ornament. Kew Bull. 151/152:138–139.

———. 1899b. Use of orchid-bark for ornament. Orchid Rev. 7:266–267.

Powell, B. H. 1868. Handbook of the economic products of the Punjab. Vol. 1. Roorkee, Lahore.

Powell, J. M. 1976a. Ethnobotany. In K. Paijmans (ed.), New Guinea vegetation, pp. 106–183. Australian National University Press, Canberra.

———. 1976b. Some useful wild and domesticated plants of the Huli of Papua. Sci. in New Guinea 4:173–201.

Pradhan, U. C. 1977. Conserving Indian orchids. Amer. Orchid Soc. Bull. 46:117–121.

Prescott, W. H. 1904. History of the conquest of Mexico. J. B. Lippincott, Philadelphia.

Pringsheim, H., and A. Genin. 1924. Über die fermentative Spaltung des Salepmannans. Pt. 6. Zeitschr. Physiol. Chem. 144:299–304.

Pringsheim, H., and G. Liss. 1928. Über das Salep-mannan. Ann. Chem. 460:32–42.

Pseudo-Apuleius. (4th century A.D.). Corpus medicorum latinorum. Vol. 4. 1924. Ed. by E. Howald and H. E. Sigerist. B. G. Teubner, Leipzig.

Puerta, G. de la. 1891. Botánica descriptiva y determinación de las plantas indígenas y cultivadas en España de uso medicinal, alimenticio, e industrial. Administración de la Revista de Medicina y Cirugía Prácticas, Madrid.

Puydt, E. de. 1880. Les orchidées. J. Rothschild, Paris.

Quiggin, A. H. 1912. Textiles. In Arts and crafts, vol. 4 of Reports of the Cambridge Anthropological Expedition to Torres Straits, pp. 63–92. Cambridge University Press, Cambridge.

Quinn, V. 1938. Roots, their place in life and legend. Frederick A. Stokes, New York.

Quisumbing, E. 1951. Medicinal plants of the Philippines. Department of Agriculture and Natural Resources, Manila, Technical Bulletin no. 16.

Radcliffe-Brown, A. R. 1964. Andaman Islanders. Free Press, New York.

Rafinesque, C. S. 1828. Medical flora. Vol. 1. Atkinson & Alexander, Philadelphia.

———. 1830. Medical flora. Vol. 2. Atkinson & Alexander, Philadelphia.

Rageau, J. 1973. Les plantes médicinales de la Nouvelle Calédonie. Trav. et Doc. de l'O.R.S.T.O.M. 23 (Paris).

Rao, R. R. 1981. Ethnobotany of Meghalaya: medicinal plants used by Khasi and Garo tribes. Econ. Bot. 35:4–9.

Raponda-Walker, A., and R. Sillans. 1961. Les plantes utiles du Gabon. In Encyclopédie biologique, vol. 56. P. Lechevalier, Paris.

Rappaport, R. A. 1967. Pigs for the ancestors. Yale University Press, New Haven.

Ratzel, F. 1896. The history of mankind. Vol. 1. Trans. by A. J. Butler. Macmillan, London.

Ray, P. G., and S. K. Majumdar. 1976. Antimicrobial activity of some Indian plants. Ec. Bot. 30:317–320.

Rayner, E. 1977. Orchids and medicine. So. Afr. Orchid J. 8:120.

Read, B. E. 1936; Chinese medicinal plants. 3d ed. Miscellaneous Publications, Peking Natural History Bulletin.

Read, B. E., and J.-C. Liu. 1927. Plantae medicinalis sinensis. Flora sinensis, ser. A, vol. 1. Department of Pharmacology, Peking Union Medical College.

Redfield, K. 1928. Remedial plants of Tepoztlán: a Mexican folk herbal. J. Washington Acad. Sci. 18:216–226.

Reeve, T. M. 1981. Orchids of the Enga province, Papua New Guinea. Aust. Orchid Rev. 46:104–110.

Regnault, J. E. J. 1902. Médecine et pharmacie chez les chinois et chez les annamites. A. Challamel, Paris.

Reinikka, M. A. 1972. A history of the orchid. University of Miami Press, Coral Gables, Fla.

Renaud, H. P. J., and G. S. Colin. 1934. Glossaire de la matière médicale marocaine. Publ. Inst. Hautes-études Maroc. 21:1–218.

Retzius, A. J. 1764. Forsok med Svensk Salep. Kung. Vetensk. Akad. Handl. 25:245–246.

——. 1806. Flora oeconomica sueciae. Vol. 2. J. Lundblad, Lund.

Rhede tot Drakestein, H. A. 1692. Hortus indicus malabaricum. Vol. 11. Van Someren, van Dyck & Boom, Amsterdam.

——. 1703. Hortus indicus malabaricum. Vol. 12. Van Someren, van Dyck & Boom, Amsterdam.

Richter, W. 1965. The orchid world. Trans. by E. Launert. Ed. by P. F. Hunt. Studio Vista, London.

Ridley, H. N. 1893. On the flora of the eastern coast of the Malay Peninsula. Trans. Linn. Soc. Lond. Bot., ser. 2, 3:267–408.

——. 1896. The Orchidaceae and Apostasiaceae of the Malay Peninsula. J. Linn. Soc. Lond. Bot. 32:213–416.

——. 1902. Fruits of the Malay Peninsula. Agric. Bull. Straits Setts. Fed. M.S. 1:531–537.

——. 1906a. List of plants used as medicines. J. Roy. Asiatic Soc. Straits Br. 45:47–53.

——. 1906b. Malay drugs. Agric. Bull. Straits Setts. Fed. M.S. 5:245–254, 269–282.

——. 1907. Materials for a flora of the Malay Peninsula. Vol. 1. Methodist Publishing House, Singapore.

——. 1912. Spices. Macmillan, London.

——. 1921. Addendum to T. A. Sprague, Plant dermatitis. J. Bot. 59:308–310.

——. 1924. Monocotyledons, vol. 4 of The flora of the Malay Peninsula. L. Reeve, London.

Rifai, M. A. 1975. Extraordinary uses of orchids in Indonesia. Rpt. First ASEAN Orchid Cong., Kasetsart University, Bangkok.

Ripley, D. 1970. The sacred grove. Victor Gollancz, London.

Robinson, C. B. 1911. Philippine hats. Philipp. J. Sci. C Botany 6:93–131.

Robinson, G. A. 1831. Friendly mission: the Tasmanian journals of George Augustus Robinson. Ed. by N. J. B. Plomley. 1966. Halstead Press, Kingsgrove, N.S.W.

Roi, J. 1955. Traité des plantes médicinales chinoises. In Encyclopédie biologique, vol. 47. P. Lechevalier, Paris.

Roig y Mesa, J. T. 1945. Plantas medicinales, aromáticas, o venenosas de Cuba. Vol. 1. Ministerio de Agricultura, Havana.

Rolfe, R. A. 1893. The history of orchid hybridisation. Pt. 1. Orchid Rev. 1:3–6.

——. 1895. Vanillas of commerce. Kew Bull. 104:169–178.

——. 1896a. A revision of the genus Vanilla. J. Linn. Soc. Lond. Bot. 32:439–478.

——. 1896b. The Cypripedium group. Orchid Rev. 4:327–334.

Roque, J. M. 1941. Flora médica guatemalteca: apuntes para la materia médica de la República de Guatemala. Tipografía Nacional, Guatemala City.

Roques, J. 1809. Plantes usuelles, indigènes et exotiques. 2d ed. Vol. 2. J. Roques, Paris.

Rosenthal, D. A. 1862. Synopsis plantarum diaphoricarum. F. Enke, Erlangen.

Roth, H. L. 1899. The aborigines of Tasmania. 2d ed. F. King, Halifax, Eng.

Roth, W. E. 1901. String and other forms of strand. North Queensland Ethnography Bulletin no. 1. Government Printer, Brisbane.

——. 1903. Superstition, magic, and medicine. North Queensland Ethnography Bulletin no. 5. Government Printer, Brisbane.

——. 1904. Domestic implements, arts and manufactures. North Queensland Ethnography Bulletin no. 7. Government Printer, Brisbane.

——. 1907. Burial ceremonies and disposal of the dead. North Queensland Ethnography Bulletin no. 9. Rec. Aust. Mus. 6:365–403.

——. 1909. Fighting weapons. North Queensland Ethnography Bulletin no. 13. Rec. Aust. Mus. 7:189–211.

——. 1910. Decoration, deformation, and clothing. North Queensland Ethnography Bulletin no. 15. Rec. Aust. Mus. 8:20–54.

Royle, J. F. 1839. Illustrations of the botany and other branches of the natural history of the Himalayan Mountains and of the flora of Cashmere. Vol. 1. W. H. Allen, London.

——. 1853. A manual of materia medica and therapeutics. J. Churchill, London.

Roys, R. L. 1931. The ethnobotany of the Mayas. Department of Middle American Research Series, Pub. no. 2. Tulane University, New Orleans.

Rumphius, G. E. 1750. Herbarium amboinense. Vol. 6. M. Uytwerf, Amsterdam.

Rupp, H. M. R. 1969. The orchids of New South Wales. Facs. with suppl. by D. J. McGillivray. Flora of New South Wales, no. 48. National Herbarium, Sydney.

S., A. B. 1889. Salep. Notes and Queries, 7th ser., 7:35.

Safford, W. E. 1905. The useful plants of the island Guam. Contrib. U.S. Nat. Herb. 9:9–404.

Said, H. M. (ed.). 1969. Hamdard pharmacopoeia of Eastern medicine. Hamdard Academy, Karachi.

Saint-Germain, L. F. de. 1943. El libro de las medicinas particulares. Real Academia de Buenas Letras, Barcelona.

Sanders, D. J. 1978. Epipactus helleborine—a European import. Amer. Orchid Soc. Bull. 47:426–427.

Sargent, O. H. 1909. Notes on the life-history of Pterostylis. Ann. Bot. 23:265–274.

Sarma, P. J. 1931. Hindu medicine and its antiquity. Ann. Med. Hist., n.s. 3:318–324.

Satyavati, C. V., M. K. Raina, and M. Sharma (eds.). 1976. Medicinal plants of India. Vol. 1. Indian Council on Medical Research, New Delhi.

Sawer, J. C. 1892. Odorographia: a natural history of raw materials and drugs used in the perfume industry. Vol. 1. Gurney & Jackson, London.

Scardavi, A. 1963. Flora medicinale della provincia di Pavia. Atti Inst. Bot. Lab. Crittogam. Univ. Pavia 20:3–158.

Schauenberg, P., and R. Paris. 1977. Guide to medicinal plants. Trans. by M. P. Jones. Lutterworth Press, London.

Schell, O. 1901. Der Volksglauben im Bergischen. Arch. Rel. W. 4:305–337.

Schelpe, E. A. C. L. E. 1961. South African epiphytic orchids. Pt. 1. J. Bot. Soc. So. Africa 47:15–18.

——. 1966. An introduction to the South African orchids. Macdonald, London.

Schmalle, H., and B. M. Hausen. 1979. A new sensitizing quinone from lady slipper (*Cypripedium calceolus*). Naturwissensch. 66:527–528.

Schramm, G. 1956. Drogen und Heilpflanzen der altchinesischen Materia medica in der Therapie von Brust- und Magenkrebs. Pharm. Zentrahl. 95:184–187.

——. 1957. Über die Bedeutung der chinesischen Droge Pai-chi für die pharmazeutische Praxis Chinas. Pharmazie 12:103.

——. 1960. Antituberkulotika, Hamostyptika, Expektorantien, und Tonika der altchinesischen Materia medica. Acta Phytotherap. 7:44–53.

Schultes, R. E., and A. Hofmann. 1980. Plants of the gods. Hutchinson, London.

Schultes, R. E., and A. S. Pease. 1963. Generic names of orchids. Academic Press, New York.

Schumacher, C. F. 1826. Medicinsk plantelaere. C. F. Schumacher, Copenhagen.

Schweinfurth, C. 1959. Classification of orchids. *In* C. L. Withner (ed.), The orchids: a scientific survey, pp. 15–43. Ronald Press, New York.

Sebire, A. 1899. Les plantes utiles du Sénégal. J.-B. Baillière, Paris.

Seeman, B. 1852–1857. The botany of the voyage of H.M.S. *Herald*. Lovell Reeve, London.

Seltman, C. 1952. The twelve Olympians. Pan Books, London.

Senghas, K. 1970. Übersicht zur Systematik und Taxonomie der Gattung Epipactus. *In* K. Senghas and H. Sundermann (eds.), Probleme der Orchideengattung Epipactus, pp. 26–37. Zeitsch. Die Orchidee.

Sheldrake, T. 1759. Botanicum medicinale. N.p., London.

Shimadzu. 1935. Letter to the editor. Orchidol Zeylan, 2:83.

Sigerist, H. E. 1951. A history of medicine. Vol. 1. Oxford University Press, New York.

——. 1961. A history of medicine. Vol. 2. Oxford University Press, New York.

Silva Maia, E. J. da. 1942. Plantas monocotiledoneas brasileiras empregadas na medicina. Rev. Flora Med. 9:59–73.

Simmonds, P. L. 1854a. The medicinal plants of Australia. Pharm. J. 13:616–618.

——. 1854b. The commercial products of the vegetable kingdom. T. F. A. Day, London.

——. 1877. Curiosities of vegetable food. J. Appl. Sci. 8, no. 87:40–41.

——. 1891. The medicinal and other useful plants of Algeria. Am. J. Pharm. 63:8–12.

——. 1892. Chinese medicines. Bull Pharm. Detroit 6:23–26.

Simmons, J. T. 1979. A checklist of orchidaceae in Northern Territory. Orchadian 6:84–86.

Singer, C. 1927. The herbal in antiquity and its transmission to later ages. J. Hellen. Stud. 47:1–52.

Singh, M. P., S. B. Malla, S. B. Rajehandari, and A. Menandhar. 1979. Medicinal plants of Nepal— retrospects and prospects. Econ. Bot. 33:185–198.

Skeat, W. W. 1900. Malay magic. Macmillan, London.

Skinner, C. M. 1925. Myths and legends of flowers, trees, fruits, and plants. J. B. Lippincott, Philadelphia.

Slaytor, M. 1977. The distribution and chemistry of alkaloids in the Orchidaceae. *In* J. Arditti (ed.), Orchid biology: reviews and perspectives, vol. 1, pp. 95–115. Cornell University Press, Ithaca, N.Y.

Sloane, H. 1707. The natural history of Jamaica. Vol. 1. H. Sloane, London.

Small, J. 1919. The application of botany in the utilization of medicinal plants. Pharm. J. 103:199–201.

Smith, E. 1729. The compleat housewife; or accomplished gentlewoman's companion. 2d ed. J. Pemberton, London.

Smith, E. L. 1923. The histology of certain orchids with reference to mucilage secretion and crystal formation. Bull. Torrey Bot. Club 50:1–17.

Smith, E. P. 1920. Plant dermatitis. J. Bot. 58:173–176.

Smith, F., and R. Montgomery. 1959. The chemistry of plant gums and mucilages. Reinhold, New York.

Smith, F. P. 1871. Contributions towards the materia medica and natural history of China. American Presbyterian Mission Press, Shanghai.

Smith, H. H. 1923. Ethnobotany of the Menomini Indians. Bull. Public Mus. City Milwaukee 4:1–174.

———. 1928. Ethnobotany of the Meskwaki Indians. Bull. Public Mus. City Milwaukee 4:175–326.

———. 1932. Ethnobotany of the Ojibwe Indians. Bull. Public Mus. City Milwaukee 4:327–525.

———. 1933. Ethnobotany of the forest Potawatomi Indians. Bull. Public Mus. City Milwaukee 7:1–230.

Smith, J. 1882. Dictionary of popular names of economic plants. Macmillan, London.

Smith, J. J. 1927. Orchids of utility. Orchid Rev. 35:323.

———. 1930. Malayan and Papuan jewel orchids. Orchid Rev. 38:3–9.

———. 1939. The genus Grammatophyllum. Orchidol. Zeylan. 6:33–36.

Smyth, R. B. 1876. The aborigines of Victoria. Vol. 1. Government Printer, Melbourne.

Soubeiran, J. L., and D. de Thiersant. 1874. La matière médicale chez les chinois. G. Masson, Paris.

Soysa, E. 1934. The romance of the orchid. Orchidol. Zeylan. 1:104–111.

——— (ed.). 1943. Orchid culture in Ceylon. Orchid Circle of Ceylon, Colombo.

Spae, D. 1847. Sobralia macrantha Lindl. Ann. Soc. Roy. Agric. Bot. Gand 3:129–130.

Specht, R. L. 1958. An introduction to the ethnobotany of Arnhem Land. In R. L. Specht and C. P. Mountford (eds.), Botany and plant ecology, vol. 3 of Record of the American-Australian Scientific Expedition of Arnhem Land, pp. 479–503. Melbourne University Press, Melbourne.

Speck, F. G. 1915. Medicine practices of the northeastern Algonquians. Proc. 19th Inter. Cong. Americanists: 303–321.

Sprague, T. A. 1928. The herbal of Otto Brunfels. J. Linn. Soc. Lond. Bot. 48:79–124.

Sprague, T. A., and E. Nelmes. 1928. The herbal of Leonhart Fuchs. J. Linn. Soc. Lond. Bot. 48:545–642.

Sprague, T. A., and M. S. Sprague. 1939. The Herbal of Valerius Cordus. J. Linn. Soc. Lond. Bot. 52:1–113.

Sprengel, C. (ed.). 1826. Systema vegetabilum. 16th ed. Vol. 3. Libraria Dieterichiana, Gottingen.

Standley, P. C. 1930. Flora of Yucatan. Field Museum of Botany, Chicago. Pub. no. 279, ser. 3, pp. 157–492.

Staner, R., and R. Boutique. 1937. Matériaux pour l'étude des plantes médicinales indigènes du Congo Belge. M. Hayez, Brussels.

Starzecka, D. C., and B. A. L. Cranstone. 1974. The Solomon Islanders. Trustees of the British Museum, London.

Stearn, W. T. 1960. Two thousand years of orchidology. Proc. 3d World Orchid Conf., London, 3:26–42.

———. 1976. From Theophrastus and Dioscorides to Sibthorp and Smith: the background and origin of the flora graeca. Biol. J. Linn. Soc. Lond. 8:285–298.

Steedman, E. V. 1930. Ethnobotany of the Thompson Indians of British Columbia. 45th Annual Report, Bureau of American Ethnology, Smithsonian Institution (1927–28), pp. 441–522.

Steenis, C. G. S. van. 1958. Magic plants of the Dayak. Sarawak Mus. J. 8:432–436.

Steenis-Kruseman, M. J. 1953. Select Indonesian medicinal plants. Bull. no. 18, Organization for Scientific Research in Indonesia, Djakarta.

Steggerda, M., and B. Korsch. 1943. Mayan remedies for diseases. Bull. Hist. Med. 13:54–82.

Steinmetz, E. F. 1957. Codex vegetabilis. E. F. Steinmetz, Amsterdam.

Sterly, J. 1970. Heilpflanzen der Einwohner Melanesiens. In Hamburger Reithe zur Kultur- und sprachwissenschaft, vol. 6. Klaus Renner, Munich.

———. 1973. Krankheiten und Krankenbehandlung bei den Chimbu im zentralen Hochland von Neu-Guinea. Arbeitsgemeinschaft Ethnomedizin, Hamburg.

———. 1974/75. Useful plants of the Chimbu, Papua New Guinea. Ethnomedizin 3:353–394.

Stewart, J., and R. Campbell. 1970. Orchids of tropical Africa, W. H. Allen, London.

Steyn, D. G. 1950. Recent investigations into the toxicity of known and unknown poisonous plants in the Union of South Africa. Onderstepoort J. Vet. Sc. 24:53–56.

Stone, E. 1962. Medicine among the American Indians. Hafner, New York.

Story, R. 1958. Some plants used by the Bushman in obtaining food and water. Botanical Survey Memoir no. 30. Division of Botany, Department of Agriculture, Pretoria.

Straatmans, W. 1971. An ethno-botanical checklist of New Guinea. New Guinea Research Unit, Australian National University, Port Moresby.

Strathern, A., and M. Strathern. 1971. Self-decoration in Mount Hagen. Duckworth, London.

Stuart, G. A. 1911. Chinese materia medica. American Presbyterian Mission Press, Shanghai.

Stutley, M., and Stutley, J. 1977. A dictionary of Hinduism. Routledge & Kegan Paul, London.

Sulit, M. D. 1934. Additional data on medicinal plants in the Maquiling National Park and vicinity. Makiling Echo (Laguna, The Philippines) 13:5–24.

Sulman, F. 1914. Wild flowers of New South Wales. Vol. 2. Angus & Robertson, Sydney.

Summerhayes, V. S. 1968. Wild orchids of Britain. 2d ed. Collins, London.

Sushruta Samhita. ca. 600 B.C., trans. 1907–1911 by K. K. L. Bhishagrata. 2 Vols. Bhishgrata, Calcutta.

Suzuki, H., and I. Keimatsu, 1932. Über die Alkaloide der chinesischen Droge "Chin-Shih-Hu." Pt. 2. J. Pharm. Soc. Japan 52:183–187 (German abstract), 1049–1060 (original Japanese).

Suzuki, H., I. Keimatsu, and M. Ito. 1932. Über die Alkaloide der chinesischen Droge "Chin-Shih-Hu." Pt. 1. J. Pharm. Soc. Japan 52:162–167 (German abstract), 996–1009 (original Japanese).

——. 1934a. Über die Alkaloide der chinesischen Droge "Chin-Shih-Hu." Pt. 3. J. Pharm. Soc. Japan 54:138–145 (German abstract), 801–819 (original Japanese).

——. 1934b. Nachtrag zum "Chin-Shih-Hu." J. Pharm. Soc. Japan 54:146–147 (German abstract), 820–823 (original Japanese).

Swainson, C. 1886. The folk lore and provincial names of British birds. Folk Lore Society, London.

Sweet, H. R. 1969. A revision of the genus Phalaenopsis. Pt. 7. Amer. Orchid Soc. Bull. 38:681–694.

Swinson, A. 1966. Kohima. 2d ed. Cassell, London.

——. 1970. Frederick Sander: the orchid king. Hodder & Stoughton, London.

Syrett, G. B. 1889. Coffee-house sign or title. Notes and Queries, ser. 7, 7:317.

Täckholm, V., and M. Drar. 1969. Flora of Egypt. Vol. 4. Cairo University Press, Cairo.

Takahashi, S., T. Namba, and Y. Hayashi. 1965. Anatomical studies on "chukanso." Jap. J. Pharmacog. 19:13–24.

Tanaka, J. 1976. Subsistence ecology of central Kalahari San, pp. 98–119. In R. B. Lee and I. De Vore (eds.), Kalahari hunter-gatherers. Harvard University Press, Cambridge.

Tanaka, T. 1976. Tanaka's cyclopedia of edible plants of the world. Keigoku, Tokyo.

Tantaquidgeon, G. 1928. Mohegan medicinal practices, weather-lore, and superstition, pp. 264–276. In F. G. Speck (ed.), Native tribes and dialects of Connecticut: a Mohegan-Pequot diary; 43d Annual Report, Bureau of American Ethnology, Smithson Institution (1925/26), pp. 199–287.

——. 1942. Study of Delaware Indian medicine practice and folk beliefs. Pennsylvania Historical Commission, Harrisburg.

Taylor, L. A. 1940. Plants used as curatives by certain southeastern tribes. Botanical Museum, Harvard University, Boston.

Taylor, R. 1848. A leaf from the natural history of New Zealand. N.p., Wellington.

——. 1870. A Maori and English dictionary. George T. Chapman, Auckland.

Tchihatcheff, P. de. 1860. Asie Mineure: description physique, statistique, et archéologique de cette contrée. Pt. 3. Gide, Paris.

Teirlinck, J. 1930. Flora magica. De Sikkel, Antwerp.

Terrac, M.-L. 1947. Contribution à l'étude des plantes médicinales de Madagascar, de la Réunion, et de l'île Maurice. P. Vuibert, Paris.

Tezozomoc, H. A. 1878. Crónica mexicana. Biblioteca mexicana. Ireneo Paz, Mexico City.

Theophrastus. ca. 300 B.C., trans. 1818. De historia plantarum, vol. 2 of Theophrasti eresii quae supersunt opera, bk. 9, 18.3–11. Trans. by J. G. Schneider. F. C. G. Vogel, Leipzig.

——. ca. 300 B.C., trans. 1916. Enquiry into plants. Vol. 2. Trans. by A. Hort. Loeb Classical Library. William Heinemann, London; Putnam, New York.

Thomale, H. 1957. Die orchideen. Eugen Ulmer, Stuttgart.

Thomas, N. W. 1906. Natives of Australia. Constable, London.

Thompson, R. C. 1924. The Assyrian herbal. Luzac, London.

——. 1949. A dictionary of Assyrian botany. British Academy, London.

Thomson, R. B., and H. B. Sifton. 1922. A guide to the poisonous plants and weeds of Canada and the northern United States. University of Toronto Press, Toronto.

Thorndike, L. 1924. Disputed dates, civilization and climate, and traces of magic in the scientific treatises ascribed to Theophrastus, pp. 73–86. *In* C. Singer and H. E. Sigerist (eds.), Essays on the history of medicine presented to Karl Sudhoff. Seldwyla, Zurich.

——. 1946. The herbal of Rufinus. University of Chicago Press, Chicago.

Thornton, R. J. 1810. New family herbal. R. Phillips, London.

Thozet, A. 1866. Notes on some of the roots, tubers, bulbs, and fruits used as vegetable food by the aborigines of northern Queensland, Australia. W. H. Buzzacott, Bulletin Office, Rockhampton.

——. 1868. List of some of the roots and fruits used as vegetable food by the aborigines of northern Queensland, Australia. Official Record of the Intercolonial Exhibition in Australasia, Melbourne, 1866–67, pp. 259–263.

Threlkeld, C. 1727. Synopsis stirpium hibernicorum. F. Davys, R. Norris & J. Worrall, Dublin.

Tiemann, F., and W. Haarmann. 1874. Über das Coniferin und seine Umwandlung in das aromatische Princip der Vanille. Ber. Deut. Chem. Ges. 7:608–623.

Timbs, J. 1861. Something for everybody. Lockwood, London.

——. 1868. Curiosities of London. Longmans, Green, Reader & Dyer, London.

——. 1872. Clubs and club life in London. Chatto & Windus, London.

Times atlas. 1972. The Times altas of the world. 4th ed. The Times, London; John Bartholomew, Edinburgh.

Tindale, N. B. 1926. Natives of Groote Eylandt and of the west coast of the Gulf of Carpentaria. Pt. 2. Rec. So. Aust. Mus., 1925–1928, 3:103–134.

Toni, E. de. 1901. Le plante lincea, cesia, columnia, stelluta e barberina. Mem. Accad. pontif. Nuovi Lincei 18:349–361.

Train, P., J. R. Henricks, and W. A. Archer. 1957. Medical uses of plants by Indian tribes of Nevada. Contrib. Flora Nevada 45:1–139.

Treide, B. 1967. Wildpflanzen in der Ernährung der Grundbevölkerung Melanesiens, vol. 16 of Veröffentlichungen des Museums für Völkerkunde zu Leipzig. Verlag Akademie, Berlin.

Tschirch, A. E. 1912. Handbuch der Pharmakognosie. Vol. 2, pt. 1. C. H. Tauchnitz, Leipzig.

Tsudsioka, S., and J. Murai. 1883. Catalogue of the collection of Japanese and Chinese drugs. N.p., Tokyo.

Tu, Y.-c. (ed.). 1933. Chih wu hsüeh tz'u tien. Commercial Press, Shanghai. Rpt. 1950, Shang wu yin shu kuan, Hong Kong.

Tucakov, J., N. Krstić, and M. Gorunović. 1962. Važnije lekovito bilje na području Leskovačkog sreza (Les plantes médicinales les plus importantes de la région du département Leskovac). Acta Pharm. Jug. 12:103–107.

Tuer, A. W. 1885. Old London street cries. Field & Tuer, London.

Turner, F. 1903. Botany of the Darling. Proc. Linn. Soc. N.S.W. 28:406–442.

Turner, J. B. 1965. Ethnobotanical notes on Simaba in central Brazil. Harvard Uni. Bot. Mus. Notes 21:59–64.

Turner, N. C., and M. A. M. Bell. 1971. The ethnobotany of the Coast Salish Indians of Vancouver Island. Econ. Bot. 25:63–99.

——. 1973. The ethnobotany of the Southern Kwatkiutl Indians of British Columbia. Econ. Bot. 27:257–310.

Turner, W. 1548. The names of herbes. J. Daye & W. Seres, London.

——. 1551. A new herball. S. Mierdman, London.

U.S. Bureau of the Census. 1974. U.S. Imports for Consumption. Report FT 146 (May). Government Printing Office, Washington.

Uhe, G. 1974. Medicinal plants of Samoa. Econ. Bot. 28:1–30.

Uniyal, M. R. 1968. Medicinal plants of the Bhagirathi Valley lying in the Uttarkashi forest division of Uttar Pradesh. Indian Forest. 94:407–420.

Uphof, J. C. 1959. Dictionary of economic plants. J. Cramer, Weinheim.

Urbina, M. 1903a. Notas acerca de las tzauhtli u orquídeas mexicanas. Ann. Mus. Nacion. Mex., ser. 2, 1:54–84.

——. 1903b. Notes about the tzauhtli. Orchid J. 1:215, 1952. (An abbreviated translation of 1903a by R. Oberg.)

Usher, G. 1974. A dictionary of plants used by man. Constable, London.

Uyldert, M. 1971. De teal der kruiden. A. J. G. Strengholt, Naarden.

Vacherot, M. 1954. Les orchidées. J.-B. Baillière, Paris.

Valenzuela, P., J. A. Concha, and A. C. Santos. 1949. Constituents, uses, and pharmacopoeias of some Philippine medicinal plants. Philipp. J. For. 6:39–111.

Vaughn, L., and V. Vaughn. 1973. An account of moth orchids: the beginning years. Amer. Orchid Soc. Bull. 42:4–12.

Venette, N. 1762. La génération de l'homme ou tableau de l'amour conjugal, considéré dans l'état du mariage. Vol. 1. N.p., London.

Vergiat, A. M. 1970. Plantes magiques et médicinales des féticheurs de l'Oubangui. J. Agric. Trop. Bot. Appl. 17:295–339.

Vidal, J. 1960. Les plantes utiles de Laos. J. Agric. Trop. Bot. Appl. 7:417–446.

Vogel, R. A. 1760. Historia materiae medicae, N.p., Leipzig.

Vogel, V. J. 1970. American Indian medicine. University of Oklahoma Press, Norman.

Vöth, W. 1973. Salep im turkischen Speiseeis. Orchidee 24:29–32.

Wagner, D. 1828. Pharmaceutisch-medicinische Botanik. D. Wagner, Vienna.

Walden, B. M. 1977. Wild flowers of Hong Kong. Sino-American, Hong Kong.

Waller, J. A. 1822. A new British domestic herbal. E. Cox, London.

Walterida. 1916. Legende van de orchidee. Reflector Weekblad 1:1235–1236 [Batavia (now Jakarta)].

Ward, J. D. U. 1937. Our forefathers ate spiders! John O'London's Weekly 38 (977):569–570, 579, 578.

Ward, K. 1928. Manipur. The Times, London, 14 November, p. 17.

Warner, W. L. 1937. A black civilization. Harper, New York.

Watling, H. 1928. Researches into Chinese orchid history. Orchid Rev. 36:295–304.

Watt, G. 1889. Dictionary of the economic products of India. Vol. 2. Superintendent of Government Printing, Calcutta.

——. 1890. Dictionary of the economic products of India. Vol. 3. Superintendent of Government Printing, Calcutta.

——. 1891. Dictionary of the economic products of India. Vol. 5. Superintendent of Government Printing, Calcutta.

——. 1893. Dictionary of the economic products of India. Vol. 6, pt. 2. Superintendent of Government Printing, Calcutta.

Watt, J. M. 1967. African plants potentially useful in mental health. Lloydia 30:1–22.

Watt, J. M., and M. G. Breyer-Brandwijk. 1932. The medicinal and poisonous plants of southern Africa. Livingstone, Edinburgh.

——. 1962. Medicinal and poisonous plants of southern and eastern Africa. 2d ed. Livingstone, Edinburgh and London.

Wealth of India. 1950. Wealth of India: raw materials. Vol. 2. Ed. by B. N. Sastri. Council for Scientific and Industrial Research, New Delhi.

——. 1952. Wealth of India: raw materials. Vol. 3. Ed. by B. N. Sastri. Council for Scientific and Industrial Research, New Delhi.

——. 1959. Wealth of India: raw materials. Vol. 5. Ed. by B. N. Sastri. Council for Scientific and Industrial Research, New Delhi.

——. 1966. Wealth of India: raw materials. Vol. 7. Ed. by S. B. Deshaprabhu. Council for Scientific and Industrial Research, New Delhi.

——. 1969. Wealth of India: raw materials. Vol. 8. Ed. by A. Krishnamurthi. Council for Scientific and Industrial Research, New Delhi.

Webb, L. J. 1959. New records of medicinal plants used by the aborigines of tropical Queensland and New Guinea. Proc. Roy. Soc. Q'land. 71:103–110.

Webb, T. T. 1933. Aboriginal medical practice in East Arnhem Land. Oceania 4:91–98.

Wedeck, H. E. 1962. Dictionary of aphrodisiacs. Peter Owen, London.

Wehmer, C. 1929. Die Pflanzenstoffe. Vol. 1. Gustav Fischer, Jena.

Weiner, M. A. 1972. Earth medicine. Macmillan, New York.

Weiss, F. E. 1917. Seeds and seedlings of orchids. Annual Report and Transactions of the Manchester Microscopical Society, 1916 (1918), pp. 32–43.

Wellmann, N. 1905. Griechische Medizin. In W. Kroll (ed.), Die Altertumswissenschaft im letzten Vierteljahrhundert, pp. 144–153. O. R. Reisland, Leipzig.

Wells, A. H. 1919. The physiological active constituents of certain Philippine medicinal plants. Pt. 3. Philipp. J. Sci. 14:1–7.

West, A. P., and W. H. Brown. 1921. Philippine resins, gums, seed oils, and essential oils. In W. H. Brown (ed.), Minor products of Philippine forests. Bull. no. 22, vol. 2, pp. 7–224. Department of Agriculture and Natural Resources, Bureau of Forestry, Manila.

White, T. C. 1938. Some economic uses of orchids. Orchidol. Zeylan. 5:74–77.

Whitlaw, C. 1829. Whitlaw's new medical discoveries. Vol. 2. C. Whitlaw, London.

Wigand, A. 1863. Über die Deorganisation der Pflanzenzelle. Jahrb. Wiss. Bot. 3:115–182.

Williams, F. E. 1930. Orokaiva society. Oxford University Press, London.

———. 1938. Papuans of the Trans-Fly. Rpt. 1969. Oxford University Press, London.

Williams, J. G., A. E. Williams, and N. Arlott. 1978. A field guide to the orchids of Britain and Europe with North Africa and the Middle East. Collins, London.

Williams, S. W. 1874. A syllabic dictionary of the Chinese language. American Presbyterian Mission Press, Shanghai.

Williamson, J. 1955. Useful plants of Nyasaland. Government Printer, Zomba. Rpt. 1972 as Useful plants of Malawi.

Williamson, R. W. 1912. The Mafulu Mountain people of British New Guinea. Macmillan, London.

Wilson, E. H. 1913. A naturalist in western China. Vol. 2. Methuen, London.

Wise, T. A. 1867. Review of the history of medicine. Vol. 1. J. Churchill, London.

Wit, H. C. D. de. 1977. Orchids in Rumphius' Herbarium amboinense. In J. Arditti (ed.), Orchid biology: reviews and perspectives, vol. 1, pp. 47–94. Cornell University Press, Ithaca, N.Y.

Withner, C. L. 1959. Introduction and History of Orchid Culture, pp. 3–14. In C. L. Withner (ed.), The orchids: a scientific survey. Ronald Press, New York.

Wong, K. C., and L.-t. Wu. 1936. History of Chinese medicine. 2d ed. National Quarantine Service, Shanghai. Rpt. 1973, AMS Press, New York.

Wong, M. 1968. Contribution à l'histoire de la matière médicale végétale chinoise. J. Agric. Trop. Bot. Appl. 15:158–197.

———. 1970. Contribution à l'histoire de la matière médicale végétale chinoise. J. Agric. Trop. Bot. Appl. 17:92–140.

Wood, H. C., J. P. Remington, and S. P. Sadtler. 1886. Wood and Bache's The dispensatory of the United States of America. 15th ed. J. B. Lippincott, Philadelphia.

Wood, J. J. 1977. Grammatophyllum scriptum. Orchid Rev. 85:323–327.

Woodville, W. 1792. Medical botany. J. Phillips, London.

Woolls, W. 1867. A contribution to the flora of Australia. F. White, Sydney.

———. 1879. Lectures on the vegetable kingdom, with special reference to the flora of Australia. C. E. Fuller, Sydney.

Wren, R. C. n.d. Potter's cyclopaedia of botanical drugs and preparations. 2d ed. Potter & Clarke, London.

Wright, J. S. 1906. A consideration of certain needed investigations in pharmacology. Proc. Indiana Acad. Sci. 1905:25–33.

Wright, W. 1787. An account of the medical plants growing in Jamaica. Lond. Med. J. 8:217–295.

Yacovleff, E., and F. L. Herrera. 1935. El mundo vegetal de los antiguos peruanos. Rev. Mus. Nac. Lima 4:31–102.

Yanovsky, E. 1936. Food plants of the North American Indians. Miscellaneous Publications, no. 237. U.S. Department of Agriculture.

Yearsley, G. G. 1976. Orchids—not just pretty flowers. Orchid Rev. 84:231–233.

Yen, D. E., and H. G. Gutierrez. 1976. The ethnobotany of the Tasaday. Pt. 1, The useful plants, pp. 97–136. In D. E. Yen and J. Nance (eds.), Further studies on the Tasaday. Panamin Foundation Research Series, no. 2. Panamin Foundation, Rizal.

Youngken, H. W. 1914. Pharmaceutical botany. Blakiston, Philadelphia.

Yule, H., and Burnell, A. C. 1903. Hobson-Jobson. New ed. Rpt. 1969. Routledge & Kegan Paul, London.

Yuncker, T. G. 1943. The flora in Niue Island. Bernice P. Bishop Mus. Bull. 178:1–126 (Honolulu).

Zepernick, B. 1972. Arzneipflanzen der Polynesier. Baessler-Archiv Beitrage zur Völkerkunst. N.s., suppl. D. Reimer, Berlin.

Zhou, J. H., F. Y. Fu, and H. P. Lei. 1965. Recent advances in the pharmacological research of medicinal plants in the People's Republic of China. Proc. 2d Inter. Pharmacol. Meeting, Prague (1963).

Zimmer, H. R. 1948. Hindu medicine. Johns Hopkins Press, Baltimore.

Zimmerman, J. G. 1764. Von der Erfahrung in der Arztenkunst. Heidegger, Zurich.

Zysk, K. 1979. In wider fields. Hemisph. Ann., pp. 200–205.

3

Orchid
Phytoalexins*

ALBERT STOESSL and JOSEPH ARDITTI

*In part, contribution No. 925 from the Research Centre, Agriculture Canada, London, Ontario, Canada, NGA 5B7. The literature survey pertaining to this chapter was concluded in January 1981. The chapter was submitted in March 1981, and the revised version was received in November 1981. Additions were made in 1982 and 1983.

Introduction: History of the Phytoalexin Concept

The concept of acquired immunity in plants seems to have originated at the turn of the century (Beauverie, 1910; Ray, 1901, Ward; 1902, 1905). The French botanist Noel Bernard, however, was probably the first researcher to recognize the phenomenon of induced chemical resistance to fungal infection in plants (Arditti, 1966; Bernard, 1909a, 1909b, 1911; Fisch, Schechter, and Arditti, 1972). While working with orchid mycorrhizae he observed that *Orchis morio* and *Loroglossum hircinum* tubers became resistant to further attacks following infection by *Rhizoctonia repens*. He suggested that immunity may have been involved and sought to determine its cause.

Bernard began his research by placing tissues from infected tubers on agar and introducing fungi. The hyphae grew toward the tissue but stopped 1 to 2 cm from it (Fig. 3-1). Following further experiments, Bernard concluded that the orchid tissue could produce a diffusible fungal inhibitor (Bernard, 1911; for reviews, see Arditti, 1979; Braun, 1963). Others confirmed his findings and showed that only living tissues could become resistant to infection (Burges, 1939; Gäumann, 1960, 1963-1964; Gäumann, Brown, and Bazzigher, 1950; Gäumann and Hohl, 1960; Gäumann and Jaag, 1945; Gäumann, Nüesch, and Rimpau, 1960; Gäumann and Kern, 1959a, 1959b; Magrou, 1924, 1936, 1938; Nobécourt, 1923, 1938). Magrou went as far as to compare the phenomenon to the production of antibodies by animals. Nobécourt showed that the defense reaction could be induced by fungal attack and that tubers killed by heating, freezing, or chloroform were incapable of reacting. He concluded (1923) that the defense compound was produced by orchids "under the influence of toxins secreted by certain fungi." Despite subsequent research (Burges, 1939) the early studies remained largely unnoticed at the time.

The next major development was the generalization of the concept of a dynamic, natural chemical defense of plants against infection, in a classic article that formally propounded the phytoalexin hypothesis (Müller and Börger, 1940). The article was based on experimental results, mainly from studies of the interaction between potatoes and *Phytophthora infestans*, but much of the hypothesis was speculative. In particular, the postulates employed to define the term "phytoalexin" as "plant warding-off substance," used for the first time by Müller and Börger in 1940, were idealized considerably. Evidence gained subsequently, mainly in experiments with potatoes, French beans, and peas, led to revisions of earlier concepts both by the original proponent of the hypothesis (Müller, 1959, 1966, 1969) and by an Australian group that carried on Müller's work (Cruickshank, 1963). The latter in particular was very influential in generating the current widespread interest in phytoalexins. Definitions and other theoretical as well as practical aspects are still a subject of controversy. Perspectives on the ongoing debates and summaries of experimental studies that have appeared at a steadily accelerating pace since the late 1960s are provided in numerous reviews (Albersheim and Anderson-Prouty, 1975; Cruickshank, 1977; Deverall, 1977; Fawcett and Spencer, 1969; Grisebach and Ebel, 1978; Gross, 1975, 1977; Kúc, 1972, 1976; Loewus and Ryan, 1981; Mahadevan, 1973; Stoessl, 1972; West, 1981).

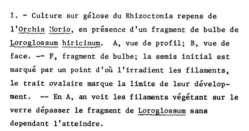

I. - Culture sur gélose du Rhizoctonia repens de
l'Orchis Morio, en présence d'un fragment de bulbe de
Loroglossum hircinum. A, vue de profil; B, vue de
face. -- F, fragment de bulbe; la semis initial est
marqué par un point d'où l'irradient les filaments,
le trait ovalaire marque la limite de leur dévelop-
ment. -- En A, an voit les filaments végétant sur le
verre dépasser le fragment de Loroglossum sans
dependant l'atteindre.

II. - Culture sur gélose du champignon de l'Orchis Mascula
en présence du bulbe de la même espèce. -- Le fragment de
bulbe est le rectangle à la base; le semis initial est le
point d'où s'irradient les filaments du champignon; la
première legne d'arrêt est marquée par des ramifications
répétées; les filaments séjournant sur le verre produisent
une invasion secondaire de la gélose; ils sont visibiles
plus bas sur le tube et se terminent par une deuxième
ligne d'arrét.

Fig. 3-1. The original figures and captions from Bernard's paper, which was the first to report on the existence of phytoalexins (Bernard, 1911).

One working definition, which probably reflects the current concepts of many researchers, is that phytoalexins are products of higher plant metabolism, absent from
healthy tissues or present only in negligible traces, which accumulate in significant
amounts in response to fungal or bacterial challenge (Stoessl, 1980). Another definition
by a group of scientists at a NATO Advanced Study Institute on Active Defense Mechanisms in Plants is that "phytoalexins are low molecular weight, antimicrobial compounds
that are synthesized by and accumulated in plants after exposure to microorganisms."
These compounds are synthesized de novo from common precursors such as acetic or
shikimic acid, but are not formed from more elaborate plant constituents through reactions such as hydrolysis or oxydation or by the action of fungal enzymes.

The compounds, of course, must show antifungal (or antibacterial) activity toward
plant pathogens in vitro, but, in addition, there should be at least a modicum of evidence
that they may be casually implicated in the disease resistance of the plants that produce
them, or, in orchids, at least in the regulation of mycorrhizae. By convention, the term
"phytoalexin" is limited to compounds of low molecular weight, of the kind commonly
regarded as secondary metabolites.

Many compounds that satisfy these criteria are now known from a range of higher
plants. Families are specific with respect to the chemical-biogenetic class or classes of
phytoalexins that they produce. Similarly, some classes of phytoalexins appear to be
family specific; others are more widely distributed. The phytoalexins of the Leguminosae, for example, are primarily pterocarpans and isoflavans, and no phytoalexins with
these structures have been found outside this family. A similar relation holds for the
phytoalexins of the Solanaceae, which are largely rearranged eudesmanes. On the other

hand, stilbenes have been found as phytoalexins in several different families, including the Leguminosae. The few known phytoalexins of the Orchidaceae are dihydrophenanthrenes.

Biogenetically, phytoalexins are clearly an inhomogenous group. That is, they are neither intrinsically related nor should they be regarded as the agents of one single defense mechanism (Stoessl, 1972, 1977, 1980), even if their effects are similar. The causes and mechanisms of their generation, as well as the extent to which they are involved in defensive functions, may not be the same in different plants. Extrapolations from the properties of one group of phytoalexins to those of another must therefore be treated with caution.

Orchid Phytoalexins: Distribution and Structure

Following several years of inactivity, research in Switzerland on the defensive reaction of orchids verified Nobécourt's work in studies of *Orchis militaris*. Subsequent intensive study by E. Gäumann and a number of collaborators led to the first intentional isolation of a postinfectional defensive agent; this crystalline substance, obtained from *Orchis militaris* (Boller *et al.*, 1957), was named orchinol. Although Müller's hypothesis had been published some thirteen years earlier, orchinol was not termed a phytoalexin at the time of its discovery. It was called Abwehrstoff (Abwehr, "defense" or "warding off"; Stoff, "substance") or Antikörper ("antibodies"; Gäumann and Jaag, 1945). The first substance to be deliberately isolated and described as a phytoalexin was pisatin (Cruickshank and Perrin, 1960; Perrin and Bottomley, 1961). Compounds now regarded as phytoalexins were known even earlier, although they were not isolated in the course of a search for defensive agents; these compounds include the stilbene pinosylvin from pines (Jorgensen, 1961) and the sesquiterpene ipomeamarone from *Ipomoea batatas* (Kúc, 1972; Uritani and Akazawa, 1955).

Orchinol (I) was isolated from tubers of *Orchis militaris* which were infected with *Rhizoctonia repens*. The yield was approximately 3 g of pure orchinol from 10 kg of tubers (Boller *et al.*, 1957). Subsequent analytical estimations indicated that tissue concentrations of orchinol can be as high as 0.92 g/kg (Gäumann and Hohl, 1960).

The structure of orchinol (I) was initially investigated by classical methods (Gäumann and Kern, 1959a; Hardegger, Schellenbaum, and Corrodi, 1963) and the information obtained was compatible with only two possible structures: either 2,4-dimethoxy-7-hydroxy-9,10-dihydrophenanthrene (I) or the 6-hydroxy isomer (II; the structures of compounds represented by roman numerals are shown in the five Structures Groups.) The latter was preferred on biogenetic grounds and the corresponding dehydro compound, 2,4-dimethoxy-6-hydroxyphenanthrene (III), was therefore synthesized by two different methods (Hardegger, Biland, and Corrodi, 1963; Hardegger, *et al.*, 1963). Direct comparison of the dehydro compound III with the product obtained by dehydrogenation of orchinol, however, showed that they were not identical; orchinol was therefore represented by I and dehydroorchinol by IV. This finding was proved correct by further spectroscopic and synthetic studies (Bowden *et al.*, 1975; Fisch and Arditti, 1972; Fisch, Flick, and Arditti, 1973; Letcher and Nhamo, 1973a; Müller *et al.*, 1974; Stoessl, Rock, and Fisch, 1974).

In subsequent work, orchinol was found by paper chromatographic methods in several European orchids in amounts that differ within and between genera (Table 3-1). For example, none of the *Ophrys* species screened produced orchinol, but all those of *Serapias* did. Within the genus *Loroglossum, L. longibracteatum* produced large amounts, whereas *L. hircinum* synthesized very little (Table 3-1). In about half the instances, the amounts detected exceeded those in *O. militaris* under the same conditions. All species that contain orchinol are members of the subfamily Orchideae. A few species that did not produce detectable amounts of orchinol included *Orchis maculata, O. ustulata,* and *Loroglossum hircinum.* Subsequently, however, traces of orchinol were found in *L. hircinum* tubers (Urech *et al.,* 1963).

	R_1	R_2	R_3	R_4	R_5	R_6
(I),	OMe	H	OMe	H	H	OH
(II),	OMe	H	OMe	H	OH	H
(V),	OMe	H	OMe	OH	H	H
(VI),	OH	H	OMe	OH	H	H
(XXXV),	OMe	H	OH	OH	OH	H
(XLII),	OMe	H	OMe	H	OMe	OH
(XLIII),	OMe	OMe	OMe	H	OMe	OH
(XLIV),	OH	OMe	OMe	H	OMe	OH
(XLV),	OH	OMe	OMe	H	OH	OH
(L),	OH	H	OH	H	H	H
(LII),	OH	H	OH	H	OH	H

Structures, group 1

	R_1	R_2	R_3	R_4	R_5	R_6
(III),	OMe	H	OMe	H	OH	H
(IV),	OMe	H	OMe	H	H	OH
(XIX),	OMe	H	OMe	OH	H	H
(XXXIII),	OMe	H	OMe	H	OH	OMe
(XXXIV),	OH	H	OH	OH	OH	H
(XXXVIII),	OMe	H	OMe	H	OMe	OH
(XXXIX),	OMe	OMe	OMe	H	OMe	OH
(XL),	OH	OMe	OMe	H	OMe	OH
(XLI),	OH	OMe	OMe	H	OH	OH
(XLIX),	OH	H	OH	H	H	H
(LI),	OH	H	OH	H	OH	H

Structures, group 2

A second major phytoalexin from orchids was reported as a product of *Loroglossum hircinum* (Hardegger, Schellenbaum, and Corrodi, 1963). The compound, loroglossol (V), is an isomer of orchinol (I). A yield of approximately 150 mg/kg was obtained from tubers of *L. hircinum* infected with *Rhizoctonia versicolor* (Urech *et al.,* 1963). The extracts contained considerably higher levels (250–400 mg/kg tuber tissue) of a third phytoalexin, hircinol (VI), a monodemethylloroglossol. Production of trace amounts of hircinol by *O. militaris* has also been reported (Urech *et al.,* 1963). The structures of the compounds were established by two independent groups a decade later. One of these groups (Letcher and Nhamo, 1973a) confirmed the structure of loroglossol (V) by an unambiguous synthesis of its O-acetyl derivative. They were then able to deduce the location of the second free hydroxy group in hircinol (VI) from its failure to form a seven-membered cyclic dioxymethylene ether when reacted with diiodomethane. The same

Table 3-1.   Synthesis of orchinol and of p-hydroxybenzyl alcohol in the bulbs of different orchids incubated with a *Rhizoctonia repens* strain from *Orchis militaris* L. (Nüesch, 1963, from Gäumann, Nüesch, and Rimpau, 1960)

Host species	Relative amounts of:	
	Orchinol	p-Hydroxybenzyl Alcohol
Aceras anthropophora (L.) R. Br.	+ +	+
Anacamptis pyramidalis (L.) Rich.	+ +	+ +
Chamaeorchis alpina (L.) Rich.	+ + +	+ +
Coeloglossum viride (L.) Hart.	+ + +	+ +
Gymnadenia albida (L.) Hartm.[a]	·+ + +	+ +
G. conopea (L.) R. Br.	?	?
G. odoratissima (L.) Rich.	+	+
Loroglossum hircinum (L.) Rich.[b]	+	+
L. longibracteatum (Biv.) Moris[c]	+ + +	+
Nigritella nigra (L.) Rchb.[d]	+ +	+
Ophrys apifera Huds.	0	0
O. arachnites (Scop.) Murray[e]	0	0
Orchis coriophora L.	?	+ +
O. latifolia L.	+	+ +
O. maculata L.	0	0
O. mascula L.	+ + +	+ +
O. militaris L.	+ +	+ +
O. morio L.	+ + +	+ + +
O. sambucina L.	+ + +	+ +
O. ustulata L.	0	?
Platanthera bifolia (L.) Rich.	0	0
Serapias lingua L.	+ + +	+ +
S. neglecta Not.	+ +	+ +
S. vomeracea Burm.	+ +	+ +

[a] *Coeloglossum albidum* Hartm.
[b] *Himantoglossum hircinum* Sprengel.
[c] *Barlia longibracteata* Parlat = *Aceras longibracteata* Rchg. = *Orchis longibracteata* Biv.
[d] *Nigritella angustifolia* Rich.
[e] *Ophrys fuciflora* Crantz.

structural conclusions were reached on the basis of a careful consideration of the IR, mass, and proton NMR spectra of orchinol, loroglossol, and hircinol (Fisch *et al.*, 1973).

A curious, though practically important feature is the weak phenolic character of the compounds, as reflected in their behavior on solvent extraction. Orchinol can be extracted by 2N NaOH from ether but not from ethyl acetate (Hardegger, Schellenbaum, and Corrodi, 1963). Loroglossol was not extracted even from ether by 1N NaOH, whereas hircinol was (Urech *et al.*, 1963).

Although the list of dihydrophenanthrene phytoalexins from orchids is now complete (phenanthrenes and dihydrophenanthrenes are known from other plant families but not as phytoalexins), a fourth compound is relevant, the red dermatogenic phenanthrenequinone cypripedin (VII), which was recently isolated from the lady slippers *Cypripedium calceolus* and *C. reginae* (Schmalle and Hausen, 1979*.) Its structure was determined by single-crystal X-ray analysis. The compound was obtained mainly from the leaves of the plant; there is no evidence that it was formed in the course of a defense reaction or that it has antifungal activity. Several other, presumably related pigments are still under investigation. The possible derivation of cypripedin from orchinol or an equivalent precursor by oxidation is suggested by the structure.

*See chapter on toxic and allergenic orchids in this volume. [Ed.]

$$Me-(CH_2)_4-\underset{\underset{H}{|}}{C}=\underset{\underset{H}{|}}{C}-CH_2-\underset{\underset{H}{|}}{C}=\underset{\underset{H}{|}}{C}-(CH_2)_7-CO-R$$

(VIII),   R = OH

(IX),   R = O — CH$_2$ — CH(OH) — CH$_2$OH

Structures, group 3

A careful search for phytoalexins in extracts from infected roots and pseudobulbs of *Cymbidium* hybrids did not detect even traces of phenanthrenes or related compounds. Two relatively weak antifungal substances were isolated and identified as linoleic acid (VIII) and its 1-monoglyceride (IX) (Stoessl, Fisch, and Arditti, 1980). It is uncertain to what extent the accumulation of these compounds occurred following fungal infection. Further, because they do not satisfy several other criteria of the hypothesis, they should not be regarded as phytoalexins.

Two interesting contradictions exist regarding the phenanthrene phytoalexins of orchids. One is the apparent diffusion of fungal inhibitors (probably orchinol) from orchid tubers into agar (Bernard, 1911), which contrasts with the inactivity of pure orchinol in this medium. A possible explanation for this phenomenon is that pure orchinol is insoluble but that it becomes soluble as a result of factors that may be present in tubers (Gäumann and Kern, 1959).

The second contradiction concerns the heat stability of orchid phytoalexins. In early reports they are described as being heat labile (Bernard, 1911; Burges, 1939; Nobécourt, 1923), which is not a property of orchinol and loroglossol. It is conceivable, however, that this phenomenon may also be due to the insolubility of these compounds—that is, that application of heat inactivates the factors or destroys the conditions that mediate their solubilization. Other explanations, however, are possible; in particular, the phenanthrenes may not be the only or most important resistance agents in the orchid tubers. Indeed, their causal involvement has still not been established definitively.

Fungal infection of *Cymbidium* leads to increased concentrations of sitosterol, stigmasterol, and campesterol in a 14:5:1 ratio (Arditti *et al.*, 1975). These compounds have also been isolated from *Arundina* and *Cattleya* (Wan *et al.*, 1971). Assays of sitosterol, stigmasterol, and campesterol in liquid cultures of *Candida lipolytica* and on a TLC plate with *Cladosporium cucumerinum* have shown that these sterols are not very active (Arditti, 1979). Ergosterol peroxide, which is also found in the extracts, proved to be somewhat more inhibitory than the other three but most probably was an artifact of extraction (Arditti *et al.*, 1972; Fisch *et al.*, 1973). Further, the ergosterol itself is produced by the fungus. Thus the sterols cannot be considered phytoalexins.

Synthesis

All three of the orchid phytoalexins and several simple derivatives have been synthesized in the laboratory. With perhaps only one or two exceptions, standard routes of phenanthrene synthesis were employed (for a review of the extensive literature on phenanthrene synthesis, see Floyd *et al.*, 1976; for more recent modifications and new routes, Bendig *et al.*, 1977; Evans *et al.*, 1977; Kende and Curran, 1978; Liepa and Summons, 1977; McDonald and Martin, 1978, and Tochtermann *et al.*, 1977).

The first synthesis in the series, that of dehydroorchinol (IV), was accomplished by Hardegger and co-workers but was not published for more than ten years (Müller *et al.*, 1974). 2-Acetyl-6-methoxynaphthalene was converted, via a Willgerodt reaction, into (6-hydroxy-2-naphthyl)acetic acid. A malonic ester synthesis with the 6-benzylether of the derived acid chloride furnished α-ethoxycarbonyl-γ-(6-benzyloxy-2-naphthyl)acetoacetic acid ester, which was cyclized to 7-benzyloxy-2,4-dihydroxy-3-ethoxycarbonylphenanthrene. Saponification, accompanied by decarboxylation, gave the 7-benzyl ether of IV in unspecified though evidently low yield. The methyl ether of IV was synthesized in analogous fashion from (6-methoxy-2-naphthyl)acetic acid. The benzyl ether resisted hydrogenolysis, as also noted by others (Stoessl, Rock, and Fisch, 1974), but could be cleaved to dehydroorchinol (IV) in approximately 25% yield by hydrochloric acid in acetic acid. It was converted into orchinol (I) in low yield by reduction to orchinol benzylether with sodium amide/hydrazine, followed by hydrogenolysis of this ether over Pd/C (Steiner *et al.*, 1974).

In an alternative approach, this group obtained orchinol (I) more directly but, apparently, serendipitously. 1,2-Dihydro-5,7-dimethoxynaphthalene (X) was converted into 6,8-dimethoxy-2-tetralone (XI) by oxidation with perbenzoic acid. Condensation of crude XI with methylvinyl ketone unexpectedly gave orchinol in a 1.8% yield. No orchinol (I) was obtained when pure XI was employed for the condensation. It was therefore suggested that the perbenzoic acid oxidation of X afforded a small amount of side product such as 6,8-dimethoxy-1-hydroxy-2-tetralone (XII), which would account for the observed formation of orchinol (Steiner *et al.*, 1974).

Structures, group 4

In another annelation study by Hardegger's group, which was published only in thesis form (Seres, 1964), 6,8-dimethoxy-1-tetralone (XIII) gave the 1-hydroxy-1-acetylide XIV, which was converted to the diene XV. This reportedly underwent a Diels-Alder reaction with vinyl acetate to give an adduct from which O-acetyl dehydroorchinol was obtained in 44% yield on dehydrogenation. The latter compound was converted, with difficulty, into dehydroorchinol (IV) by lithium aluminum hydride reduction. (Other workers, however, have found that this deacetylation can be effected with ease by base [Stoessl, Rock, and Fisch, 1974]). The route, however, was considered unsatisfactory because the overall yield of IV was "extremely low" (Seres, 1964).

Orchinol methyl ether, the O-methyl derivative of orchinol (I), has also been obtained by a new, general approach to the synthesis of dihydrophenanthrenes (Bowden *et al.*, 1975). The dihydroindole XVI, obtainable from 3,5-dimethoxyphenacyl bromide and *p*-anisidine in two steps, was hydrogenolyzed to XVII, which furnished the azosulfone XVIII on diazotization and treatment with sodium *p*-toluenensulfinate. Orchinol methyl ether was obtained by decomposing XVIII in boiling pyridine; the overall yield from phenacyl bromide was 2%.

Other successful routes to the orchid phenanthrenes have exploited the well-known photocylization of stilbenes. 2,4-Dimethoxy-7-phenanthryl acetate, the O-acetyl derivative of dehydroorchinol (IV), was obtained by oxidative photocylization of 3'-acetoxy-3,5-dimethoxystilbene, itself synthesized by Perkin condensation from 3,5-dimethoxyphenylacetic acid and 3-hydroxybenzaldehyde, followed by acetylation and decarboxylation (Letcher and Nhamo, 1973b). Dehydroorchinol acetate was the only product isolated from the photoreaction. The overall yield from the phenylacetic acid was approximately 7.5%. Attempts to reduce the compound to orchinol acetate by hydrogenation led to indiscriminate reduction of the aromatic rings. In the same communication, the authors report the successful synthesis of O-acetylloroglossol, using the approach employed earlier by the Zurich group (Hardegger, Biland, and Corrodi, 1963) for the synthesis of 2,4-dimethoxy-6-hydroxyphenanthrene (III). α-(3,5-Dimethoxyphenyl)-3-hydroxy-2-nitrocinnamic acid, again obtained by a Perkin condensation from 3,5-dimethoxyphenylacetic acid and 3-hydroxy-2-nitrobenzaldehyde, was reduced to the amino acid. On diazotization and intramolecular coupling, the phenanthrene-10-carboxylic acid was produced, which was decarboxylated after acetylation, to 3,5-dimethoxy-5-acetoxyphenanthrene (dehydroloroglossol acetate). In this case, hydrogenation over a Pt catalyst was successful, affording the O-acetylloroglossol in 6.6% yield from the phenylacetic acid.

Orchinol and loroglossol were obtained shortly afterward by a method that differed from that of Letcher and Nhamo only in details and for the first time afforded a practically useful route to the compounds (Stoessl, Rock, and Fisch, 1974). The same starting material, 3'-acetoxy-3,5-dimethoxystilbene, was used but prepared by a Wittig reaction from 3,5-dimethoxybenzyl chloride and 3-hydroxybenzaldehyde in 78% yield. Irradiation of the stilbene yielded dehydroorchinol acetate (28%) and dehydroloroglossol acetate (31%) after isolation by crystallization combined with chromatography. These compounds were hydrogenated without difficulty to orchinol acetate and loroglossol acetate, respectively, which, in turn, were hydrolyzed essentially quantitatively to orchinol (I) and loroglossol (V). The reasons for qualitative and quantitiative differences from the results of Letcher and Nhamo have not been clarified. Possible reasons are the use of Pyrex glass instead of quartz in the irradiation step and of Pd as catalyst in place of Pt for the hydrogenation. In a variation of the method, the 3'-benzyloxy-3,5-dimethoxystilbene was irradiated; the benzyl ethers of dehydroorchinol (IV) and dehydroloroglossol (XIX) were obtained in 55% yield in a ratio of 7:3. These resisted hydrogenation as well as hydrogenolysis but were converted to I and V respectively by irradiation in the presence of tributyl tin hydride (Stoessl, Rock, and Fisch, 1974). Partial demethylation of loroglossol (V) with boron tribromide furnished a small amount of hircinol (VI) which completed the formal synthesis of all orchid phytoalexins.

Note: After this chapter was written, a practical synthesis of orchinol by a novel route was reported independently by Gunter and Mander (1981) and Krautwurst and Tochtermann (1981).

Biosynthesis and Biogenetic Relations

A very plausible though hypothetical biosynthetic route to orchinol (I) was suggested not long after its structure was elucidated (Birch, 1966). The pathway, with XXI and XXII as intermediates (Scheme 1a), would account equally well for the formation of loroglossol (V; Scheme 1b), the choice between the two products depending merely on which position, a or b, is attacked in the rearrangement of intermediate XXII. Hircinol (VI) differs from loroglossol (V) only in methylation state and is almost certainly its immediate biogenetic precursor, as indicated in the scheme.

An alternative hypothetical route to I (Scheme 2a) is very similar in principle but offers the advantage of greater enzyme economy because it does not necessitate a sequence of hydroxylation, reduction, and elimination. In order to account for the formation of V and VI, however, it is necessary to postulate o-coumaric acid (XXIII), instead of p-coumaric acid (XXIV), as a prime precursor, and compounds XXV and XXVI, instead of XX and XXVII, as advanced precursors (Scheme 2b). Precursor XX is common to three of these schemes (1a, 1b, and 2a).

A central concept common to the schemes, the intramolecular oxidative phenol coupling of a dihydrostilbene, followed by a cationic rearrangement, is supported by a substantial amount of indirect evidence drawn from phytochemical relationships observed in other plant families. The intermediate XX has the typical oxygenation pattern of a stilbene formed on the well-established route from phenylalanine (XXVIII) or tyrosine (XXIX) and malonyl coenzyme A (Billek, 1964; Hillis and Hasegawa, 1962; Rupprich and Kindl, 1978; Scheme 1). The intermediate XXV required by Scheme 2b could be furnished by o-hydroxylation either at the cinnamic acid (XXX) stage, as shown, or at the stilbene stage. Two dihydrostilbenes with a 2'-hydroxy group as sole substituent in ring B, batatasin IV (XXXI) and batatasin V (XXXII), are in fact known as metabolites of *Dioscorea batatas* (Hashimoto and Tajima, 1978).

Other metabolites of the *Dioscorea* family include the phenanthrene batatasin I (XXXIII) from *D. batatas* (Hashimoto et al., 1974) and four other phenanthrenes and dihydrophenanthrenes from *D. bulbifera* and *D. prazeri* (Ireland, Schwabe, and Coursey,

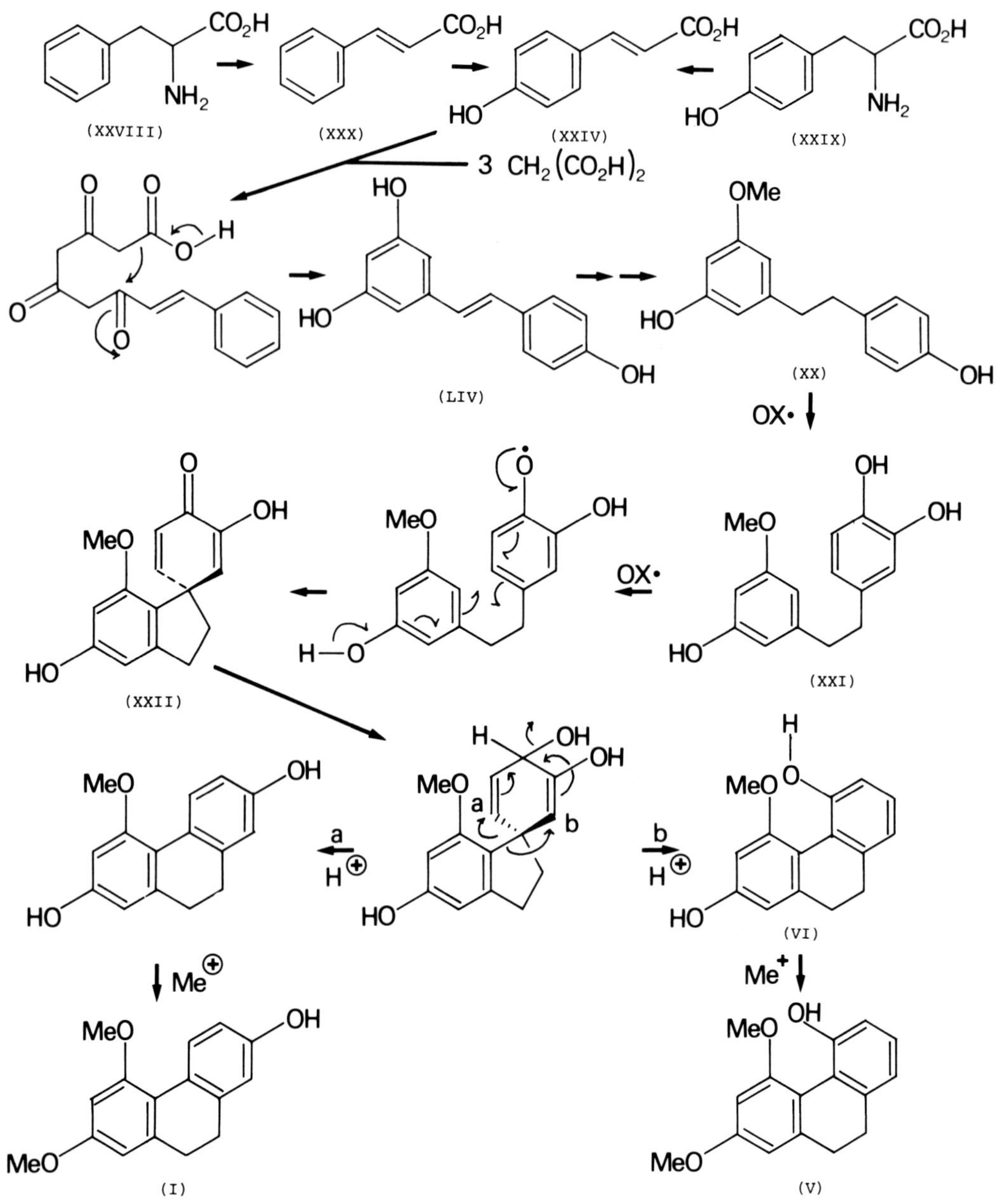

Scheme 1. A hypothetical biogenetic route to orchinol, hircinol, and loroglossol (modified from Birch, 1966)

1981; Rajaraman and Rangaswami, 1975; and Wij and Rangaswami 1978). It is significant that all five of these compounds carry hydroxy or methoxy groups at the 4, 6, and
either 5 or 7 positions (e.g., XXXIII, XXXIV, and XXXV); that is, their biosynthesis is
readily rationalized in terms of Schemes 2a or 2b, with the C-6 substituents introduced
either at the stilbene or phenanthrene stage. The routes depicted by Schemes 1a and 1b
appear somewhat less likely because they require that this substituent be introduced
after expulsion during the rearrangement of the spirodienone intermediate.

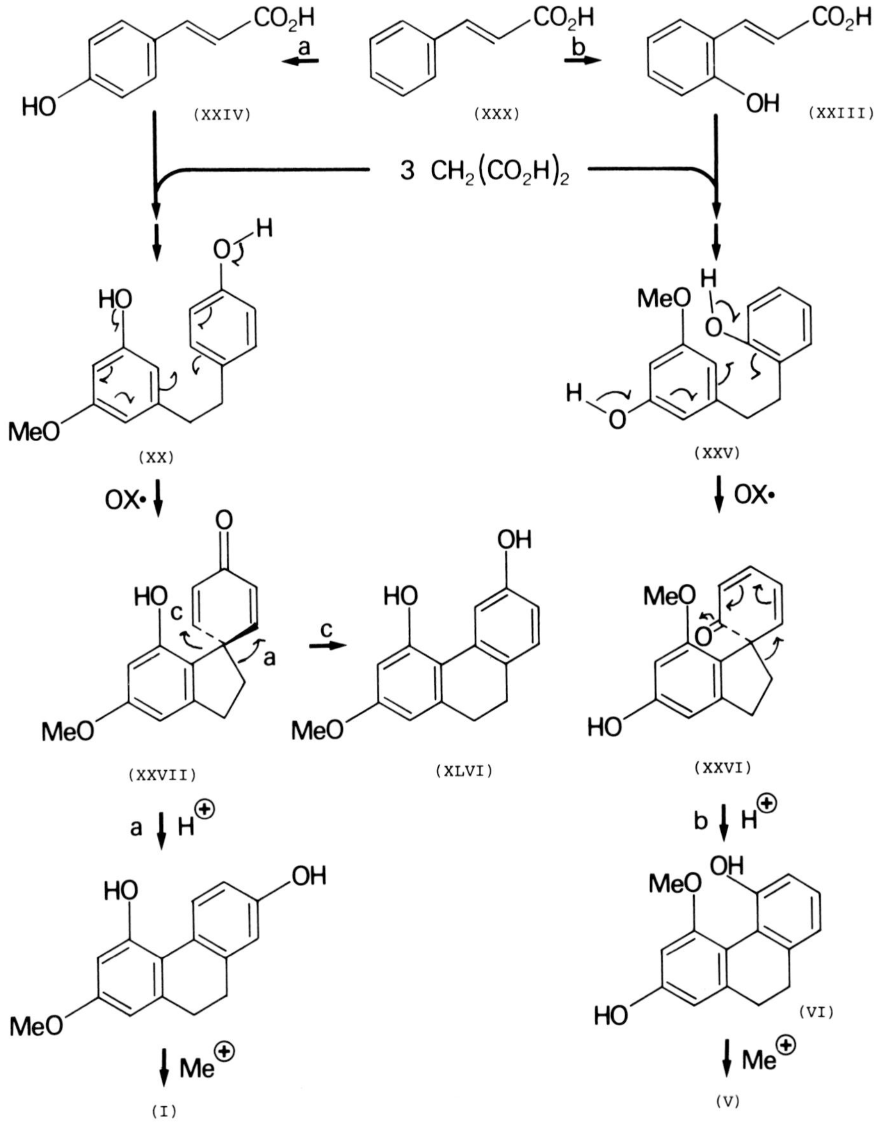

Scheme 2. An alternative route to orchinol, hircinol, loroglossol and cannabidihydrophenanthrene

A similar situation is found in the *Combretum* family from which at least three di-hydrostilbenes and nineteen phenanthrenes and dihydrophenanthrenes are known. All of the phenanthrenes and dihydrophenanthrenes are substituted with hydroxy- or methoxy- groups at the 2, 4, 6, and either the 5 or 7 position, and most also at the 3 position. The three dihydrostilbenes are similarly substituted at the 3, 4, 5, and 4′ positions. Typical examples are the dihydrostilbenes XXXVI and XXXVII, which co-occur with the phenanthrenes XXXVIII through XLI and dihydrophenanthrenes XLII through XLV in *C. psidioides* (Letcher and Nhamo, 1972, 1973a). All these com-pounds have oxygenation patterns that are compatible with Scheme 2c or with Scheme

	R_1	R_2	R_3	R_4	R_5	R_6
(XXXI),	OH	H	OMe	OH	H	H
(XXXII),	OMe	OMe	OMe	OH	H	H
(XXXVI),	OMe	OH	OMe	H	H	OH
(XXXVII),	OMe	OMe	OMe	H	H	OH
(XLVIII),	OH	H	OMe	H	OH	H

(XLVII)

	R_1	R_2	R_3
(LIII),	OH	OH	H
(LIV),	OH	OH	OH

(LV),	R = CO_2H
(LVI),	R = H

Structures, group 5

1a if the postulated loss of oxygen from the spirodienone intermediate XXII if followed by reoxygenation at a later stage.

The co-occurrence of a stilbene with the corresponding dihydrostilbene and di-hydrophenanthrene has also been observed in *Cassia garrettiana* (Hata, Baba and Kozawa, 1979). The most impressive evidence for the oxidative phenol coupling route, however, comes from the recent isolation of the dihydrostilbene XX and the spiro-dienone XXVII, both postulated as intermediates in Scheme 2a, as natural products of *Cannabis sativa,* in which they co-occur with the dihydrophenanthrene XLVI (Scheme 2c) and several related spiro compounds (Crombie and Crombie, 1978; Crombie, Crombie, and Jamieson, 1979; and Kettenes-Van den Bosch and Salemink, 1978). The intra-molecular oxidative phenol coupling of the dihydrostilbene XX to one of these spiro compounds, cannabispiran (XLVII), has been accomplished in the laboratory by the use of $K_3Fe (CN)_6$ as oxidizing agent (El-Feraly *et al.*, 1979).

Another possible biosynthetic route to the orchid phytoalexins is suggested by the occurrence in *Dioscorea batatas* of the dihydrostilbene batatasin III (XLVIII; Hashimoto *et al.*, 1974), in addition to the batatasins XXXI through XXXIII. Batatasin III (XLVIII) is the dihydro derivative of a stilbene structurally very close to the 3'-acetoxy-3,5-di-methoxystilbene, which was employed in the photosynthetic routes to orchinol (I), hircinol (VI), and loroglossol (V; Letcher and Nhamo, 1973b; Stoessl, Rock, and Fisch, 1974). It can therefore be envisaged that both the laboratory synthesis and the biosynthesis of the compounds could proceed on mechanistically similar pathways (Scheme 3, R_1 = H or Me; R_2 = H or Ac). Nevertheless, as a biosynthetic pathway, the route lacks plausibility, partly because the presence of a sole hydroxyl at the 3' position of a stilbene is a very rare feature whose biosynthetic origin is itself in need of clarification and because batatasins IV (XXXI) and V (XXXII) and the phenanthrenes and dihydrophenanthrenes of *Dioscorea* are in better accord with the oxidative phenol coupling routes (see Gorham, 1980; Ireland, Schwabe, and Coursey, 1981).

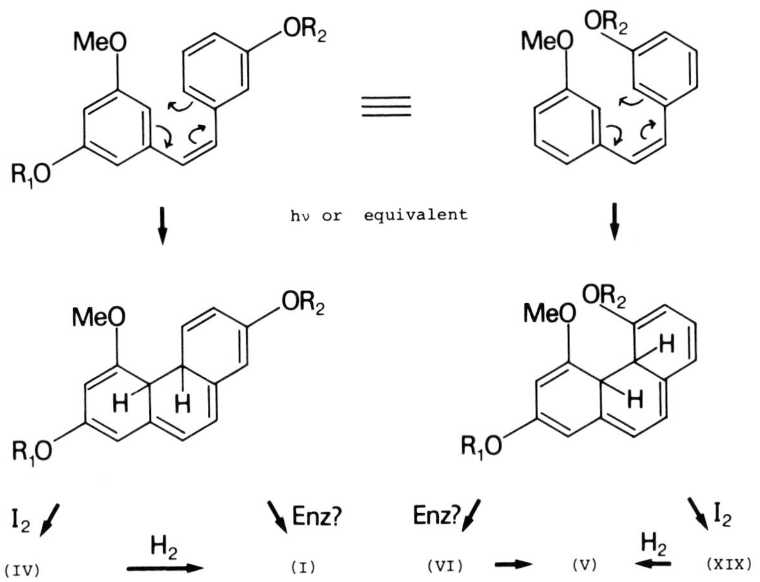

Scheme 3. "Photosynthetic" route to orchinol, hircinol, and loroglossol

A final determination regarding these and possibly other biosynthetic routes will have to be made by direct incorporation experiments. At present, however, the available data, together with the reasonable assumption that the biosynthesis of the phenanthrenes of the Orchidaceae, *Combretum*, and *Dioscorea* proceeds on essentially identical routes, strongly favor the pathways shown in Schemes 2a and 2b.

Activity and Action Spectrum

Both hircinol and orchinol are relatively nonspecific and can affect several bacteria and fungi (Tables 3-2 and 3-3). In more recent work (Ward, Unwin, and Stoessl, 1975a) it was shown that orchinol inhibits the spore germination of a range of other plant-pathogenic fungi, the ED_{50} varing from 0.3 to 1.5×10^{-4} M. Except in the case of *Monilinia fructicola* (ED_{50} 0.6×10^{-4} M), growth was less sensitive to inhibition by orchinol than germination (ED_{50} 2.2–3.5×10^{-4} M).

Table 3-2. Effects of orchinol on several soil fungi (Gäumann, Nüesch, and Rimpau, 1960)

Fungi	Inhibitory concentration of orchinol, molar
Phycomycetes	
Mucor spinosus v. Tiegh.	10^{-3}
Pythium de Baryanum Hesse	$10^{-2.5}$
Rhizopus nigricans Ehrenb.	10^{-4}
Ascomycetes	
Alternaria tenuis auct.	$10^{-2.5}$
Aspergillus clavatus Desm.	10^{-2}
Aspergillus flavus Link	10^{-2}
Aspergillus fumigatus Fres.	10^{-3}
Aspergillus niger v. Tiegh.	0
Botrytis cinerea Pers.	10^{-2}
Cladosporium fulvum Cke.	$10^{-3.5}$
Didymella exitialis (Mor.) E. Müll.	$10^{-3.5}$
Fusarium culmorum (W. G. Sm.) Sacc.	$10^{-3.5}$
Fusarium lycopersici Sacc.	10^{-4}
Fusarium Martii App. et. Wr.	10^{-4}
Fusarium solani (Mart.) App. et Wr.	10^{-3}
Neurospora sitophila (Mont.) Shear et Dodge	$10^{-3.5}$
Ophiobolus graminis Sacc.	0
Penicillium citreo-viride Biourge	10^{-2}
Pencillium citrinum Thom	0
Thielavia terricola (Gil. et Abb.) Emm.	0
Trichoderma viride Pers.	10^{-3}
Basidiomycetes	
Rhizoctonia crocorum DC.	——
Rhizoctonia Kühn from *Pinus silvestris*	10^{-3}
Rhizoctonia solani Kühn from *Solanum tuberosum*	10^{-3}

Hircinol at 50 and 100 ppm is less effective against *Candida lipolytica* BY 17 than orchinol at the same concentrations (Fig. 3-2). Growth (i.e., turbidity of a liquid culture) is almost completely inhibited by orchinol during the first six days. After that, growth increases slowly, but even after 3½ weeks the turbidity of orchinol-countering cultures is considerably lower than that of the controls (Fisch, Flick, and Arditti, 1973). Growth of the cultures accelerates after longer periods (Fig. 3-2). Reinoculation of the filter-sterilized media that were used for thirteen days to culture *C. lipolytica* BY 17 indicates that the phytoalexins were depleted. This finding is of considerable biological significance.

Reports that loroglossol is relatively inactive (Fisch, Flick, and Arditti, 1973; Hardegger *et al.*, 1963) were the result of the sparing solubility of the compound in water. It

Table 3-3. Minimal inhibitory and lethal concentrations of orchinol and hircinol (Urech *et al.*, 1963)

	(Hircinol µg ml^{-1})		(Orchinol µg ml^{-1})	
	I[a]	D[a]	I[a]	D[a]
Staph. aureus	>500		50	250
Escherichia coli	250	250	500	500
Trichophyton interdigitale	25	50	10	50
Trichophyton mentagrophytes	25	100	50	50
Endomyces albicans	50	100	50	50
Epidermophyton floccosum	100	500	100	100
Microsporum audouini	>500		100	250
Sporotrichum schenckii	>500		>500	
Aspergillus niger	500	>500	100	500

[a] I, Inhibition; D, Death.

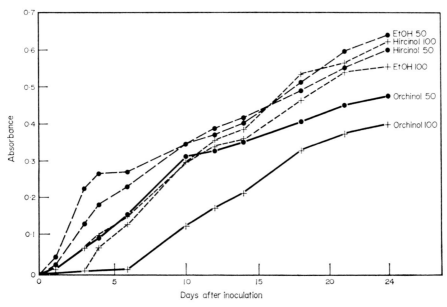

Fig. 3-2. Growth of *Candida lipolytica* on orchinol 100 and 50 ppm, hircinol 100 and 50 ppm, and ethanol (EtOH) 100 and 50 ppm (Fisch, Flick, and Arditti, 1973).

crystallizes when transferred from ethanol stock solution into aqueous culture media; this process reduces its concentration (Ward, Unwin, and Stoessl, 1975b). In fact, the activity of loroglossol was shown to be of the same order as that of hircinol and orchinol (minimum inhibitory dose of 10^{-4} to 10^{-5} M) when a dilution series was prepared directly in ethanol (Ward, Unwin, and Stoessl, 1975b).

Several phenanthrenes obtained by laboratory synthesis have high activity (Ward, Unwin, and Stoessl, 1975a; Tables 3-4 and 3-5). Some of them are more active at lower concentrations, which is probably because there is crystallization at higher levels. Both the synthetic and the naturally occurring phenanthrenes bring about rupture, distortion, and stunting of the germ-tubes produced by germinating spores. The cytoplasm of affected tubes is more granular than that of the controls and withdrawn from the walls (Ward, Unwin, and Stoessl, 1975a).

In subsequent work (Stoessl and Unwin, unpublished) it was shown that 2,4-dihydroxyphenanthrene (XLIX) and 2,4-dihydroxy-9,10-dihydrophenanthrene (L) were almost

Table 3-4. Percent inhibition of zoospore germination of *Phytophtora infestans* by orchinol and related phenanthrenes and dihydrophenanthrenes (Ward, Unwin, and Stoessl, 1975a)

	Concentration ($M \times 10^4$)							
	5	2.5	1.25	0.625	0.313	0.156	0.078	0.039
Orchinol	100r	100r	100r	81	40	21	2	0
Dehydroorchinol	100cr	100cr	100cr	100cr	100cr	100cr	83s	0
Loroglossol	90c	100cr	93crs	92crs	20s	0	0	0
Dehydroloroglossol	0c	0c	0c	50c	59c	20	16	0
Didemethylloroglossol	100	24s	21s	0	0	0	0	0

c Crystals or deposit; rrupture of germ-tube tips; sstunting and distortion of germ tubes.

Table 3-5.   Percent inhibition of spore germination of *Monilinia fructicola* by orchinol and related phenanthrenes and dihydrophenanthrenes (Ward, Unwin, and Stoessl, 1975a)

	Concentration ($M \times 10^4$)							
	5	2.5	1.25	0.625	0.313	0.156	0.078	0.039
Orchinol	100[r]	100[r]	83[rs]	51	15	0	0	0
Dehydroorchinol	0[cs]	0[cs]	0[cs]	79[c]	69[c]	64[rs]	22[rs]	0[s]
Loroglossol	35[crs]	22[crs]	21[rs]	0[s]	0[s]	0[s]	0	0
Dehydroloroglossol	0[c]	0[c]	0[c]	0[c]	0[c]	29[s]	10[s]	0
Didemethylloroglossol	81[s]	50[s]	14	0	0	0	0	0

[c] Crystals or deposit; [r] rupture of germ-tube tips; [s] stunting and distortion of germ tubes.

as active against *Monilinia fructicola* and *Phytophthora infestans* as dehydroorchinol (IV) and orchinol (I) respectively (Table 3-6). The corresponding 2,4,6-trihydroxy derivatives LI and LII were somewhat less active, but the possibility cannot be excluded that this was caused by the precipitation of the compounds during the tests as in the earlier study. The compounds are of particular interest because they are accessible by the photocyclization route from the stilbenes, pinosylvin (L) and resveratrol (LI; Stoessl and Rock, unpublished). Both stilbenes occur naturally in considerable amounts as undesirable constituents of coniferous heartwoods (Billek, 1964); they may therefore have some potential as starting materials for economically feasible syntheses of the phenanthrenes in industrial production. An additional advantage is that these stilbenes are symmetrically substituted and therefore lead to only one cyclization product in each case.

Phenanthrene derivatives applied to tomato plants through the roots and by foliage treatments delayed the course of *Fusarium* and *Verticillium* wilt (Buchenauer, 1971; Buchenauer and Grossmann, 1970). Some of the phenanthrenes were ineffective against *Phytophthora,* however. Orchinol, when used as a protectant against wheat rust, reduced the intensity of the disease considerably but had a less pronounced effect on wheat mildew when it was used as an eradicant or applied through the roots (Fawcett and Spencer, 1970). It reduced spore germination of broad bean rust, but had no effect when used as an eradicant against wheat rust; in leaf disc assays against cucumber anthracnose, cucumber mildew, and broad bean rust; or in root application against wheat rust (Fawcett and Spencer, 1970). When tested for therapeutic activity on infected cucumber cotyledons, it was not effective against powdery mildew at $1 \times 10^{-3} M$ (Ward, Unwin, and Stoessl, 1975).

Table 3-6.   Percent inhibition of germination of fungal spores by orchinol analogues (Stoessl and Unwin, unpublished)

Compound*	Fungus	Concentration ($M \times 10^4$)						
		5	2.5	1.25	.625	.325	.156	.078
XLIX	*M. fructicola*	100	100	100	100	100	0	0
XLIX	*P. infestans*	100	100	100	100	100	92	59
L	*M. fructicola*	100	100	58	14	0	0	0
L	*P. infestans*	100	100	100	100	66	44	22
LI	*M. fructicola*	100	100	0	0	0	0	0
LI	*P. infestans*	100	100	100	66	46	0	0
LII	*M. fructicola*	0	0	0	0	0	0	0
LII	*P. infestans*	100	100	72	35	0	0	0

*Compounds are identified by roman numerals in the text and structural diagrams.

Monolinolein inhibits spore germination of *Phytophthora infestans* but not of *Monilinia fructicola* and mycelium growth of *Rhizoctonia repens* M32 (Stoessl, Fisch, and Arditti, 1980).

Biological Significance

Bernard's discovery that infection by mycorrhizal fungi induces phytoalexin production (Fig. 3-1) points out the importance of these compounds in protecting orchids from infection by pathogens and in regulating mycorrhizae. Fast-growing fungi (*Fusarium solani*, for example) can invade and destroy unprotected plants very quickly. The presence of even low levels of a phytoalexin (orchinol, for instance), however, can delay invasion long enough to allow the production of effective levels of infection-induced defense compounds.

A number of fungi cannot invade tissues that contain sufficient amounts of phytoalexins or that can synthesize them rapidly enough; this assumption is supported by evidence that despite limited mechanical protection and a thin cortex, some orchid storage organs rarely rot. Only fungi that deactivate orchinol rapidly such as *Rhizoctonia solani* destroy storage organs quickly (Nüesch, 1963).

The presence of fungi in orchid roots and germinating seeds may be regarded as a form of parasitism which is localized, stabilized, and regulated, making it possible for orchids to coexist with parasitic, or potentially parasitic, fungi in a symbiotic relationship (Arditti, 1966, 1979; Knudson, 1929; and Kusano, 1911). The most effective means of regulating such symbiosis would be a slowly degradable phytoalexin present at fungistatic concentrations. A fungitoxic substance that might be degraded very slowly, or not at all, could inhibit fungi to a degree that might preclude successful symbiosis. On the other hand, the orchid would be parasitized if the fungi degraded the phytoalexin or phytoalexins rapidly. Both extremes have been reported (Bernard, 1909b; Burgeff, 1936). Continuous production of a phytoalexin or phytoalexins that may be degraded at a reasonable rate would be optimal for the establishment of orchid mycorrhiza because they could limit infection and penetration without damaging the fungus. That orchid phytoalexins are such compounds is indicated by the facts that their synthesis starts within thirty-six hours (Table 3-7) of infection, as in the case in *Orchis militaris* (Nüesch, 1963); production is continuous (Nüesch, 1963); and orchinol and hircinol are destroyed

Table 3-7. Orchinol concentration (μg/g) in tissue cylinders from bulbs of *Orchis militaris* incubated with a *Rhizoctonia repens* strain (Nüesch, 1963, from Gäumann and Hohl, 1960)

Time of incubation (days)	2-mm-thick discs, numbered from the bottom to the top					
	1	2	3	4	5	6
1	0	0	0	0	0	0
2	28	10	0	0	0	0
5	200	112	15	Traces	0	0
8	920	380	160	50	35	45
12	650	540	460	110	100	80

by *Candida lipolytica* (Fisch, Flick, and Arditti, 1973), which suggests that other fungi may do the same.

Because they are not exposed to agents that can initiate production, seedlings cultured in vitro probably do not synthesize phytoalexins. As a result, these seedlings are not resistant to attack by pathogens, which may explain why some of them perish.

Other Biological Properties

Batatasin I (XXXIII), III (XLVIII), IV (XXXI), and V (XXXII) have been claimed as endogenous plant-growth regulators of *Dioscorea batatas* (Hashimoto, Hasegawa, and Kawarda, 1972, 1974; Hashimoto and Tajima, 1978). This claim suggests that the orchid dihydrophenanthrenes and/or their putative dihydrostilbene precursors might exhibit similar properties and that these might constitute a primary function of the compounds (Stoessl, 1980). As a first approach to an investigation of this possibility, orchinol (I), loroglossol (V), hircinol (VI) and a range of simple derivatives were tested as inhibitors of indoleacetic acid, (IAA) oxidation in vitro (Lee, Rock, and Stoessl, 1978). They were found to inhibit horseradish peroxidase-catalyzed IAA degradation. A 7-hydroxy group, as in orchinol (I), conferred particularly high activity. This compound was accordingly studied more thoroughly. It competed preferentially with IAA for the ferriporphyrin group of the peroxidase, inducing a concentration-dependent lag phase in IAA oxidation. The orchinol was itself destroyed by oxidation, however, soon after the enzyme had reacted with IAA. In a similar study in a different laboratory, inhibition of IAA oxidase activity was also observed for a series of stilbenes and dihydrostilbenes structurally related to the batatasins and lunularic acid (LV; Gorham, 1978). The latter is well established as an endogenous growth regulator of liverworts (Gross, 1975). Batatasins I (XXXIII) and III (XLVIII) were found to be inactive or only very weakly active in this study, but lunularin (LVI), which is structurally related to XX, a postulated intermediate in orchinol biosynthesis, caused more than 40% inhibition. Growth-inhibitory properties of the compounds are also reported in this study (Gorham, 1978). More recently these stilbenes have been found to inhibit photosynthesis (Gorham and Coughlan, 1980).

In additional preliminary studies (Lee and Stoessl, unpublished), orchinol was found to stimulate growth in the tobacco callus assay in the absence of IAA but to have no net effect in the presence of IAA. It was inactive in the short-term pea stem elongation assay. Extension of these studies to orchid tissues are planned.

Recent Developments

1. Although only four orchid phenanthrenes and dihydrophenanthrenes were known when this chapter was first submitted to the publishers, many such compounds have now been reported from a number of Himalayan orchid species. (P. Majumder, A. K. Sarkar, and J. Chakraborty, 1982, Phytochem. 21:2712–2716, 1 phenanthrene, 10 dihydrophenanthrenes; P. L. Majumder and A. K. Sarkar, 1982, Indian J. Chem. 21B:829–831, 1 dihydrophenanthrene) and from *Dendrobium nobile* (B. Talapatra, P. Mukhopadhyay, P.

Chaudhury, and S. K. Talapatra, 1982, Indian J. Chem. 21B:386–387, 1 phenanthrene-quinone). It is not known whether any of these compounds were formed in the course of defense or other stress responses.

2. A book on phytoalexins has appeared recently (J. A. Bailey and J. W. Mansfield, eds., 1982, *Phytoalexins*, Blackie, Glasgow and London).

3. The biosynthesis of orchinol in agar-stimulated bulbs of *Orchis militaris* has now been investigated experimentally. α,β,β,3,4,5-Hexadeuteriophenylalanine was incorporated in significant amount but in an unexpected manner (A. Doux-Gayat, G. Défago, H. Kern, A. Stoessl, and J. B. Stothers, 1983, J. Chem. Soc. Chem. Commun. 157–159). This was clarified shortly thereafter in an independent study with radioactive tracers (K.-H. Fritzemeier and H. Kindl, Eur. J. Biochem., in press), which showed that biosynthesis proceeds with a biochemically novel *meta*-hydroxylation of phenylalanine and with the resultant *m*-tyrosine and 3,3′,5-trihydroxybibenzyl as true intermediates on a route very similar to that depicted in Scheme 3 in this chapter. We thank Professor Kindl for informing us of his results prior to publication.

Acknowledgments

Research on orchid phytoalexins at the University of California, Irvine, was supported in part by the Office of Naval Research (NS) Contract NR 08-796 (to J.A.). We thank Dr. Hilary Burton, U.S. Department of Agriculture, Oakland, California, for locating and providing us with copies of several key literature references; Dr. Robert Ernst for reading and commenting on the manuscript; G. Lambert for drawing the structural diagrams; and Dr. H. V. Morley, Director, London Research Centre, Department of Agriculture, Canada, for giving A. S. the opportunity to participate in the writing of this article.

Literature Cited

Albersheim, P., and A. J. Anderson-Prouty. 1975. Carbohydrates, proteins, cell surfaces and their biochemistry of pathogenesis. Annu. Rev. Plant Physiol. 26:31–52.

Arditti, J. 1966. The production of fungal growth regulating compounds by orchids. Orchid Digest 30:88–90.

———. 1967. Factors affecting the germination of orchid seeds. Bot Rev. 33:1–97.

———. 1979. Aspects of orchid physiology, pp. 421–655. *In* H. W. Woolhouse (ed.), Advances in botanical research. Academic Press, London.

Arditti, J., R. Ernst, M. H. Fisch, and B. H. Flick. 1972. Ergosterol peroxide from *Rhizoctonia repens:* Composition, conformation, and origin. J. Chem. Soc. Chem. Comm. 1972:1217–1288.

Arditti, J., B. H. Flick, A. Ehmann, and M. H. Fisch. 1975. Orchid phytoalexins. Pt. 2. Isolation and characterization of possible sterol companions. Amer. J. Bot. 62:738–742.

Beauverie, J. 1910. Essais d'immunisation des végétaux contre les maladies cryptogamiques. C. R. Acad. Sci. Paris 133:107–110.

Bendig, J., M. Beyermann, and D. Kreysig. 1977. Photodehydrocyclizations of stilbenes and stilbene-like compounds in the presence of Π-acceptors. Tetrahedron Letters: 3659–3660.

Bernard, N. 1909a. Remarque sur l'immunité chez les plantes. Bull. Inst. Pasteur 7:369–386.

———. 1909b. L'évolution dans la symbiose, les orchidées et leurs champignons commensaux. Ann. Sci. Nat. Bot., Series 9, 9:1–196.

———. 1911. Sur la fonction fungicide des bulbes d'ophrydées. Ann. Sci. Nat. Bot., Series 9, 14:221–234.

Billek, G. 1964. Stilbene in Pflanzenreich. Fortschr. Chem. Org. Naturst. 22:115–152.

Birch, A. J. 1966. Some natural antifungal agents. Chem. Ind. (London): 1173–1176.

Boller, A., H. Corrodi, E. Gäumann, E. Hardegger, H. Kern, and N. Winterhald-Wild. 1957. Über induzierte Abwehrstoffe bei Orchideen. Pt. 1. Helv. Chim. Acta 40:1062–1066.

Bowden, B. F., R. W. Read, E. Ritchie, and W. C. Taylor. 1975. Synthesis of 9,10-dihydrophenanthrenes including orchinol methyl ether. Aust. J. Chem. 28:65–80.

Braun, R. 1963. Orchinol, pp. 130–134. In H. F. Linskens and M. V. Tracey (ed.) Moderne Methoden der Pflanzen Analyse, Vol. 6. Springer Verlag, Berlin.

Buchenauer, H. 1971. Einfluss von Phenanthren- und Xanthen-Derivaten auf die *Fusarium* und *Verticillium* Welke der Tomaten. Phytopathol Z. 72:291–304.

Buchenauer, H., and F. Grossman. 1970. Therapeutic effects of fluorene, phenanthrene, and xanthene derivatives on fungal diseases of tomato. Nature 227:1267–1268.

Burgeff, H. 1936. Samenkeimung der Orchideen. Gustav Fischer Verlag, Jena.

Burges, A. 1939. The defensive mechanism in orchid mycorrhiza. New Phytol. 38:273–283.

Crombie, L., and W. M. L. Crombie. 1978. Dihydrostilbenes of Thailand cannabis. Tetrahedron Letters: 4711–4714.

Crombie, L., W. M. L. Crombie, and S. V. Jamieson. 1979. Isolation of cannabispirodienone and cannabidihydrophenanthrene. Biosynthetic relationships between the spirans and dihydrostilbenes of Thailand cannabis. Tetrahedron Letters 21:661–664.

Cruickshank, I. A. M. 1963. Phytoalexins. Annu. Rev. Phytopathol. 1:351–374.

——. 1977. A review of the role of phytoalexins in disease resistance mechanisms. Pontif. Acad. Sci. Scr. Varia. 41:503–569.

Cruickshank, I. A. M., and D. R. Perrin. 1960. Isolation of a phytoalexin from *Pisum sativum* L. Nature 187:799–800.

Deverall, B. J. 1977. Defence mechanisms of plants. Cambridge University Press, Cambridge, England.

El-Feraly, F. S., Y. M. Chan, M. A. El-Sohly, and C. E. Turner. 1979. Biomimetic synthesis of cannabispiran. Experientia 35:1131–1132.

Evans, D. A., P. A. Cain, and R. Y. Wong. 1977. A general approach to the synthesis of phenanthrenoid compounds. An alternative to oxidative phenolic coupling. J. Amer. Chem. Soc. 99:7083–7085.

Fawcett, C. H., and D. M. Spencer. 1969. Natural antifungal compounds, pp. 637–669. In D. C. Torgeson (ed.), Fungicides, Vol 2, Academic Press, New York.

——. 1970. Plant chemotherapy with natural products. Annu. Rev. Phytopathol. 8:403–418.

Fisch, M. H., and J. Arditti. 1972. Orchid phytoalexins. Amer. J. Bot. 59:672.

Fisch, M. H., R. Ernst, B. H. Flick, J. Arditti, D. H. R. Barton, P. D. Magnus, and I. D. Menzies. 1973. Identity of ergosterol '5β,8β-peroxide' J.C.S. Chem Comm. 1973:530.

Fisch, M. H., B. H. Flick, and J. Arditti. 1973. Structure and antifungal activity of hircinol, loroglossol and orchinol. Phytochem. 12:437–441.

Fisch, M. H., Y. Schechter, and J. Arditti. 1972. Orchids and the discovery of phytoalexins. Amer. Orchid Soc. Bull. 41:605–607.

Floyd, A. J., S. F. Dyke, and S. E. Ward. 1976. The synthesis of phenanthrenes. Chem. Rev. 76:509–562.

Gäumann, E. 1960. Nouvelles données sur les réactions chimiques de défense chez les orchidées. C. R. Acad. Sci. Paris 250:1944–1947.

——. 1963–1964. Weitere Untersuchungen über die chemische Infektabwehr der Orchideen. Phytopathol. Z. 49:211–232.

Gäumann, E., R. Braun, and G. Bazzigher. 1950. Über induzierte Abwehrreaktionen der Orchideen. Phytopathol. Z. 17:36–63.

Gäumann, E., and H. R. Hohl. 1960. Weitere Untersuchungen über die chemischen Abwehrreaktionen der Orchideen. Phytopathol. Z. 38:93–104.

Gäumann, E., and O. Jaag. 1945. Über induzierte Abwehrreaktionen bei Pflanzen. Experientia 1:21–22.

Gäumann, E., and H. Kern. 1959a. Über die Isolierung und den chemischen Nachweis des Orchinols. Phytopathol. Z. 35:347–356.

——. 1959b. Über chemische Abwehrreaktionen der Orchideen. Phytopathol. Z. 36:1–26.

Gäumann, E., E. Müller, J. Nüesch, and R. H. Rimpau. 1961. Über die Wurzelpilze von *Loroglossum hircinum* (L)Rich. Phytopathol. Z. 41:89–96.

Gäumann, E., J. Nüesch, and R. H. Rimpau. 1960. Weitere Untersuchungen über die chemischen Abwehrreaktionen der Orchideen. Phytopathol. Z. 38:274–308.

Gorham, J. 1978. Effect of lunularic acid analogues on liverwort growth and IAA oxidation. Phytochem. 17:99–105.

——. 1980. The stilbenoids, pp. 203–252. *In* L. Reinhold, J. B. Harborne, and T. Swain (eds.) Progress in phytochemistry, Vol. 6. Pergamon Press, Oxford, England.

Gorham, J. and S. J. Coughlan. 1980. Inhibition of photosynthesis by stilbenoids. Phytochem. 19: 2059–2064.

Grisebach, H., and J. Ebel. 1978. Phytoalexins, chemical defense substances of higher plants? Angew. Chem. Int. Ed. Engl. 17:635–647.

Gross, D. 1975. Growth regulating substances of plant origin. Phytochem. 14:2105–2112.

——. 1977. Phytoalexine und verwandte Pflanzenstoffe. Fortschr. Chem. Org. Naturst. 34:187–247.

Gunter, M. J. and L. N. Mander. 1981. Studies on reductive alkylation. A highly efficient synthesis of the phytoalexin orchinol. Aust. J. Chem. 34:675–678.

Hardegger, E., H. R. Biland, and H. Corrodi. 1963. Synthese von 2,4-dimethoxy-6-hydroxyphenanthren und Konstitution des Orchinols. Helv. Chim. Acta 46:1354–1360.

Hardegger, E., N. Rigassi, J. Seres, C. Egli, P. Müller, and K. O. Fitzi. 1963. Synthese von 2,4-Dimethoxy-6-hydroxy-9,10-dihydroyphenanthren. Helv. Chim. Acta 46:2543–2551.

Hardegger, E., M. Schellenbaum, and H. Corrodi. 1963. Über induzierte Abwehrstoffe bei Orchideen. Pt. 2. Helv. Chim. Acta 46:1171–1180.

Hashimoto, T., K. Hasegawa, and A. Kawarada. 1972. Batatasins: New dormancy-inducing substances of yam bulbils. Planta 108:369–374.

Hashimoto, T., K. Hasegawa, H. Yamaguchi, M. Saito, and S. Ishimoto. 1974. Structure and synthesis of batatasins, dormancy-inducing substances of yam bulbils. Phytochem. 13:2849–2852.

Hashimoto, T., and M. Tajima. 1978. Structures and synthesis of the growth inhibitors batatasins IV and V, and their physiological activities. Phytochem. 17:1179–1184.

Hata, K., K. Baba, and M. Kozawa. 1979. Chemical studies on the heartwood of *Cassia garrettiana* Craib. II. Nonanthraquinonic constituents. Chem. Pharm. Bull., 27:984–989.

Hillis, W. E., and M. Hasegawa. 1962. Biosynthesis of hydroxystilbenes. Chem. Ind. (London): 1330–1331.

Ingham, J. L. 1972. Phytoalexins and other natural products as factors in plant disease resistance. Bot. Rev. 38:343–424.

Ireland, C. R., W. W. Schwabe, and D. G. Coursey. 1981. The occurrence of batatasins in the Dioscoreaceae. Phytochem. 20:1569–1571.

Jorgensen, E. 1961. The formation of pinosylvin and its monomethyl ether in the sapwood of *Pinus resinosa* Ait. Can. J. Bot. 39:1765–1772.

Kende, A. S., and D. P. Curran. 1978. Total synthesis of juncusol. Tetrahedron Letters: 3003–3006.

Kettenes-Van den Bosch, J. J., and C. A. Salemink. 1978. Cannabis XIX. Oxygenated 1,2-diphenylethanes from marihuana. Rec. Trav. Chim. Pays-Bas 97:221–222.

Knudson, L., 1929. Physiological investigations on orchid germination. Proc. Int. Cong. Plant Sci. 2:1183–1189.

Krautwurst, K. D. and W. Tochtermann. 1981. Eine einfache Orchinol-Synthese. Chem. Ber. 114: 214–219.

Kúc, J. 1972. Phytoalexins. Annu. Rev. Phytopathol. 10:207–232.

——. 1976. Phytoalexins, pp. 632–652. *In* R. Heitefuss and P. H. Williams (eds.), Encycl. Plant Physiol., Vol. 4. Springer, New York.

Kusano, E. 1911. *Gastrodia elata* and its symbiotic association with *Armillaria mellea*. J. Coll. Agr. Tokyo 4:1–66.

Lee, T. T., G. L. Rock, and A. Stoessl. 1978. Effects of orchinol and related phenanthrenes on the enzymic degradation of indol-3-acetic acid. Phytochem. 17:1721–1726.

Letcher, R. M., and L. R. M. Nhamo. 1972. Chemical constituents of the *Combretaceae*. Pt. 3. Substituted phenanthrenes, 9,10-dihydrophenanthrenes, and bibenzyls from the heartwood of *Combretum psidioides*. J. Chem. Soc. Perkin Trans. 1:2941–2947.

——. 1973a. Chemical constituents of the *Combretaceae*. Pt. 4. Phenanthrene derivatives from the heartwood of *Combretum hereroense*. J. Chem. Soc. Perkin Trans. 1:1179–1181.

——. 1973b. Structure of orchinol, loroglossol, and hircinol. J. Chem. Soc. Perkin Trans. 1:1263–1265.

Liepa, A. J., and R. E. Summons. 1977. An improved phenanthrene synthesis: A simple route to (±)-tylophorine. J. Chem. Soc. Chem. Commun.: 826–827.

Loewus, F. A., and C. A. Ryan (eds.). 1981. The phytochemistry of cell recognition and cell surface interactions. Plenum Press, New York.

Magrou, J. 1924. A propos du pouvoir fungicide des tubercules d'ophrydées. Ann. Sci. Nat. Bot., Series 10, VI, 18:256–276.

——. 1936. La phagocytose chez les végétaux. 3d Internat. Cong. Comp. Path. pp. 73–80.

——. 1938. Contributions à l'étude de l'immunité humorale chez les plantes. Ann. Inst. Pasteur 60:565–600.

Mahadevan, A. 1973. Theoretical concepts of disease resistance. Acta Phytopathol. Acad. Sci. Hung. 8:391–423.

McDonald, E., and R. T. Martin. 1978. Total synthesis of juncusol. Tetrahedron Letters: 4723–4726.

Müller, K. O. 1959. The phytoalexin concept and its methodological significance. Recent Adv. Bot. 1:396–400.

——. 1966. How plants fight disease. Sci. J. (May): 3–7.

——. 1969. Die Phytoalexine, in Sicht einer allgemeinen Immunbiologie. Zentralb. Bakteriol., Parasitenkd., Infektionskr., Hyg., Abt. 2, 123:259–265.

Müller, K. O., and H. Börger. 1940. Experimentelle Untersuchungen über die Phytophthora-Resistenz der Kartoffel. Zugleich ein Beitrag zum Problem der "erworbenen Resistenz" im Pflanzenreich. Arb. Biol. Reichsanst. Land Forstwirtsch. Berlin-Dahlem 23:189–231.

Müller, P., J. Seres, K. Steiner, S. E. Helali, and E. Hardegger. 1974. Synthesen von Dehydroorchinolmethyl äther and Dehydroorchinol. Helv. Chim. Acta 57:790–795.

Nobécourt, P. 1923. Sur la production d'anticorps par les tubercules des ophrydées. C. R. Acad. Sci. Paris 17:1055–1057.

——. 1938. Le problème de l'immunité chez les végétaux. Assoc. des Diplomes de Microbiol de la Faculte de Pharm. de Nancy Bull. 10–17:9–32.

Nüesch, J. 1963. Defense reactions in orchid bulbs. Symp. Soc. Gen. Microbiol. 13:335–343.

Perrin, D. R., and W. Bottomley. 1961. Pisatin: An antifungal substance from *Pisum sativum* L. Nature 191:66–76.

Rajaraman, K., and S. Rangaswami. 1975. Structures of two new 9,10-dihydrophenanthrenes from *Dioscorea prazeri*. Indian J. Chem. 13:1137–1138.

Ray, J. 1901. Cultures et formes atténuées des maladies cryptogamiques des végétaux. C. R. Acad. Sci. Paris 133:307–309.

Rupprich, N., and H. Kindl. 1978. Enzymatic synthesis of 3,5,4'-trihydroxystilbene from *p*-coumaroyl coenzyme A and malonyl coenyme A. Hoppe-Seyler's Z. Physiol. Chem. 359:165–172.

Schmalle, H., and B. M. Hausen. 1979. A new sensitizing quinone from lady slipper (*Cypripedium calceolus*). Naturwissenschaften 66:527–528.

Seres, J. 1964. Über Orchinol und verwandte Verbindungen. Prom. No. 3528 Eidg. Techn. Hochschule, Zurich.

Steiner, K., Ch. Egli. N. Rigassi, S. E. Helali, and E. Hardegger. 1974. Zur Syntheses des Orchinols. Helv. Chim. Acta 57:1137–1141.

Stoessl, A. 1972. Antifungal compounds produced by higher plants. Rec. Adv. Phytochem. 3:143–180.

——. 1977. Biogenetic relations between some bicyclic sesquiterpenoidal stress compounds of the *Solanaceae*, pp. 61–71. *In* Z. Király (ed.) Current topics in plant pathology. Akadémiai Kiadó, Budapest.

——. 1980. Phytoalexins—a biogenetic perspective. Phytopathol. Z.: 99:251–272.

Stoessl, A., M. H. Fisch, and J. Arditti. 1980. Monolinolein as a selective fungus inhibitor from Cymbidium, Orchidaceae. Mycopathologia 70:131–134.

Stoessl, A., G. L. Rock, and M. H. Fisch. 1974. An efficient synthesis of orchinol and other orchid phenanthrenes. Chem. Ind. 17:703–704.

Tochtermann, W., R. Strickler, H. A. Klein, and E. Biegi. 1977. Zur Darstellung von (partiell hydrierten) Hydroxymethoxyphenanthrenen. Chem. Ber. 110:2456–2462.

Urech, J., B. Fechtig, J. Nüesch, and E. Vischer. 1963. Hircinol, eine antifungisch wirksame Substanz aus Knollen von *Loroglossum hircinum* (L.) Rich. Helv. Chim. Acta 46:2758–2766.

Uritani, I., and T. Akazawa. 1955. Antibiotic effect on *Ceratostomella fimbriata* of ipomeamarone, an abnormal metabolite in black rot of sweet-potato. Science 121:216–217.

Wan, A. S. C., R. T. Aexel, and H. J. Nicholas. 1971. Nonsaponifiable constituents of orchids: *Arundina* and *Cattleya*. Phytochem. 10:2267–2269.

Ward, E. W. B., C. H. Unwin, and A. Stoessl. 1975a. Postinfectional inhibitors from plants. Pt. 15. Antifungal activity of the phytoalexin orchinol and related phenathrenes and stilbenes. Can. J. Bot. 53:964–971.

——. 1975b. Loroglossol: An orchid phytoalexin. Phytopathology 65:632–633.

Ward, H. M. 1902. On the question of "predisposition" and "immunity" in plants. Proc. Cambridge Phil. Soc. 11:307–328.

———. 1905. Recent researches on the parasitism of fungi. Ann. Bot. 19:1–54.

West, C. A. 1981. Fungal elicitors of the phytoalexin response in higher plants. Naturwissenschaften 68:447–457.

Wij, M., and S. Rangaswami. 1978. Chemical components of *Dioscorea bulbifera:* Isolation and structure of a new dihydrophenanthrene (2,4,6,7-tetrahydroxy-9,10-dihydrophenanthrene) and a new phenanthrene (2,4,5,6-tetrahydroxyphenanthrene). Indian J. Chem. 16B:643–644.

4

Physiology of Germinating Orchid Seeds*

JOSEPH ARDITTI and ROBERT ERNST

*The literature review pertaining to this chapter was concluded in February 1981; the chapter was submitted in March 1981, and the revised version was received in November 1981. An addition was made in 1982.

Introduction

Orchid seeds germinate in nature only following fungal infection, that is, symbiotically. However, much (perhaps most) of the available information on their requirements and physiology has been obtained from experiments carried out under asymbiotic (i.e., artificial) conditions. Consequently, some of the data obtained from such experiments may not be entirely representative of natural conditions. Nonetheless, comparisons between symbiotic and asymbiotic seedlings suggest that conclusions based on asymbiotic experiments are generally valid and representative.

Experiments under axenic conditions were possible after L. Knudson demonstrated that at least some orchids can germinate asymbiotically on suitable media (Knudson, 1921, 1922, 1946). Using Knudson's basal media, several investigators have studied the effects of or requirements for a variety of factors in the germination of orchid seeds (for reviews see Arditti, 1967a, 1979; Fast, 1964, 1967, 1971, 1976; Stoutamire, 1974; Withner, 1959a, 1959b). Knudson's media and several others are suitable for most epiphytic or tropical orchids, or both. Some terrestrial species, however, especially those from temperate regions, are more difficult to germinate. Consequently, special media and procedures were developed or modified for terrestrial species (for reviews see Arditti, 1979; Stoutamire, 1974) from Europe (Borriss, 1969, 1970; Ernst, 1980; Fast, 1976; Hadley, 1970b; Hadley and Harvais, 1968; Harbeck, 1961, 1963, 1964, 1968a; Harvais and Hadley, 1967; Mead and Bulard, 1975; Veyret, 1969; Vöth, 1976), Canada (Harvais, 1972, 1973, 1974), Australia (Clements and Ellyard, 1979; McIntyre *et al.*, 1971, 1972a, 1972b; Veitch and McIntyre, 1972; Wrigley, 1973, 1976), South Africa (Collett, 1971; Harbeck, 1968b), and the United States (Arditti, Michaud, and Oliva, 1982; Stoutamire, 1974). Some of the research that led to the formulation of these media was practical or empirical. The rest was basic. Information from these studies together with data obtained from work with epiphytic species provide the basis of this review.

Effects and Utilization of Carbohydrates

The first studies on the suitability of using a sugar as a carbon source for germinating orchid seeds (Bernard, 1909) were made before the formulation of asymbiotic media. Comparisons between sugars became possible only after defined media were available. As a result, the first comparative studies were published not long after Knudson's initial publication (Knudson, 1916, 1921; La Garde, 1929; Quednow, 1930; Wynd, 1933b). Many studies followed (Ernst, 1967a; Ernst *et al.*, 1971a; Raghavan, 1976; for reviews see Arditti, 1967a, 1979; Withner, 1959b, 1974) that identified sugars and carbohydrates as capable or incapable of supporting germination. Species vary in their ability to germinate on several sugars (Table 4-1), but, in some instances, the physiological problems are more complex than whether an appropriate carbon source is available. The lists of suitable or unsuitable sugars are not surprising. Orchids are no exception to the rule that higher organisms generally use D-sugars. Galactose is as toxic to orchids as it is to most

Table 4-1. Sugars, polysaccharides, other carbohydrates, and carboxylic acids as carbon sources for germinating orchid seeds (Data from Arditti, 1967a, 1979; Ernst, 1967a; Ernst *et al.,* 1971a; Withner, 1959b, 1974)

Unsuitable	Remarks	Suitable	Remarks
Monosaccharides		Monosaccharides	
C-5		C-5	
D-arabinose		D-ribose	In some cases
L-arabinose		D-xylose	
D-xylose		C-6	
L-xylose		D-fructose	
C-6		αD-glucose	
D-galactose		βD-glucose	
L-glucose		D-mannose	
L-mannose		Disaccharides	
L-sorbose		C-12	
C-7		cellobiose	
Sedoheptulosan		lactose	Marginal except for *Vanilla*
Disaccharides		maltose	
C-12		melibiose	
D-lactose	Unsuitable for most species	sucrose	
Deoxysugars		trehalose	
C-6		turanose	
D-fucose		Trisaccharides	
L-fucose		C-18	
2-deoxy-D-glucose		melezitose	
L-rhamnose		raffinose	
Sugar alcohols		Tetrasaccharides	
C-4		C-24	
meso-erythritol		stachyose	
C-5		Sugar alcohols	
L-arabinitol		C-5	
C-6		D-arabinitol	
galactito!		ribitol	
myo-inositol	Protocorms survive, but fail to differentiate	xylitol	
Polysaccharides		C-6	
Starch		mannitol	
Cellulose		sorbitol	
Organic acids		Organic acids	
Citric acid		malate	
Malic acid		pyruvate	
Oxalic acid			
Pyruvic acid			
Succinic acid			
Tartaric acid			

plant tissues. It inhibits the growth of orchid seedlings and other plants at concentrations as low as 0.9 mM or 0.0125% (Arditti *et al.,* 1972; Burström, 1948; Ernst, 1967a; Ernst *et al.,* 1971a; Ordin and Bonner, 1957; Thimann, 1956) and may affect metabolism by interfering with cellulose synthesis (Ordin and Bonner, 1957) or hexokinase activity (Hele, 1953) or both.

Nuclear chromatin in galactose-treated cells appear dispersed throughout the nucleus rather than concentrated around the nuclear envelope (Ernst *et al.,* 1971a). In some instances, the nuclear envelope may evaginate into the cytoplasm, sometimes including both its membranes rather than only the outer membrane, which is more common. The membranes appear to be devoid of chromatin (Ernst *et al.,* 1971a).

Numerous unit membrane vesicles can be observed in the cytoplasm of galactose-treated cells. Myelin bodies are also present in nearly all cells, and both the vesicles and the myelin bodies exhibit a unit membrane character. A possible explanation for this finding is that these structures have been derived from the tonoplast, which was invari-

Table 4-2. Effect of glucose on *Cymbidium* protocorms (Freson, 1969)

Concentration		Effects
%	m*M*	
0	0	Protocorms do not multiply and become necrotic rapidly
0.25	13.88	Poor growth, but tissues are green
0.63	34.96	Improved multiplication, rhizoid formation, poor differentiation
1.6	88.81	Best growth, development, and chlorophyll content
4	222.02	Increased production of plantlets, reduced protocorm multiplication and chlorophyll levels
10	555.06	Protocorms do not multiply and become necrotic rapidly

ably broken. Intact dictyosomes have not been observed (Ernst *et al.*, 1971a). Amyloplasts seem normal and contain large starch grains and small lipid droplets. Mitochondria remain intact, but their cristae are slightly swollen and the matrix somewhat clumped (Ernst *et al.*, 1971a). Membranes show little or no swelling and are intact.

The size of polysaccharide molecules may pose permeability problems in orchids as in other plants, and hydrolytic enzymes may be extracellular. Permeability may also prevent the utilization of organic acids. It is not surprising that orchid seeds, which under natural conditions require mycorrhizal infection for germination, germinate well and that seedlings grow normally on trehalose and mannitol, two carbohydrates of fungal origin (Ernst, 1967a; Smith, 1973). Trehalose, which is transported into orchid seedlings by fungal hyphae (Smith, 1966, 1967), may well be a product of glucose obtained from hydrolysis of cellulose by orchid mycorrhiza (Hadley, 1968, 1969).

Inositol is a compound (sometimes classified as a vitamin or just as a growth factor) that is beneficial in low amounts (Arditti and Harrison, 1977; Leopold, 1964) but unsuitable as a carbon source (Table 4-1). Glucose, which is very common in plants and fungi either as a component of polysaccharides or as a free molecule, is also important as a starting point in many metabolic pathways. It is not surprising, therefore, that orchid seeds and seedlings can utilize glucose (Freson, 1969; Table 4-2).

Several reports indicate that a number of orchid species germinate and grow better on fructose than on glucose (Ernst, 1967a; for reviews see Arditti, 1967a, 1979; Burgeff,

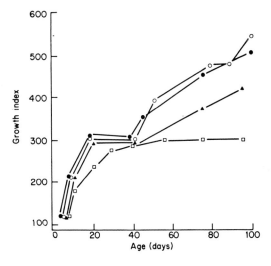

Fig. 4-1. Growth of *Cattleya aurantiaca* seedlings on sucrose (open circles), glucose (closed circles), fructose (triangles), and inositol (squares). This figure and figures 4-4, 4-5, 4-6, 4-9, and 4-10 are as redrawn in Arditti, 1979, from "Physiological Changes during the Germination of *Cattleya aurantiaca* (Orchidaceae)" by C. R. Harrison and J. Arditti, *Botanical Gazette*, vol. 139, no. 2, pp. 180–189, by permission of The University of Chicago Press. © 1978 by The University of Chicago. All rights reserved.

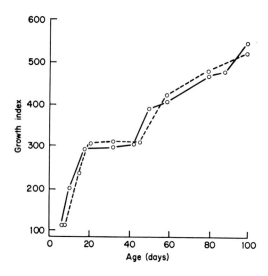

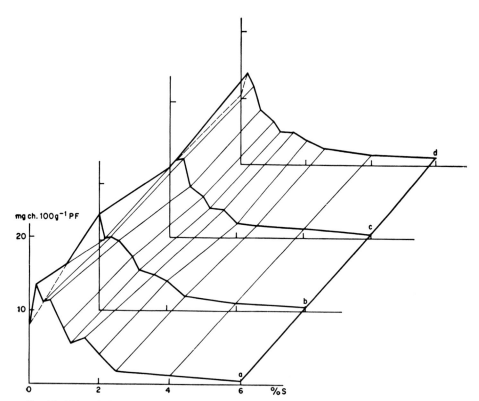

Fig. 4-2. Growth of *Cattleya aurantiaca* seedlings on cold sterilized (broken line) and autoclaved (solid line) sucrose (Harrison, 1973, as redrawn in Arditti, 1979).

Fig. 4-3. Chlorophyll levels in *Cymbidium* protocorms as affected by sucrose concentrations. Explanation of symbols: a, 23½ h at 5800 lux; b, 23½ h at 2900 lux; c, 16 h at 5800 lux; d, 16 h at 2900 lux; PF, fresh weight; S, sucrose %; 2% = 0.11 m; 4% = 0.22 m; 6% = 0.33 m; ch, chlorophyll (Vanséveren-Van Espen, 1973, as redrawn in Arditti, 1979).

1936; Withner, 1959b). For example, *Phalaenopsis* seedlings take up and/or utilize fructose in preference to glucose (Ernst *et al.*, 1971a). On the other hand, *Cattleya aurantiaca* seedlings do not grow as well on fructose as they do on sucrose or glucose (Harrison, 1973, 1977; Harrison and Arditti, 1978; Fig. 4-1).

The most commonly used sugar in orchid seed and seedling culture is sucrose. It can support growth equally well whether autoclaved or filter sterilized (Fig. 4-2), but its effects may vary depending on concentration (Fig. 4-3; Table 4-3; Homès, 1973; Homès *et al.*, 1971a, 1971b; Homès and Vanséveren-Van Espen, 1973a). Proliferation of protocorms is enhanced by supraoptimal levels of sucrose, whereas organogenesis is enhanced at suboptimal concentrations (Homès and Vanséveren-Van Espen, 1973a). In a sucrose-free medium chloroplasts have thick clusters, peripheral vesicles, thylakoids that form misshapen grana, and numerous osmophilic globules, but no starch grains. When glucose is added, the structure of the chloroplasts becomes normal within 24 hours and maximal starch accumulation occurs within four days. In *Cymbidium* protocorms chlorophyll content and photosynthetic oxygen evolution are at a maximum when they are cultured on 0.5% sucrose (Homès and Vanséveren-Van Espen, 1972, 1973a, 1973b; Vanséveren-Van Espen and Coutrez-Geerinck, 1974).

Analyses of cold-sterilized (filter) culture media containing several sugars (Table 4-4) indicate that *Phalaenopsis* seedlings release extracellular enzymes that hydrolyze α-D-glucopyranosyl-(1 → 2)-β-D-fructofuranoside and α- or β-galactopyranosyl-D-glucopyranose bonds. Hydrolysis of β-D-fructofuranosides and α-D-galactosides is inversely proportional to the increasing molecular weight of the sugars (Table 4-4). Maltose (1 →

Table 4-3. Effects of sucrose concentration on growth and development of *Cymbidium* protocorms (Vanséveren-Van Espen, 1973)

Sucrose concentration		Nature of growth or organ development	Illumination			
			23½ hours		16 hours	
%	Molarity (mM)		5800 lux	2900 lux	5800 lux	2900 lux
16	0.89	Compact masses of very pale protocorms				
		Leaves		0		
		Roots		0		
		Rhizoids		0		
2.5–10	0.14–0.56	Friable masses of pale protocorms				
		Leaves		+		
		Roots		0		
		Rhizoids		0		
2–1.6	0.11–0.09	Masses and individual green protocorms				
		Leaves		+++		
		Roots		0		
		Rhizoids		+++		
0.25–1.25	13.88–69.38	Green protocorms in groups				
		Leaves	+++	+++	+	++
		Roots	+++	+++	0	0
		Rhizoids	+++	+++	0	0
0		Small dark green protocorm masses				
		Leaves		++		
		Roots		0		
		Rhizoids		+		

Explanation of symbols: 0, no growth and/or development; +++, maximal growth and/or development.

Table 4-4. D-Hexose content of cold-sterilized oligosaccharide solutions exposed for 4 months to *Phalaenopsis* seedlings (Ernst *et al.*, 1971a)

Sugar[a]	Fractions detected by thin layer chromatography	Monosaccharide content, percentage of neutral fraction			Molar ratios of monosaccharides		
		Glucose	Fructose	Galactose	Glucose	Fructose	Galactose
Sucrose	Sucrose (s)[c], fructose, glucose	33.23	28.93	—	1.0	0.87	
Sucrose (C)[b]	Sucrose (s), fructose, glucose	4.35	4.35	—			
Maltose	Maltotriose ? (w)[c], maltose (s), glucose	2.72	—	—			
Maltose (C)	Maltotriose ? (w), maltose (s)	0.11	—	—			
Cellobiose	Cellobiose (s), glucose	1.09	—	—			
Cellobiose (C)	Cellobiose (s)	0.22	—	—			
Trehalose	Trehalose (s), glucose	1.24	—	—			
Trehalose (C)	Trehalose (s)	Trace	—	—			
Melibiose	Melibiose (s), galactose, glucose	0.63	—	3.99	1.0		6.3
Melibiose (C)	Melibiose (s)	0.07	—	0.06			
Lactose	Lactose (s), galactose, glucose	1.26	—	9.31	1.0		6.9
Lactose (C)	Lactose (s)	Trace	—	0.03			
Raffinose	Raffinose (s), melibiose (s), galactose, fructose, glucose	0.92	12.19	1.92	1.0 (0.08)[d]	13.3 (1.0)	2.1 (0.158)
Raffinose (C)	Raffinose (s), melibiose (t)[c], fructose	0.11	2.18	0.10			
Melezitose	Melezitose (s), turanose (w), sucrose (t), glucose	6.53	0.10	—	1.0 (65.3)	0.015 (1.0)	
Melezitose (C)	Melezitose (s)	0.33	0.22	—			
Stachyose	Stachyose (s), manninotriose (s), raffinose (t), galactose, fructose	—	4.79	0.68		7.0 (1.0)	1.0 (0.14)
Stachyose (C)	Stachyose (s)	—	0.16	0.17			

[a] Molecular weights: sucrose, maltose, cellobiose, trehalose, melibiose, lactose, 342.3; raffinose, melezitose, 504.4; stachyose, 684.5.
[b] (C), cold-sterilized nutrient solution not exposed to seedlings.
[c] Thin layer chromatography (TLC) intensities: s, strong; w, weak; t, trace.
[d] Value in parentheses is based on fructose content being equal to 1.0.

4-α-D glucosidic bond as in amylose), cellobiose ($1 \rightarrow$ 4-β-D bond as in cellulose), and trehalose($1 \rightarrow$ 1-α-D bond) seem to be taken up whole—that is, without external hydrolysis. These findings may explain, at least partially, the inability of most orchid seeds to germinate and their seedlings to grow and develop on polysaccharides such as starch and cellulose. The reported germination of *Miltonia* and *Odontoglossum* seeds on 1% corn or potato starch (Hayes, 1969) is an exception, possibly the result of impurities (hydrolysates such as glucose and maltose) in the starch (for a more detailed discussion see Ernst *et al.*, 1971a).

At a certain stage in their growth orchid seedlings no longer require an exogenous source of sugar. By growing *Cattleya aurantiaca* seedlings on Knudson C (KC) medium in the presence and absence of sucrose and transferring them from one combination to the other, it was possible to establish the length of the period during which they require a supply of sugar (Harrison, 1973, 1977; Harrison and Arditti, 1978). The seedlings on KC without sucrose grew to the protocorm stage, but did not produce roots and leaves (Fig. 4-4; Harrison, 1973). The seedlings on KC developed normally. After 21 days on KC, only 13% of the protocorms formed plantlets following transfer to KC without sucrose. When cultured for 28 to 30 days on KC, 50% of the protocorms transferred to KC without sucrose formed leaves and developed into larger plantlets. Seedlings with

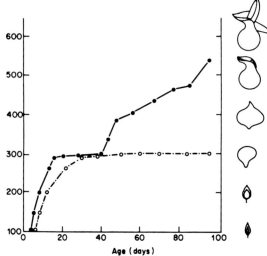

Fig. 4-4. Growth index of *Cattleya aurantiaca* seedlings cultured on Knudson C medium with (solid line) and without (broken line) sucrose.

leaves (one or more) also continued to develop following transfer to KC without sucrose. Of the protocorms that were transferred after 47 days from KC to KC without sucrose, 92% formed complete seedlings. Protocorms grown 15, 30, or 60 days on KC without sucrose required 21 to 30 days on KC before 50% formed plantlets on KC without sucrose. These findings indicate that an exogenous carbohydrate is not a requirement for growth and development after the first leaf has appeared or there is potential to generate it (Harrison, 1973, 1977; Harrison and Arditti, 1978; Figs. 4-5 and 4-6).

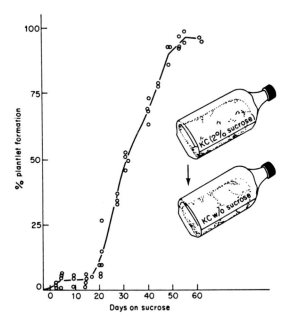

Fig. 4-5. Plantlet formation from protocorms of *Cattleya aurantiaca* as a function of the length of time on Knudson C medium with and without sucrose. Drawing represents transfer sequence.

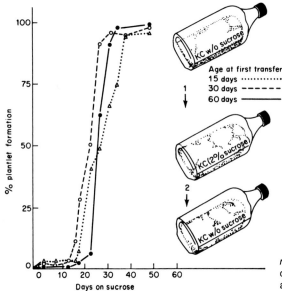

Fig. 4-6. Development of plantlets from *Cattleya aurantiaca* protocorms after a period on Knudson C without sucrose, transfer to sucrose-containing medium, and return to sucrose-free medium.

Nitrogen

Ammonia, nitrate, and urea are all suitable nitrogen sources for most germinating orchid seeds. Several species have been reported to grow better on ammonia (for reviews see Arditti, 1967a, 1979). A number of species seem unable to utilize nitrate during the early stages of germination (de Bruijne and Debergh, 1974). *Cattleya* seedlings, for example, can grow on nitrate only after a 60-day growing period (Raghavan and Torrey, 1964). Development of their ability to utilize nitrate parallels the appearance of nitrate reductase. This finding indicates that seedlings differentiate biochemically as well as morphologically (Raghavan, 1976).

Results with urea are contradictory even with species in the same genus. For example, there are reports that *Cymbidium* seedlings were inhibited (Cappelletti, 1933) and stimulated (Burgeff, 1936) by urea. The growth of *Dendrobium phalaenopsis* and *Phalaenopsis* was inhibited by urea (Burgeff, 1936), but development of *Vanilla planifolia* (Lugo-Lugo, 1955a, 1955b), *Laeliocattleya* (Magrou *et al.*, 1949), *Cattleya* (Curtis, 1947), and *Vanda* was enhanced. A culture medium formulated recently contains only urea and ammonia nitrogen (Thompson, 1977). The adverse effects of urea could be due to biuret formation during spray drying of the urea and/or sterilization.

Some of the differences in requirements or responses to urea, ammonia, and nitrate may be due to the species and/or genera used in the experiments. Others may be the result of the age of the plantlet and whether nitrate reductase was present in very young seedlings. The intimation that NH_4NO_3 is the most appropriate nitrogen source (Mitra, 1971) therefore appears reasonable.

Odontoglossum seedlings in a bark-based compost grew best when irrigated with a solution containing ammonium nitrate at a concentration of 100 mg N/l (Figs. 4-7 and 4-8; Gething, 1977). Unrooted seedlings of a *Laeliocattleya* hybrid grew best on 100 to 200

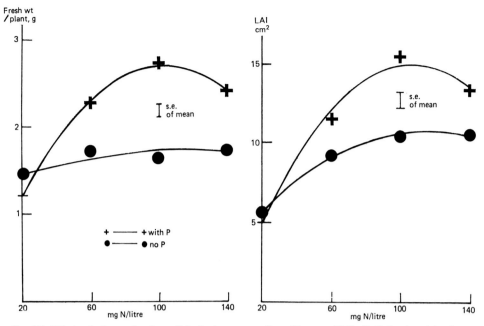

Fig. 4-7. Effects of nitrogen levels on *Odontoglossum* seedlings (January 1974). (*Left*) Fresh weight of seedlings; (*right*) leaf area index (LAI). (Gething, 1977. Reproduced with permission of the Controller of Her Majesty's Stationery Office.)

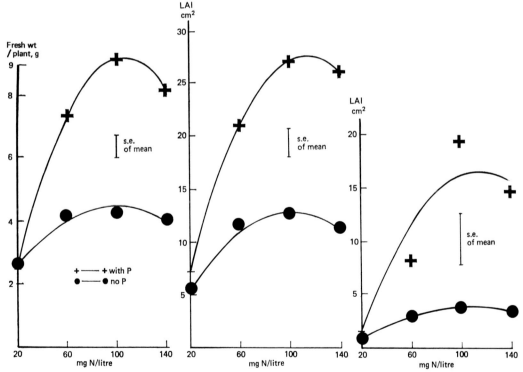

Fig. 4-8. Effects of nitrogen supply on the growth of *Odontoglossum* seedlings (October 1974). (*Left*) Fresh weight; (*middle*) leaf area index (LAI), first and second growths; (*right*) leaf area index (LAI), second growths only. (Gething, 1977. Reproduced with permission of the Controller of Her Majesty's Stationery Office.)

ppm ammonium plus urea or 100 to 200 ppm ammonium plus nitrate ions (Uesato, 1973). Following the appearance of roots, growth was best on 400 ppm ammonium plus urea or 300 ppm nitrate. A ratio of 20% to 30% NH_4^+ and 80% to 70% NO_3^- is reported to have been the most favorable (Uesato, 1973).

Nearly all amino acids and related substances have been tested in orchid seed culture media as supplements or nitrogen sources. Arginine, ornithine, and urea could replace NH_4NO_3 in *Cattleya* cultures. Phenylalanine, citrulline, tyrosine, aspartic acid, glutamic acid, glutamine, asparagine, and phenylurea could not. Proline and γ-aminobutyric acid served as moderately good sources of nitrogen (Raghavan, 1964, 1976; Raghavan and Torrey, 1964). Glycine, α-alanine, valine, α-aminobutyric acid, leucine, phenylglycine, hydroxyproline, canavanine, and threonine were inhibitory (Raghavan, 1964; Raghavan and Torrey, 1964). Shoot formation in *Cymbidium pumilum* and *C. goeringii* (Ueda and Torikata, 1968, 1969, 1972a, 1972b) was increased by arginine and aspartic acid. Results obtained from experiments with other amino acids have been extremely variable (for reviews see Arditti, 1967a, 1979; Sanford, 1974; Withner, 1959a, 1974).

Casein hydrolysate, lactalbumin hydrolysate, peptone, or tryptone are often used in culture media with varying results. (See, for example, Harvais, 1972, 1973, 1974; Mead and Bulard, 1975; Pages, 1971; Rao and Avadhani, 1963; Torikata *et al.*, 1965; Ueda and Tonkata, 1968; Vöth, 1976; Ziegler *et al.*, 1967. For reviews see Arditti, 1967a, 1979; Withner, 1959a, 1974.) Because these substances are complex mixtures which may be changed chemically during autoclaving, it is difficult if not impossible to speculate on the reasons for their effects. In experiments with *Orchis* (Mead and Bulard, 1975) casein hydrolysate could be replaced by a reconstitution of its amino acids or glutamine only. These findings may be the result of a specific requirement of *Orchis*, in that glutamine did not have a similar effect on *Cattleya* (Raghavan and Torrey, 1964). The nitrogen requirements of *Orchis laxiflora* can be satisfied with casamino acid but not inorganic nitrogen (Mead and Bulard, 1979). Organogenesis and subsequent development in *Cymbidium* are enhanced by tryptone (Kusumoto, 1978).

Nucleic acids and related compounds have had varied effects on orchid seed germination. Their effects are as difficult to evaluate as those of the complex nitrogen sources because they may also be changed by autoclaving (Arditti, 1967a). Hydroxyurea, a DNA replication inhibitor, causes malformation of *Cymbidium* protocorms (Rücker, 1975).

Mineral Nutrition

The great majority of media used for orchid seed germination and seedling culture are more concentrated than the solutions that nurture epiphytic seedlings in nature (Table 4-5; Curtis, 1946; for reviews see Arditti, 1967a, 1979; Withner, 1959a). Epiphytic orchids generally germinate well on these media, but a number of terrestrial species germinate much better on less concentrated media (Vöth, 1976). Germination of *Dactylorhiza purpurella* can occur on distilled water or a modified Pfeffer medium (Harvais, 1972). *Arundina bambusifolia* (a terrestrial orchid) seeds germinate better on the more dilute Raghavan and Torrey medium than on the Vacin and Went solution (Table 4-5; Mitra, 1971). *Vanilla planifolia* seeds germinate best on one-tenth the normal concentra-

Table 4-5. Major element composition (in millimoles) of several media used for orchid-seed germination and seedling culture and of orchid-nurturing tree trunk effluate

Ion	Burgeff				Curtis			Fast		Pfeffer	Harvais		
	Eg1	N3f	MN + N	Of/N-free	1936	modif.	1971	F, 1976	FN, 1978	Pfeffer	1973	1974	1972
Nitrate	8.40	8.40			5.71	5.71	3.96	2.77	1.36	8.76	8.76	10.37	8.76
Ammonium	3.80	3.80	7.56		2.75	2.75	7.57	2.07	0.81		0.005a	5.13a	
Nitrate : ammonium ratio	2.2	2.2			2.08	2.08	0.52	1.34	1.68		1.752a	2.02	
Phosphate	3.20	1.40	6.86	3.11	0.90	0.88	1.84	0.61	0.24	1.47	1.47	1.47	1.47
Sulfate	2.90	2.90	5.04	1.71	1.06	1.08	4.80	0.34	0.13	0.81	0.81	0.81	0.81
Chloride		3.40	3.07	1.36				2.22	0.44	1.34	1.34	1.34	1.34
Potassium	4.60	6.20	8.58	5.12	0.88	0.88	5.79	2.83	0.68	4.79	4.79	4.79	4.79
Magnesium	1.00	1.00	1.22	1.01	1.06	1.06	1.01	0.34	0.13	0.81	0.81	0.81	0.81
Calcium	4.20	4.20	0.68	0.68	1.48	1.48	0.13	0.35	0.28	3.39	3.39	1.69	3.39
Citrate		0.43									0.003a	0.08a	0.003a
Iron	0.07	0.07	0.04	0.7	0.02	0.02	10 mg chelate	0.014	0.012		0.004a	0.1a	0.004a
Manganese											0.002	0.002	0.002
Sodium			1.71										
Urea													
Ammonium : urea ratio													
Total concentration	28.17	31.8	34.76	13.69	13.86	13.86	6.91	11.54	4.08	21.37	21.38	26.59	21.38
Rankingc	20	27	31	10	11	11	5	8	2	14	15	19	15

a Estimated.
b 5.0 plus an estimated 0.13.
c Lowest = 1.

Table 4-5. Continued

Ion	Henriksson 1951	Ichihashi and Yamashita	Kaewbanrung 1967	Knudson B	Knudson C	Lucke CT-1 1976	Lugo Lugo 1955	Mead and Bulard 1975	Mead and Bulard 1979	Mead and Bulard	Murashige and Skoog	Pfeffer
Nitrate	12.72	14.38	8.48	8.48	8.40			0.99	0.99		39.4	8.73
Ammonium	3.78	3.39	3.78	7.66	7.60			0.99	0.99		20.61	
Nitrate : ammonium ratio	3.37	4.2	2.24	1.10	1.10	1.52		1	1	1	1.9	
Phosphate	3.56	3.39	3.28	2.16	1.80	1.5	1.95	2.76	2.76	2.98	1.24	1.46
Sulfate	2.90	0.70	2.97	4.79	4.80	0.20	4.79	1.43	1.43	1.43	1.50	0.81
Chloride							8.48				5.98	1.34
Potassium	3.28	7.38	4.72	1.83	1.80	0.74	1.84	1.98	1.98	1.98	20.03	4.77
Magnesium	1.01	0.70	1.01	1.01	1.00	0.20	1.01	0.97	0.97	0.97	1.50	0.81
Calcium	4.24	3.49	4.24	4.24	4.20		4.24	0.85	0.85	0.46	2.99	3.38
Citrate												
Iron	0.42		0.07	0.33	0.09		0.11	0.009	0.009	0.009		
Manganese					0.034							
Sodium							7.56					
Urea							4.16					
Ammonium : urea ratio												
Total concentration	31.91	33.43	28.55	30.5	29.72	4.16	34.14	10.06	10.06	8.91	93.25	21.3
Ranking[c]	28	29	21	25	22	3	30	7	7	6	34	13

[a] Estimated.
[b] 5.0 plus an estimated 0.13.
[c] Lowest = 1.

Table 4-5. *Continued*

Ion	Polypodium nutrient	Raghavan and Torrey	RE	Sladden modif. Burgeff	Thomale GD	Thompson	Tree trunk effluate	Vacin and Went	Veyret 1969	Modif. White 1973	Wynd	
Nitrate		2.00	11.57	8.40	10.06		0.0025	5.19	8.48	3.33	9.8	7.8
Ammonium		2.00	7.27	10.60	5.50	2.99	0.0880	7.56	7.56			
Nitrate : ammonium ratio		1	1.59	0.8	1.82		0.02	0.69	1.12			
Phosphate	1.72	2.76	2.20	2.94	2.20	2.99	0.0105	3.14	1.84	0.12	2.5	3.8
Sulfate	0.41	1.43	1.22	6.50	2.16	1.49	0.0052	4.83	4.79	4.38	1.23	9.7
Chloride							0.1430		0.01			
Potassium	2.88	1.98	6.16	2.94	6.16	3.99	0.0770	7.03	1.84	0.79	2.5	19.4
Magnesium	0.41	0.97	0.67	1.20	0.74	1.49	0.1770	1.01	1.01	2.92	1.23	3.9
Calcium		0.85	0.63	4.80		0.49	0.0250	1.95	4.24	1.27	4.9	1.9
Citrate				1.89								
Iron	0.42		0.09	0.67	0.07		0.0073	0.19	0.004	0.13[b]		
Manganese								0.04		0.03		
Sodium							0.1310			2.94		
Urea						8.99						
Ammonium : urea ratio						0.33						
Total concentration	5.84	12.99	30.46	39.94	24.3	22.43	0.686	30.94	29.77	15.91	22.16	46.5
Ranking[c]	4	9	24	26	18	17	1	26	23	12	16	33

a Estimated.
b 5.0 plus an estimated 0.13.
c Lowest = 1.

tion of Knudson B medium (Lugo-Lugo, 1955a, 1955b); *Cypripedium calceolus* germinates on a medium that is 2.5 times as dilute as the solution used for *C. reginae* (Fast, 1976; Harvais, 1973) and also less concentrated than Knudson C (Table 4-5).

An optimal mineral ion composition for *Bletilla striata* seedlings is (in mg/l) NH_4NO_3, 320; KH_2PO_4, 817; KNO_3, 202; $Ca(NO_3)_2 \cdot 4H_2O$, 945; $MgSO_4 \cdot 7H_2O$, 247 (Ichihashi, 1978). A suitable balance of ions for *B. striata* is NO_3^- 60%, $H_2PO_4^-$ 30%, and $SO_4^=$ 10% for anions and NH_4^+ 20%, K^+ 40%, Ca^{++} 30%, and Mg^{++} 10% for cations (Ichihashi, 1978). Shoot growth was promoted on a medium containing NH_4^+ 50%, K^+ 30%, Ca^{++} 10%, and Mg^{++} 10%, and NO_3^- 50%, $H_2PO_4^-$ 30%, and $SO_4^=$ 20% with a total concentration of 40 mg/l. Root growth was better on NH_4^+ 20%, K^+ 60%, Ca^{++} 10%, and Mg^{++} 10%, and NO_3^- 50%, $H_2PO_4^-$ 30%, and $SO_4^=$ 20% with a total ionic concentration of 20 mg/l. Both shoots and roots can grow at relatively low ionic concentrations (Ichihashi, 1979). On the other hand, earlier reports suggest that variations in the proportion of ions in culture media may have a limited effect (Wynd, 1933a), on germination. Anions may play a more vital role than cations in the germination of orchid seeds (Ichihashi, 1978; Wynd, 1933a). Recent work with *B. striata* seeds (Ichihashi and Yamashita, 1977) has determined the optimal range of ions and led to the formulation of a culture medium (Tables 4-5 and 4-6).

In general, it seems that medium concentration is an important factor in the germination of orchids. However, because of the limited information available, there are no clear patterns. Nonetheless, a cautious generalization can be made: lady slipper orchids (*Cypripedium, Paphiopedilum*) and temperate-climate terrestrial species appear to germinate better on more dilute media (Table 4-5; Fast, 1976; Harbeck, 1963; Harvais, 1973; Ernst, unpublished).

Prior to the development of chelating agents, the precipitation of iron was a major problem in orchid seed germination and several substances were used to ensure its availability (for reviews see Arditti, 1967a, 1979; Withner, 1959a). Currently, chelating agents such as ethylenediaminetetraacetic acid (EDTA) or commercial preparations of chelated iron are used widely to solve this problem (Fast, 1976; L. Koch, 1973; U. Koch, 1972; Mead and Bulard, 1975; Mitra, 1971; Miyazaki and Nagamatsu, 1965; Mukherjee *et al.*, 1974; Thompson, 1977 are some examples; for reviews see Arditti, 1967a, 1979; Thompson, 1977).

Comparative research has suggested that reduced phosphate levels may increase germination. The reasons are not entirely clear. One possibility is that orchid seeds may be sensitive to phosphate. Another is that high phosphate levels can lead to iron deficiency

Table 4-6. Optimal range of ions at a total medium concentration of 20 mg 1^{-1} (Ichihashi and Yamashita, 1977)

Cations	Range (% total cation concentration)	Anions	Range (% total anion concentration)
NH_4^+	16–20	NO_3^-	66–88
K^+	35–41	$H_2PO_4^-$	7–23
Ca^{2+}	34–57	SO_4^{2-}	4–14
Mg^{2+}	10		

as a result of the formation of an insoluble complex during autoclaving. On media that lack phosphorus, *Cymbidium* protocorms turn "yellow grey-green and are covered with black spots, but do not die even after 100 days" (de Bruijne and Debergh, 1974).

Several species germinate very well on media that are low in calcium (Table 4-5; Ernst, 1980; Fast, 1976; Raghavan and Torrey, 1964; Thompson, 1977; Vacin and Went, 1949; Wynd, 1933a). This is especially true for terrestrial and diandrous (i.e., lady's slipper) species. Omitting calcium from culture media has no major effect on the normal green color of the seedlings (de Bruijne and Debergh, 1974). The formation of calcium phosphate salts and their precipitation has no harmful effects either (Storey *et al.*, 1947). Orchid seeds and tubers contain low levels of calcium (Tienken, 1947; L. C. Wheeler, personal communication; Wheeler and Ramos, 1965; for reviews see Arditti, 1967a, 1979) and may therefore have limited calcium requirements.

Soaking the seeds of *Galeola septentrionalis*, a chlorophyll-free terrestrial orchid, in a solution containing several potassium salts increased germination. Potassium chloride concentrations of $5 \times 10^{-1} M$ or higher in culture media proved to be supraoptimal and $5 \times 10^{-4} M$ suboptimal. Similar treatments of *Cymbidium virescens* did not improve germination (for a review regarding the effects of potassium, lithium, and sodium on orchid seeds see Arditti, 1967a). Many of the protocorms that develop on potassium-free media are small, and the leaves of the seedlings are stunted (de Bruijne and Debergh, 1974).

Microelements are not always included in orchid seed germination media because sufficient quantities may be present in the sugar, agar, or salts. Nevertheless, improved seedling growth has been reported in some cases following the addition of microelements such as cobalt, boron, iodine, copper, manganese, and molybdenum. Hence, adding microelements to culture media is recommended, probably on the assumption that they will not be harmful and may be beneficial in appropriate concentrations (Arditti, 1967b, 1979; Harrison and Arditti, 1970; Harvais, 1972, 1973, 1974; Ichihashi and Yamashita, 1977; Kaewbamrung, 1967; U. Koch, 1972; Kusomoto and Furukawa, 1977; Miyazaki and Nagamatsu, 1965; Mukherjee *et al.*, 1974; Thompson, 1974a, 1974b, 1977; Ueda and Torikata, 1972a).

Lipids

Cells in *Cattleya aurantiaca* embryos contain lipid bodies as food reserves (Harrison, 1973, 1977; Harrison and Arditti, 1978). Protein bodies are also found, but are restricted to cells in the upper two-thirds of the embryo. Crystals consisting of proteins surrounded by membranes have been noted in degenerating cells of *Cymbidium* protocorms (Gailhofer, 1976). Except for some grains within proplastids, starch, or other carbohydrates, reserves are not found in these seeds. These findings confirm earlier reports that lipids are the major food reserves in orchid seeds (Anonymous, 1922; Poddubnaya-Arnoldi and Zinger, 1961). Indeed, analyses of *Cymbidium* seeds indicate that they contain 32% lipids (Knudson, 1929; for a review see Arditti, 1967a). As a rule, similarly high concentrations of reserve compounds are located in the endosperm and/or the cotyledons of plants, but because these structures are not present in the great majority of orchids,their embryos seem to function as storage organs also. Ultrastructural evidence tends to support this view (Harrison, 1973, 1977; Harrison and Arditti, 1978; for a review see Arditti, 1979).

The breakdown and utilization of lipid reserves in fatty seeds is associated with glyoxysomes, bodies that could not be detected in germinating *Cattleya aurantiaca* seeds (Harrison, 1973, 1977). *Cattleya* seedlings converted only 3% or less label from acetate-2-^{14}C into sugars (in contrast with 90% conversion of acetyl units in castor beans) and used their lipid reserves very slowly. Their lipid bodies were enveloped by or closely associated with mitochondria (Harrison, 1973, 1977). It seems clear, therefore, that orchids have fatty seeds in which the necessary metabolic pathways are greatly limited. The available evidence indicates that acetyl CoA generated from lipid bodies could be routed via the Kreb's cycle in mitochondria, where it is oxidized to carbon dioxide with the production of energy. This evidence may, to some degree, reflect the absence in orchids of cotyledons or endosperms, which are the organs capable of converting acetate into sugars. Their disappearance seems to have led to the loss of several biochemical capabilities.

Photosynthesis

Chlorophyll is detectable in *Cattleya aurantiaca* seedlings cultured on Knudson C medium (Knudson, 1946) 15 days after the start of the culture. The levels of chlorophylls a (Chl a) and b (Chl b) are almost equal at that time and remain comparable for 1 to 1½ months (Harrison, 1973, 1977; Harrison and Arditti, 1978), at which time the levels of Chl a increase until they reach a maximum at 180 days. Concentrations of Chl b remain unchanged (Fig. 4-9, *top*). In the absence of sucrose, chlorophyll becomes measurable after 25 days. Levels of Chl a and Chl b are comparable and remain constant (Fig. 4-9, top). Consequently, the Chl a:Chl b ratio in plantlets on KC without sucrose remains unchanged, whereas that of seedlings on KC increases (Fig. 4-9, *middle*).

Activity of ribulose-1,5-bisphosphate carboxylase (RuBPCase)*, an important component of the photosynthetic apparatus, increased rapidly between 20 and 60 days in seedlings cultured on KC and reached a plateau at a level equal to that in mature plants. On KC without sucrose, concentrations of RuBPCase rose slowly for 60 days and increased slightly after that (Fig. 4-9, *bottom*). Specific activity of the enzyme was at a maximum after 30 days on KC and decreased subsequently. On KC without sucrose the peak, evident at 60 days, was followed by a decline (Fig. 4-10, *top*).

The major enzyme involved in the initial incorporation of CO_2 by the Calvin cycle during photosynthesis is RuBPCase. Hence it is not surprising that photosynthetic capacity and RuBPCase increase simultaneously (Fig. 4-10, *bottom*). Specific activity of RuBPCase rises considerably between days 15 and 40. Enzyme levels increase when seedlings are maintained for longer periods on KC. It appears, therefore, that production of this enzyme could be one of several events that occur in seedlings when a

---

*RuBPCase was formerly called RuDPCase (the D stood for di-; the B stands for bis-), and the latter abbreviation appears in several of the figures.

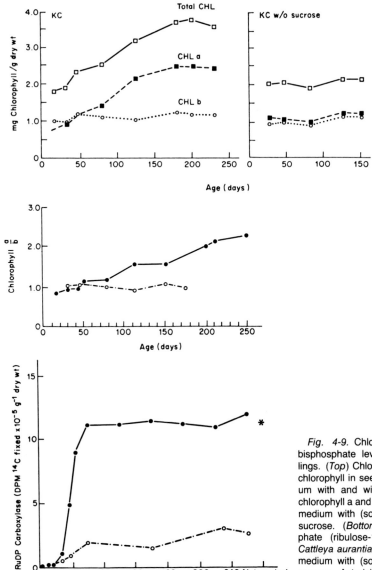

Fig. 4-9. Chlorophyll (CHL) and ribulose-1,5-bisphosphate levels in *Cattleya aurantiaca* seedlings. (*Top*) Chlorophyll a, chlorophyll b, and total chlorophyll in seedlings grown on Knudson C medium with and without sucrose. (*Middle*) Ratios of chlorophyll a and b in seedlings raised on Knudson C medium with (solid line) and without (broken line) sucrose. (*Bottom*) Activity of ribulose-1,5-diphosphate (ribulose-1,5-bisphosphate) carboxylase in *Cattleya aurantiaca* seedlings raised on Knudson C medium with (solid line) and without (broken line) sucrose. Asterisk is the level in leaves of mature plants. DPM, disintegrations per minute.

sufficient supply of carbohydrates is available. In other words, production of RuBPCase is an important biochemical event in the establishment of autotrophy and requires an exogenous source of energy (Harrison, 1973, 1977; Harrison and Arditti, 1978).

Environmental and Atmospheric Factors

The environment exerts an important effect on the physiology and development of orchid seedlings. Unfortunately, the available details are few.

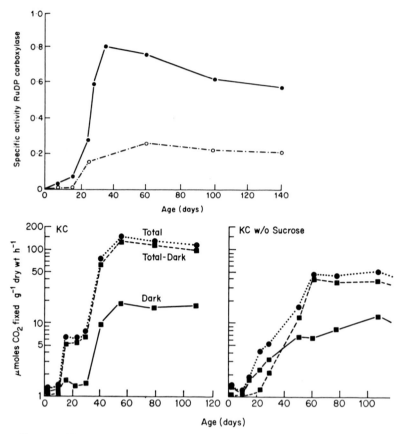

Fig. 4-10. Ribulose-1,5-bisphosphate carboxylase in *Cattleya aurantiaca* seedlings. (*Top*) Specific activity of ribulose-1,5-bisphosphate carboxylase in *Cattleya aurantiaca* seedlings raised on Knudson C medium with (solid line) and without (broken line) sucrose. (*Bottom*) Photosynthetic and dark fixation of CO_2 by *Cattleya aurantiaca* seedlings raised on Knudson C medium with or without sucrose.

Seed germination of some species in airtight containers is equal to or better than with ample gas exchange (for reviews see Arditti, 1967a, 1979). Seeds of *Calanthe discolor* and *C. discolor* × *C. sieboldii* germinate equally well in aerated and airtight culture vessels. Growth of plantlets, however, is better in aerated containers (Hasegawa *et al.,* 1978). *Cymbidium* protocorms develop shoots and roots in shallow layers of stationary liquid media. Differentiation is inhibited if the solution layer is deep, but proliferation of protocorms increases (Homès *et al.,* 1971a, 1971b). Growth and differentiation are inhibited when nitrogen is used, which tends to support findings that growth of orchid seedlings is improved with the aeration provided by glasswool pads or charcoal in media (Ernst, 1974, 1975, 1976).

Seeds of the achlorophyllous orchid *Galeola septentrionalis* germinate only in airtight vessels. Air pressure of 1.8 atmospheres enhances germination (Nakamura, 1962, 1964, 1976; Nakamura *et al.,* 1975). Oxygen at concentrations of 5% (approximately 25% of normal) and carbon dioxide 8% (26,000% of normal) respectively is essential. Ethylene at concentrations ranging from 2 to 8 $\mu l\ l^{-1}$ also enhances germination. Best germination occurs under 10% O_2 (20% is the normal content in the atmosphere), 6% CO_2 (0.032% is normal), and 84% N (80% is normal) at a pressure of 1.4 $kg\ cm^{-2}$. Tolerances were 5% to 12% O_2, 2% to 10% CO_2, and 1.1 to 2.0 $kg\ cm^{-2}$ pressure (Nakamura, 1976). Subsequent development is not influenced by CO_2 concentration of 0% to 8% and pressure between 1.0 and 1.8 $kg\ cm^{-2}$. Oxygen levels were also important, in the range of 5% to 20%, with an optimum between 10% and 15%.

Galeola septentrionalis is an underground, chlorophyll-free holomycotrophic orchid. Its inflorescence is borne above the soil. It is therefore safe to assume that for germination to occur underground, it would require low O_2 and high CO_2 levels. Such conditions have been reported, with CO_2 levels of 12% being "quite usual" and reaching 16%. Oxygen concentrations in some soils may be as low as 1% (for a review see Nakamura *et al.*, 1975). The requirement for increased pressure is not easy to explain because of the "difficulty of measuring atmospheric pressure in the soil" (Nakamura *et al.*, 1975).

The differences in atmospheric requirements of germinating orchid seeds are not surprising given the great diversity of orchids and their ability to adapt to many different ecological niches.

Illumination

Germinating orchid seeds and developing seedlings vary in their requirements and responses to light and/or photoperiods (Table 4-7; for reviews see Arditti, 1967a, 1979). Unfortunately, insufficient data make only tentative generalizations possible. It is reasonable to state, however, that epiphytic species germinate both in the light and in the dark, although they appear to require light for induction or improvement of shoot and/or root formation. Several terrestrial species respond similarly (Ueda and Torikata, 1972a; Werckmeister, 1970a, 1970b, 1971). Other species germinate better in the dark (Fast, 1976; Harvais, 1973; Vöth, 1976; for a review see Stoutamire, 1974).

A number of species develop and grow better when cultured on a dark medium such as charcoal. This phenomenon was first observed with *Cymbidium* protocormlike bodies (Werckmeister, 1970a, 1970b, 1971) and confirmed with *Paphiopedilum* and *Phalaenopsis* seedlings (Fig. 4-11; Ernst, 1974, 1975, 1976). A number of explanations have been proposed to explain this effect. One was that charcoal is a source of microelements. An analysis for elements in charcoal (Ernst, 1975) indicated that this suggestion was incorrect (Table 4-8). Water extract of charcoal had no growth-enhancing effects, and the microelements in the charcoal were also found to be impurities of media components.

A second explanation was that polarity is established by the dark medium and that it enhances formation of roots, eliminates or reduces negative- or ageotrophic effects, and improves differentiation (Werckmeister, 1971). Although it is plausible, this explanation has not been supported by findings that growth on glasswool, which is white, is better than that on dark agar medium (Ernst, 1974, 1975, 1976).

Absorption of growth-inhibiting seedling metabolites by charcoal has been proposed as another reason for the improved growth (Ernst, 1974; Werckmeister, 1970b), but seedling cultures on glasswool do not appear to offer corroboration. Growth of seedlings

Table 4-7. Effects of photoperiod, light intensity, quality, and sources of illumination on germinating orchid seeds and developing seedlings[a]

Orchid	Photoperiod (h)	Light intensity	Light quality	Remarks	Reference
Arundina bambusifolia	12	3000 lux	Philips "Natural"	Germination	Mitra, 1971
Brassocattleya	16		Cool white, warm white	Wide-spectrum Gro-Lux is better than standard	Halpin and Farrar, 1965
Calanthe discolor	16	400–500 lux	Grow lamps	Germination and growth	Hasegawa et al., 1978
C. discolor × C. sieboldii	16				
Cattleya	16		Standard Gro-Lux Wide-spectrum Gro-Lux	Gro-Lux or warm white Cool white is poorest	
Cymbidium		400–5000 lux	Diffuse daylight	Shoots and terrestrial roots develop; formation of aerial roots ceases	Werckmeister, 1970a, 1970b, 1971
Cymbidium	$23\frac{1}{2}$		Phytor	Development of protocorms	Homès et al., 1971a, 1971b
Cymbidium				"Rhizogenesis" inhibited in the dark, but etiolated shoots are formed	Homès et al., 1973
Cymbidium goeringii		8200 ergs cm^{-2} s^{-1} 73,000 ergs cm^{-2} s^{-1}	"White" (Toshiba, FL 20 SW) Vitalux (NEC FL 20 BR)	Root formation; no root formation at 4400 and 4000 ergs cm^{-2} s^{-1} under these lights or with red or blue illumination	Ueda and Torikata, 1972a
Cymbidium insigne		4000 ergs cm^{-2} s^{-2}	As above plus blue and red	Root formation. Best root formation with Vitalux. Red light not as good as blue	Ueda and Torikata, 1972a
Cypripedium calceolus				Germinates in the dark	Fast, 1976
Cypripedium reginae				Best germination in the dark	Harvais, 1973
				"Darkness-requiring dormancy"	Reyburn, 1978
Paphiopedilum seedlings				Improved growth on darkened media	Ernst, 1974, 1975, 1976
Phalaenopsis				Better growth on darkened media	Ernst, 1975, 1976
Serapias orientalis				Germination in the dark	Vöth, 1976
Terrestrial species				Light inhibits germination	Stoutamire, 1974
Various species		3000 lux		Good for germination	Mukherjee et al., 1974

[a] For a review of pre-1967 literature see Arditti, 1967a.

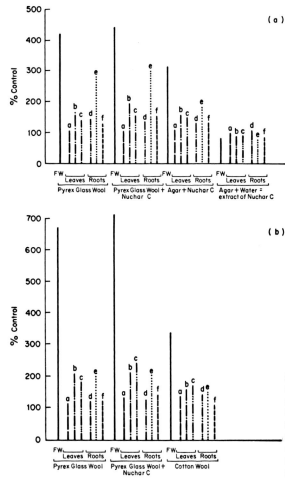

Fig. 4-11. Development of *Paphiopedilum* and *Phalaenopsis* on glasswool or on charcoal (Nuchar C)-containing medium. (A) *Paphiopedilum* seedlings cultured on Thomale GD medium, 200 days under Gro-Lux illumination. (B) *Phalaenopsis amboinensis* seedlings grown on Knudson C medium, 200 days under Gro-Lux illumination; FW, fresh weight; a, number of leaves; b, length of leaves; c, width of leaves; d, number of roots; e, length of roots; f, diameter of roots (Ernst, 1975, as redrawn in Arditti, 1979).

Table 4-8.   A semiquantitative spectroscopic analysis of Nuchar C and its water extract (based on weight of charcoal; Ernst, 1975)

Element	Nuchar C	
	Not extracted, %	Water extract %
Na	0.35	0.344
K	0.17	0.139
Ca	0.034	Trace
Mg	0.048	0.024
Mn	0.020	0.003
Si	0.36	0.24
Al	0.11	0.063
Sn	0.006	0.003
Fe	0.041	Trace
Cu	0.001	0.0007
Zn	0.002	Trace
Mo	Trace	—
B	0.0004	Trace

cultured on glasswool in liquid media is better than on charcoal-containing media. Hence absorption may not be a major factor unless dilution of inhibitors in liquid media is more rapid than in agar.

The pH of charcoal-containing media is the same as that of controls. Therefore, a more appropriate pH is apparently not a reason for the improved growth on charcoal-containing media.

Growth on charcoal or glasswool and charcoal is equally good, which suggests that improved aeration may explain the increased growth on both. Charcoal granules, each a miniature sponge as it were, may increase the amount of air in agar media, and seedlings on a glasswool platform may be similarly well aerated. In nature, seeds germinate and seedlings grow on rocks, incompletely decomposed litter, rough bark, and debris. Aeration under these conditions is undoubtedly excellent. It is therefore not surprising that growth in vitro is better when seedlings are well aerated. Overall, it appears that the effects of charcoal are not due only to the exclusion of light.

The inhibitory effects of light, which are most prevalent among terrestrial species, have been described as "part of . . . [a] protective mechanism . . . making it impossible for seedlings to develop at the soil surface when they would be subjected to drying during the growing period" (Stoutamire, 1974). It is not clear why seeds of epiphytic species, which may be subject to the same perils, do not seem to have such protective mechanisms or have a lesser need for them.

The existence of a pH-regulated or affected darkness-requiring dormancy in seeds of *Cypripedium reginae* (Reyburn, 1978) is difficult to evaluate because the results seem to be erratic. Only one of the seven cultures (pH 7.0, 6.0, 5.5, 5.0, 4.5, 4.0, 3.5) germinated in the dark at 15°C to 20°C. The rest were reported as contaminated or as "no change." Results in the light were the same (one of seven cultures germinated). When cultures were maintained for 1 month at 3°C and then moved to 15°C to 20°C, three germinated (Reyburn, 1978). These findings may be indicative of effects of darkness and/or pH, but are not rigorous enough for reasonable conclusions. Light-inhibited species become less sensitive to illumination as their seedlings develop and form leaves. There have been no comparative studies of how light quality and sources affect growth. Further generalizations are therefore not possible. (Fast, 1967; Halpin and Farrar, 1965; for reviews see Arditti, 1967a; Withner, 1959a, 1974).

Temperature

The optimal temperature for seed germination of most species is 20°C to 25°C, with the range extending from 6°C to 40°C (Arditti, 1967a, 1967b; Mukherjee *et al.*, 1974; Thompson, 1977; Withner, 1959a). Several species seem to require chilling (Stoutamire, 1974) or at least can tolerate cold storage (Vöth, 1976). However, these species also germinate best at 25°C (Harvais, 1973).

pH

Data indicate that the optimal pH for orchid seed germination is 4.8 to 5.2, with the range extending from 3.6 to 7.6 (Arditti, 1967a, 1979). Seedlings can tolerate acidity and grow well even at a pH of 3.3 to 3.7 (Ernst, 1967a, 1967b, 1974; Miyazaki and Nagamat-su, 1965). A desire to maintain an appropriate pH led to the formulation of special buffers (Burgeff, 1936; Harrison and Arditti, 1970) or media (Knudson, 1951; Sideris, 1950; Vacin and Went, 1949), all of which seem to be unnecessary. The effects of pH on a presumed darkness-requiring dormancy (Reyburn, 1978) are questionable because the results are erratic.

Vitamins

The effects of vitamins on germination have been reviewed several times during the last two decades (Arditti, 1967a, 1979; Arditti and Ernst, 1974; Arditti and Harrison, 1977; Withner, 1959, 1974). Therefore, only a brief summary will be given here.

Vitamins A, B_{12}, D, E, and T (which can be best described as a termite extract) ascorbic acid (vitamin C), biotin, folic acid, inositol (this polyol is sometimes classified as a general growth factor rather than a vitamin), niacin, pantothenic acid, pyridoxine, riboflavin, thiamine, and related compounds such as p-aminobenzoic acid, glutathione, and other substances have all been screened for their effects on orchid seed germination and seedling growth. Results have been inconsistent (Table 4-9), in part because of physiological differences between developmental stages or species. The inconsistencies could also be due to vitamins that were present as impurities in media components. If so, basal media, that is, controls, assumed to be free of vitamins, were not, and mixtures presumed to contain specific concentrations in fact included different ones. Evidence to support this assumption was obtained from experiments with niacin nearly 40 years ago (Noggle and Wynd, 1943).

Current evidence indicates that symbiotic fungi provide orchids with vitamins or their precursors (Harvais and Pekkala, 1975; Hijner and Arditti, 1973; Mariat, 1948, 1952,

Table 4-9.   Effects of vitamins on several orchids[a]

Orchid	Vitamins	Remarks	Reference
Cattleya alliance	Ascorbic acid (vitamin C) 0.5 ppm	Reduced browning of shoot apices	Uesato, 1978
Cypripedium reginae seeds and seedlings	Pantothenic acid, 0.5 ppm Pyridoxine, 0.5 ppm Thiamine, 5 ppm	Brought about increases in leaf size to "natural proportions"	Harvais, 1973
Dendrobium seeds	Pyridoxine HCl, 300 ppm Riboflavin, 300 ppm Thiamine HCl, 300 ppm	Improved germination	Mukherjee *et al.*, 1974
European terrestrial species	Niacin, 2 ppm Pyridoxine, 2 ppm Thiamine, 2 ppm	Improved germination	Borriss, 1969; Billensteiner, 1980
Orchis laxiflora	Thiamine, 0.1 mg l^{-1}	Necessary for germination	Mead and Bulard, 1979
Paphiopedilum hybrids	Riboflavin (concentration not given)	Favorable influence on germination	Flamée, 1978
	Complete vitamin mixture (Suprodyn-Roche)	Enhanced germination	
Serapias orientalis	1 tablet of Multivit B l^{-1}: Adermin, 0.5 ppm Lactoflavin, 1 ppm Niacin, 10 ppm Calcium pantothenate, 1 ppm Thiamine, 1.5 ppm	Enhanced germination	Vöth, 1976

[a]For more extensive tables see Arditti, 1967a.

1954; Stephen and Fung, 1971; Vermeulen, 1947; for reviews see Arditti, 1967a, 1979; Arditti and Ernst, 1974; Arditti and Harrison, 1977; Withner, 1959a, 1974) and other factors (Ueda and Torikata, 1974). Folic acid has had virtually no effect in orchid culture media (Table 4-10; Downie, 1949; Withner, 1951), but in one instance it stimulated germination (Mariat, 1948, 1952, 1954). Hence it seems that orchids may be self-sufficient with respect to this vitamin. Some mycorrhizal fungi require folic acid or its component moiety, p-aminobenzoic acid (Hijner and Arditti, 1973; Stephen and Fung, 1971; Vermeulen, 1947), which may be provided by *Arundina chinensis* (Stephen and Fung, 1971), *Dactylorhiza* (Vermeulen, 1947), and *Epidendrum* (Hijner and Arditti, 1973) seedlings.

Niacin enhances orchid seed germination and seed development more consistently than any other vitamin (for reviews see Arditti, 1967a, 1967b, 1977; Arditti and Ernst, 1974; Arditti and Harrison, 1977; Arditti and Tarr, 1979; Withner, 1959a, 1974). This finding indicates that orchids may have a niacin requirement that mycorrhizal fungi satisfy in nature. This assumption is supported by evidence that niacin is released into culture media by *Rhizoctonia* strains from *Dactylorhiza purpurella* (Harvais and Pekkala, 1975) and *Cymbidium* (Hijner and Arditti, 1973). Orchid seedlings and leaves synthesize niacin via the tryptophan degradation pathway (Arditti and Tarr, 1979; Cooper *et al.*, 1982; Tarr and Arditti, 1981).

Thiamine presents an interesting case of co-evolution on a physiological-biochemical level. A number of investigators have reported that this vitamin enhances germination and growth (Tables 4-9, 4-10; Arditti, 1967a, 1979; Arditti and Harrison, 1977; Withner, 1959a, 1974). In one experiment it was shown that the vitamin itself, or its pyrimidine fraction alone, was capable of enhancing germination and growth (Magrou and Mariat, 1945; Mariat, 1944, 1948, 1952). Under symbiotic conditions fungi such as *Corticium catonii* (Cappelletti, 1947) and a *Rhizoctonia* isolated from *Cymbidium* (Hijner and Arditti, 1973) provide germinating orchid seeds and developing seedlings with thiamine and its components. In other instances the fungus may obtain either thiamine or its thiazole moiety, which it requires, from the orchid.

Table 4-10. Summary of vitamin effects on germinating orchid seeds and developing seedlings (modified from Arditti and Harrison, 1977)

Vitamin	Effect
Ascorbic acid (Vitamin C)	Increased germination and growth in *Cattleya* and *Oncidium*. Promotes embryonic growth in *Cymbidium*.
Biotin	No effects on *Cattleya* and *Epidendrum*. Enhances growth and/or color in *Cattleya*, *Odontoglossum*, *Paphiopedilum*, and *Cymbidium*.
Folic acid	Mostly without effects.
Inositol	Unsuitable as sole carbon source for *Dendrobium* and *Phalaenopsis*. No effects on *Cattleya*, *Epidendrum*, and *Goodyera*. Possibly stimulates germination of *Cattleya*.
Niacin	The only vitamin reported to consistently enhance germination and development of several orchids.
Pantothenic acid	Generally without effects.
Pyridoxine	Reported to enhance germination or growth, have no effects, or be inhibitory.
Riboflavin	May not stimulate germination or does so only in some cases; enhances differentiation of plants at leaf point stage and promotes embryonic growth.
Thiamine	The vitamin itself or only its pyrimidine moiety can enhance germination and growth.
Mixtures of vitamins	Improved germination and growth.

Hormones

Results of experiments with orchid seedlings and auxins, cytokinins, and gibberellins are inconsistent and consequently inconclusive (for reviews see Arditti, 1967a, 1979; Withner, 1959a, 1974). There are several possible reasons for this inconsistency: (1) interactions may have occurred between substances because various combinations of hormones with and without additional substances, culture conditions, and seedlings were used; (2) physiological responses and requirements of species and genera may vary; (3) different forms and analogues of each hormone were used; (4) culture conditions were different in each case; (5) a wide range of dosage concentrations was used; and (6) the age of the seedlings may have affected their response.

Auxins

Auxins were first added to orchid cultures nearly 50 years ago with varying results (Burgeff, 1934; for reviews see Arditti, 1967a, 1979; Withner, 1959a, 1974). In most instances auxins, mostly indoleacetic acid (IAA), indolebutyric acid (IBA), and naphthaleneacetic acid (NAA), enhanced germination and/or seedling growth somewhat. Inhibition was reported in very few cases. In a single instance (with excised *Dendrobium* ovaries), death occurred in the absence of auxin (Israel, 1963). Overall, however, reports on the effects of auxins are inconclusive (Table 4-11).

Table 4-11. Effects of auxins on orchids[a]

Orchid	Auxin	Remarks	Reference
Chondrorhynca discolor × *Lycaste aromatica* seeds	NAA,[b] 0.1 ppm (0.54 μM)	Seed germination accelerated slightly and seedling growth and development enhanced. Protocorms died after 6 months on auxin-deficient media	Strauss and Reisinger, 1976
Bletilla sp.	NAA, 0.1 ppm (0.54 μM)	Seed germination accelerated slightly and seedling growth and development enhanced	Strauss and Reisinger, 1976
Cattleya	NAA, 1–5 mg/l or 2,4-D,[b] 0.1 mg/l	Enhanced growth of plantlets	Kusumoto, 1979a
Cattleya	NAA, 1 mg/l[c] 2,4-D, 0.1 mg/l[c] NAA 0.5–1 mg/l[c]	Maximal proliferation Stimulated shoot formation Stimulated shoot formation	Kusumoto, 1979b
Cattleya aurantiaca	NAA, 0.1 ppm (0.54 μM)	Seed germination accelerated slightly and seedling growth and development enhanced	Strauss and Reisinger, 1976
Coeloglossum viride seeds and seedlings	IAA[b], 1 ppm	No effect	Hadley, 1970b
Cymbidium	2,4-D, 0.01 mg/l[d]	Increased bud formation on protocorms, morphological aberrations	Kusumoto, 1978
	NAA, 0.01–0.1 mg/l[d] 2,4-D, 0.1 mg/l[d]	Increased bud formation Maximal shoot growth, abnormal shoots	
	NAA, 0.01–0.1 mg/l[d] NAA, 0.1 mg/l[d] NAA, 0.01 mg/l[d] NAA, 0.01–0.1 mg/l[d] 2,4-D, 0.1 mg/l	Consistent shoot growth Root formation Root development Normal protocorms Abnormal protocorms	

(continued)

Table 4-11.   Continued

Orchid	Auxin	Remarks	Reference
Cymbidium sp. seeds	K salt of NAA, above 1 ppm	Inhibitory	Torikata *et al.*, 1965
Cymbidium sp. seedlings	NAA, 0.1–1 ppm	Stimulates growth	Torikata *et al.*, 1965
Cymbidium kanran rhizome	NAA, 0.1–10 ppm	Growth slightly promoted	Sawa, 1969
Cymbidium kanran leaf-bud	NAA, 0.1–10 ppm	No differentiation	Sawa, 1969
Cymbidium madidum seeds	NAA, 0.1 ppm (0.54 μM)	Seed germination accelerated slightly and seedling growth enhanced	Strauss and Reisinger, 1976
Cymbidium virescens rhizomes and leaf buds	NAA, 0.1–10 ppm	Promotion	Sawa, 1969
Dactylorhiza (Orchis) purpurella seeds and seedlings	IAA, 1 ppm	No effect	Hadley, 1970b
Dactylorhiza (Orchis) purpurella seeds and seedlings	IAA	Results inconclusive	Harvais, 1972
Dendrobium protocorms	IBA,[b] 5 ppm; NAA, 0.5–0.8 ppm	Growth enhancement	Pages, 1971
Dendrobium seedlings	IAA, 2 mg/l; NAA, 2 mg/l	Induced callus formation, reduced percentage of normal seedlings; increased number and length of leaves	Mukherjee *et al.*, 1974
Dendrobium nobile seeds and seedlings	IAA, 0.1, 1, 10 ppm	Inhibition	Miyazaki and Nagamatsu, 1965
Goodyera repens seeds and seedlings	IAA, 1 ppm	No effect	Hadley, 1970
Miltonia spectabilis	IAA, 1 g/l to 1 × 10^{-8} g/l	Germination not "drastically stimulated"; differentiation promoted	Hayes, 1969
Miltonia spectabilis var. *moreliana*	IAA, 1 g/l to 1 × 10^{-8} g/l	Germination not "drastically stimulated"; differentiation promoted	Hayes, 1969
Odontoglossum grande	IAA, 1 g/l to 1 × 10^{-8} g/l	Germination not "drastically stimulated"; differentiation promoted	Hayes, 1969
Odontoglossum schlieperianum	IAA, 1g/l to 1 × 10^{-8} g/l	Germination not "drastically stimulated"; differentiation promoted	Hayes, 1969
Orchis (Dactylorchis) purpurella seeds and seedlings	IAA, 0.25, 0.5, or 1 ppm	Germination impeded, elongation of protocorms	Hadley and Harvais, 1968
Paphiopedilum hybrids	NAA, 1 ppm	Enhanced germination	Flamée, 1978
Phalaenopsis ovules	NAA, 0.5–1 ppm	Enhanced growth	Pages, 1971
Phalaenopsis protocorms	NAA, 10 ppm	Increased number	Uesato, 1978
Phalaenopsis shoots	NAA, 0.1 ppm	Increased number	Uesato, 1978
	NAA, 1–10 ppm	Reduced number	Uesato, 1978
Platanthera bifolia	IAA, 1 ppm	No effect	Hadley, 1969
Spathoglottis plicata seeds	2,4-D	Germination	Chennaveeraiah and Patil, 1973
Vanda cv Miss Joaquim seeds and seedlings	IAA, 25, 50, 100 ppm	Germination inhibited	Goh, 1971
Vanda cv Miss Joaquim seeds and seedlings	2,4-D, 0.1, 0.25, 0.5, 1, 2, 5, ppm	Germination inhibited	Goh, 1971
Vanda cv Miss Joaquim seeds and seedlings	2,4-D	Callus formation after 3 months	Goh, 1971
Vanda	IAA, 1 ppm	"Not very effective in the formation of seedlings"	Rao and Avadhani, 1963

[a] For a table of pre-1967 findings see Arditti, 1967a.
[b] 2,4-D, 2,4-dichlorophenoxyacetic acid; IAA, indoleacetic acid; IBA, indolebutyric acid; NAA, naphthaleneacetic acid.
[c] Combined with cytokinin.
[d] Combined with gibberellin or cytokinin.

Orchid pollinia contain large amounts of auxin, but only traces of this hormone have been detected in *Cypripedium* seeds and none in *Dendrobium* and *Calanthe* (Poddubnaya-Arnoldi, 1960; Poddubnaya-Arnoldi and Zinger, 1961). These findings and the inconsistent reports regarding the effects of auxins in culture media indicate that, in general, germinating orchid seeds and developing seedlings do not require an exogenous source of these hormones. If some do require or benefit from an exogenous source in nature, however small or large, they probably derive it from their mycorrhizae (Hayes, 1969; for a review see Arditti and Ernst, 1974). Given that at least one mycorrhizal fungus is enhanced by auxin (Downie, 1943), it is also possible that orchids provide their symbionts with the hormone.

Cytokinins

Several mycorrhizal fungi have been reported to produce cytokinins, although none is associated with orchids (Crafts and Miller, 1974; Miura and Hall, 1973). It may therefore be safe to assume that orchid mycorrhizae also produce cytokinins. If germinating orchid seeds or developing seedlings require an external source of these hormones, it is possible that this need is satisfied by the fungi under natural conditions. In vitro growth of seedlings of several species is enhanced by cytokinins. Growth in others is inhibited. In a third group, growth remains unaffected (Table 4-12; for reviews see Arditti, 1967a, 1979; Withner, 1974). Benzylamino purine (BAP) is reported to retard development and differentiation of cells and tissues of *Cymbidium* protocorms (Gailhofer and Thaler, 1975). This hormone may also bring about the appearance of enlarged mitochondria in the light. In addition, BAP induces an increase in the number of young chloroplasts and delays their degeneration (Gailhofer and Thaler, 1975). Auxin:cytokinin ratios may be important to growth in some instances (Hadley and Harvais, 1968; Uesato, 1978; see page 207).

Germinating seeds are more sensitive to higher cytokinin levels than are protocorms, which suggests that the seeds may have lower or no requirements for cytokinin (we should not assume, however, that developing embryos do not require these hormones), can synthesize enough to satisfy their own need, destroy the hormone at a slower rate than do protocorms, or a combination of these factors. On the other hand, protocorms may be unable to synthesize enough cytokinin or may deactivate it faster. Whatever the case, the effect of cytokinins on orchid seedlings is in line with their known function in other plants.

Gibberellins

Several species of basidiomycetes, a group of fungi that includes orchid mycorrhizae, produce gibberellin-like substances (Pegg, 1973; Smith, 1974; Strullu, 1974). Therefore it is possible to assume that, as with cytokinin, orchid seeds and seedlings, which may require gibberellins, obtain them in nature from their mycorrhizae. If so, the effects of gibberellic acid in orchid culture media could be expected to vary with the species and growth stage. This prediction indeed seems to hold true in several instances (Table 4-13, Fig. 4-12; Arditti, 1967a, 1979; Withner, 1959a, 1974). In general, the effects of exogenous gibberellins on the growth of orchid seedlings are mostly negative. Thus it seems that orchid seedlings synthesize as much gibberellins as they need or that seeds or seedlings have a limited ability to deactivate the hormone. Gibberellins, therefore, except when added to culture media in very small amounts, may raise actual concentrations to supraoptimal levels for most orchids.

Table 4-12. Effects of cytokinins and related substances on some orchids[a]

Orchid	Cytokinin	Remarks	Reference
Cattleya	Kinetin, 0.1–1.0 mg/l[b]	Effective plantlet growth Increased shoot growth and protocorm numbers	Kusumoto, 1979a, 1979b
	6-Benzyladenosine, 1 mg/l[b]	Promoted shoot formation	
	6-Benzyladenosine, 5 mg/l[b]	Stimulated protocorm proliferation	
Cattleya aurantiaca, unripe seeds	Benzyl adenine	Formation of protocorms not affected by low concentrations Proliferating protocorms with high concentrations Number of roots and their fresh weight and dry weight decreased with increasing concentrations Number of shoots increased by high concentrations Fresh and dry weight of protocorms and shoots decreased at low concentrations	Pierik and Steegmans, 1972
Coeloglossum viride seeds and seedlings	Kinetin, 1–10 ppm	Germination retarded, growth rate of protocorms increased	Hadley, 1970b
Cymbidium	Kinetin, 0.1–1 mg/l combined with auxin and/or gibberellin	Enhanced bud formation on protocorms and normal protocorm development	Kusumoto, 1978
Cymbidium goeringi (*Cym. virescens*) shoots	Kinetin, 10 ppm	No root formation	Ueda and Torikata, 1972a, 1972b
Cymbidium insigne shoots	Kinetin, 10 ppm	No root formation	Ueda and Torikata, 1972a, 1972b
Cymbidium cv In Mem. Cyril Strauss, protocorm	Benzyl adenine, 0.1 ppm	Development retarded	Rücker, 1974
	Benzyl adenine, 1.0 ppm	Formation of roots and root hairs inhibited	
	N-Benzyladenosine, 10 ppm	Differentiation of buds inhibited; chlorophyll synthesis inhibited	
	Kinetin, 50 ppm	Teratogenic and toxic effects, chlorophyll synthesis inhibited Mitotic and endomitotic activity stimulated by all concentrations Differentiation of cell walls occurred earlier Effects can be reversed by transplanting protocorms on cytokinin-free medium	
Cymbidium kanran rhizomes	Adenine sulfate	No effect	Sawa, 1969
Cymbidium virescens rhizomes	Adenine sulfate	No effect	Sawa, 1969
Cypripedium calceolus seeds	Kinetin or benzyl adenine, 1 ppm	Germination enhanced	Borriss, 1969
Cypripedium reginae seeds and seedlings	6(γ,γ-dimethylallyl-amino)purine	Growth impeded	Harvais, 1973
	Kinetin riboside, zeatin	No morphogenetic effects	
Dactylorhiza (*Orchis*) *purpurella* seeds and seedlings	Kinetin, 1–10 ppm	Germination impeded, growth rate of protocorms increased	Hadley, 1970b
Dactylorhiza purpurella seeds and seedlings	6(γ,γ-dimethylallyl-amino)purine	"Shoot characters" and chlorophyll formation enhanced	Harvais, 1972
	Kinetin riboside	"Root characters" suppressed	
Goodyera repens seeds and seedlings	Kinetin, 1–10 ppm	No response	Hadley, 1970b
Orchis purpurella seeds and seedlings	Kinetin	Pronounced effect on growth and development	Hadley and Harvais, 1968
Phalaenopsis	Kinetin, 1 ppm	Increased number of protocorms	Uesato, 1978
	Kinetin, 0.01 ppm	Increased number of shoots	Uesato, 1978
	Adenine	Little effect	
Platanthera bifolia seeds and seedlings	Kinetin, 1–10 ppm	Retard germination. Growth rate of protocorms increased	Hadley, 1970
Spathoglottis plicata seeds and seedlings	Kinetin, 1 ppm	Germination	Chennaveeraiah and Patil, 1973
Vanda cv Miss Joaquim seeds	Kinetin, 2 ppm	Some inhibition	Rao and Avadhani, 1963

[a] For tables of pre-1967 reports see Arditti, 1967a.
[b] Combined with auxin.

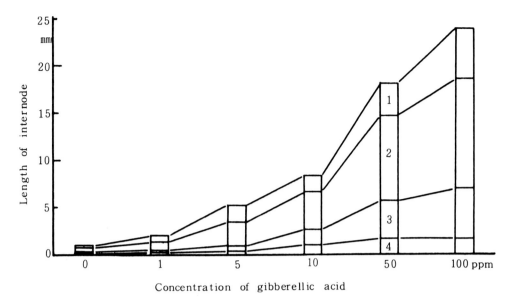

Fig. 4-12. Effects of gibberellin on internode elongation of twelve-week-old seedlings of *Cymbidium* cv Rosanna 'Pinkie' × *Cymbidium* sp. Numbers in the second column from right indicate the position of internodes (Uesato, 1978).

Other Hormones

Thyroid (Withner, 1951) and "female" (Schopfer, 1943) hormones have been added to media used to culture germinating orchid seeds and developing seedlings, but no growth-promoting effects have been reported. Reports that birth control pills enhance the growth of orchid seedlings have not been substantiated experimentally.

Interactions between Hormones

Limited information is available regarding the effects of hormonal interactions on orchid seedlings. According to recent reports (Kusumoto, 1978, 1979a, 1979b; Uesato, 1978; Figs. 4-13 through 4-20), combinations of auxins [NAA or (2,4 dichlorophenoxy) acetic acid (2,40)] and cytokinins (kinetin or benzyladenine) may enhance growth, but

Table 4-13. Effects of gibberellins on some orchids[a]

Orchid	Gibberellin	Remarks	Reference
Cypridium calceolus seeds and seedlings	GA_4, 5 ppm	Differentiation enhanced	Borriss, 1969
Dendrobium seedlings	GA	Induced callus formation; reduced percentage of normal seedlings, increased length and number of leaves	Mukherjee *et al.*, 1974
Dendrobium nobile seeds and seedlings	GA, 1, 10, 100 ppm	Enhanced rapid germination and plantlet formation. Some inhibition at 100 ppm	Miyazaki and Nagamatsu, 1965
Orchis purpurella seeds and seedlings	GA_3, 2.5, 5, 10 ppm	Enhanced protocorm survival, caused abnormal elongation of emergent shoots; did not influence the growth and overall rise of protocorms	Hadley and Harvais, 1968
Vanda cv Miss Joaquim	GA, 500 ppm	"To a certain extent inhibitory to . . . seedling formation"	Rao and Avadhani, 1963

[a] For a table listing pre-1967 findings see Arditti, 1967a.

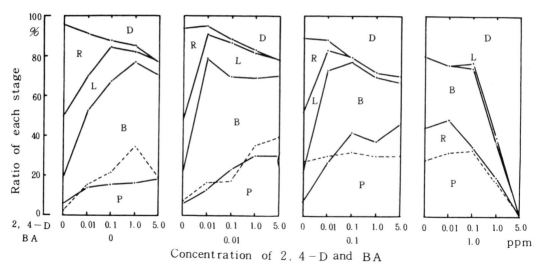

Fig. 4-13. Effects of 2,4-D and 6-benzyladenine (BA) on protocorm development and plantlet formation in *Brassolaeliocattleya* cv Norman's Bay 'Lucile' selfed. Culture period: 30 weeks. Explanation of symbols: P, protocorm stage; B, budding stage; L, leafing stage; R, rooting stage; D, death; dotted line, abnormal plantlets. (Uesato, 1978.)

the effects of these combinations vary with the hormones used, their concentrations, and ratios and the orchid.

Cytokinins, especially benzyladenine, enhanced protocorm multiplication. Simultaneous application of auxin and cytokinins had a similar effect, but the effects of concentration differed. Bud formation on *Cymbidium* protocorms was enhanced by a combination of 0.01 mg 2,4-D plus 0.1 to 1 mg GA_3/l. Shoot growth was maximal on a medium containing 0.1 mg 2,4-D plus 1 mg GA_3/l. This combination led to the formation of abnormal buds, however (Kusumoto, 1979).

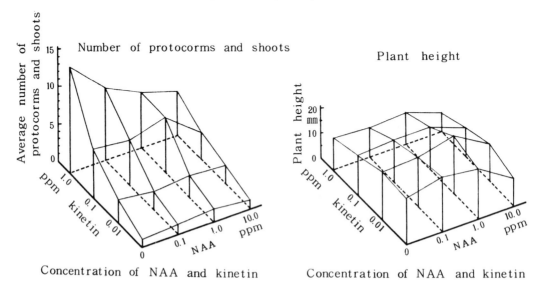

Fig. 4-14. Effects of naphthaleneacetic acid (NAA) and kinetin on the growth of *Laeliocattleya* plantlets (*Lc.* cv Princess Margaret × *Lc.* cv Bonanza 'Giant'). Culture period: 20 weeks. (Uesato, 1978.)

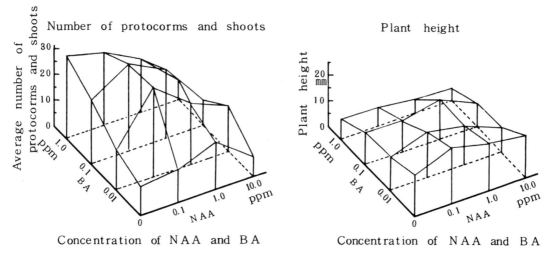

Fig. 4-15. Effects of NAA and 6-benzyladenine (BA) on the growth of abnormal protocorms of *Dendrobium* [*Dend.* cv King George × *Dend.* sp. (*nobile* type)]. Culture period: 8 weeks. (Uesato, 1978.)

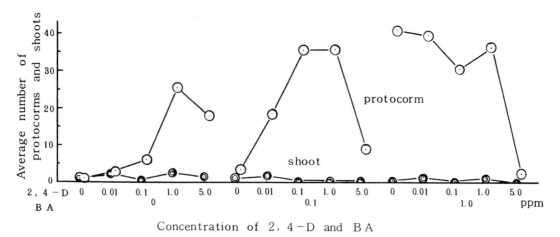

Fig. 4-16. Effects of 2,4-D and 6-benzyladenine (BA) on plantlet development from *Vanda teres* protocorms. Culture period: 30 weeks. (Uesato, 1978.)

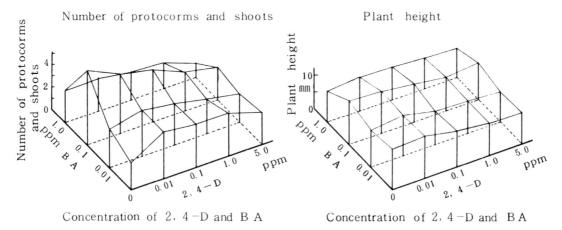

Fig. 4-17. Effects of 2,4-D and 6-benzyladenine (BA) on growth of *Laeliocattleya* cv Bonanza 'Giant' plantlets. Shoot tips with two leaves cultured for 15 weeks. (Uesato, 1978.)

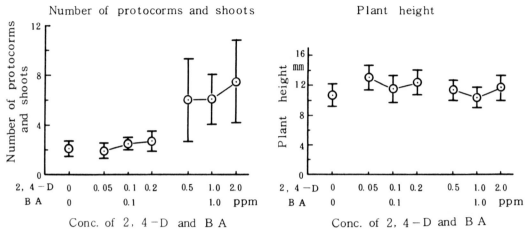

Fig. 4-18. Effects of 2,4-D and 6-benzyladenine (BA) on the growth of plantlets in *Laeliocattleya* cv Eva Robinson 'Ingham' plantlets. Shoot tips with two leaves were cultured for 15 weeks. (Uesato, 1978.)

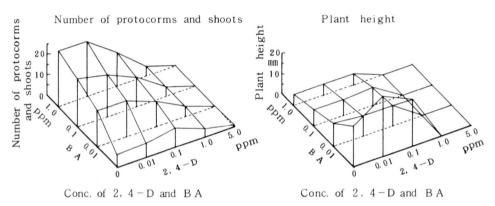

Fig. 4-19. Effects of 2,4-D and 6-benzyladenine (BA) on the growth of *Cymbidium* cv San Francisco 'Meadow Mist' protocorms. Culture period: 20 weeks. (Uesato, 1978.)

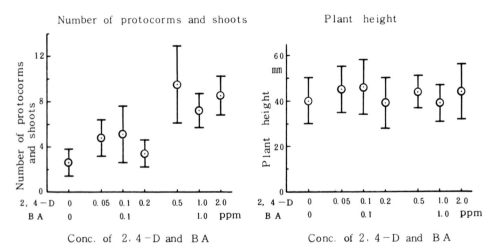

Fig. 4-20. Effects of 2,4-D and 6-benzyladenine (BA) on the growth of *Cymbidium* cv Pearlbel protocorms. Culture period: 20 weeks. (Uesato, 1978.)

Complex Additives

A large and bewildering array of complex additives have been added to orchid seed and seedling culture media. Yeast extract, coconut water, peptone, microbiological preparations (Kukulczanka and Sobieozczánski, 1974), and casein hydrolysate are among the more mundane of these additives. Bark (Frei and Dodson, 1972), sauerkraut juice, honey, salep, fish emulsion, and beef extracts are common even if unusual. Extracts of silkworm pupae and Malaysian beer can best be described as exotic (Table 4-14; Arditti, 1967a, 1979; Ernst, 1967b; Ernst et al., 1970; Withner, 1959a, 1974). The identification of complex additives that enhance growth is more important horticulturally than scientifically, but these findings may also be of interest to tissue culture researchers and investigators working with plants that do not respond to usual treatments.

Fractionations of fungi (Downie, 1949), tomato (Arditti, 1966), and banana (Arditti, 1968) suggest that their growth-enhancing fraction is insoluble in ethanol or water (Withner, 1974). This limited information leaves many substances from which to select, but suggests that the active factor or factors are not found only in fungi.

Experiments with bark substrates (Frei, 1973a, 1973b, 1976; Pollard, 1973) may not approximate natural conditions (Sanford, 1974) for four reasons. One is the addition of bark samples to a culture medium at a pH of 5.5 and autoclaving them (Frei, 1973b). This treatment could chemically modify the bark and hydrolyze and/or extract substances that may not be soluble in tree-trunk leachates under natural conditions. These substances, which may not dissolve in tree trunk effluates, that is, dilute solutions of minerals and some organic compounds (Curtis, 1946; Sanford, 1974) in cool rain water, may affect orchid seeds and seedlings. Thus in these experiments, the seedlings may have been grown on bark extracts or hydrolysates that bore minimal or no similarity to natural conditions. In fact, the bark-containing media could have been toxic due to the presence of substances produced by autoclaving via hydrolysis of larger molecules and/or alteration of existing compounds.

Second, orchid seedlings in nature are usually found in association with lichens and mosses (Frei, 1973a; Pollard, 1973), which suggests that the contact between the seedlings and the bark may be indirect.

Third, the leachates which reached the seedlings may have been modified by the passage through the lichens and mosses. During percolation, water could wash the bark and pick up solutes that can dissolve in rain water at ambient temperatures. Effluates pass through mosses and lichens before reaching the orchids. This process may result in the addition and/or removal of solutes through ion exchange, uptake, or both. Thus it is possible that not all substances leached from bark reach the orchids.

Fourth, the substances from the bark may influence the relationship between the tree, lichen, and moss. The orchids may require or depend on the lichen or moss to establish themselves, in which case the effects of substances from the bark on the mosses and lichens could be the determining factor. Actually, "those trees that had the most orchids had the most lichens and mosses. In each instance [when seedlings were removed from the trees] I found mosses and lichens between the root system of the seedling and the bark" (Frei, 1973a). Further, "it was found that the trees which [exerted] the strongest inhibition, and . . . had no orchids . . . were lacking in mosses and lichens," and "the

Table 4-14. Effect of complex additives on several orchids[a]

Orchid	Additives	Remarks	Reference
Canadian native species, seeds and seedlings	Casamino acids, yeast, and potato extracts	"Intolerant"	Harvais, 1974
Calypso bulbosa seeds and seedlings	Potato dextrose agar	Best germination	Harvais, 1974
Cattleya	Banana juice	Growth is stimulated	Kusumoto, 1979a
	Raw coconut milk	Shoot formation and protocorm proliferation are stimulated	
Cattleya	Banana juice and raw coconut milk	Proliferation of protocorm	Kusumoto, 1979b
	Yeast extract	Shoot formation is inhibited	
Cymbidium	Tryptone	Organogenesis and organ development are promoted	
	Yeast extract	Organogenesis is retarded; increased number of protocorms	Kusumoto, 1978
Cymbidium seeds and seedlings	Banana juice; banana plus apple juice; banana juice plus peptone	Promoted growth of protocorms	Kusumoto and Furukawa, 1977
Cymbidium seeds and seedlings	Tomato juice	Inferior to growth on unsupplemented Knudson C	Torikata *et al.*, 1965
	Fish extract plus peptone	Accelerated growth of protocorms	Torikata *et al.*, 1965
	Extract of silkworm pupae	Stimulated growth	Torikata *et al.*, 1965
Cypripedium calceolus *Cypripedium macrantha* *Cypripedium reginae*	Humus plus coconut milk plus banana juice plus yeast plus sugar	Germination	Muick, 1978
Cypripedium reginae seeds and seedlings	Casein hydrolysate, yeast extract	"Intolerant"	Harvais, 1973
	Potato extract	"Beneficial"	Harvais, 1973
Dactylorhiza purpurella seeds and seedlings	Casamino acids	Superior germination and growth	Harvais, 1972
	Casamino acids plus yeast extract	Further improvement of growth and survival	
Dendrobium ovules	Banana homogenate plus indolebutyric acid or NAA	"Best response"	Pages, 1971
Dendrobium protocorms	Banana homogenate with protease peptone	"Best plantlets"	Pages, 1971
	Banana homogenate plus coconut water and NAA		
Dendrobium hybrid seeds and seedlings	Banana, coconut, tomato, fish emulsion	Most suitable	Mowe, 1973
Epiphytic orchids seeds and seedlings	Bark from *Quercus* trees	Toxic or inhibitory	Frei and Dodson, 1972
European native species seeds and seedlings	Coconut water	Enhancement	Borriss, 1971
Orchis laxiflora	Casamino acids	Can satisfy requirements for nitrogen source	Mead and Bulard, 1979
Paphiopedilum hybrids	Peptone	Enhanced germination	Flamée, 1978
Paphiopedilum seeds	Peptone ("*Fleischpeptone*") or fish meal	Enhancement	Fast, 1971
Paphiopedilum seedlings	Banana	Enhancement	
Phalaenopsis protocorms	Banana	Most favorable	Ernst, 1967b
	Pineapple, fig, and tomato fruits	Pronounced increase in growth	
	Coconut milk	Strong proliferation, retarded differentiation	
	Grapes and raspberries	Retarded growth, toxic	
Phalaenopsis ovules	Coconut water plus NAA	"Best supplements"	Pages, 1971
	Coconut water plus peptone		
Serapias parviflora and *S. orientalis*	Yeast with or without peptone	"Best addition"	Vöth, 1976
Vanda cv Miss Joaquim	Tomato juice or coconut milk	Bigger seedlings formed	Rao and Avadhani, 1963
	Pollinium extract, casein hydrolysate	"Not very effective in the formation of seedling"	
	Yeast extract	"Less effective and to a certain extent inhibitory"	

[a] For a table listing pre-1967 findings see Arditti, 1967a.

inhibitors in the bark . . . were a factor . . . in the growth or lack of [growth of] moss and lichens" (Pollard, 1973).

Gamma Rays

Orchid seeds and embryos are convenient organisms for studies of radio-sensitivity because they contain very few cells. *Dendrobium nobile* seeds irradiated with 10, 20, 30, 40, 60, and 80 KR gamma rays from ^{137}Cs and ^{60}Co germinated at lower rates than controls during the first 3 weeks, and later growth was indirectly proportional to dosage. Within 6 weeks "the rate [of] each treatment reached almost constant value" (Miyazaki, 1968). Survival was similar following 10, 20, 30 KR. At 40 KR there was an abrupt decrease. Growth ceased following 60 and 80 KR. Irradiation also caused many deformities.

Morphactins

Morphactin IT 3456 at concentrations of 0.1 to 10 ppm stimulates proliferation of protocormlike body forms from shoot tips but inhibits root, shoot, and rhizoid formation. It also leads to the development of two to three shoots on one protocorm, the deformation of leaves and shoots, and the formation of secondary protocorms or leaves (Kukulczanka and Twarda-Prędota, 1973).

Surface Active Agents

Many ionic, monionic, and amphoteric biodegradable surfactants are toxic to orchid seedlings at levels higher than 100 ppm (approximately 0.3–0.4 mM). A coincidence seems to exist between the reduction of interfacial tension and phytotoxicity (Ernst *et al.*, 1971b). This finding may be the result of the effects of surfactants on cytomembranes (Healey *et al.*, 1971). Severe damage resulted after 4- and 48-hour exposure to 1000 ppm (2.9 mM) of sodium (linear) dodecylbenzene sulfonate, a common household detergent base. Chloroplasts underwent drastic changes in morphology, lost membranes, and exhibited swollen thylakoids and osmophilic granules. The disintegration of polysomes into monosomes, dispersion of chromatin, plasmolysis, and swelling of mitochondria were other effects. These ultrastructural changes were probably due to the emulsification of membrane lipids and the precipitation and dispersion of cell proteins (Healey *et al.*, 1971).

Enzymes

As mentioned above, orchid seedlings secrete several enzymes into their culture media. Ribulose-1,5-bisphosphate carboxylase is also produced by seedlings. Many additional enzymes are probably produced by germinating seeds and developing seedlings, but very few have been studied. The activity of peroxidase in *Vanda* seedlings is highest during the early stages of development and lowest during differentiation (Alvarez, 1968a; Alvarez and King, 1969). These activity levels are the exact reciprocal of IAA production by seedlings. Consequently, "temporal and spectral activity of the enzyme in the developing seedling are in accord with expectations if this enzyme, in fact, functions to control the level of IAA" (Alvarez and King, 1969). The increase of peroxidase activity, caused by exogenous IAA, indicates that the auxin also "is capable of eliciting activity of an enzyme thought to be involved in its destruction" (Alvarez and King, 1969).

An acid phosphatase produced by *Cymbidium* protocorms separates into three electrophoretic zones, each consisting of two activity bands. RNase activity produced by the same protocorms is in two zones that differ in intensity. Production of both enzymes is affected by streptomycin, but the effects vary with the time of application (Morawiecka *et al.*, 1973).

Nucleic Acids

Protocorms of *Dactylorhiza* (*Orchis*) *purpurella* grow more rapidly following mycorrhizal infection. Cortical parenchyma cells of these protocorms, which are polyploid (predominantly 32C, 64C, and 128C), produce new DNA classes. Protocorms in asymbiotic cultures enlarge and differentiate at a slower rate, and there is no evidence that their nuclei undergo endoreplication (Williamson, 1970, 1973; Williamson and Hadley, 1969). These observations suggest that the production of new DNA by *D. purpurella* protocorms requires fungal infection. Autoradiography after ^{3}H-thymidine incorporation indicated that infection of *Spathoglottis plicata* by *Tulasnella calospora* induced DNA synthesis in fully differentiated cells.

In parenchyma cells of cultured *Vanda* ovules, DNA content increases together with that of RNA and nuclear size. Feulgen staining in nuclei shows that DNA increases to 8C (Alvarez, 1968b, 1969). Hydrolysis time curves of DNA-Feulgen from senescent parenchyma cells differ from those of meristematic and normal parenchyma cells (Alvarez, 1970). Comparisons of Feulgen measurements with acridine orange dye binding suggest that "masking" or "unmasking" of phosphate groups does not occur during cellular differentiation of *Vanda* seedlings. Hence, the increased acridine orange binding is indicative of higher DNA content (Alvarez and Reyniers, 1970). *Vanda* seeds are easier to germinate asymbiotically than those of *Dactylorhiza purpurella* and other temperate zone terrestial orchids. This finding may reflect the differences in the ability of seedlings to synthesize DNA with or without mycorrhizal infection.

Further, the extremely slow growth rate of such orchids as *Taeniophyllum aphyllum* (Mutsuura *et al.*, 1962) and the much faster rate of species like *Zeuxine strateumatica* could also reflect differences in the rates of DNA synthesis. In orchids such as *Gastrodia elata*, where "the activity of [the mycorrhizal] *Armillaria mellea* determines the formation of . . . seedling . . . , renewal of . . . vegetative organs, and transformation of vegetative growth to reproductive growth," the fungus may regulate DNA and/or RNA synthesis (Zhang and Li, 1980).

Endopolyploidization also occurs regularly in some parenchyma cells of asymbiotically germinated *Cymbidium* seeds (Nagl, 1972). These cells show a disproportionate increase in nuclear DNA content and volume, which disappears after inhibition of DNA synthesis with hydroxyurea. Differentiation of the protocorm is accompanied by DNA amplification and endomitotic nuclear cycles (Nagl *et al.*, 1972; Nagl and Rücker, 1972, 1974).

Additional evidence that proper growth and differentiation require DNA synthesis has been obtained from experiments with hydroxyurea (HU). Morphological differences are apparent on 10^{-3} M HU. Protocorms were reduced in size, abnormal, and necrotic, at 5 × 10^{-7} M (Rücker, 1975).

The actions of several plant hormones on *Cymbidium* protocorms can also be explained in terms of their effects on the DNA content of the cells. Cytokinins shift DNA replication to polyploid endomitotic cells from diploid mitotic ones, thus enhancing premature and abnormal cellular differentiation (Nagl and Rücker, 1974). Auxins cause an increase in adenine/thymine (AT)-rich DNA fractions, whereas guanine/cytosine (GC) fractions are promoted by gibberellins (Nagl and Rücker, 1976). Differentiation is probably affected by differential replication of the AT and GC fractions.

The AT-rich satellite DNA from *Cymbidium* nuclei has been characterized by thermal denaturation and ultracentrifugation. It is a rare instance of a major AT fraction in plants and limited to *Cymbidium*. At the time of characterization it had not been isolated from other orchids (Capesius, 1976; Capesius *et al.*, 1975). Quinacrine, 4'6-diamidino-2-phenylindole, and Giemsa's staining technique indicate that this DNA is located within the centromere chromatin (Schweizer and Nagl, 1976). The AT-rich DNA is sensitive to hormone treatment (Capesius *et al.*, 1975; Nagl and Rücker, 1976). Appearance of the AT-rich satellite in *Cymbidium* correlates with a hormone-dependent high but variable amount of heterochromatin. Amplification of DNA may be restricted to the non-AT-rich component of the chromatin (Schweizer and Nagl, 1976). The effects of hormone treatments and different amplifications of the two DNAs suggest that they play important roles in growth and differentiation of *Cymbidium* protocorms. Whether the same holds true for other orchids is not clear.

Alkali-stable and proteinase K-resistant proteins, similar to those found in animals, have been isolated from *Cymbidium pumilum* protocorms (Capesius, Krauth and Werner, 1980).

Diversification and amplification of DNA sequences, which are the molecular basis of speciation and cladogenesis, may regulate somatic differentiation in *Cymbidium* (Nagl and Capesius, 1977).

Transmission of Viruses

Cymbidium mosaic virus is not transmitted through *Dendrobium* seeds (Yuen *et al.*, 1979).

Literature Cited

Alvarez, M. R. 1968a. Temporal and spatial changes in peroxidase activity during fruit development in *Encyclia tampensis* (Orchidaceae). Amer. J. Bot. 55:619–625.
——. 1968b. Quantitative changes in nuclear DNA accompanying postgermination embryonic development in *Vanda* (Orchidaceae). Amer. J. Bot. 55:1036–1041.
——. 1969. Cytophotometric study of nuclear proteins and nucleic acids in parenchymatous tissue of the orchid embryo. Exp. Cell Res. 57:179–184.
——. 1970. Microfluorometric comparison of Feulgen-deoxyribonucleic acid hydrolysis in meristematic and differentiated cells of the orchid embryo. Exp. Cell Res. 61:191–198.

Alvarez, M. R., and D. O. King. 1969. Peroxidase localization, activity, and isozyme patterns in the developing seedling of *Vanda* (Orchidaceae). Amer. J. Bot. 56:180–186.

Alvarez, M. R., and J. P. Reyniers. 1970. Microspectrofluorometric comparison of acridine orange dye binding in meristematic and parenchymal nuclei of the orchid embryo. Exp. Cell Res. 61:326–332.

Anonymous. 1922. Orchid mycorrhyza. Orch. Rev. 30:78–81. (Probably by Gurney Wilson.)

Arditti, J. 1966. The effects of tomato juice and some of its fractions on orchid seed germination and seedling growth. Amer. Orchid Soc. Bull. 35:175–182.

——. 1967a. Factors affecting the germination of orchid seeds. Bot. Rev. 33:1–197.

——. 1967b. Niacin biosynthesis in germinating ×*Laeliocattleya* orchid embryos and young seedlings. Amer. J. Bot. 54:291–298.

——. 1968. Germination and growth of orchids on banana fruit tissue and some of its extracts. Amer. Orchid Soc. Bull. 37:112–116.

——. 1977. Clonal propagation of orchids by means of tissue culture—a manual, pp. 202–293. *In* J. Arditti (ed.), Orchid biology: reviews and perspectives, 1. Cornell University Press, Ithaca, N.Y.

——. 1979. Aspects of the physiology of orchids. Adv. Bot. Res. 7:421–655.

Arditti, J., and R. Ernst. 1974. Reciprocal movement of substances between orchids and mycorrhizae, pp. 299–307. *In* Proc. 7th World Orchid Conf., Medellin, Colombia.

Arditti, J., and C. R. Harrison. 1977. Vitamin requirements and metabolism in orchids, pp. 157–175. *In* J. Arditti (ed.), Orchid biology—reviews and perspectives, 1. Cornell University Press, Ithaca, N.Y.

Arditti, J., P. L. Healey, and R. Ernst. 1972. The role of mycorrhiza in nutrient uptake of orchids. Pt. 2. Extracellular hydrolysis of oligosaccharides by asymbiotic seedlings. Amer. Orchid Soc. Bull. 41:503–510.

Arditti, J., J. D. Michaud, and A. P. Oliva. (1982). Seed germination of North American orchids. Pt. 1. Native California and related species of *Calypso, Epipactis, Goodyera, Piperia,* and *Platanthera.* Bot. Gaz. 142:442–453.

Arditti, J., and J. D. Tarr. 1979. Niacin biosynthesis in plants. Amer. J. Bot. 66:1105–1113.

Bernard, N. 1909. L'évolution dans la symbiose, les orchidées et leurs champignons commensaux. Ann. Sci. Nat. Bot., Series 9, No. 9:1–196.

Billensteiner, H. 1980. Asymbiotische Aussaaten europäischer Orchideen. Die Orchidee 31:35–36.

Borriss, H. 1969. Samenvermehrung und Anzucht europäischer Erdorchideen, pp. 74–78. *In* Proc. 2nd Eur. Orchid Congress.

——. 1970. Samenvermehrung und Kultur von *Habenaria dentata* (Swartz) Schlechter. Die Orchidee 21:73–79.

Burgeff, H. 1934. Pflanzliche Avitaminose und ihre Behebung durch Vitamin-zufuhr. Ber. Deutsch. Bot. Ges. 52:384–390.

——. 1936. Samenkeimung der Orchideen. G. Fischer Verlag, Jena.

Burström, H. 1948. Observations on the influence of galactose on wheat roots. Physiol. Plantarum 1:209–215.

Capesius, I. 1976. Isolation and characterization of native AT-rich satellite DNA from nuclei of the orchid *Cymbidium.* FEBS 68:255–258.

Capesius, I., B. Bierweiler, K. Bachman, and W. Rücker. 1975. An A+T-rich satellite DNA in a monocotyledonous plant *Cymbidium.* Biochim. Biophys. Acta 395:67–73.

Capesius, I., W. Krauth, and D. Werner. 1980. Proteinase K-resistant and alkali-stable bound proteins in higher plant DNA. FEBS Lett. 110:184–186.

Cappelletti, C. 1933. Osservazioni sulla germinazione asimbiotica dei semi di orchidee del genere Cymbidium. Boll. Soc. Ital. Biol. Sper. 8:288–291.

——. 1947. Ricerche fisiologiche sull simbiosi nella orchidee. Lavori di Botanica 8:57–76.

Chennaveeraiah, M. S., and S. J. Patil. 1973. In vitro morphogenesis in seed cultures of an orchid *Spathoglottis plicata,* pp. 410–411. *In* Proc. 60th Indian Sci. Congress, pt. 3.

Clements, M. A., and R. K. Ellyard. 1979. The symbiotic germination of Australian terrestrial orchids. Amer. Orchid Soc. Bull. 48:810–816.

Collett, A. 1971. Notes on the growing of *Disa uniflora.* J. Roy. Hort. Soc. 96:358–361.

Cooper, J. L., B. L. Hilton, J. Arditti, and J. B. Tarr. 1982. Niacin biosynthesis in leaf discs and seedlings of *Cattleya skinneri* (Orchidaceae). New Phytol. 91:621–628.

Crafts, C. B., and C. O. Miller. 1974. Detection and identification of cytokinins produced by mycorrhizal fungi. Plant Physiol. 54:586–588.

Curtis, J. T. 1946. Nutrient supply of epiphytic orchids in the mountains of Haiti. Ecology 27:264–266.

Curtis, J. T. 1947. Studies on the nitrogen nutrition of orchid embryos. Pt. 1. Complex nitrogen sources. Amer. Orchid Soc. Bull. 16:654–660.

de Bruijne, E., and P. Debergh. 1974. Response of *Cymbidium* protocorms to major element deficiency in a culture medium. Mededelingen Fakulteit Landbouw-wetenschappen, Ghent 39:210–215.

Downie, D. G. 1943. Notes on the germination of *Corallorhiza innata*. Trans. and Proc. Bot. Soc., Edinburgh 33:380–382.

——. 1949. The germination of *Goodyera repens* (L)R, Br. in fungal extract. Trans. and Proc. Bot. Soc., Edinburgh. 35:120–125.

Ernst, R. 1967a. Effects of carbohydrate selection on the growth rate of freshly germinated *Phalaenopsis* and *Dendrobium* seed. Amer. Orchid Soc. Bull. 36:1068–1073.

——. 1967b. Effect of select organic nutrient additives on growth *in vitro* of *Phalaenopsis* seedlings. Amer. Orchid Soc. Bull. 36:694–704.

——. 1974. The use of activated charcoal in asymbiotic seedling culture of *Paphiopedilum*. Amer. Orchid Soc. Bull. 43:35–38.

——. 1975. Studies in asymbiotic culture of orchids. Amer. Orchid Soc. Bull. 44:12–18.

——. 1976. Charcoal or glass wool in asymbiotic culture of orchids, pp. 379–383. *In* Proc. 8th World Orchid Conf., Frankfurt (1975).

——. 1980. Seed germination of Paphiopedilums. Orchid Rev. 88:235–236.

Ernst, R., J. Arditti, and P. L. Healey. 1970. The nutrition of orchid seedlings. Amer. Orchid Soc. Bull. 39:599–605, 691–700.

Ernst, R., J. Arditti, and P. L. Healey. 1971a. Carbohydrate physiology of orchid seedlings. Pt. 2. Hydrolysis and effects of oligosaccharides. Amer. J. Bot. 58:827–835.

——. 1971b. Biological effects of surfactants. Pt. 1. Influence on the growth of orchid seedlings. New Phytol. 70:457–475.

Fast, G. 1964. Erfahrungen bei der Anzucht von Orchideen. Die Orchidee 15:23–29.

——. 1967. Neue Erfahrungen mit Orchideen-Aussaaten. Die Orchidee 18:445–452.

——. 1971. Versuche zur Anzucht von Paphiopedilum aus Samen. Die Orchidee 22:189–192.

——. 1976. Möglichkeiten zur Massenvermehrung von *Cypripedium calceolus* und anderen europäischen Wildorchideen, pp. 359–363. *In* Proc. 8th World Orchid Conf., Frankfurt (1975).

Flamée, M. 1978. Influence of selected media and supplements on the germination and growth of *Paphiopedilum* seedlings. Amer. Orchid Soc. Bull. 47:419–423.

Frei, J. K. 1973a. Orchid ecology in a cloud forest in the mountains of Oaxaca, Mexico. Amer. Orchid Soc. Bull. 42:307–314.

——. 1973b. Effect of bark substrate on germination and early growth of *Ernyclia tampensis* seeds. Amer. Orchid Soc. Bull. 42:701–708.

——. 1976. The ecology of epiphytic orchids in relation to their substrates, pp. 46–62. *In* H. M. Szmant and J. Wemple (eds.), 1st Symposium on the Scientific Aspects of Orchids, Department of Chemistry, Univ. of Detroit.

Frei, J. K., and C. H. Dodson. 1972. The chemical effect of certain bark substrates on the germination and early growth of epiphytic orchids. Bull. Torrey Bot. Club 99:301–307.

Freson, R. 1969. Action du glucose sur des protocormes de *Cymbidium* Sw (Orchidaceae) cultivés in vitro. Bull. Soc. Roy. Bot. Belg. 102:205–209.

Gailhofer, M. 1976. Eiweisskristalle *in vitro* kultivierter Protokorme von *Cymbidium*. Phyton (Austria) 17:179–186.

Gailhofer, M., and I. Thaler. 1975. Einfluss von 6-benzylaminopurin auf die Feinstruktur von mito-chondrien und plastiden *in vitro* kultivierten Protokorme von *Cymbidium*. Phyton 17:159–165.

Gething, P. A. 1977. The effect of fertilizers on the growth of orchid (*Odontoglossum*) seedlings. Exp. Hort. 29:94–101.

Goh, C. J. 1971. Some effects of auxin on orchid seed germination and seedling growth, pp. 65–66. *In* International Symp. on Morphogenesis in Plant Cell, Tissue and Organ Culture VIII.4.

Hadley, G. 1968. Orchids and their symbiotic fungi. Malayan Scientist 4:23–27.

——. 1969. Cellulose as a carbon source for orchid mycorrhiza. New Phytol. 68:933–939.

——. 1970a. Non-specificity of symbiotic infection in orchid mycorrhiza. New Phytol. 69:1015–1023.

——. 1970b. The interaction of kinetin, auxin and other factors in the development of north temperate orchids. New Phytol. 69:549–555.

Hadley, G., and G. Harvais. 1968. The effect of certain growth substances on asymbiotic germination and development of *Orchis purpurella*. New Phytol. 67:441–445.

Halpin, J. E., and M. D. Farrar. 1965. The effects of four different fluorescent light sources on the growth of orchid seedlings. Amer. Orchid Soc. Bull. 34:416–420.

Harbeck, M. 1961. Erfahrungen mit der Aussaat von Orchis maculata auf sterilem Nährboden. Die Orchidee 12:67–70.

———. 1963. Einige Beobachtungen bei der Aussaat verschiedener europäischer Erdorchideen auf sterilem Nährboden. Die Orchidee 14:58–65.

———. 1964. Anzucht von *Orchis maculata* vom Samen bis zur Blüte. Die Orchidee 15:57–60.

———. 1968a. Versuche zur Samenvermehrung einiger Dactylorhiza-Arten. Die Orchidee Sonderheft (November):112–118.

———. 1968b. Aussaatversuche mit Disa uniflora. Die Orchidee 19:1–5.

Harrison, C. R. 1973. Physiology and ultrastructure of *Cattleya aurantiaca* (Orchidaceae) germination. Ph.D. Diss., University of California, Irvine.

———. 1977. Ultrastructural and histochemical changes during the germination of *Cattleya aurantiaca* (Orchidaceae). Bot. Gaz. 138:41–45.

Harrison, C. R., and J. Arditti. 1970. Growing orchids from seed. Orchid Digest 34:199–204.

———. 1978. Physiological changes during the germination of *Cattleya aurantiaca* (Orchidaceae). Bot. Gaz. 139:180–189.

Harvais, G. 1972. The development and growth requirements of *Dactylorhiza purpurella* in asymbiotic cultures. Can. J. Bot. 50:1223–1279.

———. 1973. Growth requirements and development of *Cypripedium reginae* in axenic culture. Can. J. Bot. 51:327–332.

———. 1974. Notes on the biology of some native orchids of Thunder Bay, their endophytes and symbionts. Can. J. Bot. 52:451–460.

Harvais, G., and G. Hadley. 1967. The relation between host and endophyte in orchid mycorrhiza. New Phytol. 66:205–215.

Harvais, G., and D. Pekkala. 1975. Vitamin production by a fungus symbiotic with orchids. Can. J. Bot. 53:156–163.

Hasegawa, A., M. Goi, M. Sato, and Y. Ihara. 1978. Fundamental studies on the asymbiotic seed germination of *Calanthe*. Tech. Bull. Fac. Agric. Kagawa Univ. 29:251–259.

Hayes, A. B. 1969. Observations on orchid seed mycorrhizae. Mycopathol. et Mycol. Appl. 38:139–144.

Healey, P. L., R. Ernst, and J. Arditti. 1971. Biological effects of surfactants. Pt. 2. Influence on the ultrastructure of orchid seedlings. New Phytol. 70:477–482.

Hele, M. P. 1953. The phosphorylation and absorption of sugars in the rat. Pt. 1. Hexokinase activity in the intestinal mucosa. Biochem. J. 55:857–863.

Hijner, J. A., and J. Arditti. 1973. Orchid mycorrhiza: Vitamin production and requirements by the symbionts. Amer. J. Bot. 60:829–835.

Homès, J. 1973. Modifications ultrastructurales des chloroplastes de protocormes d'Orchidées cultivés in vitro en présence de saccharose. J. Microscopie 17:66a.

Homès, J., R. Freson, M. Vermylen, and M. Michel. 1971a. Relations entre les conditions de culture et la morphogénèse chez les protocormes d'Orchidées cultivés in vitro. 96th Cong. Nat. Soc. Savantes, Toulouse 4:93–105.

———. 1971b. Relations entre les conditions de culture et la morphogénèse chez les protocormes d'Orchidées, p. 86. *In* 96th Congress Nat. Soc. Savantes, Toulouse 4.

Homès, J., and N. Vanséveren-Van Espen. 1972. Structures de plastes de protocormes d'Orchidées cultivés in vitro à diverses concentrations en saccharose. J. Microscopie 14, Coll. Annu. Soc. Française Microscopie Electronique, Nantes:55a.

———. 1973a. Effects du saccharose et de la lumière sur le développement et la morphologie de protocormes d'Orchidées cultivés in vitro. Bull. Soc. Roy. Bot. Belg. 106:89–106.

———. 1973b. Quelques formes de plastes induites par le milieu de culture dans des protocormes d'Orchidées cultivés in vitro. Bull. Soc. Roy. Bot. Belg. 106:117–121.

Ichihashi, S. 1978. Studies on the media for orchid seed germination. Pt. 2. The effect of anionic and catonic combinations relevant to seedling populations and culture periods on the growth of *Bletilla striata* seedlings. J. Jap. Soc. Hort. Sci. 46:521–529.

———. 1979. Studies on the media for orchid seed germination. Pt. 4. Influence of the characteristics of some culture media on the growth of orchid seedlings. J. Jap. Soc. Hort. Sci. 48:345–352.

Ichihashi, S., and M. Yamashita. 1977. Studies on the media for orchid seed germination. Pt. 1. The effects of balances inside each cation and anion group for the germination and seedling development of *Bletilla striata* seeds. J. Jap. Soc. Hort. Sci. 45:407–413.

srael, H. W. 1963. Production of *Dendrobium* seedlings by aseptic culture of excised ovularies. Amer. Orchid Soc. Bull. 32:441–443.

Kaewbamrung, M. 1967. Transflasking media for *Rhynchostylis* seedlings. Bull. Orchid Soc. Thailand 1:18–22.

Knudson, L. 1916. Influence of certain carbohydrates on green plants. Cornell Agric. Exp. Station Memoirs 9:1–75.

——. 1921. La germinacion no simbiotica de las semillas de orquideas. Bol. Real. Soc. Española Hist. Nat. 21:250–260.

——. 1922. Nonsymbiotic germination of orchid seeds. Bot. Gaz. 73:1–25.

——. 1929. Physiological investigations on orchid seed germination. Proc. Int. Cong. Plant Sci. 2:1183–1189.

——. 1946. A new nutrient solution for germination of orchid seed. Amer. Orchid Soc. Bull. 15:214.

——. 1951. Nutrient solutions for orchids. Bot. Gaz. 112:528–532.

Koch, L. 1973. Vergleich zweier Verfahren zur Vermehrung von *Cymbidium*—protokormen. Gartenbauwissenschaft 38:419–426.

Koch, U. 1972. Über die Aufzucht von Orchideenjungpflanzen. Zierpflanzenbau 4:131–132.

Kukulczanka, K., and J. Sobiesozczánski. 1974. The effects of microbiological S-161 preparation on the growth of meristematic *Cymbidium* Sw tissue, p. 852. *In* Proc. 19th International Hort. Congress 1B, Warsaw.

Kukulczanka, K., and B. Twarda-Prędota. 1973. Effect of morphactine on differentiation and development of *Cymbidium* protocorms cultured in vitro. Acta Soc. Bot. Poloniae 42:281–294.

Kusumoto, M. 1978. Effects of combinations of growth-regulating substances, and of organic matter on the propagation and organogenesis of *Cymbidium* protocorms cultured *in vitro*. J. Jap. Soc. Hort. Sci. 47:391–400.

——. 1979a. Effects of combinations of growth regulators, and of some supplements on the growth of *Cattleya* plantlets cultured *in vitro*. J. Jap. Soc. Hort. Sci. 47:492–501.

——. 1979b. Effects of combinations of growth regulators, and of organic supplements on the proliferation and organogenesis of *Cattleya* protocorm-like bodies cultured in vitro. J. Jap. Soc. Hort. Sci. 47:502–510.

Kusumoto, M., and J. Furukawa. 1977. Effect of organic matter on the growth of Cymbidium protocorms cultured in vitro. J. Jap. Soc. Hort. Sci. 45:421–426.

La Garde, R. V. 1929. Non-symbiotic germination of orchids. Ann. Missouri Bot. Gardens 16:499–514.

Leopold, A. C. 1964. Plant growth and development. McGraw-Hill, New York.

Lugo-Lugo, H. 1955a. Effects of nitrogen on the germination of *Vanilla planifolia* seeds. Amer. Orchid Soc. Bull. 24:309–312.

——. 1955b. The effect of nitrogen on the germination of *Vanilla planifolia* seeds. Amer. J. Bot. 42:679–684.

Magrou, J., and P. Mariat. 1945. Action de l'aneurine sur le developpement des embryons d'Orchidées. Ann. Inst. Pasteur 71:49.

Magrou, J., P. Mariat, and H. Rose. 1949. Sur la nutrition azotée des Orchidées. C. R. Acad. Sci. Paris 229:665–688.

Mariat, F. 1944. Influence favorable de la vitamine B$_1$ sur les germinations de *Cattleya*. Rev. Hort. 29:68–69.

——. 1948. Influence des facteurs de croissance sur le developpement et la differenciation des embryons d'Orchidées. Rev. Gen. Bot. 55:229–243.

——. 1952. Recherches sur la physiologie des embryons d'Orchidées. Rev. Gen. Bot. 59:324–377.

——. 1954. Action de vitamines sur les germinations d'Orchidées, pp. 428[1]–428[3]. *In* G. Bouriquet (ed.), Le vanillier et la vanille dans le monde. Paul Lechavalier, Paris.

McIntyre, D. K., G. J. Veitch, and J. W. Wrigley. 1971. Australian terrestrial orchids from seed. Mimeograph. Canberra Botanic Gardens (also in Australian Plants 6, March 1972).

——. 1972a. Australian terrestrial orchids from seed. Pt. 2. Improvements in techniques and further successes. Mimeograph. Canberra Botanic Gardens.

——. 1972b. Australian terrestrial orchids from seed. Amer. Orchid Soc. Bull. 41:1093–1097.

Mead, J. W., and C. Bulard. 1975. Effects of vitamins and nitrogen sources on asymbiotic germination and development of *Orchid laxiflora* and *Ophrys sphegodes*. New Phytol. 74:33–40.

——. 1979. Vitamins and nitrogen requirements of *Orchis laxiflora* Lamk. New Phytol. 83:129–136.

Mitra, G. C. 1971. Studies on seeds, shoot-tips and stem-discs of an orchid grown in aseptic culture. Indian J. Exp. Biol. 9:79–85.

Miura, G., and R. H. Hall. 1973. trans-Ribosylzeatin, its biosynthesis in Zea mays endosperm and the mycorrhizal fungus Rhizopogon roseolus. Plant Physiol. 51:563–569.

Miyazaki, S. 1968. On the germination and growth of the orchid seeds irradiated by gamma rays. Agric. Bull. Saga Univ. 43:101–116.

Miyazaki, S., and T. Nagamatsu. 1965. Studies on the promotion of the early growth in vitro of orchid. Pt. 1. Agric. Bull. Saga Pref. Univ. 21:131–149.

Morawiecka, B., A. Kubicz, K. Kukulczanka, A. Koch, and E. Markefka. 1973. Heterogeneity of the acid phosphatase and ribonuclease from protocorms of the orchids Cymbidium Sw. and changes occurring after treatment with streptomycin. Acta. Soc. Bot. Poloniae. 42:133–141.

Morel, G. M. 1974. Clonal multiplication of orchids, pp. 169–222. In C. L. Withner (ed.), The orchids: Scientific studies. Wiley-Interscience, New York.

Mowe, B. L. 1973. Germination and growth of Dendrobium (ionoglossum × species) in several culture media. Singapore J. Pri. Ind. 1:20–30.

Muick, F. 1978. Propagation of Cypripedium reginae from seeds. Amer. Orchid Soc. Bull. 47:306–308.

Mukherjee, T. P., S. Roy, and T. K. Bose. 1974. Seed germination and propagation of orchids. Indian Hort. 18:21–24.

Mutsuura, O., I. Ito, and R. Makahira. 1962. Studies on the germination and the development of seedlings of Taeniophyllum amphyllum (Makino) Makino. Sci. Rep. Kyoto Pref. Univ. (Nat. Sci. and Liv. Sci.) 3 Ser. A, P. 189–194:13–18.

Nagl, W. 1972. Evidence of DNA amplification in the orchid Cymbidium in vitro. Cytobios 5:145–154.

Nagl, W., and I. Capesius. 1977. Repetitive DNA and heterochromatin as factors of karyotype evolution in phylogeny and autogamy of orchids. Chromosomes Today:141–150.

Nagl, W., J. Hendon, and W. Rücker. 1972. DNA amplification in Cymbidium protocorms in vitro as it relates to cytodifferentiation and hormone treatment. Cell Diff. 1:229–237.

Nagl, W., and W. Rücker. 1972. Beziehungen zwischen Morphogenese und nuklearem DNS-Gehalt bei aseptischen Kulturen von Cymbidium nach Wuchsstoffbehandlung. Pt. 2. Pflanzen Physiol. 67:120–134.

———. 1974. Shift of DNA replication from diploid to polyploid cells in cytokinin controlled differentiation. Cytobios. 10:137–144.

———. 1976. Effects of phytohormones on thermal denaturation profiles of Cymbidium DNA: Indication of differential DNA replication. Nucleic Acid Res. 3:2033–2039.

Nakamura, S. I. 1962. Zur Samenkeimung einer Chlorophyllfreien Erdorchidee Galeola septentrionalis Reichb. f. Z. für Botanik 50:487–497.

———. 1964. Einige Experimente zur Samenkeimung einer chlorophyllfreien Erdorchidee Galeola septentrionalis Reichb. f. Mem. Coll. Agri. Kyoto Univ. No. 86 (Bot Sec. 4):1–48.

———. 1976. Atmospheric conditions required for the growth of Galeola septentrionalis seedlings. Bot. Mag. Tokyo 89:211–218.

Nakamura, S. I., T. Uchida, and M. Hamada. 1975. Atmospheric condition controlling the seed germination of an achlorophyllous orchid, Galeola septentrionalis. Bot. Mag. Tokyo 88:103–109.

Noggle, G. R., and F. L. Wynd. 1943. Effects of vitamins on germination and growth of orchids. Bot. Gaz. 104:455–459.

Ordin, L., and J. Bonner. 1957. Effect of galactose on growth and metabolism of Avena coleoptile sections. Plant Physiol. 32:212–215.

Pages, P. D. 1971. Banana homogenate, coconut water, peptone and auxins as nutrient supplements in the in vitro culture of Dendrobium and Phalaenopsis ovules. SERCA Bull. No. 2, College Laguna, Philippines.

Pegg, G. F. 1973. Occurrence of gibberellin-like growth substances in basidiomycete sporophytes. Trans. Br. Mycol. Soc. 61:277–286.

Pierik, R. L. M., and H. H. M. Steegmans. 1972. The effect of 6-benzylamino purine on growth and development of Cattleya seedlings grown from unripe seeds. Z. Pflanzenphysiol. 68:228–234.

Poddubnaya-Arnoldi, V. A. 1960. Study of fertilization in the living material of some angiosperms. Phytomorphology 10:185–198.

Poddubnaya-Arnoldi, V. A., and N. V. Zinger. 1961. Application of histochemical technique to the study of embryonic processes in some orchids. Recent Adv. in Bot. (Univ. of Toronto) Sect. 8:711–714.

Pollard, G. E. 1973. One man's opinion. Orquidea (Mex.) 3:187–190.

Quednow, K. G. 1930. Beiträge zur Frage der Aufnahme gelöster Kohlenstoffverbindungen bei Orchideen und andere Pflanzen. Bot. Archiv. 30:51–108.

Raghavan, V. 1964. Effects of certain nitrogen compounds on growing in vitro of seedlings of *Cattleya*. Bot. Gaz. 125:260–267.

——. 1976. Experimental embryogenesis in vascular plants. Academic Press, New York.

Raghavan, V., and J. G. Torrey. 1964. Inorganic nitrogen nutrition of the embryos of the seedlings of the orchid *Cattleya*. Amer. J. Bot. 51:264–274.

Rao, A. N., and P. N. Avadhani. 1963. Some aspects of in vitro culture of *Vanda* seeds, pp. 194–202. Proc. 4th World Orchid Conf.

Reyburn, A. N. 1978. The effects of pH on the expression of a darkness-requiring dormancy in seeds of *Cypripedium reginae* Walt. Amer. Orchid Soc. Bull. 47:798–802.

Rücker, W. 1974. Einfluss von Cytokininen auf Wachstum und Differenzierung in vitro kultivierter Protokorme von *Cymbidium*. Z. Pflanzenphysiol. 72:338–351.

——. 1975. Wirkung von Hydroxyharnstoff auf Entwicklung und Differenzierung in vitro kultivierter Protokorme von *Cymbidium*. Z. Pflanzenphysiol. 76:229–237.

Sanford, W. W. 1974. The ecology of orchids, pp. 1–100. *In* C. L. Withner (ed.) The orchids: Scientific studies. Wiley-Interscience, New York.

Sawa, Y. 1969. Studies on the germination of seeds and on seedling growth in terrestrial *Cymbidium*. Pt. 1. Leaf bud differentiation from rhizome of *Cymbidium virescens* Lindley and *Cymbidium kanran* Makino. Res. Reports Kochi Univ. 18. Agric. Sci. No. 4:1–4.

Schopfer, W. H. 1943. Plants and vitamins, pp. 250–253. Chronica Botanica, Waltham, Mass.

Schweizer, D., and W. Nagl. 1976. Heterochromatin diversity in *Cymbidium* and its relationship to differential DNA replication. Exp. Cell Res. 98:411–423.

Sideris, C. P. 1950. A nutrient solution for germinating of orchid seeds. Bull. Pac. Orchid Soc. Hawaii 8:337–339.

Smith, S. E. 1966. Physiology and ecology of orchid mycorrhizal fungi with reference to seedling nutrition. New Phytol. 65:488–499.

——. 1967. Carbohydrate translocation in orchid mycorrhizas. New Phytol. 66:371–378.

——. 1973. Asymbiotic germination of orchid seeds on carbohydrates of fungal origin. New Phytol. 72:497–499.

——. 1974. Mycorrhizal fungi. CRC Crit. Rev. Microbiol. 3:275–313.

Stephen, R. C., and K. K. Fung. 1971. Vitamin requirements of the fungal endophytes of *Arundina chinensis*. Can. J. Bot. 49:411–415.

Storey, W. B., H. W. Kirch, D. J. Pierce, and H. Kamemoto. 1947. Orchidology. Rep. Univ. Hawaii Agr. Exp. Station J. Bienn. ending June 1946, pp. 82–86.

Stoutamire, W. 1974. Terrestrial orchid seedling, pp. 101–128. *In* C. L. Withner (ed.). The orchids: Scientific studies. Wiley-Interscience, New York.

Strauss, M. S., and D. M. Reisinger. 1976. Effects of naphthaleneacetic acid on seed germination. Amer. Orchid Soc. Bull. 45:722–723.

Strullu, D. G. 1974. Ultrastructure des mycorrhizes: Caractérisation des principaux types. Coll. Soc. Fr. Phytopath.:339–340.

Tarr, J., and J. Arditti. 1981. Analysis of tryptophan and its metabolites by reverse-phase high-pressure liquid chromatography. New Phytol. 88:621–626.

Thimann, K. V. 1956. Studies on the growth and inhibition of isolated plant parts. V. The effects of cobalt and other metals. Amer. J. Bot. 43:241–250.

Thompson, P. A. 1974a. Growing orchids from seed. J. Roy. Hort. Soc. 99:117–122.

——. 1974b. Orchids from seed: A new basal medium. Orchid Rev. 82:179–183.

——. 1977. Orchids from seed. Royal Botanic Gardens, Kew.

Tienken, H. G. 1947. Nutrient solution. Amer. Orchid Soc. Bull. 33:111.

Torikata, H., Y. Sawa, and M. Sisa. 1965. Non-symbiotic germination and growth of the orchid seeds. Pt. 1. Studies on the medium and additive for germination of seed in *Cymbidium*. J. Jap. Soc. Hort. Sci. 34:63–70.

Ueda, H., and H. Torikata. 1968. Organogenesis in meristem cultures of *Cymbidiums*. Pt. 1. Studies on the effects of growth substances added to culture media under continuous illuminations. J. Jap. Soc. Hort. Sci. 37:240–248.

——. 1969. Organogenesis in the meristem tissue cultures of *Cymbidiums*. Pt. 2. Effects of growth substances on the organogenesis in dark culture. J. Jap. Soc. Hort. Sci. 38:188–193.

——. 1972a. Effects of light and culture medium on adventitious root formation by *Cymbidiums* in aseptic culture. Amer. Orchid Soc. Bull. 41:322–327.

——. 1972b. Organogensis and mycotrophy in *Cymbidiums*. Soc. Hort. 3rd Inter-Symp. Sub-Trop-Trop. Hort. Inst. Hort. RES (ICAR), Bangalore, India (n.p.).

——. 1974. Organogenesis in the meristem culture of *Cymbidiums*. VII. Study on the extract from mycorrhizomes of *Cymbidium goeringii* Reich. F. (*c. virescens Lindl.*). J. Jap. Soc. Hort. Sci. 43:281–285.

Uesato, K. 1973. Effects of different forms of nitrogen sources in the culture media on the growth of *Cattleya* young seedlings. No-Kasei-Kogakulu, Ryuku Daigaku No-Kasei-Kogakulu Gakututsu Hoko-ku (Ryuku Islands) 20:1–12.

——. 1978. Studies on the formation and development of protocorms in growth cycle of orchids. Bull. Coll. Agric. Univ. Ryukus 25:1–76.

Vacin, E. F., and F. W. Went. 1949. Some pH changes in nutrient solutions. Bot. Gaz. 110:605–613.

Vanséveren-Van Espen, N. 1973. Effects du saccharose sur le contenu en chlorophylles de protocormes de *Cymbidium* Sw. (Orchidaceae) cultivés in vitro. Bull. Soc. Roy. Bot. Belg. 106:107–115.

Vanséveren-Van Espen, N., and D. Coutez-Geerinck. 1974. Effets du saccharose sur les échanges gazeux de protocormes de *Cymbidium* Sw cultivés in vitro. Bull. Soc. Roy. Bot. Belg. 107:259–270.

Veitch, G. J., and D. K. McIntyre. 1972. A new medium for raising Australian terrestrial orchids from seed. Mimeograph. Canberra Botanic Gardens.

Vermeulen, P. 1947. Studies on Dactylorchis. Drukkerij Fa Schotanus and Jens, Utrecht.

Veyret, Y. 1969. La structure des semences des Orchidaceae et leur aptitude à la germination in vitro en cultures pures. Trav. Lab. "La Jaysinia" 3:89–98.

Vöth, W. 1976. Aussaat und Kultur von *Serapias parviflora* und *S. orientalis*, pp. 351–358. *In* Proc. 8th World Orchid Conf., Frankfurt (1975).

Werckmeister, P. 1970a. Über die Lichtinduktion der geotropen Orientierung von Luft- und Boden-wurzeln in Gewebekulturen von *Cymbidium*. Ber. Dtsch. Bot. Ges. 83:19–26.

——. 1970b. Die Steuerung von Vermehrung (Proliferation) und Wachstum in der Meristemkultur von *Cymbidium* und die Verwendung eines Kohle-Nährmediums. Die Orchidee 21:126–131.

——. 1971. Light induction of geotropism and the control of proliferation and growth of *Cymbidium* in tissue culture. Bot. Gaz. 132:346–350.

Wheeler, L. C., and L. J. Ramos. 1965. Mineral elements in some orchids. Unpublished mimeograph. Department of Biological Sciences, Univ. of Southern California.

Williamson, B. 1970. Induced DNA synthesis in orchid mycorrhiza. Planta (Berl.) 92:347–354.

——. 1973. Acid phosphatase and esterase activity in orchid mycorrhiza. Planta (Berl.) 112:149–158.

Williamson, B., and G. Hadley. 1969. DNA content of nuclei in orchid protocorms symbiotically infected with *Rhizoctonia*. Nature 222:582–583.

Withner, C. 1951. Effect of plant hormones and other compounds on the growth of orchids. Amer. Orchid Soc. Bull. 20:276–278.

——. 1959a. Orchid physiology, pp. 315–360. *In* C. L. Withner (ed.), The orchid: A scientific survey. Ronald Press, New York.

——. 1959b. Orchid culture media and nutrient solutions, pp. 589–599. *In* C. L. Withner (ed.), The orchids: A scientific survey. Ronald Press, New York.

——. 1974. Developments in orchid physiology, pp. 129–168. *In* C. L. Withner (ed.), The orchids: Scientific studies. Wiley-Interscience, New York.

Wrigley, J. W. 1976. The culture of Australian terrestrial orchids, pp. 397–399. Proc. 8th World Orchid Conf., Frankfurt (1975).

——. 1973. Germination and cultivation of Australian terrestrial orchids. Mimeograph. Canberra Botanic Gardens.

Wynd, F. L. 1933a. The sensitivity of orchid seedlings to nutritional ions. Ann. Missouri Bot. Gardens 20:223–237.

——. 1933b. Sources of carbohydrate for germination and growth of orchid seeds. Ann. Missouri Bot. Gardens 20:569–581.

Yuen, C. K. K. H., H. Kamemoto, and M. Ishi. 1979. Transmission of *Cymbidium* mosaic virus through seed propagation in *Dendrobium*. Amer. Orchid Soc. Bull. 48:1245–1247.

Zhang, W. J., and B. L. Li. 1980. The biological relationship of *Gastrodia elata* and *Armillaria mellea*. Acta. Bot. Sinica 22:57–63.

Ziegler, A., T. Sheehan, and R. Pesle. 1967. Influence of various media and photoperiods on growth and amino acid content of orchid seedlings. Amer. Orchid Soc. Bull. 36:185–202.

5

Carbohydrates of the Orchidaceae*

ROBERT ERNST and ELOY RODRIGUEZ

*The literature survey pertaining to this chapter was concluded in April 1980; the chapter was submitted in April 1980, and the revised version was received in May 1980.

Introduction

The carbohydrates of the Orchidaceae have received limited attention from those interested in plant physiology and phytochemistry. Nevertheless, a reasonable body of work has been produced on the reserve polysaccharides of orchid tubers, no doubt because of their commercial importance as sources of drugs and food. Furthermore, homogenates of dried orchid tubers have been used by early investigators in attempts to raise orchids from seed.

In recent years researchers have investigated a number of secondary metabolites, including the alkaloids, the flavonoids and related compounds, other glycosides, and nectars, in a search for chemotaxonomic indicators. Alkaloids of the Orchidaceae have been reviewed twice recently (Lüning, 1974; Slaytor, 1977), and orchid anthocyanins have been surveyed once (Arditti and Fisch, 1977). The coverage of glycosides in this chapter will therefore be limited to those that have not been reviewed and to those for which updated information is available.

Carbohydrates in Orchid Tubers and Roots

Early interest in the carbohydrates and mucilages of certain orchid tubers that are dried and marketed as salep (or saleb) can be traced to their use as a food and drug (Daloul, Petek, and Courtois, 1963; Ohtsuki, 1937a, 1937b; Schmidt, 1844; Sezik, 1967; see also chapter 2 in this volume), most commonly as a demulcent. The term "salep" has been traced to the Arabic word *sahlab,* an alternate for *khusy aththalab,* which according to Webster's dictionary means "the fox's testicles." Dried tubers, which generally contain 8 to 13% moisture, are derived from terrestrial orchids of the genera *Aceras, Anacamptis, Bletilla, Cremastra, Eulophia, Himantoglossum, Loroglossum, Ophrys, Orchis,* and *Serapias.* Their principal components are starch and mucilage and lesser amounts of sugars and minerals. Salep quality depends on its mucilage content, which is 40% or greater in the best grades. Its mucilage is sufficiently high in glucomannan to have served as a source of mannose.

Largely through microscopic examinations, John Lindley (1843) observed that salep of *Orchis* and other "Ophrydeae" consists not of starch, as previous workers had claimed, but a type of gum resembling bassorin (a fraction of gum tragacanth). He recognized that tubers of *Orchis maculata* contain substantial amounts of starch, which on processing can cause the salep mucilage to yield a positive iodine-starch test. This finding led to the false conclusion that salep mucilage is also a form of starch.

Schmidt (1844) subjected slices of whole orchid tubers to acid hydrolysis and isolated substantial quantities of a fermentable sugar that he identified as glucose. When it was treated with alcohol, the sugar-containing filtrate yielded a white viscid precipitate that was shown to contain 44.6% carbon, 6.3% hydrogen, and 49.1% oxygen. Schmidt identified the substance as a *Kohlenhydrat* ("carbohydrate").

At that time compounds such as sugar, starch, cellulose, gums, and pectins were placed in two categories: (1) compounds containing carbon, hydrogen, and oxygen, with the latter two in the same ratio as in water, and (2) compounds containing carbon, hydrogen, and either more or less oxygen than the ratio in water. Thus Schmidt coined the term "carbohydrate" to describe the first category: *"Es sei mir erlaubt die Ersten allgemein im Verlauf dieser Abhandlung als Kohlenhydrate zu bezeichnen."* ("Permit me to call the first ones carbohydrates in the course of this paper"). Schmidt assumed that the mucilage was an intermediate product of sugar formation.

Gans and Tollens (1888a) were the first researchers to discover the presence of mannose in naturally occurring polysaccharides. They demonstrated that the acid hydrolysis product of salep mucilage contains glucose and an additional sugar. The phenylhydrazine reaction product of the latter was identical to the phenylhydrazone of a sugar obtained by E. Fischer (1887) in the oxidation of mannitol. This new hexose was subsequently named mannose by Fischer and J. Hirschberger (1889), who confirmed its presence in hydrolyzed salep mucilage.

Gans and Tollens (1888a) determined that the melting point of mannose phenylhydrazone was 192°C to 193°C and that it dropped to 187°C to 188°C on further purification. It has since been demonstrated that D-mannose phenylhydrazone (melting at 199°C to 200°C) is difficult to recrystalize without deterioration, which lowers the melting point (Isbell and Frush, 1962). Gans and Tollens obtained an additional fraction from reaction with phenylhydrazine, which upon crystallization from alcohol gave a melting point of 202°C to 204°C. It was identified as phenylglucosazone. Its melting point has been subsequently established as 207°C (Henseke and Bautze, 1955). During its formation three moles of phenylhydrazine react with one mole of hexose. Two moles of phenylhydrazine react with one mole of hexose; the third is reduced to aniline and ammonia. As a result of this reaction, the asymmetry at C2 disappears so that the epimers D-glucose and D-mannose, as well as fructose, yield the identical phenylosazone, a fact that was not known during the nineteenth century, when Gans and Tollens were working. Even though both glucose and mannose were identified in salep mucilage, no one speculated that they were the result of the hydrolysis of a heteropolysaccharide.

A. Hilger (1903) found only D-mannose in glucomannan from salep, and this finding led him to conclude that the polysaccharide in question was composed of this sugar only. Based on elementary analysis he determined that the compound consisted of a tetrasaccharide. He derived this compound further by acetylation to yield (by his interpretation) the tetradecaacetate of the mannose tetrasaccharide, $C_{24}H_{28}O_3 (OCOCH_3)_{14}$.

Although Gans and Tollens (1888a, 1888b) clearly showed that salep mucilage yielded mannose and glucose on acid hydrolysis, H. Pringsheim and A. Genin (1924) quoted them as stating that salep consists of a polysaccharide composed exclusively of mannose residues. The results of acid hydrolysis (yielding 82% mannose) and enzymatic degradation with malt extract (yielding 81% mannose after ninety-six hours of exposure) were interpreted as constituting a nearly quantitative splitting of a "mannan." During the course of this work, mannobiose was isolated for the first time through enzymatic hydrolysis of salep mucilage and characterized as mannobiose phenylhydrazone, which melts at 199°C. The melting point of this phenylhydrazone has since been confirmed (Mukherjee *et al.*, 1961). "Salep mannan" glucomannan constitutes 27.5 to 29.5% of commercial tuber salep (Pringsheim and Liss, 1927).

Klages and Niemann (1936) methylated salep mannan and on complete hydrolysis obtained 84% 2,3,6-trimethylmannose and 1.7% 2,3,4,6-tetramethylmannose. The hexose residues of the polysaccharide therefore have a (1 → 4) linkage. The molecular weights of the methyl derivative and the polysaccharide were determined to be 5,600 and 12,000 respectively by two different methods. These are unreasonably low values and molecular weights in excess of 100,000 have been determined more recently (Buchala, Franz, and Meier, 1974; Tomoda *et al.*, 1973).

Husemann (1940) showed that polysaccharides of the salep mucilage contain acetyl groups that increase their hydrophilic properties. The polymer gave 3.5% acetic acid on alkaline or on acidic hydrolyses, with loss of water solubility. Husemann (1940) also found the polysaccharides to consist of molecules of different weights. To prevent polymer degradation, he inactivated an enzyme present in the salep tubers by boiling them with alcohol.

At a time when salep mucilage was still considered to consist of mannose homopolymers, a hexosan composed of four parts of D-mannose for each part of D-glucose was obtained from *Bletilla striata* (Ohtsuki, 1937a). The hydrolyzate of this heteropolysaccharide showed a specific rotation of +22 to 23 and yielded 77 to 81% mannose, calculated from the conversion to D-mannose phenylhydrazone.

Ohtsuki (1937b) also obtained a ratio of three moles D-mannose for each mole of D-glucose upon acid hydrolysis of salep mucilage from *Cremastra variabilis* tubers. Phenylglucosazone separated from the filtrate of the mannose phenylhydrazone upon heating. Complete hydrolysis of the glucomannan was obtained after six hours of treatment with hot, aqueous 6% sulfuric acid. It was also possible to hydrolyze this polysaccharide almost entirely with freshly prepared intestinal juice of snails. Because their enzymatic hydrolyses were less complete, previous investigators (Hérissey, 1902; Pringsheim and Genin, 1924) had failed to determine the presence of glucose.

Upon repeated methylation with dimethylsulfate, the glucomannan was converted to a derivative containing 40.9% methoxyl groups, which melt at 240°C and have a specific rotation in water of [α] D-36.1 ~ 39.7 and a cryoscopic molecular weight of approximately 3000 (Ohtsuki, 1937b). The degree of polymerization was therefore about one-half of that determined by Klages and Niemann (1936).

The finding of Ohtsuki (1937a) that salep mucilage is a glucomannan was subsequently confirmed by a number of workers (Buchala, Franz, and Meier, 1974; Courtois, Daloul, and Petek, 1963; Daloul *et al.*, 1963; Juers, Swenson, and Kurath, 1967; Petek, Courtois, and Daloul, 1963; Stepanenko *et al.*, 1961). Dry tubers of various *Orchis* species contain 25 to 30% of levorotatory polysaccharide (Daloul *et al.*, 1963). The hydrolytic effects of various enzymes, oxidation with periodic acid, and hydrolysis of the methylated glucomannan (containing approximately three moles of mannose per mole of glucose) showed it to be a linear polymer of 1 → 4 linked β-pyranoside units. The chain is initiated with mannose at the nonreducing end. Courtois *et al.* (1963) compared these results with mucilage obtained from *Orchis militaris*, *O. mascula*, *Loroglossum hircinum*, and an unidentified *Orchis* species, which were all collected in the vicinity of Paris. Complete methylation followed by hydrolysis produced several fractions but semiquantitative results (Table 5-1).

The mucilage of *O. militaris* and *O. mascula* has the same structure as that reported by

Table 5-1.   Fractions obtained following hydrolysis of methylated glucomannan (modified from Courtois *et al.*, 1963)[a]

Fraction	*Orchis militaris*	*Orchis mascula*	*Orchis* sp.	*Loroglossum hircinum*
Dimethyl-2,3-*O*-Glu	0	0	+	+
Trimethyl-2,3,6-*O*-Glu	+ +	+ +	+ +	+ +
Trimethyl-2,3,6-*O*-Man	+ + + + + +	+ + + + + +	+ + + + +	+ + + + +
Tetramethyl-2,3,4,6-*O*-Glu	0	0	+	+
Tetramethyl-2,3,4,6-*O*-Man	+	+	+	+

[a] 0, none; the number of plus signs indicates the relative amount detected.

Daloul *et al.* (1963) for Syrian salep. Mucilage of *Loroglossum hircinum* and an unknown *Orchis* species contains the same ratio of about three moles mannose per mole of glucose. The chain branches from glucose in position 6, with glucose and mannose on the non-reducing ends. Glucomannans of orchids are similar to those of deciduous and resiniferous trees.

Petek *et al.* (1963) obtained three oligosaccharide fractions having β-(1 $\rightarrow$ 4) linkage following partial acid hydrolysis of Syrian salep mucilage. These were β-mannobiose, β-mannotriose, and β-glucosidomannose. The hydrolysis fragments seemed to indicate that the polymer chain is composed of three mannose units followed by a glucose residue.

The ratios of hexoses in glucomannan from different sources of salep mucilage vary considerably. In earlier work (Stepanenko, 1960) Asian salep mucilage was shown to contain a branched, chiefly β-(1 $\rightarrow$ 4) linked glucomannan with a mannose:glucose ratio of about 2:1. More recently Juers *et al.* (1967) reported the following quantitative breakdown of glucomannan from commercial orchid tuber powder: mannose, 69.5 $\pm$ 2%; glucose, 26.6 $\pm$ 1%; acetyl, 2.1 $\pm$ 0.2%; and nitrogen, 0.11 $\pm$ 0.01%. The optical rotation of the glucomannan in 6% sodium hydroxide at 25°C as [α] 25-43.3 is in agreement with the value reported by Husemann (1940). Partial hydrolysis of the polysaccharide yielded 4-*O*-β-D-mannopyranosyl-β-D-glucopyranose, mannobiose, and mannotriose in addition to mannose and glucose.

The presence of acetyl groups in these glucomannans had already been reported by Husemann (1940) and by Ohtsuki (1937a, 1937b). In contrast, the glucomannan of four orchid species native to France was stated to contain no acetyl radicals (Courtois *et al.*, 1963).

Juers and co-workers (1967) established configuration and hydrodynamic properties of the triacetyl derivatives of salep glucomannan. The polysaccharide could be acetylated quantitatively with an acetyl content of 45.2%, yielding fractions varying in molecular weight from 615 to 4,170. The strainless conformation of pyranose rings and stereochemical analysis suggest that both mannose and glucose are present in the C1 conformation. The dependence of the light-scattering radius of gyration of the glucomannan heteropolymer on the contour length showed that its conformation was similar to other β-(1 $\rightarrow$ 4)-linked polysaccharides such as cellulose.

Recently, the chemical and physical properties of glucomannan extracted from young tubers of *Orchis morio* were compared with those of mucilage globules freed of starch and other extraneous matter from the same source. The ratio of mannose to glucose was 3.3:1 in the former and 3.6:1 in the latter (Buchala *et al.*, 1974). Both heteropolymers were methylated and fractionated following hydrolysis. The percentage of the non-reducing end groups (tetra-β-methylhexoses) and of the branch points (di-β-methylhexoses) were about twice as high in the mucilage globules as in the water-extracted glucomannan. This effect apparently occurs because the water-extracted polysaccharide is treated with α-amylase and β-amylase to degrade contaminating starch. Nitration of the polysaccharide gave an approximate DP_n value of 665. Using this value and the percentage of nonreducing end groups (tetra-O-methylhexoses) approximately seven branch points were calculated per molecule of water-extracted glucomannan. In the native polysaccharide obtained from the mucilage globules, the number of branch points may be twice as high.

Buchala and co-workers (1974) confirmed earlier findings (Husemann, 1940; Juers *et al.*, 1967) that this glucomannan contains acetyl groups. The value observed (about 5%) was greater than that reported by previous investigators. The linkage of acetyl groups was on the C2 or C3 of the mannose residue. Deacetylation of the polysaccharide yielded a water-insoluble residue.

Studies of the composition and structure of the tuber mucilage of *Bletilla striata* revealed that it was also a glucomannan (Tomodo *et al.*, 1973). This finding confirmed an earlier report (Ohtsuki, 1937b). A mannose to glucose ratio of 3:1 was determined for the heteropolymer, which is composed mainly of β-(1 → 4) linked aldohexopyranose residues. A molecular weight of 182,000 was estimated. *B. striata* glucomannan was also found to be acetylated; its acetyl content was 4.2% at position 3 of most glucose residues (Tomoda *et al.*, 1974). Presence of the ester (acetyl) group was evident from the typical infrared spectrum (Fig. 5-1). This glucomannan was composed mainly of β-(1 → 4) linked aldohexopyranose residues with (1 → 2) branching at some of the mannose units. Mannose occupies the nonreducing terminal position.

In summary, it is clear that in addition to starch the reserve polysaccharide in salep is an acetylated glucomanan.

Biosynthesis

The glucomannans of orchid tubers form in large, specialized cells that gradually fill with this mucilagenous substance. Mucilages were classified by A. B. Frank (1867) in accordance with their deposition in plant tissues as intercellular, cell membrane, and cell content types. Orchid tuber mucilages belong to the last group.

Early researchers speculated that the mucilages constitute transformation products of starch or starchlike substances (Behrens, 1883; Giraud, 1875; Schmidt, 1844). Using

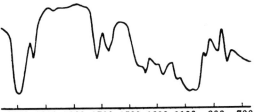

3500 2500 1900 1700 1500 1300 1100   900   700
Wavenumber (cm^{-1})

Fig. 5-1. Infrared spectrum of *Bletilla striata* tuber glucomannan. Presence of ester is shown by carbonyl absorption (C=O) at 1735 cm^{-1} and the C(=O)—O band at 1250 cm^{-1}. Absorption at 890 cm^{-1} is due to the β-glucosidic linkage. (Tomoda, Nakatsuka, and Satoh, 1974.)

staining techniques that differentiated between the mucilage, nucleus and nucleolus, and starch, R. Jaretzky and E. Bereck (1938) observed that all starch-containing cells in the outer endodermis can produce mucilage. Nuclei remain intact even in cells that have completed the process of mucilage formation, which is not the case in other plants (Jaretzky and Ulbrich, 1934; Stewart, 1919). The presence of nuclei may suggest that the mucilage of orchid tubers is a reserve substance used during shoot formation and the development of new tubers. During May the old tubers contain no mucilage. The starch remains unchanged, which is an indication that it is not readily mobilized by these plants. Conversion of the starch into mucilage may therefore facilitate its utilization during active metabolic periods.

G. Franz and H. Meier (1971) elucidated the transport of sugars in orchid tubers by following the degradation of mucilage polysaccharides in old tubers and the development of the reserve compounds in the new ones. They determined that the levels of fructose, glucose, and raffinose in old tubers are similar to those in new tubers (Table 5-2). The appearance of mannose, mannobiose, mannotriose, and maltose in old tubers is of interest because these sugars seem to be degradation products of glucomannan and starch. A similar conversion of mannan into oligosaccharides has been observed in germinating date seeds (Keusch, 1968). Neither mannose nor its oligosaccharides were found in new tubers that formed reserve polysaccharides during the same period. This finding can be taken as evidence that degradation products from the old tubers are not transported as such into the young ones. By June only small amounts of mono- and oligosaccharides can be detected (Franz and Meier, 1971); the glucomannan content in old tubers drops (Fig. 5-2) and enzymatic activity drastically decreases.

UDP-Glu and ADP-Glu may serve as precursors for starch synthesis as in other systems (Leloir, 1964; Recondo and Leloir, 1961). GDP-Man, which occurs only in the new tubers, may be the source of mannose during the formation of glucomannans, as is the case in other plants (Elbein and Hassid, 1966). In fact, glucomannan can be formed from GDP-Man as the sole substrate (Elbein and Hassid, 1966). The role of UDP-Gal in old and new tubers is not clear, but it is possibly a precursor of raffinose as in other plants (Gomyo and Nakamura, 1966; Pridham and Hassid, 1965).

Table 5-2. Soluble sugars and *myo*-inositol in old and new tubers of *Orchis morio, O. mascula,* and *Platanthera bifolia* at different times of the growth period

Sugar	Old tubers		New tubers	
	March	June	March	June
Fructose	High	High	High	High
Glucose	High	High	High	High
Mannose	Low	None	None	None
Maltose	Low	None	None	None
Maltobiose	Low	Trace	None	None
Sucrose	Medium	Medium	High	High
Maltotriose	Low	Trace	None	None
Raffinose	Low	Low	Low	Low
myo-Inositol	Low	Low	Medium	Medium

Data from Franz and Meier, 1971.

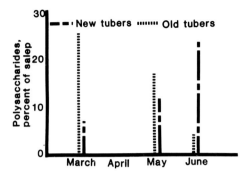

Fig. 5-2. Changes in mucilage content at beginning of the vegetative period of orchid tubers (*Orchis morio, O. mascula,* and *Platanthera bifolia*). Mucilage polysaccharide in new and old tubers. Data for April was not given. (Modified from Franz and Meier, 1971.)

The content of sugar nucleotides in old and newly formed tubers also differs substantially. During the mobilization of polysaccharides in old tubers, in May when growth takes place, only uridine diphosphate glucose (UDP-Glu) and uridine diphosphate galactose (UDP-Gal) are detected. The new tubers also contain guanosine diphosphate-D-mannose (GDP-Man) and small amounts of adenosine diphosphate glucose (ADP-Glu) (Table 5-3). Labeled sucrose injected into old tubers is partially hydrolyzed to glucose and fructose. Small amounts of raffinose are also formed. Labeled sucrose soon appears in the new tuber, pointing to a direct transport from the old one. Following prolonged incubation the label appears in the mucilage of the new tubers. Because the mucilage of old tubers is not radioactive, it can be assumed that de novo synthesis of the reserve polysaccharide occurs only in the young ones. In nature, the formation of glucomannan in *Orchis* takes place from March to July. Enzyme activity peaks during May and June (Fig. 5-3).

During the breakdown and metabolism of glucomannan and starch in *Orchis morio* tubers during the vegetation period, the mobilization of the reserve polysaccharides is facilitated by β-mannanase, amylase, β-mannosidase, β-glucosidase, and α-glucosidase (Franz, 1979). Of these enzymes, β-mannanase is the first to become active in the early spring, coinciding with glucomannan breakdown.

A particulate enzyme preparation obtained from young tubers of *Orchis morio*, harvested between May and August, catalyzed the transfer of ^{14}C-mannose from GDP-Man and incorporated the label into alkali-insoluble mannan, having the same β-(1 → 4)-D-mannopyranosyl linkage found in the glucomannan of orchid tubers (Franz, 1973). Incorporation of radioactive mannose was directly proportional to the protein content in

Table 5-3. Sugar nucleotides (in micromoles per 100 g dry weight) in orchid tubers of *Orchis morio, O. mascula,* and *Platanthera bifolia* at the start of the growth period in May

Sugar nucleotide identified	Old tubers	New tubers
Adenosine diphosphate glucose	None	0.5
Guanosine diphosphate mannose	None	2.3
Uridine diphosphate glucose	9.7	8.6
Uridine diphosphate galactose	2.4	0.9

Data from Franz and Meier, 1971.

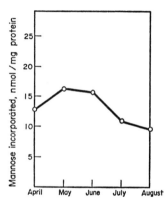

Fig. 5-3. Changes in enzyme activity during growth of *Orchis morio* tubers (Franz, 1973.)

the assay mixture. The pH optimum for this reaction is 6.5 to 6.6, and cobalt ions seem to enhance it. Mannan production was rapid during the first fifteen to twenty minutes, then leveled off (Fig. 5-4). Although the polysaccharide synthesized in vitro had the same β-(1 → 4) linkages as the naturally occurring one, it differed in that it did not contain the glucopyranosyl residues and acetyl groups, which render salep glucomannan more water soluble. The source of glucose residues in salep glucomannan is not known. Incorporation of UDP-Glu and GDP-Glu into the incubation mixture, however, did not result in modification of the alkali-soluble mannan produced from GDP-^{14}C-Man alone. The enzyme from the tuber had no GDP-Man-GDP-Glu epimerase activity (Franz, 1973).

Other Carbohydrates in Orchid Tubers

N. K. Shcherbukhina and co-workers (1969) reported the presence of a low molecular glucan in orchid salep in addition to the typical glucomannan. The glucopyranosyl units of the glucan have a α-(1 → 4) linkage.

The presence of starch in orchid tubers was already noted by Berzelius (Lindley, 1843). Tubers of a number of species of *Orchis, Ophrys, Serapias, Anacamptis,* and *Himantoglossum* were analyzed by Sezik (1967) and Baytop and Sezik (1968) for mucilage,

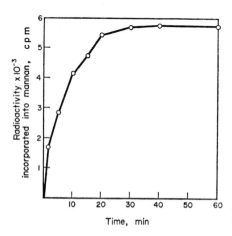

Fig. 5-4. Time course of mannan production in a standard assay with a particulate enzyme system from growing *Orchis morio* tubers. (Franz, 1973.)

Table 5.4.   Chemical analysis of orchid tubers (Sezik, 1967)

Species	Mucilage %	Starch %	Reducing sugars %	Sucrose %	N total %	Water %	Ash %
Orchis anatolica	57.04	2.75	0.91	1.11	0.88	10.36	4.91
O. italica	49.36	1.25	1.37	0.77	0.95	10.68	3.08
O. morio	32.11	25.04	2.67	0.17	0.57	10.76	3.14
O. pinetorum	50.11	0.69	2.06	0.36	0.90	11.70	1.37
O. romana	61.06	0.45	4.50	0.44	0.74	10.96	5.98
O. sancta	15.70	10.64	1.72	0.29	0.49	8.65	2.27
O. simia	29.89	1.71	1.33	0.64	0.62	10.96	5.98
O. tridentata	24.50	36.04	1.35	1.39	0.80	11.14	4.26
Ophrys fuciflora	9.60	18.78	1.05	0.49	0.64	6.40	0.49
Oph. fusca	6.82	12.77	1.01	0.70	0.72	8.60	0.24
Anacamptis pyramidalis	44.72	5.94	2.81	1.84	0.92	9.76	1.05
Serapias laxiflora	33.61	1.07	1.89	0.53	0.77	10.64	1.72
S. vomeracea	40.56	1.35	2.18	0.39	0.80	8.70	1.43
Himantoglossum longibracteatum	20.95	10.99	2.51	0.42	0.77	9.58	3.48

starch, sucrose, reducing sugars, ash, nitrogen, and water. The results are given in Table 5-4.

The species listed in Table 5-4 were collected in southwest Anatolia, Turkey. The chemical analyses revealed remarkable differences in their mucilage and starch content. According to Sezik (1967) the best grades of tuber salep for pharmaceutical use contain in excess of 40% mucilage. Starch, sugar, and nitrogen content is not considered important. Unless the ash content is 5% or lower, however, it is impossible to obtain the desired white end-product.

Carbohydrate Metabolism by Seeds and Seedlings

Orchid seeds are exceedingly small, have relatively undifferentiated embryos, and lack endosperm. Their energy storage compounds are present in starch grains and lipid droplets (Burgeff, 1936; Ernst, Arditti, and Healey, 1970). Harrison (1977) reported that starch grains were present only in proplastids and observed that the cells were packed with lipid droplets and protein bodies (Fig. 5-5). These reserves cannot be used by the seed for germination (Arditti, 1979).

Symbiotic Culture

In nature, mycorrhizae provide the orchid embryo with the nutrients needed for germination and early growth (Bernard, 1903, 1904, 1909, 1911; Burgeff, 1909, 1911, 1932, 1936).

D. G. Downie (1940) obtained germination and limited development of Goodyera repens following fungal infection in distilled water or on Pfeffer's medium. Germination was considerably better in the presence of mineral salts and was further enhanced by the addition of sugar. No germination was obtained in the absence of the fungus.

Hadley and Williamson (1971) also showed a spectacular increase in the growth of mycorrhizae-infected orchid seedlings on very low levels of sugar.

The starch levels in protocorms of Orchis purpurella grown on deionized-water Pfeffer's medium (sugar free or containing 0.1% glucose) were examined by G. Harvais and Hadley (1967). In the absence of an endophyte or sugar, protocorm development

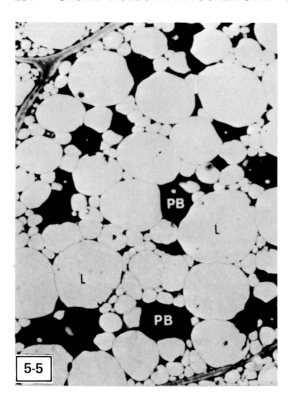

Fig. 5-5. Portion of a cell in the basal region of an ungerminated seed. L, lipid body; PB, protein body; × 3,500. (Reprinted from "Ultrastructural and Histochemical Changes during the Germination of *Cattleya aurantiaca* (Orchidaceae)," *Botanical Gazette,* vol. 138, no. 1, pp. 41–45, by C. R. Harrison, by permission of The University of Chicago Press. © 1977 by The University of Chicago. All rights reserved.)

ceased after three months; the starch levels continued to drop, however. This finding suggested that starch utilization was the result of respiration that was not accompanied by growth. No reduction in starch content occurred on glucose-containing media during the twelve-month experimental period. Fungus-free (asymbiotic) protocorms never reached the photosynthetic stage, which may have been because the glucose concentration (0.1%) in the nutrient was low.

Orchid fungi can readily break down polysaccharides such as cellulose or starch and other complex carbon sources such as lignin and gums and convert them to soluble carbohydrates. S. E. Smith (1966, 1967) demonstrated this phenomenon in translocation studies between *Rhizoctonia* and *Orchis* (Dactylorchis). Hyphae of *Rhizoctonia repens* growing on a cellulose-containing nutrient spread over a diffusion barrier to the carbon-free side of the plate, which was inoculated with seeds of *Orchis purpurella* and *Orchis praetermissa.* Growth was comparatively limited when the fungus was not supplied with cellulose.

Analysis of the *Rhizoctonia* species showed their soluble carbohydrates to consist of trehalose, glucose, and mannitol, whereas those of the *Orchis* species consisted of glucose, fructose, and sucrose. Radioactive mannitol and trehalose were detected when ^{14}C-glucose was supplied to the fungus. Following translocation by the hyphae across the diffusion barrier, labeled glucose, trehalose, and small amounts of mannitol appeared in the seedlings along with increasing levels of labeled orchid sugars (Fig. 5-6; S. E. Smith, 1967; D. Smith, Muscatine, and Lewis, 1969).

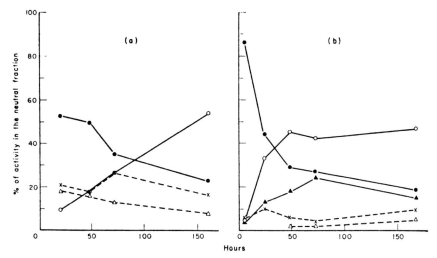

Fig. 5-6. Portion of ^{14}C in the components of the neutral fraction of mycorrhizal seedlings (*Orchis purpurella*) infected by *Rhizoctonia solani* Da (*a*) and *R. solani* Rs (*b*). ●, trehalose; ○, sucrose; X, glucose; △, fructose; and ▲, mannitol. (Smith, 1967).

Trehalose incorporated the highest proportion of the label, suggesting that it may be the principal translocated sugar. It is found in orchids only following infection, which indicates that in all likelihood trehalose is formed in the fungus and transferred as such into the seedling. Trehalose can support germination and satisfactory growth of *Phalaenopsis* (Ernst, 1967; Ernst, Arditti, and Healey, 1971) as well as *Orchis (Dactylorchis) purpurella* and *Bletilla hyacinthina* (S. E. Smith, 1973), but is less satisfactory for *Dendrobium phalaenopsis* (Ernst, 1967). Only traces of glucose were detected when *Phalaenopsis* seedlings were incubated in media that contained trehalose (Ernst, Arditti, and Healey, 1971), which indicates that trehalose is probably taken up by the seedling without extracellular hydrolysis.

Radioactive mannitol was not detected at all in the seedlings or was present only in low concentrations, (Figs. 5-6a, b; S. E. Smith, 1967). Although it is inferior to sucrose, glucose, or fructose as a carbon source, mannitol supported satisfactory asymbiotic growth of *Phalaenopsis* seedlings but proved less adequate for *Dendrobium phalaenopsis* (Ernst, 1967). Similar results were obtained with *Dendrobium nobile* (Quednow, 1930). On the other hand, *Bletilla hyacinthina* (S. E. Smith, 1973) failed to germinate on mannitol.

Goodyera repens germinated and grew well asymbiotically in the presence of 1% glucose on Pfeffer's medium containing potato extract. Trehalose gave comparable results (Purves and Hadley, 1976). Growth was slower and starch accumulation much higher in asymbiotic culture than in infected seedlings. Further, when green plantlets were exposed to $^{14}CO_2$, a higher proportion of the label was incorporated into insoluble fractions by infected seedlings than by asymbiotic ones (Purves and Hadley, 1976).

Digestion of the fungal hyphae by the orchid provides an additional mechanism for transfer of sugars (Borriss, Jeschke, and Bartsch, 1971; Dörr and Kollman, 1969; Harley, 1969; Harvais and Hadley, 1967; D. Smith, Muscatine, and Lewis, 1969); it is accompanied by high oxygen uptake (Blakeman, Mokahel, and Hadley, 1976). In nature the symbiotic relationship between the orchids and their mycorrhizae may be permanent in most cases. Under asymbiotic conditions, however, exogenous sugar may be required for relatively short periods. For *Cattleya,* for example, this period is less than two months (Harrison and Arditti, 1978).

Asymbiotic Culture

By showing that orchid seedlings require soluble sugars, Knudson (1921, 1922) pointed to the fact that mycorrhizae provide the orchids with this source of energy. Appropriate concentrations of soluble sugars, however, are not available to orchid seedlings in nature because there are competing organisms in the soil (Harley, 1969; S. E. Smith, 1966).

The list of sugars Knudson (1921, 1922) investigated for asymbiotic culture of orchids has since been expanded to include other carbohydrates. A chronology of this research was given by Withner (1959) and was reviewed by Arditti (1967, 1979). Therefore, only a summary is presented (Table 5-5).

D-hexoses and their smaller oligosaccharides can generally be used by germinating orchid seeds and seedlings. D-galactose is an exception, and its toxicity to orchids was first reported by Quednow (1930). In addition, galactose-containing oligosaccharides inhibit seed germination and seedling development in direct proportion to the degree of galactose accumulation in the culture medium (Fig. 5-7). The order of toxicity of galactose-containing sugars is lactose > melibiose > raffinose > stachiose. The appearance of free galactose in media containing these oligosaccharides suggests that there is extracellular galactosidase activity (Ernst, Arditti, and Healey, 1971).

Ultrastructural studies showed chromatin dispersal and evagination of the nuclear envelope into the cytoplasm following seedling exposure to galactose (Figs. 5-8 through 5-10). Low concentrations of glucose and fructose ruled out osmotic effects. It was therefore reasonable to assume that galactose altered the factor or factors responsible for membrane permeability. The well-defined cross-sectional structure of the unit membrane indicated that the maintenance of membrane structure was not impaired. Also, the cytoplasm contained numerous membrane vesicles and myelin bodies (Fig. 5-11). Amyloplasts had a normal appearance, but the mitochondrial cristae were slightly swollen and the matrix somewhat clumped (Figs. 5-12 and 5-13).

Plants subjected to toxic levels of galactose accumulate galactose-1-phosphate, which inhibits the formation of glucose-1-phosphate. This phenomenon may result from the inhibition of phosphoglucomutase by galactose-1-phosphate or glucose-1-phosphate formation from UDP-Glu (Göring and Reckin, 1968; Rozenfeld, 1965; Stenlid, 1957). A further effect is the inhibition of starch and cellulose synthesis (Göring and Reckin, 1968; Ordin and Altmann, 1965; Stenlid, 1957).

Galactosyl sugars are not at all uncommon in plants. For example, galactosideosucroses such as raffinose and stachyose are important translocation sugars and usually are associated with sucrose in phloem exudates or floral and extrafloral nectars, including those of orchid flowers (Baskin and Bliss, 1969; Jeffrey, Arditti, and Koopowitz, 1970; Tables 5-6 and 5-7).

Table 5-5. Carbohydrates as energy sources for asymbiotic seed germination of orchids

Carbohydrate	Orchid	Growth[a]	Reference[b]
Monosaccharides			
C-5			
D-Xylose	*Phalaenopsis* ×Doris	+ + +	Ernst, 1967
L-Xylose	*Cattleya trianaei*	0	Wynd, 1933
D-Arabinose	*Phalaenopsis* ×Doris	0	Ernst, 1967
L-Arabinose	*Cattleya trianae*	0	Wynd, 1933
D-Ribose	*Phalaenopsis* ×Doris	+	Ernst, 1967
D-Lyxose	*Phalaenopsis* ×Doris	0	Ernst, 1967
C-6			
D-Fructose	Lc. Mlle. Clementine	+ + +	Knudson, 1922
α-D-Glucose	*Cattleya* ×Angela	+	Knudson, 1922
	Laelia pumila	+ + +	Quednow, 1930
β-D-Glucose	*Phalaenopsis* ×Doris	+ + +	Ernst, 1967
L-Glucose	*Phalaenopsis* ×Doris	0	Ernst, 1967
D-Mannose	*Cattleya trianae*	+ + +	Wynd, 1933
L-Mannose	*Phalaenopsis* ×Doris	0	Ernst, 1967
D-Galactose	*Dendrobium nobile*	0	Quednow, 1930
L-Sorbose	*Phalaenopsis* ×Doris	0	Ernst, 1967
C-7			
Sedoheptulosan	*Phalaenopsis* ×Doris	0	Ernst, 1967
Disaccharides			
C-12			
Sucrose	*Cattleya mossiae*	+ + +	Knudson, 1922
Sucrose (brown)	*Cattleya* ×Belle Etoile	0	Withner, 1942
Maltose	*Cattleya trianae* hybr.	+ + +	La Garde, 1929
	Vanda suavis	0	Burgeff, 1936
Trehalose	*Phalaenopsis* ×Doris	+ +	Ernst, 1967
Cellobiose	*Phalaenopsis* ×Doris	+ +	Ernst, 1967
Turanose	*Phalaenopsis* ×Doris	+ + +	Ernst, 1967
Lactose	*Dendrobium nobile*	0	Quednow, 1930
	Phalaenopsis ×Doris	+	Ernst *et al.,* 1971
Melibiose	*Phalaenopsis* ×Doris	+	Ernst, 1967
Trisaccharides			
C-18			
Raffinose	*Cattleya trianae*	0	Wynd, 1933
	Phalaenopsis ×Doris	+ +	Ernst, 1967
Melezitose	*Phalaenopsis* ×Doris	+ +	Ernst, 1967
Tetrasaccharide			
C-24			
Stachiose	*Phalaenopsis* ×Doris	+ +	Ernst *et al.,* 1971
Polyols			
C-4			
meso-Erythritol	*Phalaenopsis* ×Doris	0	Ernst, 1967
C-5			
D-Arabinitol	*Phalaenopsis* ×Doris	+	Ernst, 1967
L-Arabinitol	*Phalaenopsis* ×Doris	0	Ernst, 1967
Xylitol	*Phalaenopsis* ×Doris	+ +	Ernst, 1967
Ribitol	*Phalaenopsis* ×Doris	+	Ernst, 1967
C-6			
Mannitol	*Dendrobium nobile*	+	Quednow, 1930
	Phalaenopsis ×Doris	+ + +	Ernst, 1967
Sorbitol	*Phalaenopsis* ×Doris	+ +	Ernst, 1967
Galactitol	*Phalaenopsis* ×Doris	0	Ernst, 1967
Cyclitol			
C-6			
myo-Inositol	*Phalaenopsis* ×Doris	0	Ernst, 1967
Deoxy-sugars			
C-6			
2-Deoxy-D-glucose	*Phalaenopsis* ×Doris	0	Ernst, 1967
L-Rhamnose	*Cattleya trianae*	0	Wynd, 1933
D-Fucose	*Phalaenopsis* ×Doris	0	Ernst, 1967
Polysaccharides			
Starch	*Cymbidium* ×Doris	0	Burgeff, 1936
Dextrin	*Dendrobium nobile*	0	Quednow, 1930
Inulin	*Cymbidium* ×Doris	0	Burgeff, 1936

[a] The number of plus signs is indicative of growth: + + +, good; + +, fair; +, marginal; 0, no growth.

[b] The first author to use a sugar is cited.

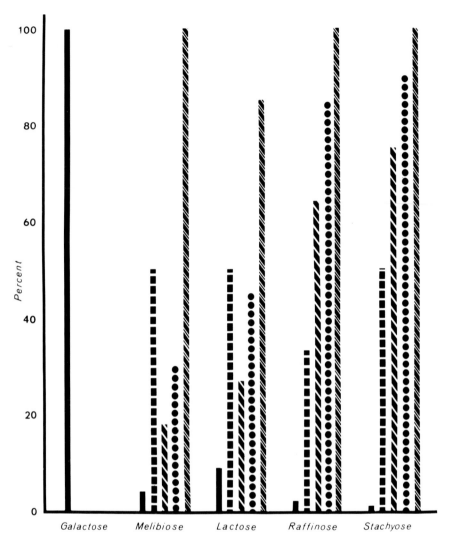

Fig. 5-7. Effect of galactose content on the differentiation, fresh weight, and survival of four-month-old *Phalaenopsis* cv Doris F$_3$ seedlings. Solid bars = galactose, percent of neutral fraction; dashes = galactose, percent of oligosaccharide; single line slants = seedling fresh weight; dots = differentiated seedlings, percent; double line slants = surviving seedlings, percent. (Ernst, Arditti, and Healey, 1971.)

Except for sucrose and several other nonreducing oligosaccharides, polyols are the only other carbohydrates translocated in the phloem of higher plants. Yet polyols have not been found to be very useful as heterotrophic carbon sources for orchids (Lewis and D. C. Smith, 1967). The relatively good growth of *Phalaenopsis* seedlings on media containing xylitol, sorbitol, or mannitol is therefore surprising (Ernst, 1967).

L-sugars and deoxy-sugars are rare as free carbohydrates. It is therefore not unexpected that these compounds do not serve as energy sources for asymbiotic propagation of orchid seedlings (Arditti, 1979; Ernst, 1967; Wynd, 1933).

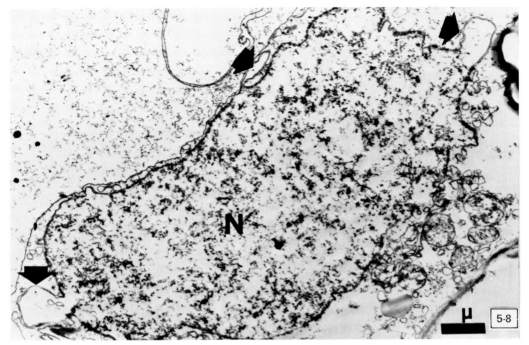

Fig. 5-8. Nucleus (N) from galactose-treated *Phalaenopsis* cv Doris F$_3$ seedling. Chromatin appears dispersed and nuclear envelope evaginates (arrows) into cytoplasm. (Ernst, Arditti, and Healey, 1971.)

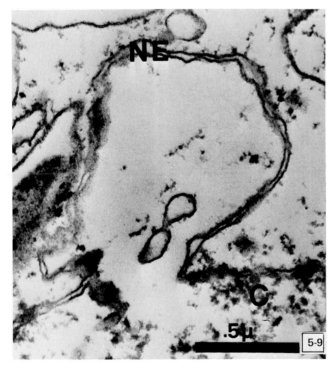

Fig. 5-9. Nuclear envelope (NE) of *Phalaenopsis* cv Doris F$_3$ seedlings evaginating into cytoplasm. Chromatin (C). (Ernst, Arditti, and Healey, 1971.)

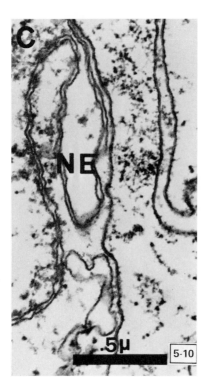

Fig. 5-10. Nuclear envelope of *Phalaenopsis* cv Doris F$_3$ seedlings folded back on cytoplasmic side. (Ernst, Arditti, and Healey, 1971.)

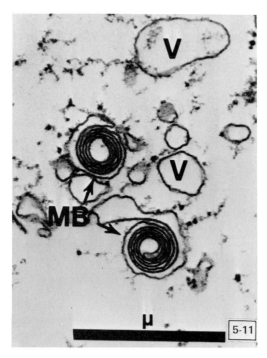

Fig. 5-11. Unit membrane vesicles (V) and myelin bodies (MB) appear in the cytoplasm of galactose-treated *Phalaenopsis* cv Doris F$_3$ seedlings. (Ernst, Arditti, and Healey, 1971.)

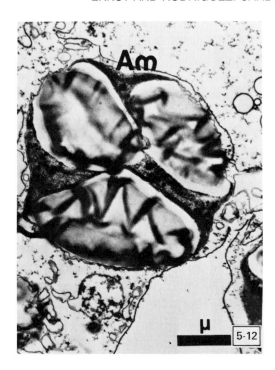

Fig. 5-12. Amyloplasts (AM) appear normal after galactose treatment of *Phalaenopsis* cv Doris F₃ seedlings. (Ernst, Arditti, and Healey, 1971.)

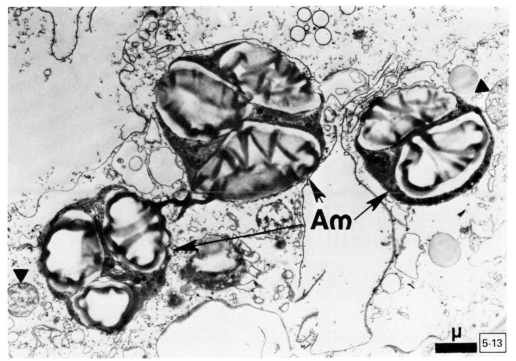

Fig. 5-13. Mitochondrial cristae appear slightly swollen (triangle) after galactose treatment of *Phalaenopsis* cv Doris F₃ seedlings. AM, amyloplasts. (Ernst, Arditti, and Healey, 1971.)

Phalaenopsis seedlings readily use the pentose sugar D-xylose (Ernst, 1967), which, although it is not an intermediate of the pentose-phosphate cycle, can be isomerized to xylulose (Pubols, Zahnley, and Axelrod, 1963), which is.

The length of time required by asymbiotically grown orchid seedlings to reach their autotrophic stage probably varies with genus and species. Harrison and Arditti (1978) reported that *Cattleya aurantiaca* seeds grown on a sucrose-containing medium for about one month develop photosynthetic ability and can continue their growth on a carbohydrate-free medium. Seedlings maintained on a sucrose-containing medium had considerably higher protein content (Fig. 5-14) and enzyme levels (see Fig. 4-9, *bottom*) than those grown on a sugar-free nutrient.

Uptake of Sugars by Leaf Slices

Bletilla hyacinthina is capable of growing on glucose and trehalose but not on mannitol (S. E. Smith, 1973). Leaf slices of this orchid were incubated in 0.5 mM and 1.0 mM solution of radioactive glucose, trehalose, and mannitol. The time required for uptake of these carbohydrates with 1.0 mM solution is shown in Figure 5-15 (S. E. Smith and F. E. Smith, 1973). Uptake rates of trehalose and mannitol were 17.8% and 33.6% of glucose respectively. Distribution of the label in the neutral, soluble fractions, following a twenty-four hour incubation in 0.5 mM solutions, showed sucrose to be the most highly labeled compound when glucose or trehalose were supplied. Mannitol was largely unaltered (Fig. 5-16). This is in line with the reported finding that *Bletilla hyacinthina* seedlings are unable to grow on nutrients containing mannitol as the sole carbon source.

Floral and Extrafloral Exudates

Probably the earliest reference to orchid nectars and their sugary ("saccharine") exudates was made by Darwin (1862) in connection with his studies on orchid pollination by insects. Shortly thereafter F. W. Burbidge (1885) pointed to the existence of "honey" glands in the sepals of *Cattleya mendelii* flowers. Fifty years later, E. Daumann (1941)

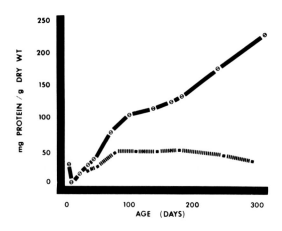

Fig. 5-14. Soluble protein content in *Cattleya aurantiaca* seedlings raised on Knudson C medium with (solid line) and without (broken line) sucrose. (Reprinted from "Physiological Changes during the Germination of *Cattleya aurantiaca* (Orchidaceae)," *Botanical Gazette*, vol. 139, pp. 180–189, by C. R. Harrison and J. Arditti, by permission of The University of Chicago Press. © 1977 by The University of Chicago. All rights reserved.)

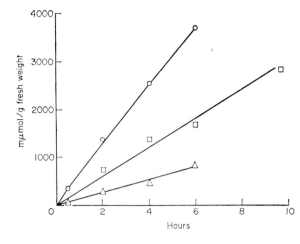

Fig. 5-15. Uptake of glucose ○, mannitol □, and trehalose △ by leaf slices of *Bletilla hyacinthina* from 1 m*M* solutions at 24°C in light (Smith and Smith, 1973.)

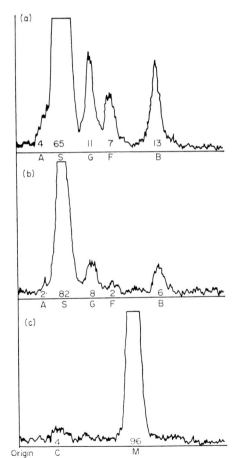

Fig. 5-16. Distribution of ^{14}C within the neutral, soluble fraction of *Bletilla hyacinthina* leaves following incubation for twenty-four hours in 0.5 m*M* glucose (*a*), trehalose (*b*), and mannitol (*c*) solutions. Solvent, methyl ethyl ketone:ethyl acetate:water, saturated with boric acid. A, B, C are unknown compounds. S, sucrose; G, glucose; F, fructose; M, mannitol. Figures under the peaks indicate their relative areas; corrections have been made for those peaks that have been truncated by scanning at this sensitivity. (Smith and Smith, 1973.)

found nectars of various orchids to contain reducing sugars. A. Frey-Wyssling and E. Häusermann (1960) identified sucrose, glucose, and fructose in the nectars of *Cymbidium traceyanum, Cymbidium lowianum,* and *Cattleya parcivaliana.* They also referred to the occurrence of "honey" drops on *Cymbidium* leaf tips. The same three sugars were also found in a *Cattleya* cultivar (Payne, 1968), in addition to a fourth unidentified one.

Percival (1961) studied a number of plants of seven orchid species and several of their hybrids. In addition to various ratios of sucrose, glucose, and fructose in each of the nectars examined, *Aerides odoratum,* an unknown *Cymbidium* species, and a *Cymbidium* hybrid also contained the trisaccharide raffinose. An additional unidentified fraction was observed in *Epipactis helleborine.* The semiquantitative method used permitted the flower nectars to be classified into three broad groups: (1) dominant sucrose nectars; (2) nectars with balanced fructose, glucose, and sucrose content; and (3) dominant fructose and glucose nectars. Most of the orchid nectars fell into the first group; all the rest fit into the third.

D. C. Jeffrey and J. Arditti (1968) separated and identified the sugars of *Catasetum discolor* and *Dendrobium chrysotoxum* and found fructose, glucose, and sucrose in both. The *Catasetum* species also contained a fourth sugar, tentatively identified as raffinose. Using the same qualitative techniques, they also analyzed the nectars of *Cattleya guttata, Cattleya loddigesii,* several hybrids of the *Cattleya* alliance, and an unknown Venezuelan *Epi-*

Table 5-6. Relative quantitative amounts of sugars from orchid nectars expressed as percent value of sucrose (modified from Baskin and Bliss, 1969)[a]

Orchid	Fructose	α-Glucose	β-Glucose	Total glucose	Raffinose
Ansellia africana	215	230	295	525	
Brassocattleya ×Nanipuakea	25	20	30	50	
Brassolaeliocattleya ×Estelle Sewall	50	195	45	240	
Cattleya aurantiaca	40	80	35	115	
Cattleya ×Edward Ayau Sr.	40	30	45	75	
Cattleyopsis lindenii	155	220	200	420	
Chysis laevis	50	35	60	95	
Cychnoches chlorochilon	20	25	40	65	
Cyrptopodium punctatum	1265	90	85	175	
Cymbidium aloifolium	20	10	15	25	
Cymbidium canaliculatum	170	100	115	215	
Diacrium bicornutum	25	10	15	25	
Epidendrum atropurpureum	80	250	170	420	
Epidendrum ×Anza	60	55	60	115	10
Epidendrum stellatum	30	15	25	40	
Laelia tenebrosa	55	55	65	120	10
Laeliocattleya ×Adolph Hecker	60	50	65	115	15
Laeliocattleya ×Paradisio	35	20	25	45	0.5
Laeliocattleya ×Mem. Walter Armacost	25	25	25	50	
Miltonidium ×Surprise	105	40	50	90	
Odontoglossum cariniferum	15	10	15	25	5
Odontoglossum ×unknown	5	15	15	30	
Phalaenopsis lueddemanniana	125	120	135	255	5
Renanthera ×Tom Thumb	10	40	45	85	
Sobralia unknown sp.	305	255	275	530	
Trigonidium obtusum	35	30	30	60	
Vanda Rothschildiana	35	40	45	85	
Zygopetalum intermedium	75	535	150	685	

[a] Values were calculated using the following equation:

$$\frac{\text{peak area (sugar analyzed)}}{100 \text{ (sucrose peak)}} \times 100 = \% \text{ sugar relative sucrose} \pm 5\%$$

dendrum species. All contained sucrose and its constituent monosaccharides, fructose and glucose. Raffinose, tentatively identified in *Cattleya loddigesii* and in a *Laeliocattleya* hybrid, was present in substantially lower levels than the other sugars (Jeffrey and Arditti, 1969).

A more quantitative comparison of relative sugar levels in the nectars of thirty orchid species and hybrids was reported by S. I. Baskin and C. A. Bliss (1969). Except for fructose, glucose, and sucrose, which were present in all exudates, only raffinose was found in greater than trace amounts (Table 5-6). It was found in six of the orchids examined. Several tentatively identified sugars (maltose, cellobiose, gentibiose, and lactose) were found at trace levels. Although lactose has been reported to occur in the fruit of *Achras sapota* (Venkataraman and Reithel, 1958) and in *Forsythia* anthers (Kuhn and Löw, 1949), it is a milk sugar rarely found in plants. Its presence in nectars is therefore surprising. Jeffrey, Arditti, and H. Koopowitz (1970) identified stachyose in three *Cymbidium* hybrids and possibly also in *Cycnoches chlorochilon* (Table 5-7). Although stachyose is much less common, the galactosyl sucroses raffinose and stachyose are frequently found together.

There is no correlation between the sugar contents of exudates and orchid pollination (Jeffrey, Arditti, and Koopowitz, 1970; Table 5-7). The study of nectar sugars may therefore be of little chemotaxonomic value. In some orchids, sugar-containing exudates attract ants that protect the plants from grazers (Table 5-7).

Table 5-7. Sugar content in floral and extrafloral exudates and pollinators of several orchid species and hybrids (Jeffrey, Arditti, and Koopowitz, 1970)

Species or hybrid	Sugars[a]	Pollinator
Aerides cornutum	"Sugar"	
A. odoratum	G, F, S, R	
Angraecum comorense	G, F, S	
A. eburneum	G, F, S, R	
A. sesquipedale	G, F, S, R, Melezitose (?)	*Xanthopan morgani predicta* (Moth)
Angraecum ×*Veitchii*	G, F, S, R (?)	
Ansellia africana	G, F, S	
Arpophyllum giganteum	G, F, S	
Ascocentrum ampulaceum	G, F, S	
Brassocattleya ×*Nanipuakea*	G, F, S, Gentiobiose (?) Melibiose (?)	
Brassolaeliocattleya ×*Marchesa*	G, F, S	
Blc ×*Sylvia Fry*	G, F, S	
Blc The Baroness × *Lc* Grandee	G, F, S	
Brassavola glauca	G, F, S	A related species, *B. digybana,* is pollinated by a sphingid moth
Catasetum discolor	G, F, S, R	*Eulaema cingulata* (bee)
Cattleya sp.[b]	G, F, S	All *Cattleya* species listed are bee pollinated
C. amethystoglossa	G, F, S	
C. aurantiaca	G, F, S	
C. bowringiana	G, F, S, and unknown oligosaccharides	
Cattleya ×Edithiae 'White Empress'	G, F, S, R	
Cattleya ×Enid 'Alba'	G, F, S	
Cattleya ×Estelle × *C. intermedia alba*	G, F, S, and a "more complicated" sugar	
C. forbesii	G, F, S	
C. guatemalensis	G, F, S, R	

(*continued*)

Table 5-7.   *Continued*

Species or hybrid	Sugars[a]	Pollinator
C. guttata alba	G, F, S	
C. intermedia	G, F, S, R (?)	
C. intermedia acquinii	G, F, S	
C. labiata	Reducing sugars	
C. loddigesii alba	G, F, S, R	
C. maxima (Horace)	G, F, S	
C. mossiae ×*L. albida*	G, F, S	*Eulaema polychroma* (bee)
C. ×Nigritian	G, F, S	
C. percivaliana	G, F, S	
C. skinneri	G, F, S, R	
C. trianaei ×Bill Taft	G, F, S	
C. trianaei ×President	G, F, S	
Cattleyopsis lindenii	G, F, S, R, Melibiose (?)	Bees
Cattleytonia ×Rosy Jewell	G, F, S	
Chysis laevis	G, F, S	
Coelogyne cristata[b]	G, F, S	
Coryanthes[b]	"Almost pure water"	All *Coryanthes* listed are bee pollinated
Cycnoches chlorochilon	G, F, S	*Eulaema cingulata* (bee—all *Cycnoches* spp. listed are bee pollinated)
C. chlorochilon male flower	G, F, S, R, Melibiose (?) St (?)	*Eulaema cingulata* (bee)
Cymbidium sp.	G, F, S	
Cymbidium aloifolium	G, F, S	*Xylocopa* sp. (bee) *Vespa cincta* (wasp)
C. canaliculatum	G, F, S	
C. canaliculatum ×Canadian	G, F, S, R (?)	
C. devonianum	G, F, S, R	
Cymbidium ×Evening Star	G, F, S, R, St (?)	
Cymbidium ×Fairy Wand	G, F, S	
Cymbidium ×King Arthur	G, D, S	
Cymbidium ×Lillian Stewart	G, F, S, T, St (?)	
Cymbidium ×Oriental Legend 'Temple Bell'	G, F, S	
Cymbidium ×Pauwelsii 'The King' × *C.* ×Ophir	G, F, S, "Unknown"	
Cymbidium ×Peter Pan 'Green Sleeves'	G, F, S, R, St	
Cymbidium ×Samarkand	G, F, S (very high F conc.)	
Cymbidium ×San Francisco	G, F, S	
Cymbidium ×Showgirl	G, F, S	
Cymbidium sp.	G, F, S, "Unknown"	
Cymbidium ×Tiger Tail	G, F, S	
Cyrtopodium punctatum	G, F, S, Melibiose (?)	*Euglossa hemichlora*
Dendrobium[b] *chrysotoxum*	G, F, S	
D. undulatum 'Bloomfeldii'	G, F, S	
Diabroughtonia ×Alice Hart	G, F, S	
Diacrium bicornutum[b] (*Caularthron bicornutum*)	G, F, S	
Epicattleya hybrid	G, F, S	
Epidendrum[b] ×Anza	G, F, S, R, Maltose (?)	*Epidendrum* listed are pollinated by bees, birds, butterflies, flies, and moths
E. atropurpureum	G, F, S, R	
E. cochleatum	G, F, S	
E. ('Hawkes')	G, F, S	
E. ×Obrienianum	G, F, S	
E. stamfordianum	G, F, S	
E. stellatum	G, F, S	
Epidendrum (unidentified Venezuelan species)	G, F, S	
Epipactis atrorubens	G, F, S	*Epipactis* listed are pollinated by bees, flies, and wasps
E. helleborine	G, F, S, Melibiose	
E. palustris	G, F, S	*Apis mellifera* (bee)
Habenaria obtusata	"Sugar"	*Aedes communis, A. canadensis canadensis, A. intrudens* (mosquito)
Laelia flava	G, F, S, R (?)	
L. millerii	G, F, S	Undet. hummingbird
L. pumila Dayana	G, F, S	

(continued)

Table 5-7. *Continued*

Species or hybrid	Sugars[a]	Pollinator
L. rubescens	G, F, S	
L. tenebrosa	G, F, S, R, Melibiose	
Laeliocattleya ×Adolph Hecker	G, F, S, R, Cellobiose	
Laeliocattleya ×Chit Chat	G, F, S, R	
Laeliocattleya ×Dorothy Fried	G, F, S, R	
Laeliocattleya ×Eva	G, F, S	
Laeliocattleya ×Golden Ray	G, F, S, R (?)	
Laeliocattleya ×Hunter's Gold	G, F, S	
Laeliocattleya ×Mem. Walter Armacost	G, F, S, Lactose	
Laeliocattleya ×Paradisio	G, F, S	
Laeliocattleya ×Valantes	G, F, S	
Listera ovata	G, F, S	*Ophinoninae* (wasp)
Miltonia warscewiczii	G, F, S	All *Miltonia* listed are bee pollinated
Miltonidium ×Surprise	G, F, S	
Mormodes igneum	G, F, S, R, St (?)	*Euglossa igniventria* *E. mixta* (bee)
Notylia	G, F, S	All *Notylia* listed are bee pollinated
Odontoglossum cariniferum	G, F, S, R, and unknown sugar	All *Odontoglossum* listed are bee pollinated
Odontoglossum 'Finest'	G, F, S	
Oncidium ampliatum[b]	G, F, S, R, Melezitose (?)	All *Oncidium* listed are bee pollinated
O. carthagenense	G, F, S, R	
O. maculatum	G, F, S	
O. nudum	G, F, S, R (?)	
O. tigrinum	G, F, S, R, Melezitose (?)	
Phaius flavus	G, F, S	All *Phaius* listed are bee pollinated
Phalaenopsis lueddemanniana	G, F, S, R, and unknown sugar	All *Phalaenopsis* listed are bee pollinated
Renanthera ×Tom Thumb	G, F, S	
Schomburgkia undulata[b]	G, F, S	All *Schomburgkia* listed are bee pollinated
Schomburgkia ×Wishful Pink	G, F, S	
Sobralia sp.	G, F, S, Melibiose (?)	All *Sobralia* listed are pollinated by birds and bees
Sophrolaeliocattleya ×Estella Jewell	G, F, S	
Spathoglottis plicata[b]	G, F, S	
Trigonidum obtusum	G, F, S	*Trigona droryana* (bee)
Vanda[b] ×Rothschildiana	G, F, S, Maltose (?)	All *Vanda* listed are bee pollinated
V. suavis (*V. tricolor*)	G, F, S	
V. teres alba 'Candide'	G, F, S	
Vanilla planifollia[b]	G, F, S, very high R conc., Melibiose, Maninotriose (?), unknown oligosaccharide	*Melipona beechii* (bee)
Zygopetalum intermedium	G, F, S	All *Zygopetalum* listed are bee pollinated
Z. mackayii	G, F, S	

[a] F, Fructose; G, glucose; R, raffinose; S, sucrose; St, stachyose.
[b] Association with ants observed in at least one species within the genus. Such association has also been observed in *Encyclia cordigera* and species of *Arundina, Gongora, Grammatophyllum,* and *Vandopsis.*

Glycosides of Orchids

Phenolic Glycosides

Phytochemical investigations of orchids have centered on their alkaloids (Lüning, 1974; Slaytor, 1977) and flavonoids (Arditti and Fisch, 1977). In addition, some of the early work dealt with phenolic glycosides derived via the shikimic acid pathway, including coumarins, quinones, and simple phenolic acid aglycones.

E. Bourquelot and M. Bridel (1914a, 1914b) observed one or more glycosides, hydro-lyzable with emulsin (β-glycosidase), in the following species of European terrestrial orchids: *Aceras anthropophora, Loroglossum hircinum, Ophrys apifera, O. aranifera, Orchis conopsea, O. latifolia, O. maculata, O. morio, O. purpurea, O. pyramidalis, O. muscifera, O. ustulata, Plantathera bifolia, Cephalanthera grandiflora, Epipactis latifolia, Limodorum abor-tivum, Neottia ovata,* and *N. nidus-avis.* Sucrose was present in each of the species except *Neottia nidus-avis.* After World War I, the same authors reported that they had isolated a crystalline glucoside from *Loroglossum hircinum,* which they named loroglossine (see Chapter 3). This glycoside forms long, colorless needles that dissolve readily in water and alcohol but not in acetic acid/ether or acetone. The compound is levorotatory and yields reducing sugar on acid or enzymatic hydrolysis (Bourquelot and Bridel, 1919).

In subsequent years, loroglossine was detected in twenty-three other orchid species (Charaux and Delauney, 1925a, 1925b, 1926; Delauney, 1924; Table 5-8). C. Charaux and P. Delauney suggested the empirical formula $C_{30}H_{12}O_{18}$, which was subsequently proved to be erroneous. Later P. Karrer and E. Matter (1947) obtained loroglossine from *Orchis latifolia, O. mascula,* and *O. maculata* and proposed an elemental formula of $C_{14}H_{20}O_8$, characterizing loroglossine as a monoglucoside, both of which are incorrect. They reported that the aglycon of loroglossine had a characteristic odor of newly mowed hay. A. Aasen, D. Behr, and K. Leander (1975) established loroglossine as being bis [4-(β-D-glucopyranosyloxy) benzyl] *erythro*isobutyltartrate (Formula 5-I). This structure was confirmed by R. Gray *et al.* (1976, 1977), who also presented evidence that the (+)-*erythro*isobutyltartaric acid component of loroglossine has the 2R,3S configuration. This finding is in agreement with the absolute configuration of this dicarboxylic acid obtained by Behr, Dahmén, and Leander (1976). Loroglossine was found to melt with decomposition at 153°C to 157°C (Aasen *et al.,* 1975) and 151°C to 153°C (Gray *et al.,*

Table 5-8. Orchids containing loroglossine

Species	References
Cephalanthera grandiflora	Delauney, 1921a, 1921b, 1921c
C. rubra	
Epipactis atrorubens	Delauney, 1923a, 1923b
E. latifolia	Delauney, 1923b
E. palustris	Charaux and Delauney, 1925a, 1926
Goodyera repens	Delauney, 1925a, 1925b
Limodorum abortivum	Delauney, 1925a, 1925b
Listera ovata	Charaux and Delauney, 1925a, 1925b, 1926
Loroglossum hircinum	Bourquelot and Bridel, 1919
Ophrys apifera	Delauney, 1921a, 1921b
O. aranifera	Delauney, 1920, 1921a, 1921b, 1921c
O. muscifera	Delauney, 1923a, 1923b
Orchis bifolia	Delauney, 1921a, 1921b, 1921c
O. conopsea	Delauney, 1923a, 1923b
O. latifolia	Delauney, 1923a, 1923b; Karrer and Matter, 1947
O. maculata	Delauney, 1923a, 1923b; Karrer and Matter, 1947
O. mascula	Delauney, 1923a, 1923b; Karrer and Matter, 1947
O. militaris	Delauney, 1923a, 1923b; Aasen *et al.,* 1975
O. morio	Delauney, 1923a, 1923b
O. purpurea	Delauney, 1923a, 1923b
O. pyramidalis	Delauney, 1923a, 1923b
O. simia	Delauney, 1921a, 1921c
O. ustulata	Delauney, 1925a, 1925b
Spiranthes autumnalis	Delauney, 1925a, 1925b

1976). Its optical properties are [α] D −34°C, c 0.36 in methanol (Aasen *et al.*, 1975) and [α] D −38°C in water (Gray *et al.*, 1976). The empirical formula of loroglossine is $C_{34}H_{46}O_{18}$, and its ultraviolet extinction coefficients in methanolic solution are 277 nm (1340), 270.5 nm (1590), and 223.5 nm (25,400) (Aasen *et al.*, 1975).

COOCH₂—⟨ ⟩—o-β-D-glucopyranoside
—OH
H——OH
COOCH₂—⟨ ⟩—o-β-D-glucopyranoside

5-I. Loroglossine

Investigation of the structure of loroglossine from *Orchis militaris* led to the isolation of a second, structurally related glycoside, which was named militarine (Aasen *et al.*, 1975), bis[4-(β-D-glucopyranosyloxy)benzyl] (R)-2-isobutylmalate (Formula 5-II). Its molecular formula $C_{34}H_{46}O_{17}$ has one less oxygen than loroglossine. The substitution of hydrogen for a hydroxyl group in the dicarboxylic acid component of militarine was shown by the formation of (R)-2-isobutylmalic acid following catalytic hydrogenation. Dahmén and Leander (1976) found a related citric acid ester of glucopyranosyloxybenzyl alcohol, tris [4(β-D-glucopyranosyloxy)benzyl]citrate (Formula 5-III), in *Vanda parishii* and named it parishin. Glucopyranosyloxybenzyl alcohol, which was also found in the extract, was assumed to be an artifact formed during the isolation.

COOCH₂—⟨ ⟩—o-β-D-glucopyranoside
—OH
H——H
COOCH₂—⟨ ⟩—o-β-D-glucopyranoside

5-II. Militarine

COOCH₂—⟨ ⟩—o-β-D-glucopyranoside
CH₂
HO-C-COOCH₂—⟨ ⟩—o-β-D-glucopyranoside
CH₂
COOCH₂—⟨ ⟩—o-β-D-glucopyranoside

5-III. Parishin

The presence of coumarin-glucosides in *Orchis militaris, O. purpurea,* and *O. simia* was claimed by H. Hérrisey and Delauney (1921). Free coumarin was not present in these orchids, but this phenolic lactone was identified in extracts hydrolyzed by emulsin or by sulfuric acid. The acid hydrolysis of a crude aqueous extract of *Dendrobium densiflorum* also yielded coumarin, 6,7-dimethoxycoumarin, and 6,7-methylenedioxycoumarin, all of which do not occur free in these plants (Dahmén, Leander, and Rosenblom, 1975). Similarly, extracts of *Dendrobium thyrsiflorum* contained 6,7-dimethoxycoumarin, 6,7-methylenedioxycoumarin, 7-hydroxy-6-methoxycoumarin, and 6,7-methylenedioxy-coumarin from *Dendrobium densiflorum* and *D. farmeri.* In each of these cases the assumption was made that these compounds occur as glycosides of the corresponding *o*-hydroxy-*trans*-cinnamic acids and that their presence in free form was an artifact of the extraction and isolation procedures.

Two *cis*- and *trans*-cinnamic acid derivatives isolated from *Dendrobium densiflorum* are densifloroside, 2-(β-D-glucopyranosyloxy)-4,5-dimethoxy-*trans*-cinnamic acid (Formula 5-IV) and its *cis* isomer (Dahmén *et al.,* 1975). The glucose is present as the pyranoside in the β-configuration. The *cis* isomer could not be completely characterized because only a small quantity was isolated.

5-IV. Densifloroside

Esters of glucose were identified (Pagani, 1976) from extracts of *Orchis sambucina*. The esters included p-coumaroyl-1-glucoside and caffeoyl-1-glucoside, along with flavonoids.

Two glycoside lactones with the elemental formula $C_{13}H_{26}O_8$ were isolated by Dahmén, Gawell, and Leander (1976). Spectrochemical and enzymatic analyses showed these compounds to be (4R,5R)-4-β-D-glucopyranosyloxy-3-methylhex-2-en-5-olide (Formula 5-V), which was named *cis*-crassinodine, and (4S,5R)-4-β-D-glucopyranosyloxy-3-methylhex-2-en-5-olide (*trans*-crassinodine) (Formula 5-VI).

5-V. *cis*-Crassinodine

5-VI. *trans*-Crassinodine

Some of these phenolic glycosides may serve as defense substances or their precursors. Thus p-hydroxybenzyl alcohol, a component of loroglossine, militarine, and parishin, was found only in fungus-infected *Orchis militaris* plants (Gaümann and Kern, 1959a, 1959b; Hardegger, Schellenbaum, and Corrodi, 1963). Glucosides similar in structure to crassinodine, isolated from two ferns, have antibiotic activity (Dahmén *et al.,* 1976).

Steroid Glycosides

A pair of closely related stigmastane steroid glycosides were obtained in crystalline form from *Dendrobium ochreatum* (Behr *et al.,* 1975). One, named dendrosteroside (Formula 5-VII), contained gentibiose in a β-linkage to the aglycone. The second had a β-D-glucopyranosyl substituent in place of the gentibiose residue (Formula 5-VIII). In addition, free aglycone was also isolated from *D. ochreatum*.

Two additional stigmastane glycosides, ochreasteroside (Formula 5-IX) and *epi*-ochreasteroside (Formula 5-X), were subsequently obtained from the same orchid species. The sugar in both is a β-D-glucopyranosyl residue. The compounds differ in the spatial arrangements of the hydroxyl group at carbon 16 (Behr and Leander, 1976).

5-VII. Dendrosteroside

5-VIII. Dendrosterone β-D-glucopyranoside

5-IX. Ochreasteroside

5-X. *epi*-ochreasteroside

Flavonoid Glycosides

Flavonoids are widely distributed in higher plants. The most common among the ten known classes are the flavones and the flavonols. They frequently occur as aglycones, but many plants produce glycosylated flavonoids. These glycosides are common in the flowers and leaves but are rarely present in the roots and stems. Flavonoids function as defensive compounds against microorganisms, effective feeding deterrents against phytophagous insects, (McClure, 1974), coloring agents, and "nectar guides" in flowers.

The anthocyanins of the Orchidaceae have been reviewed recently (Arditti and Fisch, 1977) and only an update will be presented here. Since that review the anthocyanins in

Table 5-9.   Anthocyanins and their relative concentrations (%) in the flowers of European and related orchid species (Uphoff, 1979)[a]

	Chrysanthemin	Mecocyanin	Epipactin[b]	Cyanin	Orchicyanin II	Orchicyanin I
Cypripedium calceolus	100 P					
C. reginae	100 L					
C. cordigerum	100[c]					
Listera ovata	100 P					
Epipactis atrorubens	40	30	20	10		
E. helleborine	20	40	20	10		
E. palustris	?[d]	40	60			
Calypso borealis	90			10		
Ophrys insectifera	100 L					
O. speculum	80				10	10
O. apifera L	100				—	—
P	—				40	60
Barlia robertiana[d]	10			40	40	10
Serapias lingua[d]	10?	20?		10		
Nigritella nigra	100					
Gymnadenia odorata				10	40	50
G. conopea				10	40	50
Dactylorhiza sambucina				10	30	60
D. majalis				10	30	60
D. maculata				10	20	70
Orchis ustulata	10[e]	90				
O. purpurea	10 P	?[f]		20	50	20
O. militaris				50	30	20
O. simia				10	60	30
O. longicornu				10	20	70
O. morio				10	10	80
O. mascula				5	5	90

P, petals and sepals; L, labellum.
[a] The concentrations have been rounded off and refer to flowers that have been open for 2 days.
[b] Epipactin is a characteristic orange-colored anthocyanidin glycoside of *Epipactis* species.
[c] Dark red spots on the labellum.
[d] Preliminary results.
[e] Only in buds and at the beginning of anthesis.
[f] Very small quantities.

the flowers of a number of European orchids have been examined (Uphoff, 1979a; Table 5-9). Orchids of any one species always contained the same anthocyanins, regardless of growth conditions. The sugars of these anthocyanins were almost exclusively glucose residues. In addition to common anthocyanins such as cyanidin-3-monglucoside (chrysanthemin), cyanidin-3-diglucoside (mecocyanin), and cyanidin-3,5-diglucoside (cyanin), two complex cyanin pigments were found in a number of these flowers. They were identified as "orchicyanin I" [violet color, λ max.(nm) 526, (322), 350, 267] and "orchicyanin II" [red color, λ max.(nm) 513, (312), 267; Uphoff, 1979a]. Both "orchicyanins" yield cyanin on acid or alkaline hydrolysis. The same cyanin pigment was also found in *Orchis mascula O. (Dactylorhiza) majalis*, and *O. maculata* (Uphoff, 1979b). Chrysanthemin and a similar pigment containing two moles of glucose were reported in a number of *Cymbidium* species and hybrids (Sugiyama, Kinoshita, and Kato, 1977).

In a recent chemosystematic survey the leaf flavonoids of 142 species from seventy-five genera of orchids were examined (Williams, 1979). *C*-glycosides were found in about half of the species studied (Table 5-10). Flavonols were the second most common constituents. The leaf *C*-glycosides were more common in the tropical and subtropical Laelieae and Vandinae, whereas flavonoid glycosides were characteristic of the temperate Listereae. Although a majority of the flavonoid glycosides C. A. Williams found were previously known compounds, she published the structures of three new glycosides:

Table 5-10. Orchids reported to contain flavone C-glycosides (modified from Williams, 1979)

Aerides odorata	Encyclia bractescens	Polystachya anceps
Anguloa brevilabris?	Ephemerantha fimbriata	P. angustifolia
Angraecum eburneum	Epidendrum floribundum	P. caespitifica
A. eichlerianum?	E. fragrans	P. cultriformis
Arpophyllum giganteum	E. huebneri	P. dolichophylla
Bletia purpurea	Epigeneium triflorum	P. fallax
Brassovola nodosa	Eulophia andamanensis	P. golungensis
Bulbophyllum gibbosum	E. paivaeana	P. paniculata
Calanthe vestita	Gongora quinquenervis	P. supfiana
Cattleya bowringiana	Graphorchis scripta	P. tessellata
Ceratostylis subulata	Koellensteinia graminea	Phragmipedium sargentianum
Chamaeangis	Laelia anceps	Renanthera imschootiana
odoratissima	Liparis taiwaniana	Restrepia elegans
Cochleanthes flabelliformis	Lycaste consobrina	Sarcanthus racemifera
Cymbidium atropurpureum	Masdevallia triangularis	Stanhopea devoniensis
C. finlaysonianum	Maxillaria meleagris	Stolzia repens
C. madidum	Meiracyllium trinasutum	Thunia pulchra
Dactylorhiza incarnata	Mormolyca ringens	Trichotosia elongata?
D. praetermissa?	Neomoorea wallissii	Vanda merrillii
Dendrobium chrysotoxum	Oeceoclades saundersianum	Vandopsis lissochiloides
D. moschatum?	Phalaenopsis cornu-cervi	Vanilla imperialis
Dichaea graminoides	Platanthera bifolia	Xylobium palmifolium
Diplocaulobium	P. hyperborea	Zygopetalum ×John Banks
Disa uniflora	Pleurothallis lonchophylla	
Doritis pulcherrima		

scutellarein 6-methyl ether 7-rutinoside from *Oncidium excavatum* and *O. sphacelatum;* pectolinaringenin 7-glucoside from *O. excavatum* and *Eria javanica;* and luteolin 3',4'-diglucoside from *Listera ovata*. Pectolinaringenin (Formula 5-XI) 7-glucoside and 7-rutinoside were also found in *Oncidium excavatum*. Two glucose derivatives of apigenin, vitexin (Formula 5-XII) and isovitexin (Formula 5-XIII), were isolated from *Maxillaria luteo-alba*. Vitexin was also present in *Cymbidium madidum* and in *Anguloa brevilabris*. Two Cymbidium species also contained the 7-glucoside derivatives of vitexin and isovitexin (Table 5-11). The glycoxanthones mangiferin (Formula 5-XIV) and isomangiferin were

Table 5-11. Flavonoid glycosides identified in leaves of some Orchidaceae species (Williams, 1979)

Species	Flavonoid glycosides identified
Aerides fieldingii	Quercetin and kaempferol 3-glucosides, dihydroquercetin 3-glucoside
Anguloa brevilabris	Vitexin
Cattleya bowringiana	3 Apigenin di-C-glycosides
Chamaeangus odoratissima	Chrysoeriol C-glycoside-7-O-glucoside
Cymbidium finlaysonianum	Vitexin 7-glucoside, isovitexin 7-glucoside and an apigenin di-C-glycoside
C. madidum	Vitexin 7-glucoside, vitexin, isovitexin 7-glucoside and an apigenin di-C-glycoside
Eria javanica	Pectolinarigenin and pectolinarigenin 7-glucoside
Listera ovata	Luteolin 3,4'-diglucoside
Maxillaria aff. luteo-alba	Mangiferin, isomangiferin, mangiferin isomer, vitexin, isovitexin
Mormolyca ringens	Mangiferin, isomangiferin, two unidentified xanthones with no C-sugar, a flavone C-glycoside
Neobenthamia gracilis	Quercetin and isorhamnetin 3-glucosides, quercetin 3-(6-acetylglucoside)
Oncidium excavatum	Pectolinarigenin 7-glucoside and 7-rutinoside, scutellarein 6-methyl ether 7-rutinoside
O. sphacelatum	Scutellarein 6-methyl ether 7-rutinoside, pectolinarigenin 7-rutinoside
Pleurothallis gelida	Quercetin 3-rutinoside
Polystachya fulvilabia	
P. galeata	Mangiferin and isomangiferin glucosides
P. nyanzensis	Mangiferin, isomangiferin and mangiferin sulphate
P. pachychila	Mangiferin, isomangiferin and mangiferin sulphate
Restrepia elegans	Tricin 5-glucoside, flavone C-glycoside sulphate, luteolin C-glycoside, two apigenin di-C-glycosides
Trichotosia elongata	Flavone C-glycoside, glucoside of unknown dark to dark (in UV + NH$_3$) aglycone

5-XI. Pectolinaringenin

5-XII. Vitexin

5-XIII. Isovitexin

5-XIV. Mangiferin

5-XV. Quercetin

also isolated from *Maxillaria, Mormolyca,* and *Polystachia* species (Table 5-11). Mangiferin sulfate was indicated to be present in two of the *Polystachia* species. Quercetin (Formula 5-XV) glycosides were present in *Aerides, Neobenthamia,* and *Pleurothallis* species (Table 5-11). Quercetin 3-glucoside, 7-glucoside, and 3,7-diglucoside were reported from *Orchis sambucina* by F. Pagani (1976), who also located the 3-glucoside in *O. morio.* A 3-glucoside of quercetin was also identified by S. Tira (1971) from floral segments of *O. sambucina.*

Systematic Implications of Flavonoid Glycosides

As Williams (1979) pointed out, the most temperate (Listereae) orchids produce mainly flavonol glycosides in their leaves, whereas the more tropical types (Cypripedioideae, Laelieae, and Vandinae) have largely flavone-C-glycosides. The latter are considered to be primitive in character and support the suggestion by L. Garay (1960) that orchids originated somewhere in tropical Asia.

Literature Cited

Aasen, A., D. Behr, and K. Leander. 1975. Studies on orchidaceae glycosides. 2. The structures of loroglossine and militarine, two glucosides from *Orchis militaris* L. Acta Chem. Scand. B 29:1002–1004.

Arditti, J. 1967. Factors affecting the germination of orchid seeds, Bot. Rev. 33:1–97.

——. 1979. Aspects of the physiology of orchids. Adv. Bot. Res. 7:421–655.

Arditti, J., and M. H. Fisch. 1977. Anthocyanins of the orchidaceae: Distribution, heredity, functions, synthesis and localization, pp. 117–155. *In* J. Arditti (ed.), Orchid biology: reviews and perspectives, Vol. 1. Cornell University Press, Ithaca, N.Y.

Baskin, S. I., and C. A. Bliss. 1969. Sugar occurring in the extrafloral exudates of the Orchidaceae. Phytochem. 8:1139–1145.

Baytop, T., and E. Sezik. 1968. Türk salep cesitleri üzerinde arastirmalar Recherches sur les saleps de Turquie. Istanbul. Ecz. Fak. Mec. 4:61–68.

Beguin, C. 1931. Recherche biochimique des glucides dans quelques plantes du Jura neuchâtelois. Pharm. Acta Helv. 6:195–200.

Behr, D., J. Berg, B. Karlsson, K. Leander, A. Pilotti, and A. Wiehager. 1975. Studies on orchidaceae glycosides. Pt. 1. The constitution and relative configuration of dendrosteroside, a steroid glycoside from *Dendrobium ochreatum* Lindl. Acta Chem. Scand. B 29:401.

Behr, D., J. Dahmén, and K. Leander. 1976. Studies on orchidaceae glycosides. 5. The absolute configuration of (+)-*erythro*-isobutyltartaric acid, a component of the glucoside loroglossine. Acta Chem. Scand. B 30:309–312.

Behr, D., and K. Leander. 1976. Three steroid glycosides of the stigmastane type from *Dendrobium ochreatum*. Phytochem. 15:1403–1406.

Behrens, W. 1883. Hilfsbuch zur Ausführung mikroskopischer Untersuchungen im botanischen Laboratorium. Verlag C. A. Zwetschke & Sohn, Braunschweig.

Bernard, N. 1903. La germination des Orchidées. Compt. Rend. Acad. Sci. Paris 137:483–485.

——. 1904. Recherches expérimentales sur les Orchidées. Rev. Gén. Bot. 16:405–451; 458–478.

——. 1909. L'évolution dans la symbiose, Les orchidées et leur champignons commensaux. Ann. Sci. Nat. Bot. Ser. 9:1–196.

——. 1911. Sur la fonction des bulbes d'Ophrydées. Ann. Sci. Nat. Bot. Ser. 9:221–234.

Blakeman, J. P., M. A. Mokahel, and G. Hadley. 1976. Effect of mycorrhizal infection on respiration and activity of some oxidase enzymes of orchid protocorms. New Phytol. 77:697–704.

Borris, H., E. M. Jeschke, and G. Bartsch. 1971. Elektronmikroskopische Untersuchungen zur Ultrastruktur der Orchideen-Mikorrhiza. Biol. Rundschau 9:177–180.

Bourquelot, E., and M. Bridel. 1914a. Recherche biochimique des glucosides hydrolysables par l'émulsine dans les Orchidées indigènes. J. Pharm. Chim. 10:14–18.

——. 1914b. Recherche biochimique des glucosides hydrolysables par l'émulsine dans les Orchidées indigènes. J. Pharm. Chim. 10:66–72.

——. 1919. Application de la méthode biochimique à l'étude de plusieurs espèces d'Orchidées indigènes. Decouverte d'un glucoside nouveau, la "loroglossine." C. R. Acad. Sci. 168:701–703.

Bridel, M., and P. Delauney. 1923. Sur les propriétés de la loroglossine et sur ses produits de dédoublement: Glucose et loroglossine. C. R. Acad. Sci. 177:776–778.

Buchala, A. J., G. Franz, and H. Meier. 1974. A glucomannan from the tubers of *Orchis morio*. Phytochem. 13:163–166.

Burbidge, F. W. 1885. Honey glands on the sepals of *Cattleya* flowers. Gardeners' Chronicle 24:20.

Burgeff, H. 1909. Die Wurzelpilze der Orchideen, ihre Kultur und ihre Leben in der Pflanze. G. Fischer Verlag, Jena.

——. 1911. Die Anzucht tropischer Orchideen auf Samen. G. Fischer Verlag, Jena.

——. 1932. Saprophytismus und Symbiose. Studien an tropischen Orchideen. G. Fischer Verlag, Jena.

——. 1936. Samenkeimung der Orchideen. G. Fischer Verlag, Jena.

Charaux, C., and P. Delauney. 1925a. Sur la présence du loroglosside (loroglossine) dans le *Listera ovata* B. Br. et l'*Epipactis palustris* Crantz et sur quelques nouvelles réactions de ce glucoside. C. R. Acad. Sci. 180:1770–1771.

——. 1925b. Sur la présence du loroglosside (loroglossine) dans le *Listera ovata* B. Br. et l'*Epipactis palustris* Crantz et sur quelques nouvelles réactions de ce glucoside. Bull. Soc. Chim. Biol. 7:1149–1150.

——. 1926. Sur la présence du loroglosside (loroglossine), dans le *Listera ovata* B. Br. et l'*Epipactis palustris* Crantz et sur quelques nouvelles réactions de ce glucoside. J. Pharm. Chim. 8:108–112.

Courtois, J. E., M. Daloul, and F. Petek. 1963. Recherches sur les polysaccharides des Orchidées. Pt. 2. Étude des glucomannanes de quatre espèces d'Orchidées françaises. Bull. Soc. Chim. Biol. 45: 1255–1260.

Dahmén, J., L. Gawell, and K. Leander. 1976. Studies on orchidaceae glycosides. 4. The structures and absolute configurations of *cis-* and *trans*-crassinodine, two glucosides from *Dendrobium crassinode.* Acta Chem. Scand. B 30:297–299.

Dahmén, J., and K. Leander. 1976. The structure of parishin, a glucoside from *Vanda parishii.* Phytochem. 15:1986–1987.

Dahmén, J., K. Leander, and J. Rosenblom. 1975. Studies on orchidaceae glycosides. 3. A new glycoside, 2-(β-D-glucopyranosyloxy)-4,5-dimethoxy-*trans*-cinnamic acid (densifloroside), from *Dendrobium densiflorum* Wall. Acta Chem. Scand. B 29:627–628.

Daloul, M., F. Petek, and J. E. Courtois. 1963. Recherches sur les polysaccharides des Orchidées. 1. Étude des glucomannanes du Salep de Syrie. Bull. Soc. Chim. Biol. 45:1247–1254.

Darwin, C. 1862. On the various contrivances by which British and foreign orchids are fertilized by insects and on the good effects of intercrossing. John Murray, London, pp. 44–53.

Daumann, E. 1941. Die anbohrbaren Gewebe und rudimentären Necktarien in der Blütenregion. Beih. Bot. Zbl. 61A:11.

Delauney, P. 1920. Extraction des glucosides de deux Orchidées indigènes; identification de ces glucosides avec la loroglossine. C. R. Acad. Sci. 171:435–437.

——. 1921a. Ia. Loroglossine, glucoside du "*Loroglossum hircinum*," sa presence dans diverses espèces d'Orchidées indigènes. Bull. Soc. Chim. Biol. 3:238–246.

——. 1921b. Nouvelles recherches concernant l'extraction des glucosides chez quelques Orchidées indigènes; identification de ces glucosides avec la loroglossine. C. R. Acad. Sci. 172:471–473.

——. 1921c. Présence de la loroglossine dans plusieurs espèces d'Orchidées indigènes. J. Pharm. Chim. 23:265–272.

——. 1923a. Sur la présence de la loroglossine dans onze nouvelles espèces d'Orchidées indigènes. Bull. Soc. Chim. Biol. 5:398–408.

——. 1923b. Nouvelles recherches relatives à la présence de la loroglossine dans les Orchidées indigènes. C. R. Acad. Sci. 176:598–600.

——. 1924. Contribution à l'étude des glucosides de la famille des Orchidées. Diss., les éditions de "La Vie Universitaire" Paris.

——. 1925a. Sur les glucosides de plusieurs espèces d'Orchidées indigènes. Bull. Soc. Chim. Biol. 7:1144–1147.

——. 1925b. Sur les glucosides de plusieurs espèces d'Orchidées indigènes. C. R. Acad. Sci. 180:224–225.

——. 1926. Sur les glucosides de plusieurs espèces d'Orchidées indigènes. J. Pharm. Chim. 8:104–112.

Dörr, I., and R. Kollmann. 1969. Fine structure of mycorrhiza in *Neottia nidis-avis* (L.) L. C. Rich. (Orchidaceae). Planta 89:372–375.

Downie, D. G. 1940. On the germination and growth of *Goodyera repens.* Trans. Bot. Soc. Edin. 33:36–51.

Elbein, A. D., and W. Z. Hassid. 1966. The enzymatic synthesis of a glucomannan. Biochem. Biophys. Res. Commun. 23:311–318.

Ernst, R. 1967. Effect of carbohydrate selection on the growth rate of freshly germinated *Phalaenopsis.* Amer. Orchid Soc. Bull. 36:1068–1073.

Ernst, R., J. Arditti, and P. L. Healey. 1970. The nutrition of orchid seedlings. Amer. Orchid Soc. Bull. 39:599–605, 691–700.

——. 1971. Carbohydrate physiology of orchid seedlings. Pt. 2. Hydrolysis and effects of oligosaccharides. Amer. J. Bot. 58:827–835.

Fischer, E. 1887. Verbindungen des Phenylhydrazins mit den Zuckerarten. II. Ber. 20:821–834.

Fischer, E., and J. Hirschberger. 1889. Über Mannose. II. Chem. Ber. 22:365–369.

Frank, A. B. 1865. Zur Kenntnis der Pflanzenschleime. J. prakt. Chemie 95:479–498.

——. 1867. Über die anatomische Bedeutung und die Entstehung der vegetabilischen Schleime. Jahrb. wiss. Bot. 5:161–200.

Franz, G. 1973. Biosynthesis of salep mannan. Phytochem. 12:2369–2373.

——. 1979. Metabolism of reserve polysaccharides in tubers of *Orchis morio* L. Planta Med. 36:68–73.

Franz, G., and H. Meier. 1971. Bildung und Abbau des Schleimpolysaccharids (Salepmannan) von Orchideenknollen. Planta Med. 19:326–332.

Frey-Wyssling, A., and E. Häusermann. 1960. Deutung der gestaltlosen Nektarien. Schweiz. Bot. Ges. 70:150–162.

Gans, R., and B. Tollens. 1888a. Über Quitten- und Salepschleim. Ann. Chem. 249:245–257.

———. 1888b. Mannose oder Isomannitose aus Salepschleim. Ber. 21:2150–2152.

Garay, L. 1960. On the origin of the orchidaceae. Bot. Mus. Leaflets, Harvard Univ. 19:57–87.

Gäumann, E., and H. Kern. 1959a. Über die Isolierung und den chemischen Nachweis des orchinols. Phytopathol. Z. 35:347–356.

———. 1959b. Über chemische Abwehrreaktionen bei Orchideen. Phytopathol. Z. 36:1–26.

Giraud, L. 1875. Die Untersuchung des Schleimes der Quittensamen, des Leims, des Salep, des *Fucus crispus*. Jahresb. Pharm. 10:299–301.

Gomyo, T., and M. Nakamura. 1959. Biosynthesis of raffinose from uridine diphosphate galactose and sucrose by an enzyme preparation of immature soybeans. Agr. Biol. Chem. Tokyo 30:425–427.

Göring, H., and E. Reckin. 1968. Einfluss der D-Galaktose auf den Kohlenhydratstoffwechsel pflanzlicher Gewebe. Flora A. 159:82–103.

Gray, R. W., A. Guggisberg, K. P. Segebarth, M. Hesse, and H. Schmid. 1976. Über die Konstitution von Loroglossin. Helv. Chim. Acta 59:645–649.

———. 1977. Die Konstitution des Loroglossins. Helv. Chim. Acta 60:1304–1311.

Hadley, G. 1975. Organization and structure of orchid mycorrhiza, pp. 335–351. *In* F. E. Sanders, B. Mosse, and P. B. Tinker (eds.), Endomycorrhizas. Academic Press, London.

Hadley, G., and B. Williamson. 1971. Analysis of the post-infection growth stimulus in orchid mycorrhiza. New Phytol. 70:445–455.

Hardegger, E., M. Schellenbaum, and H. Corrodi. 1963. Über induzierte Abwehrstoffe bei Orchideen. II. Helv. Chim. Acta 46:1171–1180.

Harley, J. L. 1969. Mycorrhiza in the orchidaceae, pp. 191–229. *In* J. L. Harley (ed.), The biology of mycorrhiza. Leonard Hill, London.

Harrison, C. R. 1977. Ultrastructure and histochemical changes during the germination of *Cattleya aurantiaca* (Orchidaceae). Bot. Gaz. 138:41–45.

Harrison, C. R., and J. Arditti. 1978. Physiological changes during the germination of *Cattleya aurantiaca* (Orchidaceae). Bot. Gaz. 139:180–189.

Harvais, G., and G. Hadley. 1967. The development of *Orchis purpurella* in asymbiotic and inoculated cultures. New Phytol. 66:217–230.

Henseke, G., and M. Bautze. 1955. Über Osonhydrazone. Pt. 4. Mitteil.: Zur Kenntnis der Mischosazone. Chem. Ber. 88:62–69.

Hérrisey, H. 1902. Sur la digestion de la mannane des tubercules d'Orchidées. C. R. Acad. Sci. 134:721–723.

Hérrisey, H., and P. Delauney. 1921. Présence dans plusieurs Orchidées indigènes de glucosides fournissant de la coumarine par hydrolyse. Bull. Soc. Chim. Biol. 3:573–579.

Hilger, A. 1903. Zur Kenntnis der Pflanzenschleime. Ber. 36:3197–3203.

Husemann, E. J. 1940. Über die Konstitution von Salepmannan. Mitteilung über makromolekulare Verbindungen. J. prakt. Chem. 155:241–260.

Isbell, H. C., and H. L. Frush. 1962. α-D-Mannose from ivory-nut meal, pp. 145–147. *In* R. L. Whistler and M. L. Wolfrom (eds.), Methods in carbohydrate chemistry, vol. 1. Academic Press, New York.

Jaretzky, R., and E. Bereck. 1938. Der Schleim in den Knollen von *Orchis purpureus* Huds. und *Platanthera bifolia* (L.) Rchb. Arch. Pharm. 276:17–27.

Jaretzky, R., and H. Ulbrich. 1934. Die intraplasmatischen Vorgänge bei der Schleimbildung in den Samen von *Linium usitatissimum* L. und in den Wurzeln von *Althaea officinalis* L. Arch. Pharm. 272:796–811.

Jeffrey, D. C., and J. Arditti. 1968. Sugar content of orchid nectar. Orchid Rev. 76:315–316.

———. 1969. The separation of sugars in orchid nectars by thin layer chromatography. Amer. Orch. Soc. Bull. 38:866–868.

Jeffrey, D. C., J. Arditti, and H. Koopowitz. 1970. Sugar content in floral and extrafloral exudates of orchids: Pollination, myrmecology and chemotaxonomy implications. New Phytol. 69:187–195.

Juers, D. H., H. A. Swenson, and S. F. Kurath. 1967. Configuration and hydrodynamic properties of fully acetylated salep glucomannan. J. Polym. Sci. 5:361–375.

Karrer, P., and E. Matter. 1947. Über Loroglossin. Helv. Chim. Acta 30:2096–2100.

Keusch, L. 1968. Die Mobilisierung des Reservemannans in keimenden Dattelsamen. Planta 78:321–350.

Klages, F., and R. Maurenbrecher. 1938. Die Konfiguration des Steinnuss- und Salepmannans und über den Gültigkeitsbereich der Hudsonschen Superpositionsregeln bei Mannosederivaten. Ann. 535:175–204.

Klages, F., and P. Niemann. 1936. Über die Konstitution des Salepmannans und die übrigen Kohlenhydrate aus Tubera Salep. Ann. Chem. 523:224–234.

Knudson, L. 1921. La germinacion no simbiotica de las semillas de orquideas. Bol. Real Soc. Española Hist. Nat. 21:250–260.

——. 1922. Non-symbiotic germination or orchid seeds. Bot. Gaz. 73:1–25.

Kuhn, R., and I. Löw. 1949. Über ein Vorkommen von Milchzucker im Pflanzenreich. Chem. Ber. 82:479–481.

LaGarde, R. 1929. Non-symbiotic germination of orchids. Ann. Missouri Bot. Gardens 16:499–514.

Leloir, L. F. 1964. Nucleoside diphosphate sugars and saccharide synthesis. Biochem. J. 91:1–8.

Lewis, D. H., and D. C. Smith. 1967. Sugar alcohols (polyols) in fungi and green plants. New Phytol. 66:143–184.

Lindley, J. 1843. Bemerkungen über die Anatomie der Ophryden-Wurzeln. Isis von Oken. 6:449–450.

Lüning, B. 1974. Alkaloids of the Orchidaceae, pp. 349–382. In C. L. Withner (ed.), The orchids:Scientific studies. John Wiley & Sons, New York.

McClure, J. 1974. The physiological role of flavonoids. In J. B. Harboune, T. J. Mabry, and H. Mabry (eds.), The flavonoids. Academic Press, London.

Mukherjee, A. K., D. Choudhury, and P. Bagchi. 1961. Constitution of the galactomannan from the kernel of green Palmyra palm nut (Borassus flabellifer Linn.). Can. J. Chem. 39:1408–1418.

Ohtsuki, T. 1937a. Studien über "Cremastramannan," das Mannan des japanischen Saleps. Acta Phytochim. 10:1–28.

——. 1937b. Untersuchung über das Bletillamannan, ein Mannan aus den Knollen von Bletilla striata. Acta Phytochim. 10:29–41.

Ordin, L., and A. Altmann. 1965. Inhibition of phosphoglucomutase activity in oat coleoptiles by air pollutants. Physiol. Plantarum 18:790–797.

Pagani, F. 1976. Fitocostituenti di orchidaceae. Nota I. Componenti della Orchis sambucina L., Orchis morio L. Boll. Chim. Farm. 115:407–412.

Payne, J. H. 1968. New light on the nectar of Cattleya flowers. Rev. Orchid Soc. S. Calif. 7:9.

Percival, M. S. 1961. Types of nectars in angiosperms. New Phytol. 60:235–281.

Petek, F., J. E. Courtois, and M. Daloul. 1963. Recherches sur les polysaccharides des orchidées. Pt. 3. Identification de trois oligosaccharides isolés après hydrolyse acide partielle du Salep de Syrie. Bull. Soc. Chim. Biol. 45:1261–1266.

Pridham, J. B., and W. Z. Hassid. 1965. Biosynthesis of raffinose. Plant Physiol. 40:984–986.

Pringsheim, H., and A. Genin. 1924. Über die fermentative Spaltung des Salepmannans. Pt. 6. Mitteilung über Hemicellulosen. Z. physiol. Chem. 140:299–304.

Pringsheim, H., and G. Liss. 1927. Über das Salep-Mannan. Ann. Chem. 460:32–42.

Pubols, M. H., J. C. Zahnley, and B. Axelrod. 1963. Partial purification and properties of xylose and ribose isomerase in higher plants. Plant Physiol. 38:457–461.

Purves, S., and G. Hadley. 1976. The physiology of symbiosis in Goodyera repens. New Phytol. 77: 689–696.

Quednow, K. G. 1930. Beiträge zur Frage der Aufnahme gelöster Kohlenstoffverbindungen durch Orchideen und andere Pflanzen. Bot. Arch. 30:51–108.

Recondo, E., and L. F. Leloir. 1961. Adenosine diphosphate glucose and starch synthesis. Biochem. Biophys. Res. Comm. 6:85–88.

Rozenfeld, E. L. 1965. Kimia i obmen uglevodov, pp. 335–347. In 3d Konferensii po Probleme Khimiya i Oben Uglevodov, Moscow.

Schmidt, C. 1844. Über Pflanzenschleim und Bassorin. Ann. Chem. 51:29–62.

Shcherbukhina, N. K., B. N. Stepanenko, and V. D. Shcherbukhin. 1969. Structure of water-soluble polysaccharides from salep and of the polysaccharide Erumuran. Rast. Resur. 5:398–406. C.A. 1970, 72:28868 z.

Sezik, E. 1967. Turkiye'nin salepgilleri tikari salep cesitleri ve ozellikle Mugla salebi uzerinde arastirmalar. Doctoral Diss., Istanbul University, No. 34, pp. 1–76.

Slaytor, M. B. 1977. Phytochemistry. The distribution and chemistry of alkaloids in the orchidaceae, pp. 95–115. *In* J. Arditti (ed.), Orchid biology: reviews and perspectives, 1. Cornell University Press, Ithaca, N.Y.

Smith, D., L. Muscatine, and D. Lewis. 1969. Carbohydrate movement from autotrophs to heterotrophs in parasitic and mutualistic symbiosis. Biol. Rev. Cambridge 44:17–90.

Smith, S. E. 1966. Physiology and ecology of orchid mycorrhizal fungi with reference to seedling nutrition. New Phytol. 6:488–499.

——. 1967. Carbohydrate translocation in orchid mycorrhizas. New Phytol. 66:371–378.

——. 1973. Asymbiotic germination of orchid seeds on carbohydrates of fungal origin. New Phytol. 72:497–499.

Smith, S. E., and F. A. Smith. 1973. Uptake of glucose, trehalose and mannitol by leaf slices of the orchid *Bletilla hyacinthina*. New Phytol. 72:957–964.

Stenlid, G. 1957. A comparison of toxic effects of some sugars upon growth and chloride accumulation in young wheat roots. Physiol. Plantarum 10:807–823.

Stepanenko, B. N., E. M. Afanas'eva, L. V. Slozhenikina, T. T. Bolotina, R. A. Baksova, and N. K. Rudakova. 1961. The reserve heteropolysaccharides in plants. Abstr. Comm. p. 441. *In* Proc. 5th Intern. Congress Biochem., Moscow, Sec. 17.

Stepanenko, B. N., and V. D. Shcherbukhina. 1964. A study of the so called Salep-Manna. Biokhimiia 29:41–46.

Stewart, A. W. 1919. Stereo chemistry, 2d ed. Longman, Green, London.

Sugiyama, A., M. Kinoshita, S. Kako, and H. Ohno. 1977. Studies on the flower color of *Cymbidium*. Pt. 1. Properties of anthocyanins in the flowers. J. Jap. Soc. Hort. Sci. 46:72–80.

Sunding, P. 1963. Nektarier has *Cattleya* Lndl. og de ekstraflorale nektarier has noen andre orchidéslekter. Blythia 21:110–115.

Tira, S. 1971. Monocotyledonae, Orchidaceae, Isoquercitrin from *Orchis sambucina*. Phytochem. 10:1975–1976.

Tomoda, M., S. Nakatsuka, and N. Satoh. 1974. Plant Mucilages. Pt. 9. The location of the O-acetyl group and the nature of the branches in *Bletilla*-glucomannan. Chem. Pharm. Bull. 22:2710–2713.

Tomoda, M., S. Nakatsuka, M. Tamai, and M. Nagata. 1973. Plant Mucilages. Pt. 8. Isolation and characterization of a mucous polysaccharide, "Bletilla-glucomannan," from *Bletilla striata* tubers. Chem. Pharm. Bull. 21:2667–2671.

Uphoff, W. 1979a. Anthocyanins in the flowers of European orchids. Experientia 35:1013–1014.

——. 1979b. Die Farbstoffe der gefleckten Blätter von *Orchis* und *Dactylorhiza*. Die Orchidee 30:184–186.

Venkataraman, R., and F. J. Reithel. 1958. Carbohydrates of Sapotaceae. Pt. 1. The origin of lactose in *A. sapota*. Arch. Biochem. Biophys. 75:443–452.

Williams, C. A. 1979. The leaf flavonoids of the orchidaceae. Phytochem. 18:803–813.

Wihtner, C. L. 1942. Nutrition experiments with orchid seedlings. Amer. Orchid Soc. Bull. 11:112–114.

——. 1959. Orchid physiology, pp. 315–360. *In* C. L. Withner (ed.), The orchids. Ronald Press, New York.

Wrigley, T. C. 1960. Ayapin, scopoletin and 6,7-dimethoxycoumarin from *Dendrobium thyrsiflorum* (Reichb. f.). Nature 188:1108.

Wynd, F. L. 1933. Sources of carbohydrate for germination and growth of orchid seedlings. Ann. Missouri Bot. Gardens 20:569–581.

Additional Literature

Bhatnagar, J. K., S. S. Handa, and S. C. Duggal. 1971. Chemical investigations on *Microstylis wallichi*. Planta Med. 20:156–161.

Damirov, I. A. 1949. Mucilagenous plants of Azerbaidzhan. Med. Prom. S.S.S.R. 3:30–31 (C.A. 1950, 44:798 i).

Homès, J., and N. Vanséveren-Van Espen. 1973. Quelques formes de plastes induites par le milieu de culture dans des protocorms d'orchidées cultivés in vitro. Bull. Soc. Roy. Bot. Belg. 106:117–121.

Kobayashi, K. 1944. A constituent of *Onychium japonicum*. J. Pharm. Soc. Japan 64:35.

Meyer, A. Beiträge zur Kenntnis pharmaceutisch wichtiger Gewächse. Pt. 8. Ueber die Knollen der einheimischen Orchideen. Arch. Pharm. 24:273–286.

Plekhanova, N. V., A. Berdikeev, G. P. Fedorchenko, and L. V. Zenchenko. 1976. D-Mannose by acid hydrolysis of initial raw material, neutralization of hydrolyzate, deposition of end product by decomposing phenylhydrazone of mannose by known methods. Russian Patent 530,685 (C. A. 1977, 86:45035 g).

Politis, I. 1914. Sulla presenza del glicogeno nelle fanerogame e sua relazione col'ossalato di calcio. Atti Ist. Bot. Univ. Padua 14:385–396.

Rodkiewicz, B., and A. Gorska-Brylass. 1968. Callose in the walls of developing megasporocytes and megaspores. Acta Soc. Bot. Pol. 37:19–25.

Slozhenikina, L. V., V. D. Shcherbukhina, and B. N. Stepanenko. 1963. A study of erumuran and salepmannan by infrared spectroscopy. Dokl. Akad. Nauk SSSR 153:960–963 (C. A. 1964, 60:9348 b).

Stepanenko, B. N., N. K. Shcherbukhina, R. A. Baksova, V. D. Shcherbukhin, and K. Dovletmuradov. 1966. Simple method of D-mannose isolation from *Eremurus* roots and from *Orchis* tubers. Prikl. Biokhim. i Mikrobiol. 2:39–44.

Stepanenko, B. N., and N. K. Shcherbukhina. 1963. Chemical nature of the so-called salep-mannan. Dokl. Akad. Nauk. SSSR 151:967–970 (C. A. 1964, 59:15364 f).

Tomoda, M., and S. Kimura. 1976. Plant Mucilages. Pt. 12. Fourteen oligosaccharides obtained from *Bletilla*-glucomannan by partial acetolysis. Chem. Pharm. Bull. 24:1807–1812.

6

Toxic and Allergenic Orchids*

BJÖRN M. HAUSEN

*The literature review pertaining to this chapter was concluded in February 1983; a preliminary draft of the chapter was submitted in November 1981, and the revised version was received in March 1983.

Introduction

It is not really ironic that the most beautiful flowers in the plant kingdom also have some adverse effects. Our daily experience indicates that this is the case with all fine things in the world. Although the Orchidaceae are the largest of the plant families, with 25,000 to 35,000 species in 750 genera (Williams, 1979), their economic importance is largely confined to the floral industry. Orchids are very rarely ingested as food or used medicinally. Thus the hazardous effects of ingestion or of direct contact are confined to people who use some orchids as drugs or handle them as ornamentals. The available phytochemical information on orchid constituents is very limited in relation to the total number of known species. Since the *Chemical Abstracts* and the *Index Medicus* list only a handful of publications on toxic and allergenic properties of orchids, it is not surprising that our knowledge on the subject is comparatively scant.

Orchids are admired throughout the world as very beautiful flowers, but only a single species, *Vanilla planifolia* Andrews, is of worldwide economic importance as a food or condiment and is commercially cultivated and processed for the purpose. Though several other species are also cultivated as food or as remedies in various places about the world, they are of local interest only. Some 20 to 60 species used in this manner are listed by Brøndegaard (1965), Ghose (1955), Lawler and Slaytor (1969), and Miller (1959).[1]

Orchids are used as remedies for toothache, headache, and diarrhea, and as vermifuges, tonics, and antipyretics. The dried tubers have been used as the basis of a food variously known as salep, saloop, sahlep, and tubera salep (see Chapter 2). Grieve (1971) lists ten species used for the preparation of tubera salep, mainly such *Orchis* species as *O. mascula* L., *O. morio* L., *O. ustulata* L. and *Dactylorhiza majalis* (Rchb.) Hunt et Summerh. syn. *O. latifolia* auct. non L. Miller (1959) says that powdered roots of these *Orchis* species prepared as salep were used as the basis of a drink in London before coffeehouses became popular. Salep extracts are said to possess aphrodisiac properties; perhaps these alleged powers explain their continued use (though no reliable information is available about the extent of that use). The German pharmacopoeia, *Deutsches Arzneibuch,* listed tubera salep (which was not recognized as an official drug) as recently as the 1960s.

Because of their sedative properties, root extracts of *Cypripedium reginae* Walter and probably also of *C. calceolus* L. have been used in North America since the mid-nineteenth century. The drugs are known as cypripedin and American valerian (MacDougal, 1895). Such a drug was listed as "nerve root" in the *Merck Index* as recently as 1976 (Windholz *et al.,* 1976).

Miller (1959) reports that *Corymborchis longiflora* (Hooker f.) Burkill causes vomiting and poisoning in residents of India and the Malay Peninsula when they chew it and swallow the juice. Additional species may have similar effects, but none have been documented. Most cases of poisoning are restricted to areas where orchids are used as nutrients or drugs.

---

[1]The uses of these and other orchids are discussed in Chapter 2 [Ed.].

Toxic Effects

Phytochemical research has revealed the occurrence of alkaloids (Lüning, 1974; Slaytor, 1977), anthocyanins (Arditti *et al.*, 1977), coumarins (Wrigley, 1960), flavonoids (Pagani, 1976; Williams, 1979), glucosides (Delauney, 1920, 1921, 1925; Hérissey and Delauney, 1922; Hardegger and Schellenbaum, 1963), phenolic compounds (Ishi *et al.*, 1979), lipids (Holman and Nichols, 1972), sugars (Jeffrey *et al.*, 1970), terpenes (Holman and Heimermann, 1973), and other compounds (Hegnauer, 1963) in orchids. Although some of these chemicals may be considered to be poisonous, no case of human poisoning was reported in the literature between 1900 and 1982. Generally, coumarin and its derivatives are known to cause bleeding when they are taken orally frequently and in high dosage (*e.g.*, as ratsbane; Meyler, 1978). Tannins are considered to be carcinogenic (Hueper and Conway, 1969; Oler *et al.*, 1976). Their concentration in flowers is so low, however, and their use as drugs so limited, that their hazards need not cause us serious concern. Some observations and reports, however, point to possible poisonous properties of orchid plants. One of the most informative contributions is that of Ghose (1955), who reported that bees dropped off the blossoms of *Cymbidium devonianum* Paxton nectaries in India and were found to be dull and numb. Although no uncommon sugars

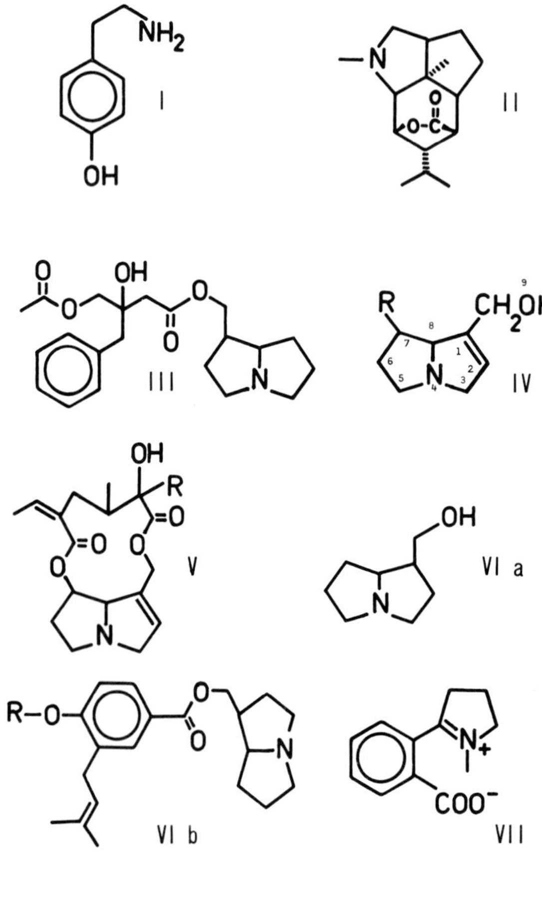

Fig. 6-1. Toxic compounds in plants of the Orchidaceae and Compositae. I: Tyramine from *Cattleya sp.* II: Dendrobine from *Dendrobium nobile.* III: Phalaenopsine (= Phalaenopsine T) from *Phalaenopsis amabilis.* IV: Basic structure of necins (R = H, OH). V: Retrorsine (R = CH_2OH), Senecionine (R = CH_3) from *Senecio* species. VI: (a) Laburnine from *Vanda sp.;* (b) Malaxin (R = sugar) from *Malaxis sp.* VII: Shihunine from *Dendrobium lohohense.*

were detected in the nectar (Jeffrey *et al.,* 1970), it is possible that it could contain unknown toxic components.

Among the very few experiments with extracts of orchid plants are those of Ormerod and White (1929). They studied the pharmacological effects of leaves and stems of *Cypripedium calceolus* var. *pubescens* (Willd.) Correll (*C. parviflorum* Salisb.) and *Amerorchis rotundifolia* (Banks ex Pursh) Hultén (*Orchis rotundifolia* Banks ex Pursh) in frogs, guinea pigs, and rats. *A. rotundifolia* was ineffective, but *C. calceolus* var. *pubescens* exhibited such definite pharmacological effects in frogs as an increase of the contractility of the heart, marked vasoconstriction, and a drop in blood pressure. Ormerod and White attributed these properties to an unknown orchid constituent of glucosidic character.

Recently Maille, Morel, and Gautheret (1974) demonstrated the presence of the phenolic amine tyramine in leaves of *Cattleya* species (Fig. 6-1, I). Tyramine is a vasoconstrictor, and so increases blood pressure. Fortunately exposure to the very popular ornamental *Cattleya* species is restricted to manual contact, which is harmless, so far as we know.

A case of severe inflammation of the eyes (conjunctivitis) of a six-year-old girl, with swelling of the lids and development of vesicles on the horny layer, was recently reported by the physician who treated her (Dr. E. Brodmann, personal communication). The girl had rubbed her eyes after touching an *Arachnis* hybrid. Because the reactions developed after approximately one hour and disappeared two days later, this phenomenon must be interpreted as a primary irritation due to unknown substances in or on the orchid (possibly but not likely a fungicide or insecticide).

Alkaloids

Early investigations of orchid alkaloids date to the end of the last century (Wildeman, 1892; Droog, 1896) and the beginning of this century (Boorsma, 1902; Wester, 1921), but most of them were screening studies. Little was known about isolated compounds themselves until 1964, when B. Lüning started the first systematic investigation of Orchidaceae alkaloids. His studies provided new knowledge about these constituents and increased our understanding of structural relationships (Lüning, 1964, 1974; Lüning *et al.,* 1966).

Scattered throughout the earlier alkaloid investigations in the 1930s are several reports on a single species: *Dendrobium nobile* Lindley. This orchid has been used in China as a tonic and antipyretic since ancient times (Onaka *et al.,* 1965) and is still in use there and in Hong Kong and Japan. The drug, originally from southwestern China, was called *chin-shih-hu* in Chinese and *sekkoku* in Japanese (Chen and Chen, 1935a, 1935b; Inubishi *et al.,* 1964a, 1964b). In 1930 *Dendrobium nobile* was already being cultivated as an ornamental plant (Chen and Chen, 1935b), and hybrids of this species are now relatively inexpensive and extraordinarily popular with horticulturists. Successful attempts to isolate alkaloids from *Dendrobium nobile* were initiated by Chen and Suzuki and their colleagues in 1932–1936. The Chen studies were the only ones that were also concerned with the pharmacological actions of the isolated alkaloid dendrobine (Fig. 6-1, II). Chen and Chen (1935a, 1935b) demonstrated its toxicity in mice, rabbits, and guinea pigs.

Dendrobine produced a moderate hyperglycemia and diminished cardiac activity; when applied in larger doses, it lowered the blood pressure and suppressed respiration. The minimal lethal doses were 20 mg/kg for mice, 22 mg/kg for guinea pigs, and 17 mg/kg for rabbits. Larger doses caused convulsions that were apparently central in origin, not secondary to respiratory or circulatory failure; death soon followed (Chen and Chen, 1935b). A detoxification of dendrobine was possible with sodium amytal (sodium isoamyl ethyl barbiturate), which acted as an antidote. Rabbits poisoned by a lethal dose of 360 mg/kg dendrobine-HCl could be saved by simultaneous administration of 100 mg/kg sodium amytal (Chen and Rose, 1936).

Since Lüning's initial study in 1964, more than 2,000 orchids have been investigated for alkaloids (Lüning, 1974; Slaytor, 1977; Lawler and Slaytor, 1969; Hartley et al., 1973). But other than a single short note (Lüning et al., 1966) on the lethal dose of Phalaenopsine, 75 mg/kg in mice (Fig. 6-1, III), the literature contains no information on the pharmacological or toxic effects of orchid alkaloids.

Most of the Orchidaceae alkaloids fall into one of two classes: (1) alkaloids of the pyrrolizidine type and (2) those of the dendrobine type (Fig. 6-1, II). In his list of orchids screened for the occurrence of alkaloids, Lüning (1974) notes 214 species in 64 genera with an alkaloid content higher than 0.1%. The majority of alkaloids were isolated from the genera Dendrobium (32), Liparis (28), Malaxis (18), Phalaenopsis (17), and Eria (14). Dendrobium is the genus richest in alkaloids, the most important of which are the pyrrolizidine-based compounds.

Although there has been no known case of human poisoning by orchid alkaloids, the pyrrolizidine alkaloids require careful study since they are well known for their toxicity. Poisoning by Senecio and Heliotropium alkaloids in particular has been studied in detail by Willmot and Robertson (1920), Selzer and Parker (1951), Bras and Hill (1956), Hill (1960), and Braginskii and Bobokhodzev (1965). Pyrrolizidine alkaloids are hepatotoxic, and their carcinogenicity has been demonstrated in rats (for a review see Hirono, 1979).

Structure and activity characteristics of the pyrrolizidine alkaloids have been discussed by Schoental (1957, 1968) and Mattocks (1968, 1971). For toxicity the alkaloid must possess a 1-hydroxymethyl-pyrrolizidine structure, a double bond in 1,2 position (such 1-hydroxymethyl-1,2-dehydro-8α-pyrrolizidine compounds are called necins), and one hydroxy group each, in positions 7 and 9 (Fig. 6-1, IV).

The most hepatotoxic properties are developed when the hydroxy groups are esterified, as for example in the cyclic diesters retrorsine and senecionine (Fig. 6-1, V).

According to Schoental (1968), the presence of an additional hydroxy group in position 7 (Fig. 6-1, IV) imparts greater water solubility. Thus an increased rate of excretion results in lower hepatotoxicity. Replacement of hydroxyls by chlorine, acetoxy, or methoxy groups increases the toxicity. Monoesters are less active. Nonesters are not likely to be hepatotoxic. The absence of the double bond between positions 1 and 2 (Fig. 6-1, IV) eliminates liver toxicity completely (Chen and Rose, 1940).

Semisynthetically prepared pyrrolizidine alkaloids with branched side chains have stronger hepatotoxicity than those with straight chains (Schoental, 1968). Structurally the pyrrolizidine alkaloids of the Orchidaceae do not have two of the essential requirements for liver toxicity: a double bond in the 1,2 position and a hydroxy group or esterification in position 7, as for example malaxin from *Malaxis longusta* Schltr. and laburnine from *Vanda cristata* Lindley (Fig. 6-1, VI).

Another *Dendrobium* species used medicinically, in the form of a drug that is known in Japanese as *chukanso*, is *D. lohohense* Tang & Wang. It contains the phthalide-pyrrolidine alkaloid shihunine, which occurs in the plant as the betaine (Fig. 6-1, VII; Inubishi *et al.*, 1964a, 1964b). There have been no reports of human poisoning from this species.

And so our present knowledge of orchid poisoning in humans can be summed in two words: no evidence. The lack of any such reports can be attributed to the fact that very few orchids are known to be toxic and even fewer are used as a food or drug (tubera salep, vanilla, *shin-shih-hu*, *chukanso*). If the risk of poisoning exists, it is probably low. The possibility of adverse effects must be taken into consideration, however, if and when orchid species that contain pyrrolizidine alkaloids become more popular as drugs. For the present, since most orchids are touched but not ingested, the sensitizing effects described below are of more interest than their toxic properties.

Sensitizing Effects

Without exception the sensitizing effects of orchids are the result of direct contact between human skin and flowers, stems, roots, or other parts of the plant. The lesions are either of a primary irritant nature (like the burning and redness one experiences after touching a nettle) or allergenic, that is, expressions of a specific hypersensitivity.

Immunological Basis

All hazardous effects of orchids to the human skin described to date are of type IV allergy (also called contact allergy, cell-mediated allergy, or allergy of the delayed type), according to the classification of Coombs and Gell (1975). The definition of contact allergy is "an acquired, altered and specific capacity of the body to react to foreign substances by a pathological reaction based on specific sensitized T-lymphocytes." In delayed allergy the characteristic lesions of the skin develop 24 to 48 hours after contact with the plant. The essential fact is that contact allergy is not inheritable, but is acquired by steady or occasional direct contact with the material that causes it.

Contact allergy is induced when substances of low molecular weight come in contact with the skin during the handling of orchids. After penetration of the horny layer of the skin, the compounds are taken up by Langerhans cells in the epidermis or macrophages in the dermis, or both. These cells are specifically adapted to capture foreign material and present the allergen to T-lymphocytes in association with their surface antigens (in humans, HLA-D/DR antigens). The T-lymphocytes recognize the antigens as "altered self" and as a result produce specifically sensitized new lymphocytes, divided into effector and memory cells. On renewed contact with the allergen, the sensitized effector T-lymphocytes attract other cells, and together they release lymphokines that produce finally the clinical effect of dermatitis.

Allergic contact dermatitis usually occurs at the site of contact with the plant. It consists of itching, pustules, vesicles, and even bullae. The clinical symptoms start with mild pruritus and erythema; a burning sensation follows. Later, papules, vesicles, and exudation appear. Continued contact with the plant results in thickening and swelling, followed by fissures and lichenification.

The first reactions involve the skin of the hands, forearms, and eyelids. In due course the lesions spread to the face, neck, and other parts of the body where particles of the sensitizing material are carried by the hands. Plant parts may also become trapped between clothing and the skin. Characteristically, every renewed contact with the sensitizer produces a stronger outbreak of dermatitis. Attacks become more frequent, and lesions increase in severity. Generally, all clinical symptoms subside within a short time when the victim ceases contact with the offending plant, as on weekends, holidays, and other absences from the place where orchids are handled. Dermatitis affects primarily people who handle the plants frequently or steadily—florists, breeders, orchid hobbyists, nursery workers, collectors, and plant scientists.

Primary Irritant and Sensitizing Orchids

Orchid dermatitis was recognized long before the term "allergy" was formulated by the pediatrician Clemens von Pirquet in 1910. At first (and unfortunately in most non-medical journals even today) all damaging effects of plants to the human skin were considered to be the result of poisoning. A hundred years ago allergic contact dermatitis and primary irritant dermatitis could not be distinguished from each other. It is still impossible to separate them on the basis of their clinical appearance. Histological determinations (Skoog, 1980) or epicutaneous tests must be carried out. Positive reactions to patch tests even in high dilution are limited to very allergic persons. Subtoxic doses produce negative results in nonsensitive individuals.

H. H. Babcock (1875) suffered severe dermatitis on the hands and face after extensive collection of field-grown lady's slippers such as *Cypripedium reginae* Walter and *C. calceolus* var. *pubescens* (Willd.) Correll (*C. pubescens* Willd.). That the effects were allergic is evident in his observation that "in each season the poisoning had appeared on the day after he had collected" the orchids (delayed reaction) and that the suffering had become "more extensively than ever before" (every renewed contact produces a stronger outbreak of dermatitis). Babcock was convinced that the effects produced by the orchids were similar to those caused by poison ivy (*Rhus radicans* L. and six subspecies). He inquired whether anyone else had had a similar experience. His request was repeated in several journals (e.g., G. T., 1887), and two responses were published in the following years.

R. E. Kunze (1879) wrote that tons of *C. pubescens* were brought to the market every year for the manufacture of a tincture called cypripedin without any known cases of poisoning. H. G. Jesup (1893), however, confirmed Babcock's observation by citing two additional cases of *C. pubescens* "poisoning," which today must be interpreted as allergic contact dermatitis. He also drew attention to the book *Dermatitis venenata* by J. C. White (1887), which contains reports that support the hypothesis that this species is allergenic rather than toxic.

During the same period D. T. MacDougal (1894, 1895) published his observations and experiments with *C. pubescens,* the state flower of Minnesota. Fourteen hours after he rubbed freshly broken leaf material onto his arm, he suffered a violently inflamed skin reaction with severe swelling from the shoulder to the fingertips. Although this case must be considered to be a primary irritant reaction, MacDougal noted after further experiments with nine of his students that response varied among individuals: some reacted, others did not. He suggested that the source of the "poisonous" substances might be the glandular hairs that cover the stems and leaves. His suggestion was proved to be accurate (Swanson *et al.*, 1980; Holman *et al.*, 1981). MacDougal's experiments motivated Nestler in Prague (1907) to experiment on himself by rubbing leaves and extracts of orchids several times into the skin of his arms. Initially, applications of *Cypripedium acaule* Aiton, *C. calceolus* L., *C. calceolus* var. *pubescens*, *C. montanum* Douglas ex Lindley, and *C. reginae* produced no visible result. A month after the first application of *C. reginae*, however, strong itching developed at the site, followed by redness and vesicles. These lesions must now be interpreted as allergic eczematous reactions. They are indicative of the beginning of an allergic status due to direct and frequent contact with the secretions and ether extracts of the orchids. Nestler himself noticed that the "poison" acted only after the passage of time: four weeks were necessary to induce sensitivity. Nestler's assumption that the "toxic" substance of *C. reginae* might be a red quinone is remarkable, as the allergens that my colleagues and I have now isolated from this orchid are orange and red quinones (Hausen, 1979).

No instances of orchid dermatitis were described between the two world wars. After 1945 interest in the raising and breeding of orchids was renewed. One case of dermatitis following contact with wild *C. reginae* was reported from North America (Culver, 1951). In a second case from Europe, hobby breeding of *C. reginae* was the source of dermatitis (Beierlein, 1957). Another author (Sadovsky, 1957) denied the existence of a *Cypripedium*-caused contact allergy; he reported that he had handled these plants for years without suffering from a "skin rash." Two other publications in the 1950s (Anonymous, 1952, 1953) only repeated the older literature, and one note (Anonymous, 1953) is clearly a summary of MacDougal's long paper of 1894–95.

Recently R. A. Hardie and V. S. Rajan (1981) surveyed 53 employees associated with the commercial cultivation of orchids in Singapore. They found only a single case of allergy, and could not identify the species (Rajan, personal communication). Their report presented no further details.

Since there are no reports on patch tests other than those from Singapore, and since Nestler's speculation regarding the presence of a quinone suggested an interesting possibility, my colleagues and I initiated experiments with animals and chemical studies to determine the nature of the sensitizing constituent or constituents in orchids. We started by studying the native lady's slipper *Cypripedium calceolus* L. (which in Germany and the United States, as in other countries, is protected by law).

Thin-layer-chromatographic screening of leaves from 148 plants (collected with permission) revealed the presence of quinonoid substances. The "short ether extract" (we extracted the sensitizing constituents by dipping the plant for 60 to 90 seconds into peroxide-free diethyl ether [Hausen, 1977]) was used in sensitizing experiments with albino guinea pigs of the Pirbright-white strain. Only quinone containing fractions of the ether extract elicited positive reactions in the sensitized guinea pigs. Similar results were obtained with extracts of field-collected plants of the American lady's slipper *C. reginae* (provided by Dr. W. Jürgen Schrenck of North Chicago). These extracts, which also contained quinonoid constituents, elicited positive reactions in guinea pigs as well as cross-reactions in *C. calceolus*–sensitive animals. The plant material from the United States (and later from Europe), however, was too meager to permit the isolation of sufficient amounts of the relevant compounds for structure elucidation.

Separation, purification, and X-ray crystallography of a red quinone from European *C. calceolus* which elicited the strongest reactions in the sensitized guinea pigs led to the identification of the substance as 2,8-dimethoxy-7-hydroxy-1,4-phenanthrene quinone (Fig. 6-2, I), which we called cypripedin (Schmalle and Hausen, 1979). In 1979 two additional quinonoid constituents were detected in field material of *C. calceolus* flowers from northern Germany. No quinones other than cypripedin, however, could be iso-

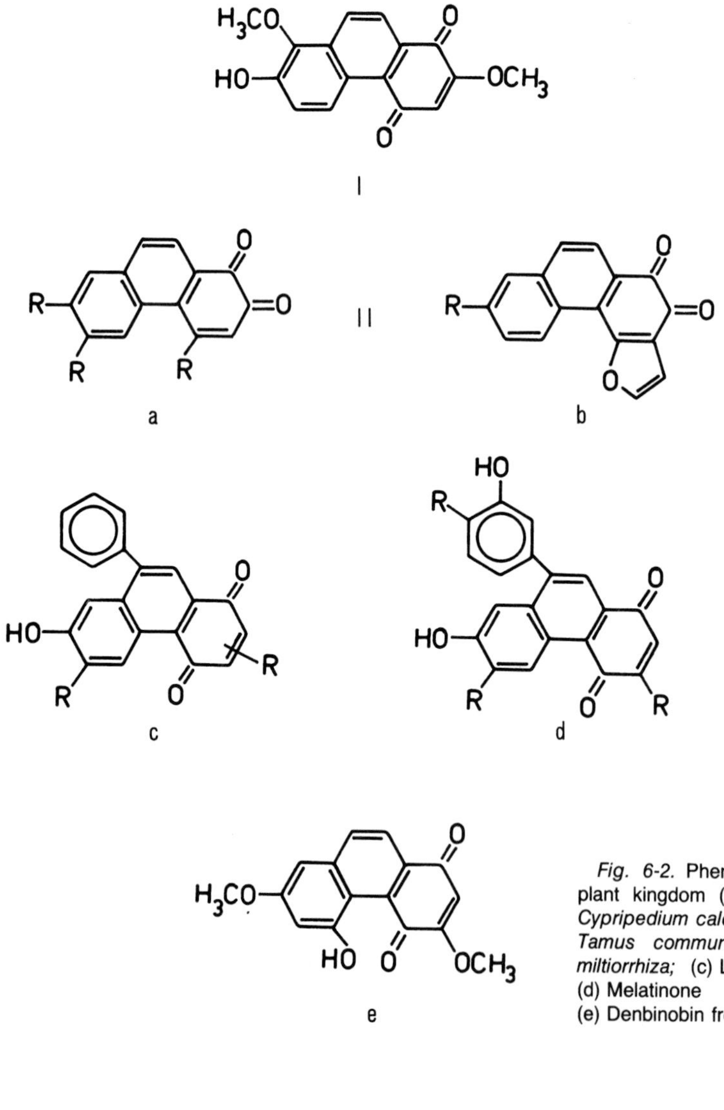

Fig. 6-2. Phenanthrene quinones found in the plant kingdom (R = OCH₃). I: Cypripedin from *Cypripedium calceolus*. II: (a) Tamus quinone from *Tamus communis*; (b) Tanshinone from *Salvia miltiorrhiza*; (c) Latinone from *Dalbergia latifolia*; (d) Melatinone from *Dalbergia melanoxylon*; (e) Denbinobin from *Dendrobium nobile*.

lated from horticulturally grown plants from Graz, Austria. As far as we could determine from the literature, this quinone is the first found in orchids and has not been reported from natural sources before.

Phenanthrene quinones are very rare in the plant kingdom. For example, only very small amounts (1 mg) of a 4,6,7-trimethoxy-1,2-phenanthrene quinone were isolated from the rhizome of *Tamus communis* L. (Fig. 6-2, IIa) after difficult separation and purification procedures (Reisch *et al.*, 1972). Another example is tanshinone I from the roots of *Salvia miltiorrhiza* BGE (Labiatae), whose structure was elucidated by Wessely and his colleagues (Wessely and Wang, 1940; Wessely and Bauer, 1942) as methylfurano-7-methoxy-1,2-phenanthrene quinone (Fig. 6-2, IIb). This structure was later confirmed by synthesis (Baillie and Thomson, 1968). Recently two phenanthrene quinones were isolated by O'Criodain and his co-workers (1981) from commercial tropical wood species—latinone (Fig. 6-2, IIc) from *Dalbergia latifolia* Roxb. (East Indian rosewood) and melatinone (Fig. 6-2, IId) from the African blackwood *Dalbergia melanoxylon* Guill. & Perr. (D. M. X. Donnelly, personal communication, 1981). Both timbers are known for their sensitizing properties.

Phenolic phenanthrene phytoalexins (Fig. 6-3, I) have been discovered in several orchid species, as for example orchinol in *Orchis militaris* L. and loroglossol and hircinol in other genera (Hardegger *et al.*, 1963; Urech *et al.*, 1963; Letcher and Nhamo, 1973; Fisch *et al.*, 1973; Alvarenga *et al.*, 1976; see also Chapter 3 of this volume). Production of phytoalexins is induced by mycorrhizal fungi that are required for germination (Gäumann *et al.*, 1950; Arditti, 1979). It seems reasonable to hypothesize that these phytoalexins could be oxidized to phenanthrene quinones. Of the 15 possible phenanthrene quinones, only 4 (Fig. 6-3, II) have been synthesized to date; 1,2-, 1,4-, 3,4-, and 9,10-phenanthrene quinone (Fittig and Ostermayer, 1873; Fieser *et al.*, 1929a, 1929b, 1929c, 1929d; Becker, 1969). Six of the remaining possible isomers were prepared by Newman and Childers (1967) as their hydroquinones. However, attempts to obtain the corresponding quinones from the precursing dihydroxyphenanthrenes through oxidation failed (Fieser, 1929d). For example, 4,5- and 4,7-dihydroxyphenanthrene did not oxidize to the expected 4,5- and 4,7-phenanthrene quinone, but yielded the purple 5-hydroxy-1,4-phenanthrene quinone and the red 7-hydroxy-1,4-phenanthrene quinone (Fig. 6-4, Ia,b). Similar results were obtained with monohydroxyphenanthrenes, for example, the 4-hydroxy derivative. On the other hand, oxidation of 2,7-dihydroxyphenanthrene produced a high yield of the dark-red 7-hydroxy-1,2-phenanthrene quinone, that is, the *ortho*quinone (Fig. 6-4, Ic,d; Newman and Childers, 1967).

Generally, Newman and his co-workers observed that hydroxy and methoxy phenanthrenes as well as hydroxy-methoxy phenanthrenes were oxidized under proper conditions to either the ortho- or the paraphenanthrene quinone. Thus it is possible that the sensitizing 2,8-dimethoxy-7-hydroxy-1,4-phenanthrene quinone (cypripedin) in *Cypripedium calceolus* could be an oxidation product of a phenanthrene that may be present in *Cypripedium* species. These considerations suggest the existence of other phenanthrene quinones with potential sensitizing capacity. Furthermore, Hopff and Schweizer (1962) have shown that several phenanthrene quinones are highly reactive in

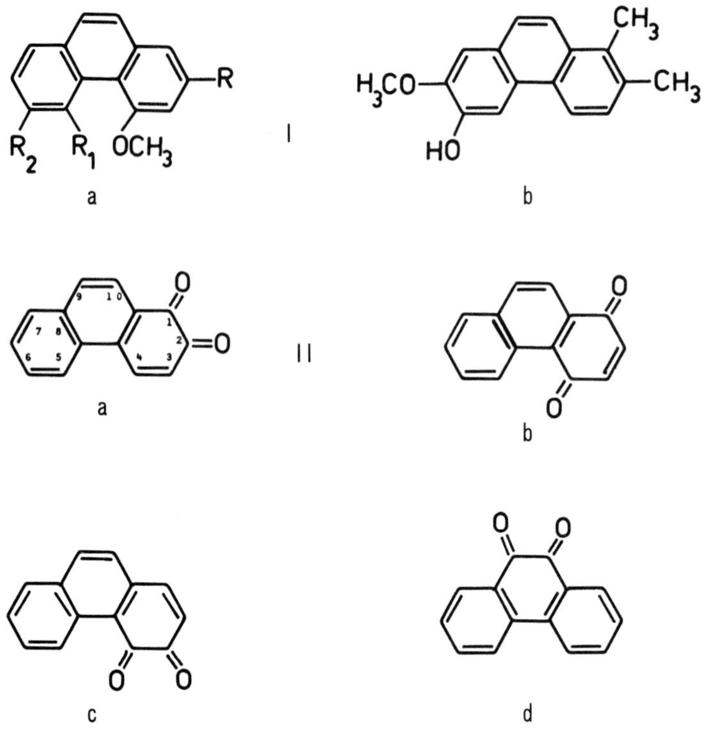

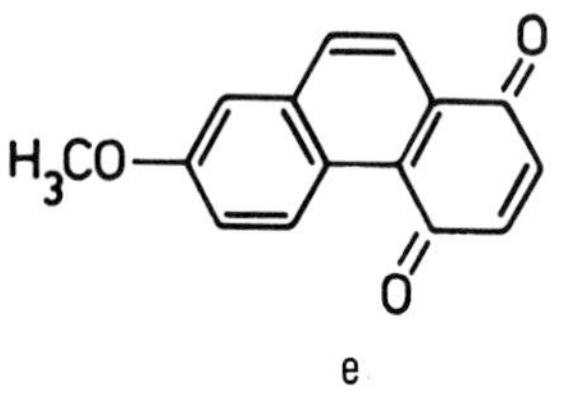

Fig. 6-3. Naturally occurring phytoalexins of the phenanthrene type and experimentally prepared phenanthrene quinones. I: (a) Orchinol (R = OCH_3, R_1 = H, R_2 = OH); Loroglossol (R = OCH_3, R_1 = OH, R_2 = H); Hircinol (R = R_1 = OH, R_2 = H); (b) Micandrol-E. II: (a) 1,2-phenanthrene quinone; (1-10, counting of carbon atoms in phenanthrenes); (b) 1,4-phenanthrene quinone; (c) 3,4-phenanthrene quinone; (d) 9,10-phenanthrene quinone; (e) 7-methoxy-1,4-phenanthrene quinone.

nucleophilic substitution. Nucleophilic attack of NH_2 and SH groups of surface antigens in Langerhans cells and macrophages is essential for the binding of proteins which produces an "altered self" structure, which is necessary for the induction of contact allergy. Finally, it is possible that oxidation may also take place in the skin itself following penetration of the precursor (phenanthrene). If so, the·presence of the quinone itself in the plant is not absolutely necessary.

In the course of our studies concerning structure-sensitizing capacity relationships my colleagues K. Krohn and K. Paavilainen of Braunschweig, West Germany, synthesized five phenanthrene quinones which do not occur naturally and differ only in the number and position of their methoxy groups. The first of these quinones, 7-methoxy-1,4-phenanthrene quinone (Fig. 6-3, IIe), revealed a very high sensitizing capacity in guinea pig sensitization experiments (unpublished). Further studies with six recently synthesized phenanthrene quinones have shown them to be strong sensitizers (unpublished).

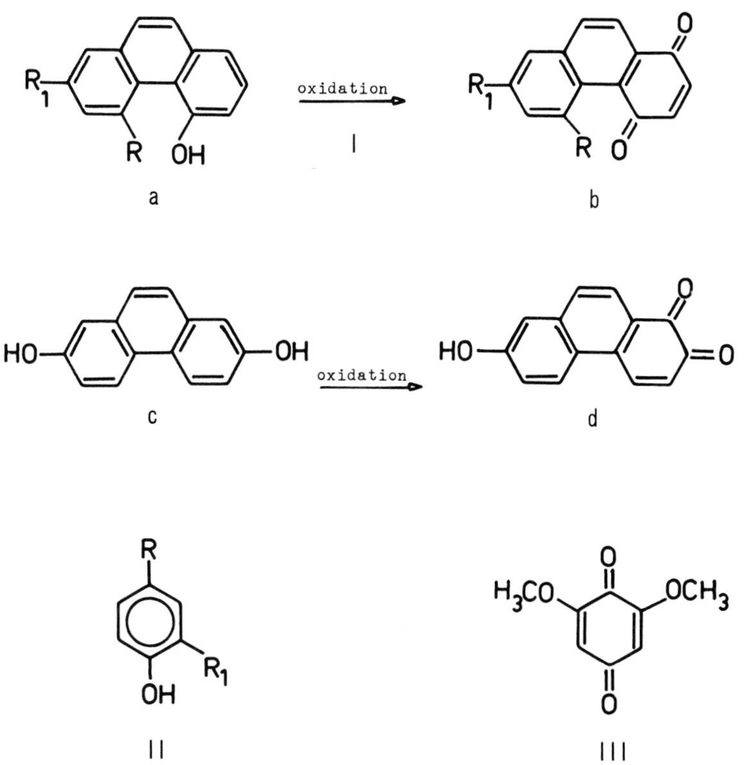

Fig. 6-4. Results of oxidation attempts with dihydroxyphenanthrenes; aromatic compounds in *Vanilla* capsules; contact allergen of *Cymbidium sp.* I: (a) 4,5-dihydroxyphenanthrene (R = OH, R_1 = H); 4,7-dihydroxyphenanthrene (R = H, R_1 = OH); (b) 5-hydroxy-1,4-phenanthrene quinone (R = OH, R_1 = H); 7-hydroxy-1,4-phenanthrene quinone (R = H, R_1 = OH); (d) 7-hydroxy-1,2-phenanthrene quinone. II: Vanillin (R = CHO, R_1 = OCH₃); Vanillyl alcohol (R = CH₂OH, R_1 = OCH₃); Ethyl vanillin (R = CHO, R_1 = OC₂H₅); III: 2,6-dimethoxy-1,4-benzoquinone.

Paphiopedilum Species

In answer to a questionnaire published in *Die Orchidee* (Hausen, 1978), three individuals reported having had eczematous reactions following frequent contact with lady's slipper hybrids. We were able to visit the nurseries of two respondents and to perform epicutaneous tests. The first patient developed dermatitis on the hands and forearms after frequent handling of approximately 500 cultivated plants of *Paphiopedilum haynaldianum* (Rchb. f.) Pfitzer. Patch tests with leaves, petals, and stems as well as with two quinones isolated from the plant after thin-layer chromatographic separation gave strongly positive responses. The subject also reacted to *P. fairieanum* (Lindley) Pfitzer, but not to *P. spicerianum* (Rchb. f.) Pfitzer. Because of insufficient plant material we have been unable to isolate the quinones in quantities sufficient for structure elucidation. In the second case the patient reacted to three of the four isolated quinones and also to extracts of *Phalaenopsis* cultivars. This more recent case holds out hope for a continuation of the chemical investigations. It would not be surprising, however, if their structures were found to be similar to the phenanthrene quinone from *Cypripedium calceolus* (Fig. 6-2, I). This view is supported by the fact that *Paphiopedilum* and *Cypripedium* species are so closely related botanically that until recently taxa that are today included in *Paphiopedilum* were classified as part of the genus *Cypripedium* (Hausen, 1980).

Vanilla

The flavoring properties of the capsules of *Vanilla planifolia* Andrews (the only orchid that is of major economic importance as a condiment) have been known for centuries. Before the flavoring and characteristic properties develop, the capsules must be fermented and dried. The major part of the world's vanilla production takes place in Réunion (Bourbon), Madagascar, Tahiti, and Central and South America (Jackson, 1875; Busse, 1899). During harvest the vanilla capsules are not fragrant, since the constituents are still bound to sugars. After fermentation the compounds are cleaved into the active substances vanillin (an aldehyde), vanillyl alcohol, esters, and glucose (Fig. 6-4, II). Vanillin is the major component of vanilla, but ethyl vanillin is more intensive in vanilla odor and taste than vanillin itself (Arana, 1944; Garros-Patin and Hahn, 1954; Arctander, 1969).

Vanillin, synthetic or from natural sources, is used throughout the world as a flavoring agent, in high-priced luxury perfumes, soaps, creams, and lotions, and in tobacco, chocolate, ice cream, and thousands of other formulations. Its most remarkable use is as a masking agent in evil-smelling industrial products, such as rubber, plastic, and fiberglass (Arctander, 1969).

Cases of contact dermatitis have been described since 1883 (Layet, 1883). The dermatitis that affected workers who handled the capsules during cultivation, harvesting, and fermentation was referred to as "vanillism" (Hutchinson, 1892/93; Drevon, 1899). At first vanillism was attributed to a mite (Arnozan, 1883), but later it was demonstrated that the capsules themselves were responsible.

Numerous cases of allergic contact dermatitis (delayed type of allergy) induced by vanilla capsules and extracts in household items and foods have been reported. However, most of the other reactions have been immediate (type I), such as allergic rhinitis, bronchial asthma, gastrointestinal complications, and urticaria (Table 6-1). Consumption of vanilla in ice cream, cake, beverages, liqueurs, and so on has in some cases caused urticarial eruptions with swelling of the face and arms, or strong generalized itching, headache, and nausea (Milian, 1936). Since most bakers, beverage makers, and homemakers come into contact with vanilla capsules, some researchers have tested their major component, the pure vanillin, on their allergic respondents. N. Hjorth (1961) and W. G. van Ketel (1973) found positive reactions to 10% concentrations. It is not possible to determine from these reports, however, whether vanilla itself caused stronger reactions than the pure vanillin.

We have studied a case of perfume dermatitis that was called to our attention by Dr. G. Heidbreder of Hamburg, West Germany. A 15-year-old girl developed redness, papules, and vesicles behind both ears after frequent use of vanilla perfume imported from Spain. Epicutaneous tests with the perfume produced moderate reactions after open application and strong reactions under occlusive conditions (patch test). Tests in controls

Table 6-1. Primary irritant or sensitizing effects noted after contact with or ingestion of vanilla and its products

Year	Author	Effects noted
1883	Layet	Occupational dermatoses in 6 individuals who handled fermented vanilla.
1883	Arnozan	"Vanillism," assumed to be caused by a mite.
1886	Morrow	"Poisoning" by ice cream containing vanilla; dermatitis in pickers of vanilla capsules.
1887	White	Irritation in persons employed in vanilla plantations and in curing establishments in Mexico.
1892/93	Hutchinson	Occupational vanillism in 3 workers in a vanilla factory.
1893	White	Dermatitis on the face, wrists, and forearms of the manager of a vanilla commission house.
1895	Guerin	Conjunctivitis and dermatitis after handling of vanilla capsules in Guadeloupe.
1896	Gieseler	Vanillism, attributed to preparation of vanilla with cardol (cashew nut oil).
1897	Arning	Symptoms similar to those of vanillism in persons who extracted vanillin from wood.
1897	Arning	Chronic eczema due to crystallization of vanillin on the surface of vanilla capsules.
1899	Drevon	An unknown number of persons reported to suffer from vanilla dermatitis.
1899	Audeoud	Dermatitis of the face and hands in pickers of vanilla capsules.
1906	Brocq and Fage	Dermatitis of the face and hands of a person employed by a vanilla commission house.
1906	Anonymous	Skin eruptions caused by vanilla (no details).
1907	Hiley	Doubtful case of vanilla dermatitis, possibly formaldehyde allergy.
1907	Gaucher and Malloizel	Dermatitis of the face due to occupational handling and cleaning of vanilla.
1907	Claverie	Occupational dermatitis in capsule pickers severe enough to require absence from work.
1909	Brétin	Dermatitis caused by leaves of vanilla plant; skin eruptions during artificial pollination on plantations.
1911	Clarac and Grall	Several cases of vanillism.
1914	Leggett	Excoriation of the scalp, face, and arms after use of hair lotion containing vanilla extract.
1924	Peshkin	Hand dermatitis in pharmacists and druggists who handled vanilla.
1929	Nestler	No effects noted after vanilla capsules were rubbed on skin.
1929	Lortat-Jacob and Solvante	Occupational dermatitis due to cutting of vanilla for chocolate flavoring; epicutaneous tests with vanillin negative.
1930	Touton	Painful dermatitis (urticaria?) after ingestion of vanilla ice cream.
1934	Sincke	Sensitization by vanilla capsules; epicutaneous tests with vanillin negative.
1936	Milian	Two cases of vanilla dermatitis (no details given).
1936	Blasko	Dermatitis of the face due to occupational cleaning of vanilla capsules in a warehouse.
1936	Zündel	17 positive patch tests with vanilla in 2,000 subjects with dermatitis.
1939	Downing	Dermatitis of the hands in pastry cooks, confectioners, chocolate dippers ("vanillism").
1939	Gougerot and Basset	Six cases of dermatitis on the face, hands, and forearms of workers who handled vanilla.
1943	Klauder	Dermatitis in workers who sorted vanilla capsules and prepared beverages; tests positive.
1947	Sequeira *et al.*	Erythema, papules, and vesicles in confectioners.
1949	Urbach and Gottlieb	Vanilla dermatitis in housewives.
1950	Tzanck and Sidi	Dermatitis more frequently noted as result of natural vanilla than of synthetic or imitation vanilla.
1954	Bui-Xuan-Nhuan	Several cases of contact dermatitis due to natural and artificial vanilla.
1954	Caujolle and Meynier	Poisoning and irritation attributed to intermediate products of synthetic vanillin.
1961	Hjorth	Vanilla allergy noted in 34 of 73 subjects who were also allergic to balsam of Peru; in some subjects vanilla (10%) produced positive reactions; in one case bullous reactions of the hands were noted after consumption of vanilla ice cream.
1970	Pirilä	Flare-up of allergic reactions in a subject sensitive to balsam of Peru after ingestion of $\frac{1}{3}$ teaspoon of vanilla sugar.
1970	Fisher	Dermatitis of the face linked with vanilla extracts in tobacco smoke.
1972	Hjorth and Weismann	Positive patch tests with vanilla in chefs and sandwich makers.
1973	van Ketel	Vanilla allergy due to ointment scented with vanilla; reactions to vanillin (10%) positive.
1975	Larsen	Cosmetic dermatitis due to perfume; no reaction to vanillin (undiluted) after 48 hours.
1975	Mitchell	Positive reactions to vanillin in 8 of 142 subjects sensitive to balsam of Peru.
1977	Opdyke	Negative reactions to human maximization tests with vanilla and vanillin in 25 volunteers.

remained negative. As the quantity of the perfume left after the multiple tests was not sufficient for the preparation of fractions, a newly imported sample was analyzed chemically. Thin-layer chromatographic separation revealed that it contained vanillin, ethyl vanillin, cinnamic aldehyde, and 3,5-dimethoxy-4-hydroxy benzaldehyde. Renewed epicutaneous tests with these constituents and further fractions (all 1% in petrolatum) remained negative. A chemical analysis of the small amount left in the first perfume bottle revealed that some of the constituents found in the second bottle were not present, but that it did contain a quinone. The first perfume sample was much darker than the second. Therefore it is possible that after frequent opening of the bottle, oxygen from the air led to oxidation products that might have been responsible for the exzematous reactions. These products were not present in the new sample. When the girl discontinued use of the perfume, no further dermatitis occurred. No flare-up reactions were detected following consumption of foods that contained vanilla.

Altogether it is clear from previous reports that vanillin itself does not function as the main sensitizer of vanilla. The substance is known to produce occasional reactions in people who have been previously sensitized to vanilla and sometimes in those allergic to the benzoin rosins in balsam of Peru (Hjorth, 1961; Pirilä, 1970; Mitchell, 1971, 1975). Tests with vanilla capsules produced stronger responses than the pure compound. Rudzki (1976) noted immediate reactions to 1% and 2% concentrations of ethyl vanillin in individuals sensitive to balsam of Peru, but no response after 24 hours. Opdyke's (1977) human maximization tests with vanillin (2 and 5% in petrolatum) carried out in 25 volunteers could not demonstrate sensitization either.

In our sensitization experiments conducted by the open epicutaneous method and in the guinea pig maximization test we obtained strong reactions with vanilla capsule extracts and very weak responses with vanillin. Elicitation studies with vanillyl alcohol, ethyl vanillin (Fig. 6-4, II), cinnamic aldehyde, and vanillin itself in various concentrations, as well as several fractions isolated from the ethanol extract of the capsules in vanilla-sensitive animals, revealed that vanilla is a strong sensitizer, but vanillin and related constituents have weak sensitizing and eliciting properties. The threshold of primary irritation by vanillin is greater than 30%. Of 10 guinea pigs sensitized with pure vanillin, only 5 demonstrated a moderate reaction to a concentration of 20%. Thus vanillin can be regarded as only a minor sensitizer, probably a secondary allergen (elicitor) in vanilla-sensitive individuals. However, the first fraction of the vanilla capsule ethanol extract, separated by preparative thin-layer chromatography, gave strong reactions. Consequently, some still unknown constituent or constituents may prove to be the main sensitizer in *Vanilla planifolia* allergy.

Besides *V. planifolia,* other members of the same genus have been said to cause dermatitis: *V. griffithii* Rchb. f. (Ridley, 1921), *V. claviculata* Sw. (Anonymous, 1952), *V. pompona* Schiede, and *V. tahitensis* J. W. Moore (Desoille *et al.,* 1946).

Other Ornamental Orchids

A case of contact allergy caused by a *Cymbidium* hybrid and confirmed by positive epicutaneous tests was reported recently by Shoji (1981). The sensitizing properties of this ornamental and very popular orchid were established by positive results in experimental sensitization work with guinea pigs. Chemical separation of the extracts revealed the presence of two quinones. The structure of one was elucidated as 2,6-dimethoxy-1,4-benzoquinone (Fig. 6-4, III) by X-ray crystallographic analysis. In the patient as well as in the sensitized animals only this quinone elicited strong reactions; the second gave negative reaction in the patient and produced only weak responses in animals (Hausen and Shoji, 1982). Subsequently, screening tests for quinones in available ornamental field-grown and commercial orchid extracts were performed in my laboratory (Table 6-2). Phytochemical screening for potential sensitizers should preferably be performed by the Craven test, which is specific for benzo- and naphthoquinones and probably also for certain coumarins (R. H. Thomson, personal communication). A positive color reaction requires the presence of a labile hydrogen or halogen atom adjacent to the carbonyl group of the quinone or its equivalent (Craven, 1931). This condition is fulfilled by all quinonoid primary sensitizers isolated to date. Table 6-2 demonstrates that Craven-positive constituents were detectable in the investigated species and also in the tubera salep extract that is derived from at least 10 *Orchis* species (Grieve, 1971). No great importance is attributed to the detection of Craven-positive constituents in fermented vanilla capsules, since the fractions that contained such compounds produced only moderate reactions in our sensitized guinea pigs.

Recently a new phenanthrene quinone, called denbinobin (3,7-dimethoxy-5-hydroxy-1,4-phenanthrene quinone; Fig. 6-2, IIe) has been isolated from an Indian form of *Dendrobium nobile* Lindley in concentrations of 0.002% (Talapatra *et al.*, 1982). Although I could not detect this quinone in cultivars of this orchid bred in middle Europe, its chemical structure suggests a potential sensitizing power. Efforts to synthesize it in greater amounts and to determine its sensitizing capacity experimentally are in progress.

Conclusion

It is clear from this review that we know little about the toxic and sensitizing effects of orchids, but may speculate a great deal. Studies of the poisonous and allergenic compounds in this family are still at their beginnings. No case of poisoning has been described, but contact allergy caused by several ornamental species must be considered to

Table 6-2. Phytochemical screening for quinonoid constituents in orchid species and orchid extracts: thin-layer chromatographic separation of ether and ethanol extracts

Species	Plant part	Craven reaction	Number of spots
Phalaenopsis hybrids	Petals	Blue	1
Cymbidium hybrids	Leaves, flowers, stems	Blue	2
Dendrobium nobile Lindley	Petals	Blue	1
Paphiopedilum sp.	Whole plant	Blue/green	2–4
Cypripedium reginae Walter	Leaves, petals	Blue	2
Paphiopedilum fairieanum (Rchb. f.) Pfitzer	Whole plant	Blue	2
Ophris sp.	Whole plant	Blue	2
Vanilla planifolia Andrews	Fermented capsules	Blue/green	2
Orchis mascula L.	Whole plant	Blue	Several
Tubera salep (*Orchis* species)	Root extracts	Blue	1

be established. As breeding and sales of orchids become more popular, the risk of delayed hypersensitivity in nursery workers and florists will undoubtedly increase. An interesting aspect of this situation is the finding that phenanthrene quinones appear to play a greater role as contact sensitizers than has hitherto been recognized, not only in the Orchidaceae but in the plant kingdom generally. Further identification of orchid constituents will contribute a great deal to our understanding of the relationships between chemical structure and biological activities as they relate to sensitizing effects.

Literature Cited

Alvarenga, M. A. de, O. R. Gottlieb, and M. T. Magalhaes. 1976. Methylphenanthrenes from *Sagotia racemosa*. Phytochem. 15:844–845.

Anonymous. 1906. A skin eruption produced by vanilla. Lancet 2:1478.

———. 1952. Poisonous orchids. Orchid J. 1:20.

———. 1953. More on poisonous orchids. Orchid J. 2:67.

Arana, F. E. 1944. Vanilla curing. Vanilla chemistry. Puerto Rico Agric. Experim. Stat. Bull. 42:1–17.

Arctander, S. 1969. Perfume and flavour chemicals. 2 vols. Montclair, N.J.

Arditti, J. 1979. Aspects of the physiology of orchids. Adv. Bot. Res. 7:421–655. Academic Press, London.

Arditti, J., and M. H. Fisch. 1977. Anthocyanins of the Orchidaceae, pp. 117–155. *In* J. Arditti (ed.), Orchid Biology: reviews and perspectives, vol. 1. Cornell University Press, Ithaca, N.Y.

Arning, E. 1897a. Vanilleausschlag. Dtsch. Med. Wochenschr. 23:435–436.

———. 1897b. Vanille-Ekzem. Berlin. Klin. Wochenschr. 34:509.

Arnozan. 1883. Note sur l'acare de la vanille. Rév. d'Hyg. Police Sanitaire 5:724–726.

Audeoud, H. 1899. Note sur le vanillisme professionnel. Rév. Méd. Suisse Rom. 10:627–633.

Babcock, H. H. 1875. Poisoning by *Cypripedium*. Pharmacist 8:1.

Baillie, A. C., and R. H. Thomson. 1968. Naturally occurring quinones. Pt. 11. The tanshinones. J. Chem. Soc. C., pp. 48–52.

Becker, H. D. 1969. New synthesis of 1,2-phenanthrenequinone. J. Org. Chem. 34:2026–2027.

Beierlein, H. 1957. Allergischer Hautausschlag, verursacht durch den amerikanischen Prachtfrauenschuh (*Cypripedium reginae*). Orchidee 8:95.

Blasko, G. E. 1936. Étude sur le vanillisme professionnel. Med. thesis, University of Paris.

Boorsma, W. 1902. Orchidaceae. Bull. Inst. Bot. Buitenzorg 14:36–37.

Braginskii, B., and I. Bobokhodzev. 1965. Hepato-splenomegaly against the background of heliotropic toxicosis. Sov. Med. 28:57–60.

Brandänge, S., and B. Lüning. 1969. Studies on Orchidaceae alkaloids. Pt. 12. Pyrrolizidine alkaloids from *Phalaenopsis amabilis* B1 and *Ph. mannii* Rchb. f. Acta Chem. Scand. 23:1151–1154.

Bras, G., and K. R. Hill. 1956. Veno-occlusive disease of the liver. Lancet 2:161–163.

Brétin, P.-M. 1909. L'origine végétale de certaines dermites. Med. thesis, University of Lyon.

Brocq, L., and Fage. 1906. Eruption des erythemateuse et papuleuse causée par la vanille. Bull. Soc. Franc. Dermat., pp. 404–407.

Brøndegaard, V. J. 1965. Farmakognosiens orkidéer. Svensk. Farm. Tidskr. 69:938–944.

Bui-Xuan-Nhuan. 1954. Le vanillisme. *In* G. Bouriquet (ed.), Le vanillier et la vanille dans le monde, pp. 647–662. Paul Lechevalier, Paris.

Busse, W. 1899. Vanille. Arb. Kaiserl. Gesundheitsamt 15:1–113.

Caujolle, F., and D. Meynier. 1954. Toxicité de la vanille. Ann. Pharm. France 12:42–49.

Chen, K. K., and A. L. Chen. 1935a. The alkaloid of Chin-shih-hu. J. Biol. Chem. 111:653–658.

———. 1935b. The pharmacological action of dendrobine, the alkaloid of Chin-shih-hu. J. Pharmacol. Exper. Therap. 55:319–325.

Chen, K. K., and C. L. Rose. 1936. Detoxification of dendrobine by "Sodium Amytal." Proc. Soc. Experim. Biol. Med. 34:553–554.

———. 1940. The action and toxicity of platyphylline and seneciphylline. J. Pharmacol. Experim. Therap. 68:130–140.

Clarac, A., and C. Grall. 1911. "Vanillisme." Traite Prat. Pathol. Exot. Clin. Thérap. T. V.:246–250.

Claverie, G. 1907. Essai sur le vanillisme professionnel. Med. thesis, University of Paris.

Coombs, R. R. A., and P. G. H. Gell. 1975. Classification of allergic reactions responsible for clinical hypersensitivity and disease, pp. 761–781. *In* P. G. H. Gell, R. R. A. Coombs, and H. Lachmann (eds.), Clinical aspects of immunology, 3d ed. Blackwell, Oxford.

Craven, R. 1931. A sensitive colour reaction for certain quinones. J. Chem. Soc., pp. 1605–1606.

Culver, C. 1951. Johnny Ladyslipperseed. Am. Orchid Soc. Bull. 20:609–611.

Delauney, P. 1920. Contribution à l'étude des glucosides de la famille des Orchidées. Compt. Rend. Acad. Sci. 171:435–437.

——. 1921. Chimie végétale. Compt. Rend. Acad. Sci. 172:471–473.

——. 1925. Chimie biologique. Compt. Rend. Acad. Sci. 180:224–225.

Desoille, H., A. Meyer, and A. Massinot. 1946. Quelques notions étiologiques sur le vanillisme. Arch. Mal. Prof. 7:120–121.

Downing, J. G. 1939. Cutaneous eruptions among industrial workers. Arch. Derm. 39:12–32.

Drevon. 1899. Vanillisme. Ann. d'Hyg. Méd. Colon. 2:529–532.

Droog, E. de. 1896. Contribution à l'étude de la localisation microchimique des alcaloides dans la famille des Orchidées. Mém. Cour. Autr. Mém. Acad. Roy. Belg. 55:1–35.

Fieser, L. F. 1929a. Some derivatives of 3,4-phenanthrenequinone. J. Amer. Chem. Soc. 51:940–952.

——. 1929b. 1,2-phenanthrenequinone. J. Amer. Chem. Soc. 51:1896–1906.

——. 1929c. The sulfonation of phenanthrene. J. Amer. Chem. Soc. 51:2460–2470.

——. 1929d. Disulfonation. J. Amer. Chem. Soc. 51:2471–2486.

Fisch, M. H., B. H. Flick, and J. Arditti. 1973. Structure and antifungal activity of hircinol, loroglossol, and orchinol. Phytochem. 12:437–441.

Fisher, A. A. 1970. Sieben Gewürze aus dermatologischer Sicht. Hautarzt 21:295–297.

Fittig, R., and E. Ostermayer. 1873. Über das Phenanthren. Liebigs Ann. Chemie 166:361–387.

G. T. 1887. Editorial. Bot. Gaz. 12:275–276.

Garros-Patin, J., and J. Hahn. 1954. La chimie de la vanille, pp. 559–675. *In* G. Bouriquet (ed.), Le vanillier et la vanille dans le monde. Paul Lechevalier, Paris.

Gaucher, P. C., and Malloizel. 1907. Eruption chez les vanilleurs. Bull. Soc. Franc. Dermat., pp. 59–60.

Gäumann, E., R. Braun, and G. Bazzigher. 1950. Über induzierte Abwehrreaktionen bei Pflanzen. Phytopathol. Z. 17:36–63.

Ghose, B. N. 1955. Wirtschaftliche und giftige Orchideen. Orchidee 6:53–54.

Gieseler, T. 1896. Zur Kasuistik und Ätiologie der sogenannten Vanillevergiftungen. Med. thesis, University of Bonn.

Gougerot, H., and A. Basset. 1939. Dermatite éczemateuse professionnelle à la vanille. Bull. Soc. Franc. Dermat. 46:1329–1333.

Grieve, M. 1971. A modern herbal. Dover, New York.

Guerin. 1895. Manifestations oculaires du vanillisme. Ann. d'Oculist., pp. 284–286.

Hardegger, E., H. R. Biland, and H. Corrodi. 1963a. Synthese von 2,4-dimethoxy-6-hydroxyphenanthren und Konstitution des Orchinols. Helv. Chim. Acta 46:1354–1360.

Hardegger, E., M. Schellenbaum, and H. Corrodi. 1963b. Über induzierte Abwehrstoffe bei Orchideen. Helv. Chim. Acta 46:1171–1181.

Hardie, R. A., and V. S. Rajan. 1981. A survey of orchid growers. Contact Derm. 7:122–123.

Hartley, T. G., E. A. Dunstone, J. S. Fitzgerald, S. R. Johns, and J. A. Lamberton. 1973. A survey of New Guinea plants for alkaloids. Lloydia 36:217–319.

Hausen, B. M. 1977. A simple method for extracting crude sesquiterpene lactones from Compositae plants for skin tests, chemical investigations, and sensitizing experiments in guinea pigs. Contact Derm. 3:58–60.

——. 1978. Kontaktallergie durch Frauenschuh (*Cypripedium sp*). Orchidee 29:[134].

——. 1979. New allergenic quinones in orchids. Arch. Derm. Res. 264:102–103.

——. 1980. Allergic contact dermatitis to quinones in *Paphiopedilum haynaldianum*. Arch. Derm. 116:327–328.

Hausen, B. M., A. Shoji, and O. Jarchow. In press. Orchid allergy. 2,6-dimethoxy-p-benzoquinone, the main contact allergen of *Cymbidium sp*. Arch. Derm.

Hegnauer, R. 1963. Chemotaxonomie der Pflanzen. Birkhäuser Verlag, Stuttgart and Basel.

Hérissey, H., and P. Delauney. 1922. Présence des glucosides qui donnent du coumarin à l'hydrolyse. J. Pharm. Chim. 25:298–305.

Hiley, R. F. 1907. Dermatitis due to vanilla. Lancet 1:469.

Hill, K. R. 1960. The worldwide distribution of senecosis in man and animal. Proc. Roy. Soc. Med. 53:281–283.

Hirono, I. 1979. Naturally occurring carcinogenic substances. Gann 24:85–102.

Hjorth, N. 1961. Eczematous allergy to balsams. Munksgaard, Copenhagen.

Hjorth, N., and K. Weismann. 1972. Occupational dermatitis in chefs and sandwich makers. Contact Derm. Newsletter, no. 11, p. 30.

Holman, R. T., and W. H. Heimermann. 1973. Identification of components of orchid fragrances by gas chromatography–mass spectrometry. Amer. Orchid Soc. Bull. 42:678–682.

Holman, R. T., and P. C. Nichols. 1972. Characterization of the lipids of some orchids. Phytochem. 11:333–337.

Holman, R. T., W. P. Cunningham, and E. S. Swanson. 1981. A closer look at the glandular hairs on the ovaries of Cypripediums. Am. Orchid Soc. Bull. 50:683–687.

Hopff, H., and H. R. Schweizer. 1962. Zur Kenntnis der Reaktivität polycyclischer Chinone. Helv. Chim. Acta 45:312–331.

Hueper, W. A., and W. D. Conway. 1969. Tannins and tannic acid, pp. 36 and 365. In W. A. Hueper (ed.), Chemical carcinogenesis and cancer. Charles C. Thomas, Springfield, Ill.

Hutchinson, J. 1892/93. An eruption caused by vanilla. Arch. Surgery 4:49–50.

Inubishi, Y., H. Ishii, B. Yasui, T. Konita, and T. Harayama. 1964. Isolation and characterization of alkaloids of the Chinese drug "Chin-shih-hu." Chem. Pharm. Bull. 12:1175–1180.

Inubishi, Y., Y. Tsuda, T. Konita, and S. Matsumoto. 1964. Shihunine, a new phthalide-pyrrolidine alkaloid. Chem. Pharm. Bull. 12:749–750.

Ishii, M., S. Uemoto, K. Fujieda, M. Nonaka, Y. Shoyama, Y. Miyahara, and I. Nishioka. 1979. A new biologically active phenolic from Cattleya trianaei. Phytochem. 18:1211–1213.

Jackson, J. R. 1875. Vanilla. Pharmacist 8:168–170.

Jeffrey, D. C., J. Arditti, and H. Koopowitz. 1970. Sugar content in floral and extrafloral exudates of orchids. New Phytol. 69:187–195.

Jesup, H. G. 1893. Is Cypripedium spectabile poisonous to the touch? Bot. Gaz. 18:142–143.

Ketel, W. G. van. 1973. Allergy to cumarin and cumarin derivatives. Contact Derm. Newsletter no. 13:355.

Klauder, J. V. 1943. Actual cases of certain occupational dermatoses. Arch. Derm. 48:579–600.

Kunze, R. E. 1875. Rhus versus Cypripedium. Bull. Torrey Club 6:22.

Larsen, W. G. 1975. Cosmetic dermatitis due to perfume. Contact Derm. 1:142.

Lawler, L. J., and M. Slaytor. 1969. Distribution of alkaloids in New South Wales and Queensland Orchidaceae. Phytochem. 8:1959–1962.

Layet, A. 1883. Étude sur le vanillisme, ou accidents causées par la vanille. Rév. d'Hyg. Police Sanitaire 5:711–724.

Leggett, W. 1914. Vanilla as a skin irritant. Brit. Med. J. 1:1351–1352.

Letcher, R. M., and L. R. M. Nhamo. 1973. Structure of orchinol, loroglossol, and hircinol. J. Chem. Soc. Perk. 1:1263–1265.

Lortat-Jacob and Solvante. 1929. Éruption érythémateuse par vanille. Bull. Soc. Franc. Dermat. 1:9–11.

Lüning, B. 1964. Studies on Orchidaceae alkaloids. Screening of species for alkaloids. Acta Chem. Scand. 18:1507–1516.

———. 1974. Alkaloids of the Orchidaceae, pp. 349–382. In C. L. Withner (ed.), The orchids. Scientific Studies. Wiley-Interscience, New York.

Lüning, B., H. Tränckner, and S. Brandänge. 1966. Studies on Orchidaceae alkaloids. V. A new alkaloid from Phalaenopsis amabilis Bl. Acta Chem. Scand. 20:2011.

MacDougal, D. T. 1894. On the poisonous influence of Cypripedium spectabile and Cypripedium pubescens. Minnesota Bot. Stud. 1:32–36.

———. 1895. Poisonous influence of various species of Cypripedium. Minnesota Bot. Stud. 1:450–451.

McLean, E. K. 1970. The toxic actions of pyrrolizidine (Senecio) alkaloids. Pharmacol. Rev. 22:429–483.

Maille, M., G. Morel, and R. Gautheret. 1974. Mise en evidence d'une amine phénolique dans diverses Orchidées du genre Cattleya Compt. Rend. Acad. Sci., ser. D, 278:2217–2218.

Mattocks, A. R. 1968. The toxicity of pyrrolizidine alkaloids. Nature 217:723–728.

———. 1971. Hepatotoxic effects due to pyrrolizidine alkaloid N-oxides. Xenobiotica 1:563–565.

Meyler, L. (ed.). 1978. Side effects of drugs, vol. 7, pp. 482–500. Excerpta Medica, Amsterdam.

Milian, G. 1936. Dermatoses artificielles d'origine végétale, pp. 791–803, 855, 857–859. In Darier, J., R. Sabouraud, H. Gougerot, G. Milian, L.-M. Pautrier, R. Ravaut, A. Sezary, and C. Simon (eds.), Nouvelle pratique dermatologique, vol. 4. Masson, Paris.

Miller, M. A. 1959. Orchids of economic use. Amer. Orchid Soc. Bull. 28:157–162, 268–271, 351–354.

Mitchell, J. C. 1971. The skin and chemical additives in foods. Arch. Derm. 104:329–331.

———. 1975. Patch testing with some compounds of balsam of Peru. Contact Derm. 1:391–392.

Morrow, P. A. 1886. Ice-cream poisoning; vanillism. Med. Rec. (New York) 30:108.

Nestler, A. 1907. Das Sekret der Drüsenhaare der Gattung *Cypripedium* mit besonderer Berücksichtigung seiner hautreizenden Wirkung. Ber. Dtsch. Bot. Ges. 23:554–556.

———. 1929. Hautreizende Pflanzen. Umschau 33:611–613.

Newman, M. S., and R. L. Childers. 1967. Attempted preparation of new phenanthrenequinone types. J. Org. Chem. 32:62–66.

O'Criodain, T. O., M. O'Sullivan, M. J. Meegan, and D. M. X. Donnelly. 1981. Latinone, a phenanthrene-1,4-quinone from *Dalbergia latilolia*. Phytochem. 20:1089–1092.

Oler, A., M. Neal, and E. Mitchell. 1976. Tannic acid: acute hepatotoxicity following administration by feeding tube. Food Cosm. Toxicol. 14:565–569.

Onaka, T., S. Kamata, T. Maeda, Y. Kawazoe, M. Natsume, T. Okamoto, F. Uchimara, and M. Shimizu. 1965. The structure of nobilonine, the second alkaloid of *Dendrobium nobile*. Chem. Pharm. Bul. 13:745–747.

Opdyke, D. L. J. 1977. Vanillin. Monographs in fragrance raw materials suppl. to Food Cosm. Toxicol. 15:633–638.

Ormerod, M. J., and F. D. White. 1929. A preliminary pharmacological investigation of extracts of certain Western Canadian plants, sec. 4. Trans. Roy. Soc. Can. 23:189–194.

Pagani, F. 1976. Fitocostituenti di Orchidaceae. Pt. 1. Componenti della *Orchis sambucina* L., *Orchis morio* L. Boll. Chim. Farm. 115:407–412.

Peshkin, M. M. 1924. Bronchial asthma and other allergic manifestations in pharmacists. Amer. J. Pharmacy 96:524–529.

Pirilä, V. 1970. Das endogene Ekzem. Allergie u. Asthma 16:15–19.

Pirquet, C. von. 1910. Allergie. August Hirschwald, Berlin.

Reisch, J., M. Bathory, I. Novak, K. Szendrei, and E. Minker. 1972. Stickstofffreie Phenanthrenderivate als Pflanzeninhaltsstoffe. Herba Hung. 11:61–71.

Ridley, H. N. 1921. *In* T. A. Sprague, Plant dermatitis. J. Bot. 59:308–310.

Rudzki, E. 1976. Immediate reactions to balsam of Peru, cassia oil, and ethylvanillin. Contact Derm. 2:360–361.

Sadovsky, O. 1957. Allergischer Hautausschlag durch Orchideen? Orchidee 8:126.

Schmalle, H., and B. M. Hausen. 1979. A new sensitising quinone from lady slipper (*Cypripedium calceolus*). Naturwiss. 66:527–528.

Schoental, R. 1957. Hepatotoxic action of pyrrolizidine (*Senecio*) alkaloids in relation to their structure. Nature 179:361–363.

———. 1968. Chemical structures and pathological effects of pyrrolizidine alkaloids. Israel J. Med. Sci. 4:1133–1145.

Selzer, G., and R. G. F. Parker. 1951. Senecio poisoning exhibiting as Chiari's syndrome. Amer. J. Pathol. 27:885–907.

Sequeira, J. H., J. T. Ingram, and T. R. Brain. 1947. Diseases of the skin. 5th ed. J. & A. Churchill, London.

Shoji, A. 1981. Contact dermatitis caused by ornamental plants. 11th Symp. Japan. Antigen Res. Group, Osaka, p. 4.

Sincke, G. E. 1934. Überempfindlichkeit gegen Vanille. Dermatol. Wochenschr. 99:1480–1481.

Skoog, M.-L. 1980. Measurement and differentiation of the cellular infiltrate in experimental toxic contact dermatitis. Acta Derm.-Venerol. 60:239–244.

Slaytor, M. B. 1977. The distribution and chemistry of alkaloids in the Orchidaceae, pp. 95–115. *In* J. Arditti (ed.), Orchid Biology: reviews and perspectives, vol. 1. Cornell University Press, Ithaca, N.Y.

Swanson, E. S., W. P. Cunningham, and R. T. Holman. 1980. Ultrastructure of glandular ovarian trichomes of *Cypripedium calceolus* and *C. reginae* (Orchidaceae). Amer. J. Bot. 67:784–789.

Suzuki, H., I. Keimatsu, and M. Ito. 1932. Alkaloids of the Chinese drug "Chin-shih-hu." II. Dendrobine. J. Pharm. Soc. Japan 52:1049–1060.

———. 1934. Alkaloids of the Chinese drug "Chin-shih-hu." Pt. 3. Dendrobine. J. Pharm. Soc. Japan 54:802–823.

Talapatra, B., P. Mukhopadhyay, P. Chaudry, and S. K. Talapatra. 1982. Denbinobin, a new phenanthraquinone from *Dendrobium nobile* Lind. (Orchidaceae). Ind. J. Chem. 21B:386–387.

Touton, H. 1930. Hautschädigungen durch pflanzliche Nahrungs- und Genussmittel. Naturwiss. 18:121–126.

Tzanck, A., and E. Sidi. 1950. Les dermatoses allergiques. Masson, Paris.

Urbach, E., and P. M. Gottlieb. 1949. Allergy, pp. 373–419. 2d ed. Grune & Stratton, New York.

Urech, J., B. Fechtig, J. Nüesch, and E. Vischer. 1963. Hircinol, eine antifungisch wirksame Substanz aus Knollen von *Loroglossum hircinum* (L.) Rich. Helv. Chim. Acta 46:2758–2766.

Wessely, F. von, and A. Bauer. 1942. Über Chinonfarbstoffe aus der Reihe eines Phenanthronfurans. Pt. 2. Über die Konstitution des Tanshinons I. Ber. Dtsch. Chem. Ges. 75:617–625.

Wessely, F. von, and S. Wang. 1940. Über einen neuartigen natürlichen Chinonfarbstoff aus der Klasse eines Phenanthronfurans. Ber. Dtsch. Chem. Ges. 73:19–24.

Wester, D. H. 1921. Mikrochemische Untersuchung einiger gezüchteter Orchideae auf Alkaloide und Gerbstoffe. Ber. Dtsch. Pharm. Ges. 31:179–183.

White, J. C. 1887. Dermatitis venenata. Cupples & Hurd, Boston.

——. 1893. Poisoning by vanilla. Boston Med. Surg. J. 79:440–441.

Wildeman, E. de. 1892. Présence et localisation d'un alcaloide dans quelques Orchidées. Bull. Soc. Belg. Microscop. 18:101–108.

Williams, C. A. 1979. The leaf flavonoids of the Orchidaceae. Phytochem. 18:803–813.

Willmot, F. C., and G. W. Robertson. 1920. Senecio disease or cirrhosis of the liver due to Senecio poisoning. Lancet 2:848–849.

Windholz, M., S. Budavari, L. Y. Straumtsos, and M. N. Fertig (eds.). 1976. The Merck Index. 9th ed. Merck, Rahway, N.J.

Wrigley, T. C. 1960. Ayapin, Scopoletin, and 6,7-dimethoxy-coumarin from *Dendrobium thyrsiflorum*. Nature 188:1108.

Zündel, W. 1936. Erfahrungen mit Hautfunktionsprüfungen an 2000 Patienten. Arch. Derm. (Berlin) 173:435–472.

SYSTEMATICS

7

A Reassessment of the Sectional Limits in the Genus *Cymbidium* Swartz*

CHRISTOPHER J. SETH and PHILLIP J. CRIBB†

*The literature survey pertaining to this chapter was concluded in December 1981. The chapter was submitted in January 1982, and the revised version was received in March 1982.

†The help of P. Taylor and J. Wood of the Royal Botanic Gardens, Kew, and of Dr. G. Seidenfaden of Borsholmgard, Denmark, is gratefully acknowledged.

Introduction

The genus *Cymbidium* is one of the most important orchid genera horticulturally, yet no attempt has been made to revise or monograph it in this century. The accounts that do exist are of a regional nature, limited mostly to works by J. J. Smith (1905), Holttum (1964), Seidenfaden and Smitinand (1961), Pradhan (1979), Lin (1977), and Wu and Chen (1980). Nearly all recent accounts of *Cymbidium* in the Indian subcontinent are based on work by J. D. Hooker (1890) and King and Pantling (1898).

R. Schlechter (1924) revised the sectional limits of *Cymbidium* and chose to place in the genus *Cyperorchis* Bl. all species that have a slender column, a distinct pollinial shape, and a lip that is united at its base to the sides of the column. P. F. Hunt (1970), however, rejected this separation because he considered the differences to be insufficient and far from clear-cut enough to distinguish *Cyperorchis* from *Cymbidium*. Furthermore, he decided that the presence of four pollinia rather than two in many *Cymbidium* species was as distinguishing a characteristic as those Schlechter recognized. Hunt amended the sectional nomenclature in light of this conclusion (Table 7-1).

In this study, the infrageneric classification of the genus has been reconsidered. An attempt has also been made to collate all the information on synonymy published since Schlechter's account. Whenever possible, types have also been cited. A total of 53 groups of *Cymbidium* are considered in this chapter. Abbreviations for herbaria and other abbreviations are given at the end of the chapter.

Taxonomy

Cymbidium *Sw.* in Nov. Acta Soc. Sci. Upps. 6:70 (1799); Schltr. in Fedde, Repert. 20:96 (1924); Hunt, P. F. in Kew Bull. 24:93 (1970).
Jensoa Raf., Fl. Tellur. 6:38 (1836)
Cyperorchis Bl. in Rumphia 4:47 (1848)
Iridorchis Bl., Orch. Arch. Ind. 90, t. 26 (1858)
Arethusanthe Finet in Bull. Soc. Bot. Fr. 44:179 (1897).

The genus comprises perennial epiphytic, lithophytic, or terrestrial herbs, which have vegetative buds developing from the base of the previous growth. Pseudobulbs are ovoid or spindle-shaped, often hidden by overlapping leaf bases. Roots are thick, spongy, elongate, and branching and arise from the base of new growth. Leaves, if present, are few to numerous, distichous, thick, rigid, and fleshy or leathery, usually long and narrow or occasionally lanceolate, and are articulated near the base. Inflorescence racemose, densely or laxly flowered, arising from near the base of the current and rarely from the previous year's growth. The peduncle is erect, arching, or pendent and is often enclosed at the base by large, leafy bracts. Flowers are often large, showy, and fragrant. Sepals and petals are free and subsimilar and spread or converge above. The lip has three lobes, that are free or attached at the base to the sides of the column; the callus is of two or

Table 7-1. A comparison of the major subdivisions of the genus *Cymbidium*

Schlechter (1924) sections	P. F. Hunt (1970) sections	Proposed in this study
Cymbidium Sw.	*Cymbidium* Sw.	*Cymbidium* subgen. *Jensoa*
Macrorhizon	Macrorhizon	Pachyrhizanthe
Geocymbidium	Geocymbidium	Geocymbidium
Maxillarianthe	Maxillarianthe	Maxillarianthe
Jensoa	Jensoa	Jensoa
		Cymbidium subgen. *Cymbidium*
Himantophyllum	Himantophyllum	Himantophyllum
Eucymbidium	Cymbidium	Cymbidium
		Suavissimum
		Floribundum
Austrocymbidium	Austrocymbidium	Austrocymbidium
Bigibbarium	Bigibbarium	Bigibbarium
Cyperorchis Bl.		*Cymbidium* subgen. *Cyperorchis*
Eucyperorchis	Cyperorchis	Cyperorchis
Iridorchis	Iridorchis	Iridorchis
		Eburnea
Annamaea	Annamaea	Annamaea
Parishiella	Parishiella	Parishiella

rarely three, usually prominent keels, sometimes hairy, parallel, or converging above. The column is slightly or strongly curved, weakly to strongly winged, and is concave on the ventral surface. There are either two unequally lobed pollinia or four pollinia that are transversely ovoid, obovoid, or quadrangular and somewhat compressed. They are usually more or less sessile and are attached to the rostellum by a common stipe.

Major revisions of the sectional limits in the genus have been undertaken by Schlechter (1924) and Hunt (1970). The relationship between the sections proposed by these authors and those suggested here differ in some respects (Tables 7-1 and 7-2).

Table 7-2. The subdivision of *Cymbidium*

Subgenus	Sections	Characteristic flower shape	Number of pollinia	Attachment of the lip	Pollinia shape and orientation
Jensoa	Pachyrhizanthe Geocymbidium Maxillarianthe Jensoa		Four in two pairs	At the base of the column, hinged, free to move	(side view)
Cymbidium	Himantophyllum Cymbidium Suavissimum Floribundum		Two each, with two usually unequal lobes		
	Austrocymbidium		(cross section seen from above)		

(continued)

Table 7-2. Continued

Subgenus	Sections	Characteristic flower shape	Number of pollinia	Attachment of the lip	Pollinia shape and orientation
	Bigibbarium				
Cyperorchis	Iridorchis Parishiella			Lower part of the lip attached to the sides of the column, fixed, not free to move	
	Annamaea				
	Cyperorchis Eburnea				

Key to the Subgenera of *Cymbidium*

1. Pollinia 4, in unequal pairs; lip with a callus in which the keels meet at the apex to form a short tube . . . . subgen. **Jensoa**
   Pollinia 2, each unequally lobed 2
2. Lip attached to base of column or column-foot, hinged and free from column margins at base . . . . subgen. **Cymbidium**
   Lip united at its base to the base and sides of the column, fixed and not free to move easily . . . . subgen. **Cyperorchis**

Subgen. **Jensoa** *Seth & Cribb* comb. & stat. nov.

Jensoa Raf., Fl. Tellur. 6:38 (1835). Type: *C. ensifolium* (Sw.) Lindl.

   Although the species of this subgenus show the most interesting range of vegetative variation and shape and size of their tepals, two features of their floral morphology are particularly distinctive. The anther contains four pollinia of two unequal pairs, and the apices of the two keels meet on the lip to form a short tube.

Key to Sections in Subgenus *Jensoa*

1. Plants saprophytic, lacking chlorophyll; leaves scalelike . . . . sect. **Pachyrhizanthe**
   Plants autotrophic; leaves properly developed 2
2. Leaves lanceolate, petiolate (except in *C. caulescens*); pseudobulbs fusiform . . . .
   . . . . sect. **Geocymbidium**
   Leaves linear, not petiolate; pseudobulbs linear 3

3. Inflorescences 1- or rarely 2-flowered .... sect. **Maxillarianthe**
   Inflorescences 3- to many-flowered .... sect. **Jensoa**

A. sect. **Pachyrhizanthe** *Schltr.* in Fedde, Repert. Beih. 4:73 (1919). Lectotype: *C. aberrans* (Finet) Schltr.

C. sect. *Macrorhizon* Schltr. in Fedde, Repert. 20:101 (1924); P. F. Hunt in Kew Bull. 24:94 (1970). Type: *C. macrorhizon* Lindl. *Synon. nov.*

Plants are saprophytic and lack normal leaves. Although several saprophytic species of *Cymbidium* have been described, all are apparently assignable to one species, *C. macrorhizon* (Seidenfaden, personal communication).

1. **C. macrorhizon** *Lindl.,* Gen. Spec. Orch. 162 (1833); Hook. f. Fl. Brit. India 6:9 (1890); Duthie in Ann. Roy. Bot. Garden Calcutta 9:134, t. 114 (1906); Seidenfaden & Smitinand, Orch. Thailand 3:501, t. 370 (1961); Pradhan, Indian Orchids 2:470 (1979). Type: Kashmir, *Royle* s.n. (holo. K).

Bletia nipponica Franch. & Sav., Enum. Pl. Japon. 2:511 (1879). Type: Japan, *Savatier* (holo. P).

Cymbidium nipponicum (Franch. & Sav.) Rolfe in Orch. Rev. 3:39 (1895); Garay & Sweet, Orch. S. Ryukyu Isls. 142 not t. 17 a, b (1974).

C. pedicellatum Finet in Bull. Soc. Bot. France 47:268, t. 9A (1900). Type: Japan, *Savatier* (holo. P).

Yoania aberrans Finet in Bull. Soc. Bot. France 47:274, t. 9 (1900). Type: not cited, but holo. probably at P.

Aphyllorchis aberrans (Finet) Schltr. in Engl. Bot. Jahrb. 45:387 (1911).

Cymbidium aberrans (Finet) Schltr. in Fedde, Repert. Beih. 4:264 (1919).

C. aphyllum Ames & Schltr. in Fedde, Repert. Beih. 4:73 (1919) *non* (Roxb.) Sw. Type: Szechuan, *Wilson* 4714 (holo. AMES).

C. szechuanensis S. Y. Hu in Quart. J. Taiwan Mus. 26:140 (1973). Type: as for *C. aphyllum* Ames & Schltr.

DISTRIBUTION: Northern India, Thailand, Indochina, China, Japan, and the Ryukyu Islands.

B. sect. **Geocymbidium** *Schltr.* in Fedde, Repert. 20:101 (1924); P. F. Hunt in Kew Bull. 24:94 (1970). Type: *C. lancifolium* Hook.

This section contains a small number of species that for the most part have stalked, lanceolate leaves. The most widely distributed of these species is *C. lancifolium*. Plants of this species recently introduced from Papua New Guinea have been mistakenly referred to *C. papuanum* Schltr.

2. **C. caulescens** *Ridley* in J. Fed. States Mus. 5:167 (1915); Seidenfaden & Smitinand, Orch. Thailand 3:501, t. 371 (1961). Type: Malaya, *Robinson* (holo. SING; iso. K!)

DISTRIBUTION: Malaya.

3. **C. lancifolium** *Hook.,* Exotic Fl. 1: t. 51 (1823); Loddiges, Bot. Cab. 10: t. 927 (1824); Lindl., Gen. Spec. Orch. 164 (1833); Hook. f., Fl. Brit. India 6:9 (1890); King &

Pantling in Ann. Roy. Bot. Garden Calcutta 8: 185, t. 247 (1898); J. J. Smith, Orch. Java 6:476 (1905); Schltr. in Fedde, Repert. Beih. 4:269 (1919); Seidenfaden & Smitinand, Orch. Thailand 3:512 (1961); Holttum, Orch. Malaya, ed. 3, 518 (1964); Garay & Sweet, Orch. S. Ryukyu Isls. 143 (1974); Lin, Nat. Orch. Taiwan 2:119 (1977) excl. syn. *C. syunitianum* Fuk. Type: Nepal, *Wallich* (holo K!).

C. cuspidatum Bl., Bijdr. 8:379 (1825). Type: Java, *Blume* (holo. L.)

C. javanicum Bl., Bijdr. 8:380 (1825). Type: Java, *Blume* (holo. L.)

G. gibsonii Lindl. in Paxton's Fl. Gard. 3:144, t. 301 (1857). Type: India, *Gibson* (holo. K.)

C. kerrii Rolfe ex Downie in Kew Bull.:381 (1925). Type: Thailand, *Kerr* 227 (holo. K.).

C. nagifolium Masamune in Bot. Mag. Tokyo 44 (250):220 (1930) Type: Yakusima, *Masamune* (holo. ? TI).

C. aspidistrifolium Fuk. in Bot. Mag. Tokyo 48 (571):438, t. 2 and 3 (1934); S. Y. Hu in Quart. J. Taiwan Mus. 26:134 (1973). Type: Taiwan, *Fukuyama* 4137 (holo. herb. Fukuyama).

DISTRIBUTION: Northeastern India, Nepal, Burma, Thailand, Indochina, Malaysia, Sumatra, Java, Papua New Guinea, China, Taiwan, Japan, and the Ryukyu Islands.

Wu and Chen (1980) consider the leaf margins, flower color, and flowering time of *C. lancifolium* (including *C. nagifolium*) as distinguishing it from *C. javanicum* (including all the other synonyms).

On the type sheet in Lindley's herbarium, however, one leaf has a serrate margin and the others entire ones. No discernible pattern could be seen in the other specimens in the Kew herbarium and, thus, for now, *C. lancifolium* is treated as one rather variable species needing further study.

4. **C. maclehoseae** *S. Y. Hu* in Chung Chi J. 11:15 (1972). Type: Hong Kong, *Hu* 9369 (holo. AMES).

DISTRIBUTION: Hong Kong.

5. **C. papuanum** *Schltr.* in Fedde, Repert. Beih. 1:952 (1913). Type: New Guinea, *Schlechter* 18680 (holo. B †).

DISTRIBUTION: New Guinea.

NOTE: The species type has been destroyed. Its identity, therefore, remains a mystery.

6. **C. syunitianum** *Fuk.* in Bot. Mag. Tokyo 49:757 (1935). Type: Taiwan, *Sasaki* 4688 (holo. herb. Fukuyama).

DISTRIBUTION: Taiwan.

C. sect. **Maxillarianthe** *Schltr.* in Fedde, Repert. 20:101 (1924); P. F. Hunt in Kew Bull. 24:94 (1970). Type: *C. goeringii* (Rchb. f.) Rchb. f.

Species of this section are terrestrial with ovoid pseudobulbs, long and narrow leaves, and one- or sometimes two-flowered inflorescences.

7. **C. goeringii** (*Rchb. f.*) *Rchb. f.* in Walp. Ann. 3:547 (1852); Garay & Sweet, Orch. S. Ryukyu Isls. 143 (1974); Wu & Chen in Act. Phyt. Sinica 18:299 (1980). Type: Japan, *Goering* 592 (holo. W).

Maxillaria goeringii Rchb. f. in Bot. Zeit. 3:334 (1845).

Cymbidium virescens Lindl. in Bot. Reg. misc. 37 (1838); Schltr. in Fedde, Repert. Beih. 4:272 (1919), *non* Willd. (1805). Type: Japan, hort. Rollissons ex *Siebold* (holo. K).

C. virens Lindl. in Walp. Ann. 6:626 (1861) *sphalm.* for *C. virescens*.

C. formosanum Hay., in J. Coll. Sc. Univ. Tokyo 30:335 (1911); Schltr. in Fedde, Repert. Beih. 4:267 (1919); Lin, Nat. Orch. Taiwan 2:112 (1977). Type: Taiwan, *Nakahara* (holo. TI).

C. forrestii Rolfe ex Downie in Notes Roy. Bot. Garden Edinb. 8:23 (1913); Schltr. in Fedde, Repert. Beih. 4:267 (1919). Type: China, *Forrest* 415 (holo. K).

C. serratum Schltr. in Fedde, Repert. Beih. 4:73 (1919). Type: China, *Esquirol* (holo. B †; copy of holo. K).

C. yunnanense Schltr. in Fedde, Repert. Beih. 4:273 (1919). Type: China, *Maire* 6425 (holo. B †).

C. pseudovirens Schltr. in Fedde, Repert. Beih. 12:351 (1922). Type: China, *Limpricht* 304 (holo. B †).

C. tortisepalum Fuk. in Bot. Mag. Tokyo 48:304, t. 1 (1931); Liu & Su in Fl. Taiwan 5:948 (1978). Type: Taiwan, *Fukuyama* 3983 (holo. herb. Fuk.).

C. gracillimum Fuk. in Trans. Nat. Hist. Soc. Formosa 22:413 (1932). Type: Taiwan, *Fukuyama* 3220 (holo. herb. Fukuyama).

C. uniflorum Yen. Icon. Cymb. Amoy. A-Z (1964). Type: publication not seen.

C. longibracteatum Wu & Chen in Act. Phytotax. Sin. 11:31 (1966). Type: China, *Y. L. Fee* 2064 (holo. PE).

C. tortisepalum var. *viridiflorum* Ying, Coll. Illn. Ind. Orch. Taiwan 415 (1977).

C. formosanum Hay. var. *gracillimum* (Fuk.) Liu & Su in Fl. Taiwan 5:943 (1978).

C. goeringii var. *serratum* (Schltr.) Wu & Chen in Acta Phytotax. Sin. 18:300 (1980).

C. goeringii var. *longibracteatum* (Wu & Chen) Wu & Chen in Acta Phytotax. Sin. 18:300.

C. goeringii var. *tortisepalum* (Fuk.) Wu & Chen in Acta Phytotax. Sin. 18:300.

DISTRIBUTION: China, Korea, the Ryukyu Islands, and Japan.

NOTE: The synonymy above is taken largely from the account of Chinese *Cymbidium* species by Wu and Chen (1980). They accept that the three varieties listed above at the end of the synonymy occur in China, in addition to the typical one.

8. **C. mackinnoni** *Duthie* in J. As. Soc. Bengal 71:40 (1902) and in Ann. Roy. Bot. Garden Calcutta 9:135, t. 115 (1906). Type: India, *Mackinnon* 22709 (holo. CAL; iso. K).

D. sect. **Jensoa** (*Raf.*) *Schltr.* in Fedde, Repert. 20:102 (1924); P. F. Hunt in Kew Bull. 24:94 (1970). Type: *C. ensifolium* (L.) Sw.

Species of this section are closely related to the species in the previous section. These species have few- to many-flowered inflorescences, however. Indeed, Wu and Chen

(1980) have united these sections under section *Maxillarianthe*. The one-flowered habit is quite distinctive, however, and although we realize their close affinity, we prefer to follow Hunt (1970) and distinguish them.

9. **C. aliciae** *Quisumbing* in Philipp. J. Sci. 72(4):486 (1940) and in Orch. J. 3:63, t. 28 (1954). Type: Philippines, Luzon, *Quisumbing* (holo. PNH)

DISTRIBUTION: The Philippines.

10. **C. cyperifolium** *Wall.* ex *Lindl.*, Gen. Spec. Orch. 163 (1833); Hook. f. in Fl. Brit. India 6:13 (1890); King & Pantling in Ann. Roy. Bot. Garden Calcutta 8:186, t. 248 (1898); Duthie in Ann. Roy. Bot. Garden Calcutta 9:135 (1906); Seidenfaden & Smitinand, Orch. Thailand 3:508 (1961). Type: India, Sylhet, *Wallich* 7353 (holo. K!).
C. haematodes Lindl., Gen. Spec. Orch. 162 (1833). Type: Sri Lanka, *Macrae* 12 (holo. K!).
C. viridiflorum Griff., Itin. Notes 126 (1848). Type: India, *Griffith* 5264 (holo. K!).

DISTRIBUTION: Northern India, Sikkim, Sri Lanka, Burma, Thailand, and China.

11. **C. ensifolium** *(L.) Sw.* in Nov. Act. Soc. Upsal. 6:77 (1799). Lindl., Gen. Spec. Orch. 162 (1833); Rchb. f. in Walp., Ann. Bot. 6:622 (1864); Hook. f., Fl. Brit. India 6:13 (1890); Schltr. in Fedde, Repert. Beih. 4:266 (1919); Seidenfaden & Smitinand, Orch. Thailand 3:511 (1961); Holttum, Orch. Malaya, ed. 3, 523, t. 152 (1964); Garay & Sweet, Orch. S. Ryukyu Isls. 145 (1974). Type: China, *Osbeck* (holo. ? LINN) (Plate 7-1).
Epidendrum ensifolium L., Sp. Plant., ed. 1, 954 (1753).
Limodorum ensatum Thunb., Fl. Japon. 29 (1784). Type: based on same type as *E. ensifolium* L.
C. xiphiifolium Lindl. in Bot. Reg. 7: t. 529 (1821). Type: China, *Hume* (holo. K).
C. ensifolium var. *estriatum* Lindl. in Bot. Reg. 23: t. 1976 (1837). Type: cult. Hort. Soc. London (holo. K).
C. ensifolium var. *striatum* Lindl. in Bot. Reg. 23: t. 1976 (1837). Type: China or Japan, *Fothergill* (holo. K).
C. estriatum (Lindl.) Steud., Nom. Bot. 2:460 (1840).
C. micans Schauer in Nov. Act. Nat. Cur. 19, suppl. 1:433 (1843). Type: China, Kwang-tung, *Meyen* (holo. K).
C. munronianum King & Pantling in J. As. Soc. Bengal 64:338 (1895). Type: Sikkim, *Pantling* 256 (holo. CAL; iso. K).
C. gyokuchin Mak. in Iinuma, Somoku-Dzusetsu, ed. 3, 4:1181 (1912). Type: not cited, but probably in MAK or TI.
C. shimaran Mak. in Iinuma, Somoku-Dzusetsu, ed. 3, 4: 1183 (1912). Type: as above.
C. yakibaran Mak. in Iinuma, Somoku-Dzusetsu, ed. 3, 4:1182 (1912). Type: as above.
C. yakibaran var. *albomarginatum* in Iinuma, Somoku-Dzusetsu, ed. 3, 4:1182 (1912). Type: as above.
C. yakibaran var. *niveo-marginatum* Mak. in Iinuma, Somoku-Dzusetsu, ed. 3, 4:1182 (1912). Type: as above.
C. arrogans Hay., Icon. Pl. Formos. 4:76 (1914). Type: Taiwan, *Hayata & Sasaki* (holo. ? TAI).

C. misericors Hay. Icon. Pl. Formos. 4:79 (1914). Type: Taiwan, *Hayata & Soma* (holo. ? TAI).

C. rubigemmum Hay., Icon. Pl. Formos. 6:81 (1916). Type: Taiwan, *Soma* (holo. ? TAI).

C. sundaicum Schltr. in Fedde, Repert. Beih. 4:266 (1919). Type: Java, *J. J. Smith* (cited in J. J. Smith, Orch. Java 478 [1905]).

C. ensifolium var. *munronianum* (King & Pantling) Tang & Wang in Acta Phytotax. Sin. 1:91 (1951).

C. kanran var. *misericors* (Hay.) Ying, Coll. Illn. Ind. Orch. Taiwan: 440 (1977).

C. ensifolium var. *rubigemmum* (Hay.) Liu & Su in Fl. Taiwan 5:940 (1978).

C. ensifolium var. *misericors* (Hay.) Liu & Su in Fl. Taiwan 5:942 (1978).

C. ensifolium var. *yakibaran* (Mak.) Wu & Chen in Acta Phytotax. Sin. 18:296 (1980).

C. ensifolium var. *susin* Yen, Icon. Cymb. Amoy. D-b 1 (1964). Type: publication not seen.

DISTRIBUTION: Northern India, Sikkim, Thailand, Indochina, (?) Malaya, Sumatra, Java, Borneo, New Guinea, China, Hong Kong, Taiwan, the Ryukyu Islands, and Japan.

NOTE: The above is taken largely from Wu and Chen (1980), who recognize the two varieties listed at the end of the synonymy as distinct from the typical variety.

12. **C. faberi** *Rolfe* in Kew Bull. :198 (1896); Schltr. in Fedde, Repert. Beih. 4:266 (1919); Liu, Native Orchids of Taiwan 2:109 (1977). Type: China, Chekiang, *Faber* (holo. K).

C. scabroserrulatum Mak. in Bot. Mag. Tokyo 16:154 (1902). Type: Taiwan, *Makino* (holo. herb. MAK or TI).

C. oiwakensis Hay., Icon. Pl. Formos. 6:80 (1916); Schltr. in Fedde, Repert. Beih. 4:270 (1919). Type: Taiwan, *Hayata* (holo. TAI).

C. cerinum Schltr. in Fedde, Repert. Beih. 12:350 (1922). Type: China, Szechuan, *Limpricht* 1392 (holo. B †).

C. fukienense Yen, Icon. Cymb. Amoy. A-1 (1964). Type: publication not seen.

C. szechuanicum Wu & Chen in Acta Phytotax. Sin. 11:33 (1966). Type: China, Szechuan, *Wu* 2040 (holo. PE).

C. omeiense Wu & Chen in Acta Phytotax. Sin. 32 (1966). Type: China, Mt. Omei, *Y. L. Fee* 2099 (holo. PE).

C. faberi var. *szechuanicum* (Wu & Chen) Wu & Chen in Acta Phytotax. Sin. 18:299 (1980).

C. faberi var. *omeiense* (Wu & Chen) Wu and Chen in Acta Phytotax 299 (1980).

The last two varieties are treated as distinct from the typical variety recognized by Wu and Chen (1980).

DISTRIBUTION: China and Taiwan.

13. **C. gonzalesii** *Quisumbing* in Philipp. J. Sci. 72:485 (1940). Type: Philippines, Luzon, *Quisumbing* 5783E (holo. PNH).

DISTRIBUTION: Philippines.

NOTE: This species may prove to be conspecific with *C. ensifolium.*

14. **C. kanran** *Mak.* in Bot. Mag. Tokyo 16:10 (1902) and in Iinuma, Somoku-Dzusetzu, ed. 3, 4:1056; 1180 (1912); Schltr. in Fedde, Repert. Beih. 4:269 (1919); Garay & Sweet, Orch. S. Ryukyu Isls. 144 (1974); Lin, Native Orch. Taiwan 2:116 (1977). Type: Taiwan, *Makino* (holo. probably in MAK or TI).

C. kanran var. *latifolium* Mak. in Iinuma, Somoku-Dzusetzu, ed. 3, 4:5, t. 5 (1912). Type: not cited, but probably in MAK or TI.

C. oreophilum Hay., Icon. Pl. Formos. 4:80, t. 38c (1914). Type: Taiwan, *Hayata* (holo. ? TAI).

C. misericors var. *oreophilum* Hay., Icon. Pl. Formos. 81 (1914). Type: Taiwan, *Hayata* (holo. ? TAI).

C. purpureo-hiemale Hay. Icon. Pl. Formos. 81 (1914). Type: Taiwan, *Hayata* (holo. ? TAI).

C. linearisepalum Yam. in Trans. Nat. Hist. Soc. Formos. 20:40 (1930). Type: Taiwan; publication not seen but probably holo. TAI.

C. linearisepalum forma *atropurpureum* Yam., Suppl. Icon. Pl. Formos. 5:12 (1932). Type: Taiwan, *Takashi Noya* A (holo. TAI).

C. linearisepalum forma *atrovirens* Yam., Suppl. Icon. Pl. Formos. 5:12 (1932). Type: Taiwan, *Takashi Noya* B (holo. TAI).

C. linearisepalum var. *atropurpureum* (Yam.) Masamune in Trop. Hort. 3:30 (1933).

C. linearisepalum var. *atrovirens* (Yam.) Masamune in Trop. Hort. 3:30 (1933).

C. sinokanran Yen, Icon. Cymb. Amoy. G-I (1964). Type: publication not seen.

C. sinokanran var. *atropurpureum* (Yam.) Yen, Icon. Cymb. Amoy. G-2 (1964). Type: publication not seen.

C. kanran var. *purpureohiemale* (Hay.) Ying, Coll. Illn. Ind. Orch. Taiwan 440 (1977).

DISTRIBUTION: China, Japan, Taiwan, and the Ryukyu Islands.

NOTE: The synonymy above follows that given by Wu and Chen (1980).

15. **C. koran** *Mak.* in Iinuma, Somoku-Dzusetzu, ed. 3, 4:1055; 1179 (1912). Type: holo. not cited, but probably in MAK or TI.

DISTRIBUTION: Japan.

16. **C. poilanei** *Gagn.* in Bull. Mus. Hist. Nat. Paris, series 2, 3:681 (1931). Type: Kampuchea *Poilane* 316 (holo. P).

DISTRIBUTION: Indochina.

17. **C. siamense** *Rolfe* ex *Downie* in Kew Bull. 382 (1925); Seidenfaden & Smitinand, Orch. Thailand 3:509 (1961). Type: Thailand, *Kerr* 242 (holo. K).

DISTRIBUTION: Thailand.

18. **C. sinense** (*Andr.*) *Willd.,* Sp. Plant., ed. 4:111 (1805); Lindl., Gen. Spec. Orch. 162 (1833); Hayata, Icon. Pl. Formos. 83 (1914); Schltr. in Fedde, Repert. Beih. 4:272 (1919); Garay & Sweet, Orch. S. Ryukyu Isls. 146 (1974); Liu, Native Orch. Taiwan 2:126 (1977); Wu & Chen in Acta Phytotax. Sin. 18:297 (1980) (Plate 7-2).

Epidendrum sinense Andr., Bot. Rep. 3: t. 216 (1802). Type: China, cult. *Hibbert* (lecto. plate cited above).

Cymbidium fragrans Salisb. in Trans. Hort. Soc. London 1:298 (1812). Type: based on *E. sinense* above.

C. chinense Heynh., Nom. Bot. 2:179 (1840). Sphalm. for *C. sinense.*

C. hoosai Mak. in Bot. Mag. Tokyo 16:23 (1902). Type: Taiwan, *Masamune* (holo. ? TI or MAK).

C. albojucundissimum Hay., Icon. Pl. Formos. 4:74 (1914). Type: Taiwan, *Hayata* (holo. ? TAI).

C. sinense var. *margicoloratum* Hay., Icon. Pl. Formos. 6:82 (1916). Type: publication not seen.

C. sinense forma *margicoloratum* (Hay.) Fuk. in Masamune, Short Fl. Formos. 287 (1936).

C. sinense forma *albojucundissimum* (Hay.) Fuk. in Trans. Nat. Hist. Soc. Formos. 22:415 (1932).

C. sinense var. *albojucundissimum* (Hay.) Masamune in Trop. Hort. 3:31 (1933).

C. sinense var. *bellum* Yen, Icon. Cymb. Amoy. E-a. 1. (1964). Type: publication not seen.

C. sinense var. *album* Yen, Icon. Cymb. Amoy. F-a 1. (1964). Type: publication not seen.

DISTRIBUTION: Northern India, Sri Lanka, China, Hong Kong, Taiwan, and the Ryukyu Islands.

19. **C. tosyaense** *Masamune* in Trans. Nat. Hist. Soc. Formosa 25:14 (1935). Type: Taiwan, *Masamune* (holo. ? TAI).

DISTRIBUTION: Taiwan.

subgen. **Cymbidium.** Type: *C. aloifolium* (L.) Sw.

This typical subgenus consists of six sections, two of which are newly established here. The subgenus contains predominantly epiphytic species distinguished by their two usually deeply and unequally bilobed, transversely ovoid, compressed pollinia attached by a short stipe to the rostellum. The lip is hinged to the base of the column or, in section *Bigibbarium*, to a short column-foot, and the ligulate or lanceolate sepals and petals usually spread, in rare instances forming a hood over the column.

Key to Sections in Subgenus *Cymbidium*

1. Leaves linear or ligulate; not noticeably stalked, column lacking a foot 2
   Leaves broadly lanceolate, stalked; column with a short but obvious foot . . . . sect.
   Bigibbarium
2. Pollinia transversely ovoid; petals lanceolate to linear-lanceolate 3
   Pollinia more or less upright, ovoid; petals oblong-ovate, ovate, or narrowly obovate
   . . . . sect. **Austrocymbidium**

3. Petals more or less porrect, forming a hood over the column 4
   Petals spreading, do not form a hood over the column 5
4. Scape pendulous; sepals and petals acute . . . . sect. **Himantophyllum**
   Scape erect; sepals and petals obtuse or rounded at apex . . . . sect. **Floribundum**
5. Leaves ligulate, thick, and fleshy, rigid; scapes arcuate or pendulous sect. **Cymbidium**
   Leaves linear-lanceolate, leathery but not rigid; scapes erect . . . . sect. **Suavissimum**

E. sect. **Cymbidium**. P. F. Hunt in Kew Bull. 24:94 (1970). Type: *C. aloifolium* (L.) Sw.
A section of four widely distributed, rather variable, and often confused species distinguished by their thick, rigid, fleshy, ligulate leaves and arching or pendulous scapes. A fuller account of this group is given by Seth (Kew Bull., in press)

20. **C. aloifolium** (*L.*) *Sw.* in Nov. Act. Soc. Sci. Ups. 6:73 (1799); Salisbury in Trans. Hort. Soc. London 1:298 (1812); Loddiges, Bot. Cab. 10: t. 967 (1824); Lindl., Gen. Spec. Orch. 165 (1833), and in J. Linn. Soc. Bot. 3:27 (1859); Rchb. f. in Walpers, Ann. Bot. 6:624 (1864); Hook. f., Fl. Brit. Ind. 6:8 (1890); King & Pantling in Ann. Roy. Bot. Garden Calcutta 8:189, t. 252 (1898); J. J. Smith, Orch. Java 6:482 (1905); Duthie in Ann. Roy. Bot. Garden Calcutta 9:136 (1906); Hayata, Icon. Pl. Formos. 4:74, t. 37 (1914). Lectotype: Illustration in Rheede, Hort. Malab. t. 8 (1703).

Epidendrum aloifolium L., Sp. Plantarum, ed. 1:953 (1753).

E. pendulum Roxb., Pl. Coast Coromandel 1:35, t. 44 (1795). Lectotype: illustration cited above.

E. aloides Curtis, Bot. Mag. 11: t. 387 (1797), sphalm. for *E. aloifolium*.

Cymbidium pendulum (L.) Sw., Nov. Act. Soc. Sci. Ups. 6:73 (1799); Veitch, Man. Orch. Pl. 2:21 (1894) *pro parte;* Cogn. & Goos., Dict. Icon. Orch. Cymbid. t. 6 (1899); Schltr. in Fedde, Repert. Beih. 4:271 (1919) & 20:104 (1924).

Aerides borassii Buch. Ham. ex J. E. Smith in Rees, Cyclop. 39: Addend. Aerides 8: (1819). Type: India, Mysore, *Buchanan-Hamilton* (holo., BM).

C. wallichii Lindl., Gen. Spec. Orch. 165 (1833). Type: Attran River, *Wallich* 7352 (lecto. K).

C. erectum Wight, Ic. Pl. Ind. Or. 5:21, t. 1753 (1852); Rchb. f. in Walpers, Ann. Bot. 6:623 (1864). Type: India, *Wight* (holo. K!).

C. simulans Rolfe in Orch. Rev. 25:175 (1917); Seidenfaden & Smitinand, Orch. Thailand 1:508 (1961); Holttum, Orch. Malaya, ed. 3:623 (1964); Backer & Bakhuisen, Fl. Java 3:395 (1968). Type: Sikkim, *Pantling* 268 (lecto. K).

C. intermedium H. G. Jones in Reinwardtia 9:71 (1974). Type: India, Bombay, cult. *Jones* C/85 (holo. herb. Jones).

DISTRIBUTION: Sri Lanka, India, Sikkim, southern China, Hong Kong, Burma, Thailand, Malaya, Andaman Islands, Sumatra, Java, Borneo, and Taiwan.

21. **C. atropurpureum** (*Lindl.*) Rolfe in Orch. Rev. 11:190 (1903); Quisumbing in Orch. J. 3:63 (1954); Holttum, Orch. Malaya, ed. 3:520, t. 151 (1964); Backer & Bakhuisen, Fl. Java 3:396 (1968). Type: ? Java, hort. *Rollissons* (holo. K!).

C. pendulum (L.) Sw. var. *atropurpureum* Hook. f. in Bot. Mag. 94: t. 5710 (1865).

C. pendulum sensu Vidal, Phan. Cunn. Phil. 150 (1885) *non* Sw.

C. finlaysonianum Wall. ex Lindl. var. *atropurpureum* (Hook. f.) Veitch. Man. Orch. Pl. 2:16 (1894).

DISTRIBUTION: Malaya, Sumatra, Java, Borneo and the Philippines.

22. **C. bicolor** *Lindl.*, Gen. Spec. Orch. 164 (1833) and Bot. Reg. 25:46, misc. 69 (1839); Rchb. f. in Walpers, Ann. Bot. 6:625 (1864); Hook. f., Fl. Brit. India 6:11 (1890) *excl. syn.* Type: Sri Lanka, *Macrae* 54 (holo. K!).
Cymbidium aloefolium sensu Bl., Bijdr. 378 (1825) *non* (L.) Sw.
C. pubescens Lindl. in Bot. Reg. 26: misc. 75 (1840) and 27: t. 38 (1841); Hook. f., Fl. Brit. Ind. 6:11 (1890); J. J. Smith, Orch. Java 6:483 (1905) and Fig. Atlas t. 368 (1911); Ridley, Fl. Malay. Pen. 4:145 (1924); Ames and Quisumb. in Philipp. J. Sci. 49:491 (1932); Quisumb. in Orch. J. 3:63 (1954); Seidenfaden & Smitinand, Orch. Thailand 1:507 (1961); Holttum, Orch. Malaya, ed. 3:522 (1964); Backer and Bakhuizen, Fl. Java 3:395 (1968). Type: Singapore, *Cuming* (holo. K!).
C. mannii Reichb. f. in Flora 55:274 (1872). Type: Assam, *Mann* (W, holo.).
C. pendulum sensu Duthie in Ann. Bot. Garden Calcutta 9:136 (1906) *excl. cit. non* (L.) Sw.
C. pulchellum Schltr. in Fedde, Repert. 8:570 (1910). Type: Sarawak, *Schlechter* 15846 (holo. B †).
C. flaccidum Schltr. in Fedde Repert. 12:109 (1913) and in Fedde, Repert. Beih. 4:267 (1919). Type: China, Szechuan, *Esquirol* 2728 (holo. B †).
C. celebicum Schltr. in Fedde, Repert. 21:197 (1925). Type: Sulawesi, Schlechter 20629 (holo. B †).
C. rectum Ridley in J. Roy. As. Soc. Str. Br. 82:198 (1920) and Fl. Malay. Penins. 4:146 (1924). Type: Malaya, *Williams* in *Ridley* 11370 (holo., SING; iso. K!).

DISTRIBUTION: Sri Lanka, India, Sikkim, China, Burma, Andaman Islands, Thailand, Malaya, Sumatra, Java, Borneo, Sulawesi, and the Philippines.

23. **C. finlaysonianum** *Wall.* ex. *Lindl.*, Gen. Spec. Orch. 164 (1833); Hook. f., Fl. Brit. Ind. 6:11 (1980); Veitch, Man. Orch. Pl. 2:16 (1894); J. J. Smith, Orch. Java 6:481 (1905) and Fig. Atlas. t. 366 (1911); Ridley, Fl. Malay. Penins. 4:145 (1924); Schltr. in Fedde, Repert. 21:197 (1925); Quisumb. in Orch. J. 3:63 (1954); Seidenfaden & Smitinand, Orch. Thailand 1:507 (1959); Holttum, Orch. Malay., ed. 3:520, t. 150 (1964); Backer & Bakhuizen, Fl. Java 3:396 (1968). Type: Cochinchina, *Finlayson* in *Wallich* 7358 (holo. K!) (Plate 7-3).
C. pendulum sensu Bl., Bijdr. 379 (1825); sensu Lindl. Gen. & Spec. Orch. 165 (1833) *excl. syn.* and Bot. Reg. 26: t. 25 (1840) *non* (L.) Sw.
C. pendulum (L.) Sw. var. *brevilabre* Lindl. in Bot. Reg. 30: t. 24 (1842). Type: Philippines, hort. Loddiges, *Cuming* (holo. K!).
C. tricolor Miq. in Choix Pl. Buitenz. t. 19 (1864). Type: Java, cult. Buitenzorg (Bogor) Bot. Gard. (holo. U).

DISTRIBUTION: Thailand, Indochina, Malaya, Sumatra, Java, Borneo and the Philippines.

F. sect. **Himantophyllum** *Schltr.* in Fedde, Repert. 20:103 (1924); P. F. Hunt in Kew Bull. 24:94 (1970). Type: *C. dayanum* Rchb. f.

A small section of one or possibly two epiphytic species distinguished by their stiff, leathery, linear leaves and their pendulous scapes and petals, which are shorter than the sepals and form a hood over the column.

24. **C. dayanum** Rchb. f. in Gard. Chron. 710 (1869); Holttum, Orch. Malaya, ed. 3, 519 (1964); Backer & Bakhuizen, Fl. Java 3:395 (1968); Garay & Sweet, Orch. S. Ryukyu Isls. 144 (1974); Lin, Native Orch. Taiwan 2:103 (1977); Wu & Chen in Acta Phytotax. Sin. 18:301 (1980). Type: Assam, cult. *Day* (holo. W.) (Plate 7-4).

C. leachianum Rchb. f. in Gard. Chron. 10:106 (1878). Type: Taiwan, cult. *Leach* ex *Corner* (holo. W).

C. pulcherrimum Sander in Gard. Chron. 1891:712 (1891). Type: India, cult. *Sander* (holo. not located).

C. simonsianum King & Pantling in J. As. Soc. Bengal 64:338 (1895) and in Ann. Roy. Bot. Garden Calcutta 8:188, t. 250 (1898); Hayata, Icon. Pl. Formos. 4:82, t. 39 (1914). Type: Sikkim, *Pantling* 51 (holo. CAL; iso. K).

C. acutum Ridl. in J. Linn. Soc. 32:334 (1896). Type: Malaya, *Elphinstone* (holo. SING; iso. K).

C. alborubens Mak. in Bot. Mag. Tokyo 16:11 (1902). Type: Japan, *Makino* (holo. ? TI or MAK).

C. marginatum Mak. in Iinuma, Somoku-Dzusetzu, ed. 3, 4:1183 (1912). Type: not cited, but holo. probably in TI or MAK.

C. angustifolium Ames & Schweinf. in Ames, Orchid 6:212 (1920). Type: Borneo, Kiau, *Clemens* 74 (holo. AMES).

DISTRIBUTION: Northern India, Sikkim, Thailand, Malaya, Sumatra, Java, Borneo, Sulawesi, Philippines, China, Taiwan, the Ryukyu Islands, and Japan.

25. **C. sutepense** *Rolfe* ex *Downie* in Kew Bull. 382 (1925); Seidenfaden & Smitinand, Orch. Thailand 3:2 (1961). Type: Thailand, *Kerr* 113 (holo. K).

DISTRIBUTION: Thailand.

NOTE: Seidenfaden (personal communication) considers this species conspecific with the previous species.

G. sect. **Suavissimum** *Seth & Cribb* sect. nov. foliis elongatis lineari-lanceolatis coriaceis, scapo erecto, petalis ligulatis sepalis similibus brevioribus distinguendum. Type: *C. suavissimum* Sander ex Curtis.

This section contains only the one species, which is distinguished by its very long linear-lanceolate leaves and its erect inflorescence and ligulate petals, which are much shorter than the similarly shaped sepals.

26. **C. suavissimum** *Sander* ex *Curtis* in Gard. Chron. 84:137; 157, t. 6 (1928); P. Taylor in Curtis's Bot. Mag. 180: n.s. t. 671 (1974). Type: prov. unknown, cult. *Sander* (holo. not located).

DISTRIBUTION: Burma.

H. sect. **Floribundum** *Seth & Cribb* sect. nov. foliis lineari-lanceolatis coriaceis, scapo erecto brevi, sepalis oblongis lanceolatis vel ovatis, petalis supra columnam cucullum facientibus, polliniis ovoideis erectis vel suberectis distinguendum. Type species: *C. floribundum* Lindl.

Another monotypic section based on the horticulturally important species *C. floribundum,* which Schlechter placed in sect. *Jensoa.* It is more similar to the previous three sections, but is distinguished from them by its linear-lanceolate leathery leaves, short, erect scape, petals that are shorter than the sepals and that form a hood over the column, and its ovoid erect or suberect pollinia.

27. **C. floribundum** *Lindl.,* Gen. Spec. Orch. 2 (1833); Schltr. in Fedde, Repert. Beih. 4:267 (1919). Type: illustration at Hort. Soc. London (copy of illustration K).

C. pumilum Rolfe in Kew Bull. 130 (1907); Schltr. in Fedde, Repert. Beih. 4:271 (1919); Lin, Native Orch. Taiwan 2:123 (1977). Type: China, Yunnan, *Manberg* (holo. K).

C. illiberale Hayata, Icon. Pl. Formos. 4:78 (1914); Schltr. in Fedde, Repert. Beih. 4:268 (1919). Type: Taiwan, *Hayata* (holo. TAI).

C. floribundum var. *pumilum* (Rolfe) Wu & Chen in Acta Phytotax. Sin. 18:301 (1980).

DISTRIBUTION: China, Taiwan.

I. Sect. **Austrocymbidium** *Schltr.* in Fedde, Repert. Beih. 20:104 (1924); P. F. Hunt in Kew Bull. 24:94 (1970). Type: *C. canaliculatum* R. Br.

A section of possibly five species, three of which are found only in Australia. They are the only members of the genus to be found there. These three species have been adequately revised by Dockrill (1969).

The species of this section are characterized by their oblong-ovate or narrowly obovate sepals and petals, mobile lip attached at the base of the column, entire or two-ridged callus, and two unequally lobed, ovoid, more or less erect pollinia joined to the rostellum by a short, broad stipe.

C. chloranthum and *C. hartinahianum* have been tentatively included in this section because of the similarity of their floral morphology to that of the Australian species.

28. **C. canaliculatum** *R. Br.,* Prodr. Fl. Nov. Holl. 331 (1810); Lindl., Gen. Spec. Orch. 164 (1833); Dockrill, Austr. Indig. Orch. 1:630 (1969). Type: Australia, *R. Brown* 5530 (holo. BM; iso. K).

C. hillii F. Muell. in Regel, Gartenfl. 138 (1879). Type: Australia, cult. Brisbane Bot. Gard. (holo. MEL).

C. sparkesii Rendle in J. Bot. 36:221 (1898). Type: Australia, *Sparkes* (holo. BM; iso. K).

DISTRIBUTION: Australia.

29. **C. chloranthum** *Lindl.* in Bot. Reg. 29:68 (1843); Holttum, Orch. Malaya, ed. 3, 519 (1964); Backer & Bakhuisen, Fl. Java 3:396 (1968). Type: ? Nepal, cult. *Loddiges* (holo. K).

C. variciferum Rchb. f. in Bonplandia 4:324 (1856). Type: not cited, but holo. probably at W.

C. sanguinolentum Teijm. & Binn. in Tidjdschr. Nederl. Ind. 24:318 (1862); J. J. Smith, Orch. Java 6:480 (1905); Ames, Orchid 6:214 (1920). Type: Java, *Teijm. & Binn.* 902 (holo. BO).

C. sanguineum Teijm. & Binn. in Cat. Hort. Bogor. 51 (1866). Sphalm. for *C. sanguinolentum.*

DISTRIBUTION: Malaya, Sumatra, Java, and Borneo.

30. **C. hartinahianum** *Comber & Nasution* in Bull. Kebun Raya 3:1 (1977). Type: Sumatra, *Nasution & Bukit* 6 (holo. BO).

DISTRIBUTION: Sumatra.

31. **C. madidum** *Lindl.* in Bot. Reg. 26:9 (1840); Dockrill, Austr. Indig. Orch. 1:634 (1969). Type: Australia, cult. *Rollissons* (holo. K) (Plate 7-5).

C. iridifolium A. Cunn. in Lindl. Bot. Reg. 25:34 (1839) *non* Roxb. (= *Oberonia iridifolia*) *non* Sw. (= *Oncidium iridifolium*). Type: Australia, *Cunningham* (holo. K).

C. albuciflorum F. Muell., Frag. 1:188 (1858). Type: Australia, *W. Hill* (holo. MEL).

C. leai Rendle in J. Bot. 36:221 (1898). Type: Australia, *Lea* (holo. BM).

C. queeneanum Klinge in Acta Hort. Petrop. 17:137 (1898). Type: Australia, *Persich* (holo. LE).

C. leroyi St. Cloud in N. Queensl. Nat. 24:3 (1955). Type: Australia, *Le Roy* (holo. QRS).

DISTRIBUTION: Australia.

32. **C. suave** *R. Br.,* Prodr. Fl. Nov. Holland. 331 (1810); Lindl., Gen. Spec. Orch. 164 (1833); Dockrill, Austr. Ind. Orch. 1:638 (1969). Type: Australia, *R. Brown* (holo. BM).

C. gomphocarpum Fitzg. in J. Bot. 21:203 (1883). Type: Australia, *Fitzgerald* (holo. BM).

DISTRIBUTION: Australia.

J. Sect. **Bigibbarium** *Schltr.* in Fedde, Repert. 20:105 (1924); P. F. Hunt in Kew Bull. 24:94 (1970). Type: *C. devonianum* Paxt.

Another monotypic section based on the distinctive species *C. devonianum.* It is characterized by its lanceolate-petiolate leaves, oblong-lanceolate sepals, mobile three-lobed lip attached to the apex of a short but distinctive column-foot, and two unequally lobed, ovoid, more or less erect pollinia borne on a short stipe.

C. sikkimense was based on a mixed collection of two species. The flowers undoubtedly belong to *C. devonianum*, whereas the leaves belong to a species of section *Cymbidium.*

33. **C. devonianum** *Paxt.* Mag. Bot. 10:97 (1843); Hook. f., Fl. Brit. India 6:10 (1890); King & Pantling in Ann. Roy. Bot. Garden Calcutta 8:190 (1898). Type: India, cult. *Duke of Devonshire* ex *Gibson* (holo. not located) (Plate 7-6).

C. sikkimense Hook. f., Fl. Brit. India 6:9 (1890). Type: Sikkim, *J. D. Hooker* (in part) (holo. K).

DISTRIBUTION: Northern India and Sikkim.

subgen. **Cyperorchis** *(Bl.) Seth & Cribb* comb. & stat. nov. Type: *C. elegans* Lindl.
Cyperorchis Bl. in Rumphia 4:47 (1848); Schltr. in Fedde, Repert. 20:105 (1924).
Iridorchis Bl., Orch. Arch. Ind. 90, t. 26 (1858).
Arethusanthe Finet in Bull. Soc. Bot. Fr. 44:179 (1897).

Five sections make up this subgenus, which is characterized by the fusion of the basal margins of the lip to the basal part of the column so that the lip is not mobile and by the dorsal sepal, which is mostly hooded over the column.

Key to Sections of Subgenus *Cyperorchis*

1. Rostellum not beaked; pollinia ovoid, transverse; pseudobulbs ovoid 2
   Rostellum beaked; pollina ovoid to quadrangular, erect; pseudobulbs fusiform or subcylindrical 4
2. Lip with 3 keels; lateral sepals do not spread widely, so the flower is twice as tall as broad in front view . . . . sect. **Annamaea**
   Lip with 2 keels; lateral sepals spread widely; flower is broader than it is tall in front view 3
3. Leaves are less than 20 cm. long; petals porrect, forming a hood over the column with the dorsal sepal . . . . sect. **Parishiella**
   Leaves more than 25 cm. long; petals spread, do not form a hood over the column . . . . sect. **Iridorchis**
4. Sepals and petals do not spread widely, especially at the base; sepals, petals, and lip very narrow; pollinia ovoid . . . . sect. **Cyperorchis**
   Sepals and petals spread widely; sepals, petals, and lip not especially narrow; pollinia ± quadrangular . . . . sect. **Eburnea**

K. sect. **Iridorchis** *P. F. Hunt* in Kew Bull. 24:94 (1970). Type: *C. giganteum* Lindl.
The species of this section and those of sections *Annamaea* and *Eburnea* have contributed largely to the production of modern-day large-flowered hybrids. The flowers of the species in this section are large, ornamental, and shaped like modern commercial cymbidiums.

This section is characterized by its arching inflorescences, large flowers with spreading petals and sepals, hooded dorsal sepal, large lip bearing two prominent heels, and transversely ovoid pollinia. The species are mostly epiphytic.

34. **C. iridioides** *D. Don* Prod. Fl. Nep. 36 (1825); Wu & Chen in Acta Phyt. Sinica 18:302 (1980). Type: Nepal, *Wallich* (holo. BM).
C. giganteum Lindl., Gen. Spec. Orch. 163 (1833) and J. Proc. Linn. Soc. Bot. 3:29 (1859);
    Hook. f., Fl. Brit. India 6:12 (1890); King & Pantling in Ann. Roy. Bot. Garden Calcutta 8:191 (1898); Schltr. in Fedde, Repert. Beih. 4:267 (1919). Type: Nepal, *Wallich* (holo. K).

Iridorchis gigantea (Lindl.) Bl., Coll. Orch. Arch. Ind. Jap. 90, t. 26 (1858).
C. wilsonii Rolfe in Orch. Rev. 12:79 (1904); Masters in Gard. Chron., series 3, 35:157, t.
    166 (1904). Type: China, Yunnan, *Wilson* (holo. K).
Cyperorchis gigantea (Lindl.) Schltr. in Fedde, Repert. 20:107 (1924).
Cymbidium giganteum cv. Wilsonii. Taylor & P. Woods in Curtis's Bot. Mag., n.s. t. 704
    (1976).

DISTRIBUTION: Northern India, Nepal, Sikkim, and China.

NOTE: Wu and Chen (1980) treat *C. wilsonii* as a distinct species differing in pseudobulb
and leaf size from *C. iridioides*.

    35. **C. hennisianum** *Schltr.* in Orchis 12:46 (1918). Type: Burma, *Hennis* (holo. B †).
Cyperorchis hennisiana (Schltr.) Schltr. in Fedde, Repert. 20:107 (1924).

DISTRIBUTION: Burma.

    36. **C. hookerianum** *Rchb. f.* in Gard. Chron. 1866:7 (1866); Bateman in Curtis's Bot.
Mag. 92: t. 5574 (1866). Type: cult. *Veitch* (holo. W).
C. grandiflorum Griff., Notul. 3:342 (1851); Hook. f., Fl. Brit. India 6:12 (1890); King &
    Pantling in Ann. Roy. Bot. Gard. Calcutta 8:192, t. 256 (1898); Schltr. in Fedde,
    Repert. Beih. 4:268 (1919); Seidenfaden & Smitinand, Orch. Thailand 3:505, t. 374
    (1961) *non* Sw. (1799) (= *Pogonia grandiflora*). Type: Bhutan, *Griffith* 698 (holo. CAL)
    (Plate 7-7).
C. grandiflorum var. *punctatum* Cogn., J. des Orch. 76 (1893). Type: cult. *L. Linden* (holo.
    BR).
Cyperorchis grandiflora (Griff.) Schltr. in Fedde, Repert. 20:107 (1924).

DISTRIBUTION: Nepal, Northern India, Sikkim, China, and Thailand.

    37. **C. insigne** *Rolfe* in Gard. Chron. 35:387 (1904); Seidenfaden & Smitinand, Orch.
Thailand 3:506 (1961). Type: Annam, *Bronchart* 43 (holo. K).
C. sanderi Sander in Gard. Chron. 37:115 (1905). Type: Annam, cult. *Sander* ex *Micholitz*
    (holo. not located).
Cyperorchis insignis (Rolfe) Schltr. in Fedde, Repert. 20:108 (1924).

DISTRIBUTION: Indochina and Thailand.

    38. **C. longifolium** *D. Don,* Prodr. Fl. Nepal. 36 (1825); Lindl., Gen. Spec. Orch. 163
(1833); Hook. f., Fl. Brit. India 6:13 (1890); King & Pantling in Ann. Roy. Bot. Garden
Calcutta 8:191, t. 254 (1898). Type: Nepal, *Wallich* (holo. BM).
C. erythraeum Lindl. in J. Proc. Linn. Soc. Bot. 3:30 (1859). Type: Sikkim, *J. D. Hooker* 229
    (holo. K).
Cyperorchis longifolia (D. Don) Schltr. in Fedde, Repert. 20:108 (1924).

DISTRIBUTION: Northern India, Sikkim, and China.

NOTE: For a discussion of the application of this name, see *C. elegans*.

39. **C. lowianum** *Rchb. f.* in Gard. Chron. n.s. 11:332 (1879); Seidenfaden & Smitinand, Orch. Thailand 3:504 (1961). Type: Burma, cult. *Low* ex *Boxall* (holo. W) (Plate 7-8).
Cyperorchis lowiana (Rchb. f.) Schltr. in Fedde, Repert. 20:108 (1924).
Cymbidium hookerianum var. *lowianum* (Rchb. f.) Wu & Chen in Acta Phytotax. Sin. 18:303 (1980).

DISTRIBUTION: Northern India, Burma, Thailand, Indochina, and China.

NOTE: Wu and Chen (1980) consider this species a variety of *C. hookerianum*.

40. **C. schroederi** *Rolfe* in Gard. Chron. 37:243 (1905); Summerh. in Curtis's Bot. Mag. 163: t. 9637 (1942). Type: Annam, cult. *Schroeder* ex *Micholitz* (holo. K).
Cyperorchis schroederi (Rolfe) Schltr. in Fedde, Repert. 20:108 (1924).

DISTRIBUTION: Indochina.

41. **C. tracyanum** *Hort.* ex *O'Brien* in Gard. Chron., series 3, 8:178 (1890); Rolfe in J. Hort. 513 (1890); Seidenfaden & Smitinand, Orch. Thailand 3:504 (1961). Type: cult. *Tracy* (holo. not located).
Cyperorchis tracyana (Hort. ex O'Brien) Schltr. in Fedde, Repert. 20:108 (1924).

DISTRIBUTION: Burma and Thailand.

L. sect. **Parishiella** (*Schltr.*) *P. F. Hunt* in Kew Bull. 24:94 (1970). Type: *C. tigrinum* Par. ex Hook.
Cyperorchis sect. Parishiella Schltr. in Fedde, Repert, 20:108 (1924).
A monotypic section distinguished from the previous section, which it closely resembles, by its smaller flowers, in which the petals and dorsal sepal form a hood over the column, and by its shorter leaves, which are less than 20 cm. long.
42. **C. tigrinum** *Par.* ex *Hook.* in Curtis's Bot. Mag. t. 5457 (1864); Hook. f. Fl. Brit. India 6:9 (1890); Seidenfaden & Smitinand, Orch. Thailand 3:514 (1961). Type: Burma, *Parish* 144 (holo. K) (Plate 7-9).
Cyperorchis tigrina (Par. ex Hook.) Schltr. in Fedde, Repert. 20:108 (1924).
Cymbidium evrardii Guill. in Bull. Soc. Bot. France 77:339 (1930). Type: Annam, *Evrard* 1238 (holo. P).

DISTRIBUTION: Burma, Thailand, and Indochina.

M. sect. **Annamaea** (*Schltr.*) *P. F. Hunt* in Kew Bull. 24:94 (1970). Type: *C. erythrostylum* Rolfe.
Cyperorchis sect. Annamaea Schltr. in Fedde, Repert. 20:108 (1924).

A monotypic section consisting of a quite distinctive species, *C. erythrostylum*. It is distinguished from other species in the genus by its lateral sepals, which are twice as tall as broad and which hang more or less vertically rather than spreading laterally. The pollinia resemble those of the preceding section in shape and orientation, but the lip bears three keels, suggesting a possible relationship with the following section.

43. **C. erythrostylum** *Rolfe* in Gard. Chron. 2:247 (1905). Type: Indochina (Cochinchina), *Micholitz* (holo. K).

DISTRIBUTION: Indochina.

N. sect. **Cyperorchis** (*Bl.*) *P. F. Hunt* in Kew Bull. 24:94 (1970). Type: *C. elegans* Lindl. *Cyperorchis* Bl. in Rumphia 4:47 (1848); Schltr. in Fedde, Repert. 20:105 (1924).

The six species in this section are distinguished by sepals and petals that do not spread, at least in their basal part, a two- or three-keeled narrow lip, two unequally lobed, obovoid to subquadrangular pollinia, and a beaked rostellum.

C. roseum and *C. sigmoideum* are placed here, only tentatively following their inclusion in *Cyperorchis* by Backer and Bakhuisen (1968).

44. **C. cochleare** *Lindl.* in J. Proc. Linn. Soc. Bot. 3:38 (1859); King & Pantling in Ann. Roy. Bot. Garden Calcutta 8:194, t. 260 (1898). Type: Sikkim, *J. D. Hooker* 235 (holo. K). *Cyperorchis cochleare* (Lindl.) Bentham in J. Linn. Soc. 18:317 (1881); Hook. f., Fl. Brit. India 6:15 (1890); Schltr. in Fedde, Repert. 20:106 (1924).

DISTRIBUTION: Northern India and Sikkim.

45. **C. elegans** *Lindl.*, Gen. Spec. Orch.:163 (1833) and in J. Proc. Linn. Soc. Bot. 3:28 (1859); King & Pantling in Ann. Roy. Bot. Gard. Calcutta 8:194, t. 259 (1898). Type: Nepal, *Wallich* 7354 (holo. K). *Cyperorchis elegans* (Lindl.) Bl., Rumphia 4:47 (1848) and in Mus. Bot. Lugd. Bat. 1:48 (1849); Hook. f. in Fl. Brit. India 6:14 (1890); Schltr. in Fedde, Repert. 20:107 (1924). *C. densiflorum* Griff., Notul. 3:337 (1851). Type: Assam, Khasia Hills, *Griffith* 229 (holo. CAL). *Cyperorchis babae* Kudo ex Mas. in J. Jap. Bot. 8:258, t. 1 & 2 (1932); T. P. Lin, Nat. Orch. Taiwan 2:131 (1977). Type: Taiwan, *Kudo* (holo. ?TI)

DISTRIBUTION: Nepal, Sikkim, Northeast India, Burma, China, and Taiwan.

46. **C. mastersii** *Griff.* ex *Lindl.* in Bot. Reg. 31: t. 50 (1845); King & Pantling in Ann. Roy. Bot. Garden Calcutta 8:195, t. 261 (1898). Type: hort. *Loddiges* (holo. K.) (Plate 7-10). *C. affine* Griff., Notul. 3:336 (1851); Lindl. in J. Proc. Linn. Soc. Bot. 3:28 (1859); Rchb. f. in Gard. Chron. 810 (1878). Type: India, *Griffith* (holo. CAL; iso. K). *C. micromeson* Lindl. in J. Proc. Linn. Soc. Bot. 3:29 (1859). Type: India, *Griffith* (holo. K). *Cyperorchis mastersii* (Griff. ex Lindl.) Bentham in J. Linn. Soc. 18:318 (1881); Hook. f., Fl. Brit. India 6:15 (1890); Schltr. in Fedde, Repert. 20:107 (1924).

DISTRIBUTION: Northern India and Sikkim.

47. **C. roseum** *J. J. Smith,* Orch. Java 6:475 (1905); Holttum, Orch. Malaya, ed. 3, 518 (1964). Types: Java, *Bosscha* (syn. BO); *Ader* (syn. BO); *Kessler* (syn. BO), and *Raciborski* (syn. BO).
Cyperorchis rosea (J. J. Smith) Schltr. in Fedde, Repert. 20:107 (1924); Backer & Bakhuisen, Fl. Java 3:394 (1968).

DISTRIBUTION: Java, Sumatra, and Malaya.

48. **C. sigmoideum** *J. J. Smith* in Bull. Dép. Agr. Ind. Néerl. 13:5 (1907); Schltr. in Fedde, Repert. 20:104 (1924). Type: Java, *Connell* (holo. BO).
Cyperorchis sigmoidea (J. J. Smith) Backer & Bakhuisen in Fl. Java 3:394 (1968).

DISTRIBUTION: Java.

C. parishii var. *sanderae* Sander ex Rolfe in Orch. Rev. 12:163 (1904). Type: cult. *Sander* (holo. K).
Cyperorchis parishii (Rchb. f.) Schltr. in Fedde, Repert. 20:108 (1924).

DISTRIBUTION: Burma.

49. **C. whiteae** *King & Pantling* in Ann. Roy. Bot. Garden Calcutta 8:193, t. 258 (1898). Type: Sikkim, *Pantling* 425 (holo. CAL; iso K).

DISTRIBUTION: Sikkim.

P. section **Eburnea** *Seth & Cribb* sect. nov. affinis sect. *Cyperorchis* (Bl.) P. F. Hunt sed polliniis quadrangularibus, sepalis petalisque patentibus satis differt. Type: *C. eburneum* Lindl.
This section of three species is closely related to the previous one but differs from it in that its flowers open widely and its pollinia are quadrangular. In common with section *Cyperorchis,* it has a beaked rostellum, similarly orientated pollinia, and a three-keeled lip.
50. **C. banaënse** *Gagn.* in Bull. Mus. Hist. Nat. Paris series 2, 22:626 (1950). Type: Annam, *Poilane* 29022 (holo. P).

DISTRIBUTION: Indochina.

51. **C. eburneum** *Lindl.* in Bot. Reg. 33: t. 67 (1847) and in J. Linn. Soc. 3:28 (1859); Hook. f., Fl. Brit. India 6:11 (1890); King & Pantling in Ann. Roy. Bot. Garden Calcutta 8:196, t. 262 (1898). Type: cult. *Loddiges* (holo. K) (Plate 7-11).
C. syringodorum Griff., Notul. 3:338 (1851). Type: India, *Griffith* (holo. K).
Cyperorchis eburnea (Lindl.) Schltr. in Fedde, Repert. 20:107 (1924).

DISTRIBUTION: Nepal, Northern India, Sikkim, Burma, and China.

52. **C. parishii** *Rchb. f.* in Trans. Linn. Soc. 30:144 (1874); Menninger in Amer. Orch. Soc. Bull. 34:892 (1964); Cribb in Orch. Rev. 83:332 (1975). Type: Burma, *Parish 56* (holo. W; iso. K) (Plate 7-12).
C. eburneum var. *parishii* (Rchb. f.) Hook. f., Fl. Brit. India 6:12 (1890).

The Interspecific Hybridization of Cymbidium

The interspecific hybridization data (Table 7-3) have been taken from F. K. Sander's *Complete List of Orchid Hybrids,* which records successfully flowered and registered hybrid grexes. Although no record exists of the crosses that have failed, one could assume that many crosses that are not listed have been tried. Species in sections *Cyperorchis* and *Iridorchis* have large, attractive flowers. For this reason, many crosses using these species have been attempted. Conversely, crosses using species with small, dull flowers have been infrequently or never attempted.

All of the species listed in Table 7-3 have shown varying degrees of compatibility with *Cymbidium* hybrids. In addition, the following species have produced seed with hybrids

Table 7-3. Compatibility of *Cymbidium* species

Species	C. goeringii	C. ensifolium	C. kanran	C. sinense	C. aloifolium	C. atropurpureum	C. bicolor	C. finlaysonianum	C. dayanum	C. pumilum	C. canaliculatum	C. chloranthum	C. madidum	C. suave	C. devonianum	C. giganteum	C. hookerianum	C. insigne	C. longifolium	C. lowianum	C. schroederi	C. tracyanum	C. tigrinum	C. erythrostylum	C. elegans	C. mastersii	C. eburneum	C. parishii
C. goeringii (as C. virescens)	X									X		X																
C. ensifolium		X		X	X	X				X	X									X	X							
C. kanran			X																	X		X						
C. sinense (as C. hoosai)				X						X			X							X								
C. aloifolium (incl. C. pendulum)					X		X	X		X										X								X
C. atropurpureum		X				X																						
C. bicolor (incl. C. pubescens)		X		X	X																							
C. finlaysonianum		X		X				X			X	X																
C. dayanum									X															X				
C. pumilum	X	X	X							X	X	X	X			X		X		X	X	X	X		X			
C. canaliculatum		X		X			X	X		X		X	X															
C. chloranthum													X											X				
C. madidum	X							X		X	X		X	X	X													
C. suave										X			X	X													X	
C. devonianum				X						X	X		X		X		X			X		X		X			X	
C. giganteum																X	X	X		X		X	X	X			X	X
C. hookerianum (as C. grandiflorum)																X	X	X		X		X					X	X
C. insigne										X					X	X	X	X		X	X	X	X	X			X	X
C. longifolium																			X					X				
C. lowianum		X	X	X						X					X	X	X	X		X	X	X	X	X		X	X	X
C. schroederi																		X		X	X							
C. tracyanum		X		X						X						X	X	X		X		X		X			X	X
C. tigrinum										X					X		X			X			X				X	
C. erythrostylum		X								X		X			X		X			X		X					X	
C. elegans							X	X							X	X		X						X				
C. mastersii																X	X			X		X					X	X
C. eburneum										X			X	X	X	X	X			X		X		X			X	X
C. parishii					X													X		X								X

but not with other species: *C. lancifolium* (1973), *C. gracillimum* (1970), *C.* "niveo-mar-ginatum" (1961), *C. faberi* (1971), and *C. suavissimum* (1975).

Only three intergeneric hybrids have been recorded. The first, × *Phaiocymbidium* Chardwarense (1902), is a cross of *C. giganteum* and *Phaius grandifolius*. The authenticity of this cross, however, is a subject of doubt. Rolfe (1911), for one, was convinced that the hybridizer made an error in his records. The other two crosses, × *Grammatocymbidium* Emil Anderson (1966), a hybrid of *C. pendulum* (*aloifolium*) and *Grammatophyllum measure-sianum*, and × *Ansidium* Pasatiempo (1967), a hybrid of *C. madidum* and *Ansellia gigantea*, are far more likely. Both of these crosses reflect the generic affinities of *Cymbidium*.

Excluded Species

The following species, which were originally assigned to *Cymbidium*, have been ex-cluded from this account. The names are excluded for various reasons, mainly because they are now correctly classified in other genera. No attempt, however, has been made to ensure that the disposition given is authoritative.

Cymbidium

aculeatum Sw. in Nov. Act. Soc. Sci. Ups. 6:77 (1799)	= *Eulophia aculeata*
adenoglossum Lindl. in J. Linn. Soc. 6:134 (1862)	= *Eulophia adenoglossa*
alatum Roxb., Hort. Beng.: 63; Fl. Ind. 3:459	= *Thecostele alata*
allagnata Buch.-Ham. ex Wall. Cat. n. 7327	= *Vanda roxburghii*
aloefolium Heyne, ex Wall. Cat. n. 7331	= *Diplocentrum recurvum*
altissimum Sw. in Nov. Act. Soc. Sci. Ups. 6:74 (1799)	= *Oncidium altissimum*
altum Willd., Sp. Pl. 4:105	= *Bletia verecunda*
amabile Roxb., Hort. Beng.: 63; Fl. Ind. 3:457	= *Phalaenopsis amabilis*
andersonii Lamb. in Andr. Bot. Rep.: t. 651	= *Cyrtopodium andersonii*
angolense Rchb. f., Flora 48:188 (1865)	= *Eulophia angolensis*
aphyllum Sw. in Nov. Act. Soc. Sci. Ups. 6:73 (1799)	= *Dendrobium aphyllum*
appendiculatum Don, Prod. Fl. Nep.: 36	= *Cremastra wallichiana*
assamicum Linden in Ill. Hort. 28:95 (1881) nomen	
autumnale Sw. in Nov. Act. Soc. Sci. Ups. 6:72 (1799)	= *Earina mucronata*
Ballianum Hort. ex Orch. Rev. 12:85 (1904)	- hybrid
bambusifolium Roxb., Hort. Beng.: 63; Fl. Ind. 3:460	= *Arundina bambusifolia*
bituberculatum Hook., Exot. Fl. 2: t. 116	= *Liparis bituberculata*
boreale Sw. in Nov. Act. Soc. Sci. Ups. 6:76 (1799)	= *Calypso borealis*
boweri F. Muell. in Wing, South S. Record (Aug. 1883)	- Solomon Isles
buchanani Rchb. f. in Flora 64:329 (1881)	- S. Africa
calcaratum Schltr. in Ann. Mus. Col. Marseille, Series 3:181 (1913)	- Madagascar
calceolaria Willd., Sp. Pl. 4:97	= *Epidendrum calceolariae*
candidum H. B. K., Nov. Gen. Sp. 1:324	- Colombia
carnosum Griff., Notul. 3:339	= *Eulophia* sp.
clypeolum Willd., Sp. Pl. 4:99	= *Liparis clypeolum*
coccineum Sw. in Schrad. J. 2:214 (1799)	= *Ornithidium coccineum*
Cooperi Rolfe in Orch. Rev. 22:94 (1914)	- hybrid
corallorrhiza Sw. in Vet. Acad. Handl. Stockh.: 238 (1800)	= *Corallorhiza innata*
cordatum Londes in Mém. Soc. Nat. Mosc. 1:282 (1811)	= *Listeria cordata*
cordigerum H. B. K., Nov. Gen. Sp. 1:341	= *Epidendrum atropurpureum*

corniculatum Spreng., Syst. 3:722 = *Pleurothallis emarginata*
crispatum Thunb., Pl. Bras. Dec. 2:18 - Brazil
cucullatum Sw. in Nov. Act. Soc. Sci. Ups. 6:73 (1799) = *Brassavola cucullata*
cylindricum Heyne ex Wall. Cat. sub. n. 7317 = *Aerides cylindricum*
dependens Lodd., Bot. Cab. 10:936 = *Cirrhaea loddigesii*
diurnum Sw. in Nov. Act. Soc. Sci. Ups. 6:75 (1799) - Venezuela
echinocarpon Sw. in Nov. Act. Soc. Sci. Ups. 6:71 (1799) = *Dichaea echinocarpa*
equitans Sw. in Nov. Act. Soc. Sci. Ups. 6:72 (1799) = *Oberonia brevifolia*
erectum Sw. in Schrad. J. 2:226 (1799) = *Cephalanthera pallens*
falcatum Sw. in Schrad. J. 2:226 (1799) = *Cephalanthera falcata*
flabellatum Spreng., Syst. 3:724 = *Cymbidiella flabellata*
flabellifolium Griseb., Fl. Brit. W. Ind.: 629, sphalm. = *Zygopetalum cochleare*
flabelliforme Sw. in Nov. Act. Soc. Sci. Ups. 6:73 (1799) = *Zygopetalum cochleare*
flavescens Llanos, Fragm.: 96 = *Cleisostoma amabile*
floridum Lindl., Gen. Sp. Orch.: 121 = *Bletia florida*
Florinda Hort. ex Orch. Rev. 21;346 (1913) - hybrid
Fuerstenbergianum Schltr. in Orchis 12:47 (1918) - hybrid
furvum Willd., Sp. Pl. 4:103 = *Vanda furva*
fuscescens Griff., Icon. Pl. As. 3: t. 319 = *Tainia latifolia*
Gammieanum King & Pantling in J. As. Soc. Beng. 64:339
  (1895) - natural hybrid
gibsonii Wall. ex Voigt, Hort. Suburb. Calc.:627 - nomen
glandulosum H. B. K., Nov. Gen. Sp. 1:340 - Venezuela
glaucum Sw. in Nov. Act. Soc. Sci. Ups. 6:71 (1799) = *Dichaea glauca*
Glebelandense Hort. ex Orch. Rev. 19:51 (1911) - hybrid
globosum Sw. in Nov. Act. Soc. Sci. Ups. 6:72 (1799) = *Epidendrum globosum*
graminoides Sw. in Nov. Act. Soc. Sci. Ups. 6:71 (1799) = *Dichaea graminoides*
grandiflorum Sw. in Nov. Act. Soc. Sci. Ups. 6:76 (1799) = *Pogonia grandiflora*
guttatum Willd., Sp. Pl. 14:102 = *Oncidium luridum*
hirsutum Willd., Sp. Pl. 4:94 = *Elleanthus caravata*
humblotii Rolfe in Gard. Chron. 2:8 (1892) = *Cymbidiella humblotii*
humile Sm. ex Lindl., Coll. Bot.: sub. t. 37 = *Coelogyne humilis*
huttoni Hook. f., Bot. Mag.: t. 5676 - Java
hyacinthinum Sm., Exot. Bot. 1:117 = *Bletia hyacinthina*
hyemale Muhl. ex Willd., Sp. Pl. 4:107 = *Aplectrum hyemale*
I'ansonii Rolfe in Orch. Rev. 8:191 (1900) - hybrid
imbricatum Roxb., Hort. Beng. 63; Fl. Ind. 3:460 = *Pholidota imbricata*
inconspicuum Wall. ex Hook. f. in Ann. Bot. Garden Calc.
  5:46 (1895) = *Saccolabium inconspicuum*
iridifolium Roxb., Hort. Beng. 63; Fl. Ind. 3:458 = *Oberonia iridifolia*
iridifolium Sw. ex Steud. Nom., ed. 2:460 = *Oncidium iridifolium*
iridioides Don, Prod. Fl. Nep. 36 = ? *Coelogyne* sp.
ixioides Don, Prod. Fl. Nep. 36 = *Spathoglottis ixioides*
japonicum Miq. sphalm. *C. javanicum*
juncifolium Willd., Sp. Pl. 4:102 = *Oncidium cebolleta*
latifolium Spreng., Syst. 3:725 = *Maxillaria latifolia*
latifolium Sw. in Schrad. J. 2:225 (1799) = *Epipactis latifolia*
liliifolium Sw. in Nov. Act. Soc. Sci. Ups. 6;76 (1799) = *Liparis liliifolia*
limbatum Hook. ex Lindl., Gen. Sp. Orch.: 165 - Trinidad
lineare Herb. Heyne, ex Wall. Cat. sub. n. 7312 = *Saccolabium wightianum*
lineare Sw. in Nov. Act. Soc. Sci. Ups. 6:72 (1799) = *Isochilus linearis*
loeselii Sw. in Nov. Act. Soc. Sci. Ups. 6:76 (1799) = *Liparis loeselii*

luteum Willd., Sp. Pl. 4:106   = *Chloraea crispa*
lycopodioides Willd., Sp. Pl. 4:98 (1805)
magnificum Schltr. in Orchis 12:47 (1918)   - hybrid
Mandaianum Hort. ex Orch. Rev. 20:167 (1912)   = *C. I'Ansonii*
marginatum Lindl., Bot. Reg.: t. 1530   = *Maxillaria gracilis*
meyenii Schau. in Nov. Act. Nat. Cur. 19, Suppl. 1:433 (1843)   = *Arundina meyenii*
minimifolium Thw. ex Hook. f., Fl. Brit. Ind. 6:37 in syn.
    (1890)   = *Sarcochilus minimifolius*
montanum Sw. in Nov. Act. Soc. Sci. Ups. 6:72 (1799)   - Jamaica
moschatum Willd., Sp. Pl. 4:98   = *Dendrobium moschatum*
muricatum Sw. in Nov. Act. Soc. Sci. Ups. 6:71 (1799)   = *Dichaea muricata*
nervosum Sw. in Nov. Act. Soc. Sci. Ups. 6:76 (1799)   = *Liparis nervosa*
nitidum Roxb., Hort. Beng. 63; Fl. Ind. 3:459   = *Coelogyne ocellata*
nitidum Wall. ex Don, Prod. Fl. Nep. 35   = *Coelogyne nitida*
nodosum Sw. in Nov. Act. Soc. Sci. Ups. 6:73 (1799)   = *Brassavola nodosa*
nutans Sw. in Nov. Act. Soc. Sci. Ups. 6:77 (1799)   = *Geodorum purpureum*
ochroleucum Lindl., Gen. Sp. Orch. 168   = *Maxillaria camaridii*
odontorrhizum Willd., Sp. Pl. 4:110   = *Corallorhiza odontorrhiza*
ovatum Willd., Sp. Pl. 4:101   = *Dendrobium chlorops*
pallens Sw. in Schrad. J. 2:225 (1799)   = *Cephalanthera pallens*
palustre Sw. in Schrad. J. 2:225 (1799)   = *Epipactis palustris*
parviflorum Reinw. ex Lindl. in J. Linn. Soc. 3:55 (1859)   = *Eria reinwardtii*
pedicellatum Sw. in Schrad. J. 2:224 (1799)   = *Eulophia aculeata*
pictum R. Br., Prod. 331   = *Geodorum pictum*
plantaginifolium Willd., Sp. Pl. 4:101 (1805)
plicatum Harv. ex Lindl. in Hook., Comp. Bot. Mag. 2:203
    (1836)   = *Eulophia aculeata*
praecox Sm. ex Lindl., Coll. Bot.: sub. t. 37   = *Pleione praecox*
praemorsum Buch.-Ham. ex Wall. Cat. n. 7325   = *Acampe praemorsa*
praemorsum Sw. in Nov. Act. Soc. Sci. Ups. 6:75 (1799)   = *Acampe excavata*
proliferum Sw. in Nov. Act. Soc. Sci. Ups. 6:71 (1799)   = *Ponera prolifera*
pulchellum Sw. in Nov. Act. Soc. Sci. Ups. 6:75 (1799)   = *Calopogon pulchellus*
purpureum Drapier, Herb. Amat. 5:313 (1831)
purpureum Loisel.   - untraced
purpureum Steud., Nom., ed. 2:559, in syn., sphalm.   = *Ornithidium vestitum*
pusillum Sw. in Nov. Act. Soc. Sci. Ups. 6:74 (1799)   = *Oncidium iridifolium*
ramosissimum Presl., Rel. Haenk 1:98   - S. America
reflexum R. Br., Prod. 331   = *Liparis reflexa*
reptans Sw. in Nov. Act. Soc. Sci. Ups. 6:71 (1799)   = *Bulbophyllum nutans*
rhodochilum Rolfe in Orch. Rev. 10:184 (1902)   = *Cymbidiella rhodochila*
rigidum Willd., Sp. Pl. 4:106   = *Tetramicra rigida*
Rosefieldense Hort. ex Orch. Rev. 20:57 (1912)   - hybrid
roseum Cooper in Orch. Rev. 30:105 (1922)   - hybrid
rubrum Sw. in Schrad. J. 2:226 (1799)   = *Cephalanthera rubra*
sagamiense (Nakai) Makino & Nemoto, Fl. Jap., ed. 2:1631
    (1931)   = *Pachyrhizanthe sagamiensis*
sandersoni Harv., Gen. S. Afr. Pl., ed. 2:360   = *Ansellia gigantea*
satyrium Buch.-Ham. ex Wall. Cat. n. 7334   = *Saccolabium buccosum*
scarabaeiforme Parish ex Rchb. f. in Gard. Chron.:842 (1865)   = *Luisia psyche*
scriptum Steud., Nom., ed. 1:248   = *Eulophia scripta*
scriptum Sw. in Schrad. J. 2:218 (1799)   = *Grammatophyllum speciosum*
serrulatum Sw. in Nov. Act. Soc. Sci. Ups. 6:72 (1799)   = *Epidendrum serrulatum*
spathulatum Moon, Cat. Pl. Ceylon 60 (1824)   = *Epidendrum spathulatum*

speciosissimum Don, Prod. Fl. Nep. 35	= *Coelogyne cristata*
speciosum Reinw. ex Lindl. in J. Linn. Soc. 3:23 (1859)	= *Arundina densa*
spinescens Reinw. ex Lindl. in J. Linn. Soc. 3:14 (1859)	= *Dendrobium spinescens*
squamatum Sw. in Vet. Acad. Handl. Stockh. 21:238 (1800)	= *Dipodium squamatum*
stapeliaeflorum Teijsm. & Binn. in Tijdschr. Nederl. Ind. 24:319 (1862)	= *Grammatophyllum stapeliaeflorum*
stapeloides Link & Otto, Ic. Pl. Sel.: 111, t. 52	= *Zygopetalum stapeloides*
stenopetalum Reinw. ex Lindl., Fol. Orch. Coelog. 14	= *Coelogyne longifolia*
stephensi Ridley in J. Bot. 71 (1900)	= *Grammatophyllum stapeliaeflorum*
striatum Sw. in Nov. Act. Soc. Sci. Ups. 6:77 (1799)	= *Bletia hyacinthina*
strictum Don, Prod. Fl. Nep. 35	= *Coelogyne elatum*
subulatum Sw. in Nov. Act. Soc. Sci. Ups. 6:73 (1799)	- Jamaica
tabulare Sw. in Nov. Act. Soc. Sci. Ups. 6:77 (1799)	= *Eulophia tabularis*
tabulare (L.f.) Sw. in Schrad., J. Bot. 2:224	= *Satyrium tabulare*
tenuifolium Lindl., Gen. Sp. Orch.: 167	= *Luisia tenuifolia*
tenuifolium Wight, Ic.: t. 1689 (non text)	= *Luisia teretifolia*
tenuifolium Willd., Sp. Pl. 4:103 (1805)	
teretifolium Sw. in Nov. Act. Soc. Sci. Ups. 6:72 (1799)	= *Epidendrum teretifolium*
tesselatum Sw. in Nov. Act. Soc. Sci. Ups. 6:75 (1799)	= *Vanda roxburghii*
tesselloides Roxb., Hort. Beng. 63; Fl. Ind. 3:463	= *Vanda roxburghii*
testaefolium Sw. in Nov. Act. Soc. Sci. Ups. 6:71 (1799)	= *Pleurothallis testaefolia*
tetrapetalum Sw. in Nov. Act. Soc. Sci. Ups. 6:74 (1799)	= *Oncidium tetrapetalum*
tribuloides Spreng., Syst. 3:721	= *Pleurothallis tribuloides*
trichocarpon Sw. in Nov. Act. Soc. Sci. Ups. 6:71 (1799)	= *Dichaea trichocarpa*
trifidium Sw. in Schrad., Neues. J. 1:76 (1805)	= *Bletia verecunda*
trinerve G. F. W. Mey, Prim. Fl. Esseq. 258	- Guiana
tripterum Sw. in Schrad., J. 2:214 (1799)	= *Coelia baueriana*
triquetrum Sw. in Nov. Act. Soc. Sci. Ups. 6:74 (1799)	= *Oncidium triquetrum*
triste Roxb., Hort. Beng. 63; Fl. Ind. 3:461	= *Luisia teretifolia*
triste Willd., Sp. Pl. 4:99	= *Luisia* sp.
umbellatum Spreng., Pugill. 2:82	= *Cirrhopetalum thouarsii*
undulatum Sw. in Nov. Act. Soc. Sci. Ups. 6:74 (1799)	= *Oncidium carthagenense*
ustulatum Bolus in J. Linn. Soc. 20:469 (1884)	= *Eulophia* sp.
utriculatum Sw. in Nov. Act. Soc. Sci. Ups. 6:75 (1799)	= *Govenia utriculata*
variegatum Sw. in Nov. Act. Soc. Sci. Ups. 6:74 (1799)	= *Oncidium variegatum*
verecundum Sw. in Nov. Act. Soc. Sci. Ups. 6:75 (1799)	= *Bletia verecunda*
vestitum Sw. in Nov. Act. Soc. Sci. Ups. 6:70 (1799)	- Jamaica
vexilliferum La Llave & Lex., Nov. Veg. Desc. fasc. 2:11	- Mexico
violaceum H. B. K., Nov. Gen. et Sp. 1:341	= *Cattleya violacea*
virescens Willd., So. Pl. 4:106	= *Chloraea piquichen*
Winnianum Hort. ex Reichenbachia, 2, 6: t. 75 (1894)	- hybrid
Woodlandense Hort. ex Orch. Rev. 21:38 (1913)	- hybrid
xilophyllum Sw. in Schrad. J. 2:226 (1799)	= *Cephalanthera ensifolia*
Zaleskianum Linden, Lindenia: t. 778	- natural hybrid

Species and Synonyms

NAME

Aerides borassii Smith ex. Buch.-Ham. = 20
Aphyllorchis aberrans Schltr. = 1
Bletia nipponica Fr. & Sav. = 1

Cymbidium aberrans (Finet) Schltr. = 1
Cym. acutum Ridley = 24
Cym. affine Griff. = 46
Cym. albo-jucundissimum Hayata = 18
Cym. alborubens Makino = 24
Cym. albuciflorum F. Muell = 31
Cym. **aliciae** Quis. 9
Cym. aloefolium Bl. = 22
Cym. aloides Curtis = 20
Cym. **aloifolium** (L.) Sw. 20
Cym. aloifolium sensu Wall. = 23
Cym. angustifolium Ames & Schweinf. = 24
Cym. aphyllum Ames & Schltr. = 1
Cym. arrogans Hayata = 11
Cym. aspidistrifolium Fukuyama = 3
Cym. **atropurpureum** (Lindl.) Rolfe 21
Cym. babae Kudo ex Masamune = 45
Cym. **banaënse** Gagnep. 50
Cym. **bicolor** Lindl. 22
Cym. **canaliculatum** R.Br. 28
Cym. **caulescens** Ridl. 2
Cym. celebicum Schltr. = 22
Cym. cerinum Schltr. = 12
Cym. chinense Heynh. = 18
Cym. **chloranthum** Lindl. 29
Cym. **cochleare** Lindl. 44
Cym. cuspidatum Bl. = 3
Cym. **cyperifolium** Wall. 10
Cym. **dayanum** Rchb. f. 24
Cym. densiflorum Griff. = 45
Cym. **devonianum** Paxt. 33
Cym. **eburneum** Lindl. 51
Cym. eburneum var. *parishii* Hk.f. = 52
Cym. **elegans** Lindl. 45
Cym. **ensifolium** Sw. 11
Cym. ensifolium var. *estriatum* Lindl. = 11
Cym. ensifolium var. *misericors* (Hay.) Liu & Su = 11
Cym. ensifolium var. *munronianum* (K. & P.) Tang & Wang = 11
Cym. ensifolium var. *rubigemmum* (Hay.) Liu & Su = 11
Cym. ensifolium var. *striatum* Lindl. = 11
Cym. ensifolium var. *susin* Yen = 11
Cym. ensifolium var. *yakibaran* (Mak.) Wu & Chen = 11
Cym. erectum Wight = 20
Cym. erythraeum Lindl. = 38
Cym. **erythrostylum** Rolfe 43
Cym. estriatum Lindl. = 11
Cym. evrardii Guill. = 42
Cym. **faberi** Rolfe 12
Cym. faberi var. *omeiense* (Wu & Chen) Wu & Chen = 12
Cym. faberi var. *szechuanicum* (Wu & Chen) Wu & Chen = 12
Cym. **finlaysonianum** Lindl. 23
Cym. finlaysonianum var. *atropurpureum* Veitch = 22

Cym. flaccidum Schltr. = 22
Cym. **floribundum** Lindl. 27
Cym. floribundum var. *pumilum* (Rolfe) Wu & Chen = 27
Cym. formosanum Hayata = 7
Cym. formosum var. *gracillimum* (Fuk.) Liu & Su = 7
Cym. forrestii Rolfe = 7
Cym. fragrans Salis. = 18
Cym. fukienense Yen = 12
Cym. gibsonii Lindl. = 3
Cym. **giganteum** Wall. ex Lindl. = 34
Cym. **goeringii** (Rchb. f.) Rchb. f. 7
Cym. goeringii var. *serratum* (Schltr.) Wu & Chen = 7
Cym. goeringii var. *longibracteatum* (Wu & Chen) Wu & Chen = 7
Cym. goeringii var. *tortisepalum* (Fuk.) Wu & Chen = 7
Cym. gomphocarpum Fitzg. = 32
Cym. **gonzalesii** Quis. 13
Cym. gracillimum Fukuyama = 7
Cym. grandiflorum Griff. = 36
Cym. grandiflorum var. *punctatum* Cogn. = 36
Cym. gyokuchin Makino = 11
Cym. haematodes Lindl. = 10
Cym. **hartinahianum** Comber & Nasution 30
Cym. **hennisianum** Schltr. 35
Cym. hillii F. Muell. = 28
Cym. **hookerianum** Rchb. f. 36
Cym. hookerianum var. *lowianum* (Rchb. f.) Wu & Chen = 39
Cym. hoosai Makino = 18
Cym. illiberale Hayata = 27
Cym. **insigne** Rolfe 37
Cym. intermedium H. G. Jones = 20
Cym. iridifolium A. Cunn. = 31
Cym. **iridioides** D. Don 34
Cym. javanicum Bl.
Cym. **kanran** Makino 14
Cym. kanran var. *babae* (Kudo ex Mas.) Ying = 45
Cym. kanran var. *latifolium* Mak. = 14
Cym. kanran var. *misericors* = 11
Cym. kanran var. *purpureohiemale* (Hay.) Ying = 14
Cym. kerrii Rolfe ex Downie = 3
Cym. **koran** Makino 15
Cym. **lancifolium** Hook. 3
Cym. leachianum Rchb. f. = 24
Cym. leai Rendle = 31
Cym. leroyi St. Cloud = 31
Cym. linearisepalum Yamamoto = 14
Cym. linearisepalum forma *atropurpureum* Yam. = 14
Cym. linearisepalum var. *atropurpureum* (Yam.) Mas. = 14
Cym. linearisepalum forma *atrovirens* Yam. = 14
Cym. linearisepalum var. *atrovirens* (Yam.) Mas. = 14
Cym. longibracteatum Wu & Chen = 7
Cym. **longifolium** Don 38
Cym. **lowianum** Rchb. f. 39

Cym. **mackinnoni** Duthie 8
Cym. **maclehoseae** S. Y. Hu 4
Cym. **macrorhizon** Lindl. 1
Cym. **madidum** Lindl. 31
Cym. mannii Rchb. f. = 20
Cym. marginatum Mak. = 24
Cym. **mastersii** Griff. ex Lindl. 46
Cym. micans Schauer = 11
Cym. micromeson Lindl. = 46
Cym. misericors Hayata = 11
Cym. misericors var. *oreophilum* Hay. = 4
Cym. munronianum K. & P. = 11
Cym. nagifolium Masamune = 3
Cym. nipponicum (Fr. & Sav.) Rolfe = 1
Cym. oiwakensis Hayata = 12
Cym. omeiense Y. S. Wu & S. C. Chen = 12
Cym. oreophilum Hayata = C. kanran Makino
Cym. **papuanum** Schltr. 5
Cym. **parishii** Rchb. f. 52
Cym. parishii var. *sanderae* Rolfe = 52
Cym. pedicellatum Finet = 1
Cym. pendulum (Roxb.) Sw. = 20
Cym. pendulum var. *atropurpureum* Lindl. = 21
Cym. pendulum var. *brevilabre* Lindl. = 23
Cym. pendulum sensu Bl. = 23
Cym. pendulum sensu Duthie = 22
Cym. pendulum sensu King & Pantling = 22
Cym. pendulum sensu Lindl. = 23
Cym. pendulum sensu Vidal = 21
Cym. **poilanei** Gagnepain 16
Cym. pseudovirens Schltr. = 7
Cym. pubescens Lindl. = 22
Cym. pulchellum Schltr. = 22
Cym. pulcherrimum Sander = 24
Cym. pumilum Rolfe = 27
Cym. purpureo-hiemale Hayata = 14
Cym. queeneanum Klinge = 31
Cym. rectum Ridl. = 22
Cym. **roseum** J. J. Sm. 47
Cym. rubrigemmum Hayata = 11
Cym. sanderae Sand. ex Rolfe = 3
Cym. sanderi Sand. = 37
Cym. sanguineum Teijsm. & Binn. = 29
Cym. sanguinolentum Teijsm. & Binn. = 29
Cym. scabroserrulatum Makino = 12
Cym. **schroederi** Rolfe 40
Cym. serratum Schltr. = 7
Cym. shimaran Makino = 11
Cym. **siamense** Rolfe ex Downie 17
Cym. **sigmoideum** J. J. Sm. 48
Cym. sikkimense Hook. f. = 33
Cym. simonsianum K. & P. = 24
Cym. simulans Rolfe = 20

Cym. **sinense** (Andr.) Willd. 18
Cym. sinense forma *albojucundissimum* (Hay.) Fuk. = 18
Cym. sinense var. *albojucundissimum* (Hay.) Mas. = 18
Cym. sinense var. *album* Yen = 18
Cym. sinense var. *bellum* Yen = 18
Cym. sinense var. forma *margicoloratum* (Hay.) Fuk. = 18
Cym. sinense var. *margicoloratum* Hay. = 18
Cym. sinokanran Yen = 14
Cym. sinokanran var. *atropurpureum* (Yam.) Yen = 14
Cym. sparkesii Rendle = 28
Cym. **suave** R. Br. 32
Cym. **suavissimum** Sander ex Curtis 26
Cym. sundaicum Schltr. = 11
Cym. **sutepense** Rolfe ex Downie 25
Cym. syringodorum Griff. = 51
Cym. **syunitianum** Fukuyama 6
Cym. szechuanensis S. Y. Hu = 1
Cym. szechuanicum Y. S. Wu & S. C. Chen = 12
Cym. **tigrinum** Par. ex Hook. 42
Cym. tortisepalum Fukuyama = 7
Cym. tortisepalum var. *viridiflorum* Ying = 7
Cym. **tosyaense** Masamune 19
Cym. **tracyanum** Hort. ex O'Brien 41
Cym. tricolor Miq.
Cym. uniflorum Yen. = 7
Cym. variciferum Rchb. f. = 29
Cym. virens Lindl. = 7
Cym. virescens Lindl. = 7
Cym. viridiflorum Griff. = 10
Cym. wallichii Lindl. = 20
Cym. **whiteae** King & Pantling 49
Cym. wilsonii (Rolfe ex Cooke) Rolfe = 34
Cym. yakibaran Makino = 11
Cym. yakibaran var. *albomarginatum* Makino = 11
Cym. yakibaran var. *niveomarginatum* Makino = 11
Cym. yunnanense Schltr. = 7
Cym. xiphiifolium Lindl. = 11
Cyperorchis babae Kudo ex Masamune = 45
Cyper. cochleare Benth. = 44
Cyper. eburnea (Lindl.) Schltr. = 51
Cyper. elegans Bl. = 45
Cyper. gigantea (Lindl.) Schltr. = 34
Cyper. grandiflora (Griff.) Schltr. = 36
Cyper. hennisiana (Schltr.) Schltr. = 35
Cyper. insignis (Rolfe) Schltr. = 37
Cyper. longifolia (Don) Schltr. = 38
Cyper lowiana (Rchb. f.) Schltr. = 39
Cyper. mastersii Benth. = 46
Cyper. parishii (Rchb. f.) Schltr. = 52
Cyper. rosea (J. J. Smith) Schltr. = 47
Cyper. schroederi (Rolfe) Schltr. = 40
Cyper. sigmoidea (J. J. Smith) Back. & Bakh. = 48
Cyper tigrina (Parish) Schltr. = 42

Cyper. tracyana (Rolfe) Schltr. = 41
Epidendrum aloides Curtis = C. aloifolium (L.) Sw.
E. aloifolium L. = C. aloifolium (L.) Sw.
E. ensifolium L. = 11
E. pendulum Roxb. = C. aloifolium (L.) Sw.
E. sinense Andr. = 18
Iridorchis gigantea (Lindl.) Bl. = 34
Maxillaria goeringii Rchb. f. = 7
Orchis abortiva Rudb. = 20
Yoania aberrans Finet = 1

Abbreviations for Herbaria

AMES	Orchid Herbarium of Oakes Ames, Cambridge, Massachusetts
B	Botanisches Museum, Dahlem, Berlin, Germany
BM	British Museum (Natural History), London, England
BO	Herbarium Bogorense, Lembaga Biologi Nasional, Bogor, Java
BR	Jardin Botanique National de Belgique, Meise, Belgium
BRI	Botanical Museum and Herbarium, Brisbane, Australia
C	Botanical Museum and Herbarium, Copenhagen, Denmark
CAL	Central National Herbarium, Calcutta, India
E	Royal Botanic Garden, Edinburgh, Scotland
Fukuyama	Private herbarium of Fukuyama
G	Conservatoire et Jardin Botaniques, Geneva, Switzerland
Jones	Private herbarium of H. G. Jones
K	Royal Botanic Gardens, Kew, Surrey, England
KUN	Kunming Institute of Botany, Academia Sinica, Kunming, Yunnan, People's Republic of China
L	Rijksherbarium, Leiden, Netherlands
LAE	Division of Botany, Department of Forest, Lae, Papua New Guinea
LE	Komarov Botanical Institute, Academy of Sciences, Leningrad, USSR
LINN	The Linnaean Society of London, England
MAK	Makino Herbarium, Tokyo, Japan
MEL	National Herbarium of Victoria, Melbourne, Australia
NSW	National Herbarium of New South Wales, Sydney, Australia
P	Musée National d'Histoire Naturelle, Laboratoire de Phanerogamie, Paris, France
PE	Institute of Botany, Academia Sinica, Peking, China
QRS	Queensland Research Station, Atherton, Queensland, Australia
S	Swedish Museum of Natural History, Stockholm, Sweden
SING	Botanic Gardens, Singapore
SZ	Department of Biology, National Sichuan University, Chengdu, Sichuan, People's Republic of China
TAI	The Herbarium, Department of Botany, National Taiwan University, Taipei, Taiwan
TI	Botanical Institute, Tokyo, Japan
U	Institute for Systematic Botany, Utrecht, Netherlands
UPS	University of Uppsala, Uppsala, Sweden
W	Naturhistorisches Museum, Vienna, Austria
Z	Institüt für Systematische Botanik der Universität Zürich, Zurich, Switzerland

Full addresses of these herbaria can be obtained from Holmgren, P. K. and W. Keuken. 1974. *Index Herbariorum,* ed. 6. Vol. 1. Utrecht, Netherlands.

Other Abbreviations

†	destroyed
!	seen by authors
excl. cit.	excluding citations listed
excl. syn.	excluding listed synonymy
holo.	holotype, the sole element (usually an herbarium specimen) used as the type by the author of a name or the element designated or indicated by him as the type
iso.	isotype, a duplicate specimen of the holotype
isosyn.	isosyntype, a duplicate of a syntype, not cited in the prologue
lecto.	lectotype, an element subsequently designated or selected from among syntypes to serve as the definitive type
non Sw.	not in the sense of Sw.
not t.	not plate
s.n.	without number
syn.	syntype, any of two or more elements used as types by the author of a name, whether or not designated by him as such
synon. nov.	newly placed in synonymy
t.	plate

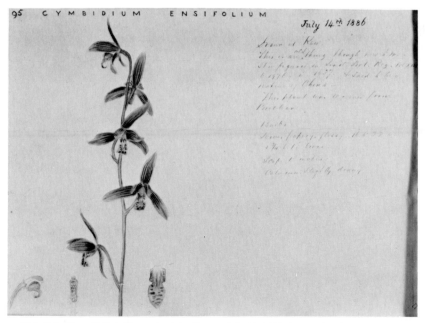

Plate 7-1. C. ensifolium. Drawn by John Day on July 14, 1886, from a plant flowering at Kew. (Plates 7-1 through 7-12: Crown copyright; reproduced with the permission of the Controller of Her Majesty's Stationery Office and the Director of the Royal Botanic Gardens, Kew.)

Plate 7-2. C. sinense. Drawn by John Day on March 1, 1885, from a plant flowered by Lees.

Plate 7-3. C. finlaysonianum. Drawn by John Day on July 27, 1886, from a plant mistakenly labeled *C. pendulum,* flowering at Kew.

Plate 7-4. C. dayanum. Drawn by John Day on November 11, 1868, from a plant collected by his nephew in Assam.

Plate 7-5. C. madidum. Drawn by John Day on June 24, 1884, from a plant flowered by W. Bull.

Plate 7-6. C. devonianum. Drawn by John Day on March 15, 1883, from a plant grown by W. Bull.

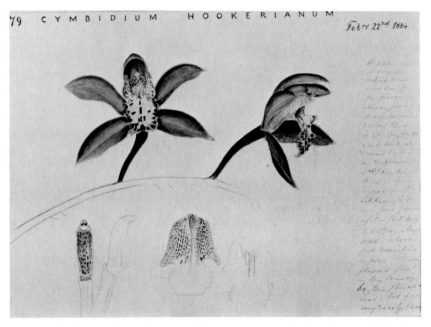

Plate 7-7. C. hookerianum. Drawn by John Day on February 22, 1884, from a plant flowered by J. Veitch.

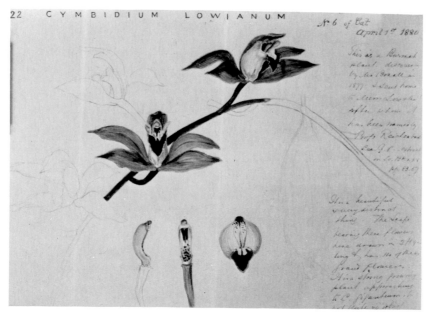

Plate 7-8. C. lowianum. Drawn by John Day on April 1, 1880, from a plant in his own collection.

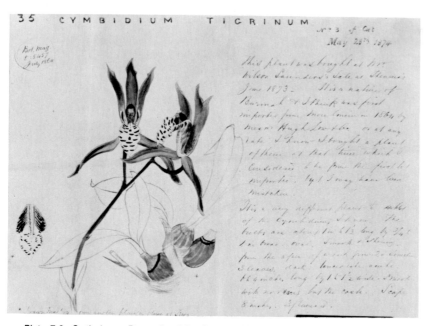

Plate 7-9. C. tigrinum. Drawn by John Day on May 28, 1874, from a plant in his own collection purchased from the collection of Wilson Saunders at Stevens' Sale Room.

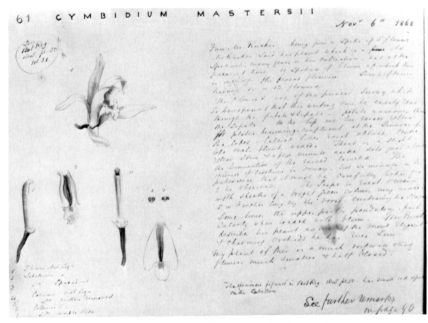

Plate 7-10. *C. mastersii.* Drawn by John Day on November 6, 1868, from an inflorescence given him by Mr. Rucker.

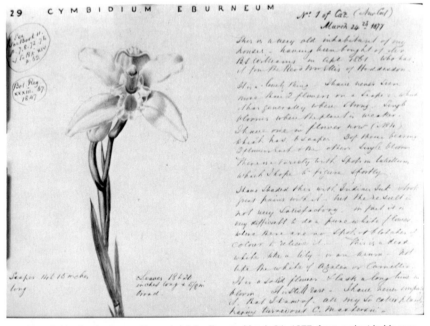

Plate 7-11. *C. eburneum.* Drawn by John Day on March 24, 1877, from a plant in his own collection purchased from B. S. Williams in April 1861.

Plate 7-12. *C. parishii.* Drawn by John Day on July 5, 1878, from a plant in his own collection purchased from Hugh Low & Co. in May 1870, the first time this species flowered in cultivation in Europe.

Literature Cited

Backer, C. A., and R. C. Bakhuisen. 1968. Cymbidium Swartz. Flora of Java 3:394–396.

Blume, C. L. 1848. Trib. Vandeae. Rumphia 4:47.

——. 1849. Cyperorchis Bl. Mus. Bot. Lugd. Bat. 1:48.

——. 1858. Collection des orchidées les plus remarquables de l'Archipel Indien et du Japon, Vol. 1, pp. 90–93.

Dockrill, A. W. 1969. Australian indigenous orchids, Vol. 1, pp. 619–639. Soc. Growing Aust. Plants, Sydney.

Duthie, J. F. 1906. The orchids of north western Himalaya. Ann. Roy. Bot. Garden Calcutta 9:133–138.

Garay, L. A., and H. R. Sweet. 1974. Orchids of the southern Ryukyu Islands, pp. 141–148. Bot. Illus., Harvard University, Cambridge.

Holttum, R. E. 1964. A revised flora of Malaya, Vol. 1, 3d ed., pp. 517–526. Government Printing Office, Singapore.

Hooker, J. D. 1890. The flora of British India, Vol. 6, pp. 8–16. L. Reeve, Ashford, Kent.

Hunt, P. F. 1970. Notes on Asiatic orchids, 5. Kew Bull. 24:93–94.

King, G., and R. Pantling. 1898. The orchids of the Sikkim-Himalaya. Ann. Roy. Bot. Garden Calcutta 8:184–196.

Lin, T. P. 1977. Native orchids of Taiwan, Vol. 2, pp. 101–134. Ji-Chyi Wang, Chiayi, Taiwan.

Lindley, J. 1830–1840. Genera and species of orchidaceous plants, pp. 161–172. Ridgways, London.

——. 1859. Contributions to the orchidology of India. J. Proc. Linn. Soc. (Botany) 3:27–30.

Menninger, E. D. 1961. Catalog of Cymbidium species with synonyms and excluded species. Amer. Orchid Soc. Bull. 30:865–876.

Pradhan, U. 1979. Indian orchids, Vol. 2. Kalimpong, India, pp. 465–480. Pub. by author.

Rheede, H. 1703. Horti Malabarici 12:17, t. 8.

Rolfe, R. A. 1903. Cymbidium atropurpureum. Orch. Rev. 11:190–191.

——. 1915. Cymbidium pendulum. Orch. Rev. 23:252.

——. 1917. Cymbidium aloifolium and its allies. Orch. Rev. 25:173–175.

Roxburgh, W. 1795. Epidendrum pendulum. Plants of the Coast of Coromandel, Vol. 1, p. 35, t. 44.

Rudbeck, O. 1701. Campi Elysii, Vol. 2, p. 224.

Sander, F. K. 1921. Sander's complete list of Orchid Hybrids to January 1946, with addenda for 1946–60, 1961–70, 1971–75.

Schlechter, R. 1924. The genera Cymbidium Sw. and Cyperorchis Bl. Feddes Repertorium 20:96–110.

Seidenfaden, G., and T. Smitinand. 1961. The orchids of Thailand, Vol. 3, pp. 498–514. Siam Society, Bangkok.

Smith, J. J. 1905. Die Orchideen von Java, Vol. 6 of Der flora von Buitenzorg, pp. 474–484. E. J. Brill, Leiden.

——. 1911. Die Orchideen von Java, figuren atlas, Vol. 4. E. J. Brill, Leiden.

Swartz, O. 1799. Cymbidium. Nov. Act. Soc. Sci. Ups. 6:70–78.

Wu, Y. S., and S. C. Chen. 1980. A taxonomic review of the orchid genus Cymbidium in China. Acta Phyt. Sinica 18:292–307.

APPENDIX

Chromosomes in Orchids: Counting and Numbers*

RYUSO TANAKA and HARUYUKI KAMEMOTO

*Submitted in July 1980.

Studies of orchid chromosomes have produced knowledge of considerable practical value to orchid breeders. Since increases in chromosome number are generally accompanied by improved horticultural characteristics, orchid breeders have learned that determining chromosome number is an important tool in breeding. Such terms as diploids, triploids, tetraploids, and aneuploids are now in common use among orchidologists.

Every orchid plant is composed of a great many cells, and in the nuclei of the cells are very small bodies known as chromosomes. The chromosomes carry genes, the determiners of heredity.

The chromosome number in any one species is generally constant—40 for species of *Cattleya*, 38 for *Vanda*, 38 for *Phalaenopsis*. These numbers represent two sets of chromosomes; one set is derived from the pollen parent, and the other from the seed-bearing parent. The combination of these two sets of chromosomes is called a diploid (*di*, two; *ploid*, fold). Reduction division, or meiosis, results in the production of eggs and pollen, each possessing only one set of chromosomes. The fusion of egg and pollen in fertilization restores the diploid number, thereby maintaining a constant number of chromosomes for the species. Occasionally, however, changes in chromosome numbers occur, some of which are increases in multiple sets of chromosomes. Plants with three sets of chromosomes are *triploids* (*tri*, three); those with four sets are *tetraploids* (*tetra*, four); those with five sets are *pentaploids* (*penta*, five); those with six sets are *hexaploids* (*hexa*, six). Triploids, tetraploids, pentaploids, hexaploids, and higher ploids are collectively referred to as *polyploids* (*poly*, many). Polyploids, along with *haploids* (*monoploids*) and diploids, are also termed *euploids* (*eu*, good or advantageous) because they possess chromosome numbers that are exact multiples of a given set.

An individual with a chromosome number that is not an exact multiple of a chromosome set is an *aneuploid* (*an*—not). In Cattleyas the euploid numbers are 20 (haploid), 40 (diploid), 60 (triploid), 80 (tetraploid), 100 (pentaploid), and so on. Plants with numbers deviating from the above euploids, such as 41, 42, 58, 59, 61, 62, 81, 82, are correctly termed *aneuploids*.

Characteristics of Polyploids and Aneuploids

An increase in ploidy in orchids is often accompanied by an increase in the size of the plant parts. Plants are stockier; leaves are darker green, wider, and thicker; and flowers are of improved form. Because of the increased width and substance of the sepals and petals, the flowers are often erect, sturdy, and compact, desirable characteristics for exhibition.

Because increase in ploidy results in improvement of individual flowers, more award-

NOTE: The portion of this appendix that precedes the list of chromosome numbers is taken with some modification from "Chromosome Numbers of Orchids in Hawaii," by H. Kamemoto, R. Tanaka, and K. Kosaki, *Hawaii Agricultural Experimental Station Bulletin* 127, pp. 1–28, 1961.

winning orchids are tetraploids than triploids. For cut flowers, however, an important consideration is floriferousness, and it appears that this characteristic is generally inversely related to increased ploidy. Triploidy appears to be the most desirable level for cut-flower production in *Cattleya* as well as in *Cymbidium*. At this level, improved flower quality is obtained without sacrificing flower production.

Not all polyploids have superior characteristics. Since genes are the ultimate determiners of heredity, a duplication of a poor set of genes in a tetraploid will accentuate inferior qualities. Conversely, a diploid with desirable genes can produce flowers of higher quality than a triploid or tetraploid with poor genes. A combination of desirable genes and polyploidy should be the aim in breeding for award-winning plants.

When diploids already have genes for heavy substance, an increase in ploidy can result in "too-heavy" substance, which can cause crippling. Many tetraploid yellows are notorious for this characteristic. It has been noted in some crosses that triploidy substantially reduces the malformation of flowers among yellows.

For cut-flower production among *Vanda* and *Dendrobium*, the diploids have maintained their importance. A superior commercial cut flower variety, which will probably remain in commercial production, is the diploid *Vanda* Miss Joaquim. *Dendrobium* Jacquelyn Thomas and *D.* Neo Hawaii, which are also diploids, have demonstrated their value as cut flowers among dendrobiums.

Occasionally, plants with one or two additional chromosomes appear. Morphological differences are not always clearly evident among *Cattleya* plants with 41, 42, or 43 chromosomes. Also, aneuploids on the polyploid level, such as those with 61, 62, 79, 81, 82, 83, 101, and 102 chromosomes, often do not exhibit detectable morphological variations from their corresponding euploids (60, 80, and 100). On the other hand, aneuploids with chromosome numbers that deviate considerably from the euploids may exhibit differences in plant vigor and morphological characteristics. Their breeding behavior may also be adversely affected.

Breeding Behavior of Polyploids and Aneuploids

The best orchid stud plants are tetraploids because they are fertile and produce offspring that are relatively uniform. Variations in degree of fertility occur among tetraploids depending upon the constitution of the chromosome complements. If all four sets are uniform, such as tetraploid strap-leaved *Vanda* (*autotetraploid*, SSSS), fertility may be reduced as a result of irregularity in meiosis, which leads to the formation of univalents, bivalents, trivalents, and tetravalents. On the other hand, tetraploid semi-terete *Vanda* (*allotetraploid*, SSTT) exhibits less irregularity at meiosis because normal chromosome pairing can occur within similar sets of strap and terete *Vanda* chromosomes.

Tetraploids can be selfed or crossed with other tetraploids to produce further tetraploids. When crossed with diploids, triploids will result; when crossed with triploids, variable offspring may be predicted.

Triploids are generally of low fertility and often represent a dead end in breeding. The reason for this poor fertility is the high irregularity in reduction division. Because there are three sets of chromosomes, distribution of chromosomes to the poles is unequal, resulting in pollen and eggs with varying chromosome numbers, many of which are nonfunctional. Occasionally, restitution of nuclei will give rise to functional unreduced eggs and pollen.

Some triploids produce offspring. The chances of success with triploids are improved if they are used as the seed-bearing parent instead of the pollen parent. The resulting progenies can be expected to be highly variable because of the wide range in products from reduction division. For example, triploid *V.* Nellie Morley × diploid strap-leaved *Vanda* has resulted in individuals with 38, 39, 52, 57, 70, 71, 73, 75, 76, and 95 chromosomes. Triploid *Dendrobium* Lady Constance × diploid *D. phalaenopsis* has produced seedlings with 38, 42, 46, 51, 52, 57, and 75 chromosomes. This type of cross can therefore be expected to yield diploid, triploid, tetraploid, and pentaploid offspring in addition to aneuploids. Some pentaploids might be anticipated from triploid × tetraploid crosses, as has been the case with triploid *C.* Rembrandt × tetraploid *Lc.* Pasadena, which produced pentaploid *Lc.* Rosa Kirsch. Variability can also be expected, however, as shown in the cross triploid *C. bowringiana* 'Splendens' × tetraploid *Blc.* Wendell Hoshino, which produced individuals with chromosome numbers of 100, 79, 70, and 71.

Pentaploids generally appear to be more fertile than triploids. Studies on meiosis in pentaploid strap-terete *Vanda* plants have revealed that usually two sets of chromosomes reach either pole and that the chromosomes of the extra set assort at random. Thus, in crosses involving the pentaploids *V.* Nora Potter, *V.* Colorful, and *V.* Roberta Chun with diploid strap-leaved *Vanda*, the chromosome numbers of offspring ranged from 59 to 68, with the majority having from 65 to 68 chromosomes. These are aneuploids between the triploid and tetraploid levels.

Aneuploids with deviations of one or two chromosomes from the euploid level apparently do not exhibit adverse morphological characteristics or breeding behavior, and, therefore, might practically be included with the euploids. Aneuploid *Cattleya* plants with 61 or 62 chromosomes will show poor fertility, similar to triploids with 60 chromosomes, whereas aneuploids with 81 or 82 chromosomes will be fertile, similar to tetraploids with 80 chromosomes.

Those aneuploids with chromosome numbers more or less intermediate between the triploid and tetraploid levels can be expected to be low in fertility because of chromosome imbalance.

Sterility among Diploids

Although orchidologists generally attribute sterility in orchids to triploidy and aneuploidy, many diploids also exhibit sterility. Sterility can result from incompatibility of genes, male sterile genes, or genes that cause irregularities such as asynapsis, stickiness, and supernumerary cell divisions in meiosis. Translocations, inversions, and deletions of chromosomes may also result in sterility. The most common cause of sterility encountered among diploid orchids is probably a lack of homology of parental chromosomes in primary hybrids. Normal chromosome pairing at meiosis is often a prerequisite to fertility. In interspecific hybrids, partial pairing or complete lack of pairing results in poor fertility. Generally, hybrids of distantly related species are lower in fertility than those of closely related species. Since efforts in Hawaii have been directed toward producing increased numbers of intergeneric hybrids, sterility problems will undoubtedly be encountered. On the other hand, improvements in germination technique involving ovule culture may successfully surmount some sterility barriers encountered with the usual seed germination methods.

Technique for Counting Chromosomes

The technique for making routine counts is not difficult to master if approximate counts suffice. Although accurate counts are necessary in scientific research, counts of plus or minus one or two chromosomes are usually satisfactory for practical purposes, particularly when chromosome numbers are at the triploid and higher polyploid levels.

The Microscope

Except for *Paphiopedilum* plants, which possess large chromosomes that can be counted with a high, dry objective (40×), orchids require a microscope equipped with an oil-immersion lens (90 to 100×) and 10 to 15× oculars. The optical system should be clean and perfectly aligned to give a clear image.
The following equipment and supplies are also needed:
   Microscope illuminating lamp
   Green filter
   Slides and cover slips
   Vials with stoppers
   Alcohol lamp
   Tweezers and dissecting needles
   Sharp knife or razor blades
   Wax pencil
   Orcein stain
   Glacial acetic acid
   Ethyl alcohol (95%)
   Chloroform
   Concentrated hydrochloric acid
   8-hydroxyquinoline
   Paraffin
   Gum mastic
   Immersion oil
   Blotting paper

Preparation of Aceto-Orcein Stain

Prepare 100 ml. of 45% acetic acid by pouring 45 ml. of glacial acetic acid in 55 ml. of distilled water. Place 1 g of orcein in the acetic acid and heat to dissolve orcein. Cool the solution, filter, and transfer the stain into a medicine dropper bottle. The stain is now ready for use.

Preparation of 8-Hydroxyquinoline Solution

Pretreatment of root tips with 8-hydroxyquinoline will cause contraction and improve spreading of chromosomes and thereby facilitate counting. Prepare 0.002 M solution of 8-hydroxyquinoline (molecular weight = 145.15) by dissolving 0.029 g of 8-hydrooxyquinoline in 100 ml. of distilled water.

Preparation of Fixing Fluids

The fixing fluid should kill the cells rapidly with a minimum of shrinkage, swelling, distortions, and production of artifacts. Any of the following fixing fluids is satisfactory:
1. Modified Carnoy's
   2 parts 95% ethyl alcohol
   1 part chloroform
   1 part glacial acetic acid
2. Carnoy's
   3 parts ethyl alcohol
   1 part glacial acetic acid
3. 45% acetic acid

Preparation of Hydrochloric Acid-Alcohol Mixture

Hydrochloric acid is used to soften tissues so that they may be spread easily. One can use 1N hydrochloric acid at 140°F (60°C) or a 1:1 mixture of concentrated hydrochloric acid (12N) and 95% ethyl alcohol at room temperature.

Preparation of Paraffin-Gum Mastic Mixture

Heat 1 part of gum mastic with 9 parts of paraffin until they melt and form a mixture. Cool to solidify. This mixture is used to seal cover slips.

Root Smear Technique for Counting Chromosomes of Orchids

1. Sever active root tips, about 1 mm long, and place in a small vial containing 0.002 M 8-hydroxyquinoline solution for 3 to 5 hours at about 65°F (18°C).
2. Wash with water.
3. Fix with 2:1:1 mixture of 95% ethanol, chloroform, and glacial acetic acid for at least 10 minutes at about 50°F (10°C).
4. Hydrolyze with 1N HCl at 140°F (60°C) for 3 to 5 minutes.
5. Wash with water.
6. Place in 45% acetic acid for 10 minutes. (It may also be stored for several days in refrigerator.)
7. Transfer the root to a clean slide and cover with 45% acetic acid to keep roots from drying.
8. Remove root cap under a dissecting microscope.
9. Separate cells with needles.
10. Blot out acetic acid, add 1 to 2 drops of aceto-orcein, and place slide in a chamber saturated with 45% acetic acid for 10 to 30 minutes.
11. Place cover glass, tap cover with the point of a needle or slide tapper, and remove excess stain.

12. When cells are well spread, heat slide for a few seconds. Prevent boiling.
13. Place bibulous paper over slide and press firmly with thumb to flatten cells and remove excess stain.
14. Seal edges of cover glass with paraffin-gum mastic mixture or dental wax.
15. Count chromosomes with a compound microscope under an oil immersion lens.

Pollen Mother Cell (PMC) Smear Technique for Counting Chromosomes of Orchids

1. Carefully slit open a young bud with a surgical knife and sample a small portion of a pollinium to determine the stage of development.
2. Place on slide and fix with 45% acetic acid at 50°F (10°C) for 5 minutes.
3. Replace 45% acetic acid with 1% aceto-orcein and stain for a few minutes.
4. Place a cover glass, heat, and press firmly to remove excess stain.
5. Examine under the microscope. If the stage of meiosis is too early to sample, seal the bud with scotch or masking tape to prevent drying and resample at an appropriate time.
6. If the PMCs are at metaphase division, remove pollinia and treat with 45% acetic acid at 50°F (10°C) for 10 minutes.
7. Place a portion of the pollinia on a slide and add a drop of aceto-orcein. Keep in chamber for 5 minutes. Prepare additional slides to ensure adequate numbers of analyzable figures.
8. Place a cover glass, tap gently, and remove excess stain.
9. Heat gently. Do not allow to boil.
10. Press firmly and seal with dental wax.
11. Count chromosomes with a compound microscope under an oil immersion lens.

Chromosome Numbers in Orchids

Plant name	Chromosome number n	Chromosome number 2n	Reference	Plant name	Chromosome number n	Chromosome number 2n	Reference
Acampe longi- folia		38	Kamemoto et al., 1964	Aceras anthro- pophora		42	Heusser, 1938
Acp. ochracea		38	Kamemoto et al., 1964		21	42	Barber, 1942
						42	Kliphuis, 1963
Acp. papillosa		38	Kamemoto et al., 1964			42	Löve & Kjell- quist, 1973
		38	Tara & Kame- moto, 1970	Acineta superba		40, 42	Daker & Jones, 1970
		36	Mehra & Kash- yap, 1978	Acroanthes monophyllos	15–17		Stenar, 1937
	18, 19		Mehra & Seh- gal, 1978	(= Malaxis monophylla)			
Acp. prae- morsa		38	Kulkarni & Jorapur, 1979	Ada elegantula		60	Charanasri & Kamemoto, 1975
Acp. wightiana		38	Barganur, 1972	A. species		60	Charanasri & Kamemoto, 1975
Acanthe- phippium pictum		48	Tanaka, 1965b	Aerangis biloba		50	Shindo & Kamemoto, 1963b
A. striatum	20		Mehra & Vij, 1970			50	Jones, 1967
						50	Ar-rushdi, 1971
A. sylhetense	20		Mehra & Vij, 1970	Aergs. citrata		ca. 50	Jones, 1967
				Aergs. compta		51	Jones, 1967

Plant name	n	2n	Reference	Plant name	n	2n	Reference
		Chromosome number				Chromosome number	
Aergs. kotschyana		50, ca. 50	Jones, 1967	Aer. ringens		38	Kulkarni & Jorapur, 1979
Aergs. rhodosticta		42	Jones, 1967	Aer. suavissima		ca. 38	Jones, 1967
Aergs. species		50, ca. 50, 200	Jones, 1967	Aer. vandarum		38	Chardard, 1963
Aergs. ugandensis		ca. 50	Jones, 1967			38	Sharma & Chatterji, 1966
Aeridachnis unnamed (Aerides odoratum × Arachnis maingayi)	variable	38	Shindo & Kamemoto, 1963a	Aer. williamsii		38	Jones, 1967
				Aeridostylis Springtime	variable 19–76	38	Tanaka & Kamemoto, 1961
Aerides biswasianum	19		Mehra & Vij, 1970	A. unnamed (Aerides odoratum × Rhynchostylis gigantea)	variable	38	Shindo & Kamemoto, 1963
Aer. crassifolium		38	Kamemoto et al., 1964				
Aer. crispum	19		Chardard, 1963				
		38	Kulkarni & Jorapur, 1979	Aeridovanda unnamed (Vanda Tatzeri × Aerides lawrenceae)	variable	38	Tanaka & Kamemoto, 1961
Aer. falcatum	19		Chardard, 1963				
		38	Kamemoto et al., 1964	Agrostophyllum brevipes	20		Mehra & Vij, 1970
Aer. fieldingii		38	Kamemoto et al., 1964	A. callosum	20		Mehra & Vij, 1970
Aer. flabellatum		38	Kamemoto et al., 1964			38	Mehra & Sehgal, 1978
Aer. hitchongii		40	Chardard, 1963	A. khasianum	20		Mehra & Vij, 1970
Aer. houllettianum		38	Kamemoto et al., 1964	A. myrianthum	20		Mehra & Vij, 1970
		38	Tara & Kamemoto, 1970	Amblostoma tridactylum		40	Blumenschein, 1960
Aer. japonicum		38	Yuasa, 1936	Amitostigma gracile		42	Tanaka, 1965b
	19	38	Sugiura, 1939	A. keiskei		42	Mutsuura & Nakahira, 1958
		38	Miduno, 1940b			42	Tanaka, 1965b
		38	Kamemoto, 1959b			42	Tanaka, 1971
		38	Mutsuura & Nakahira, 1960	A. lepidum		44	Tanaka, 1965b
		38	Sinoto & Shoji, 1962	Anaecamptis pyramidalis		20, 40	Fuchs & Ziegenspeck, 1923
		38	Tanaka, 1965b		18	36	Heusser, 1938
Aer. lawrenceae		40	Eftimiu-Heim, 1941		18		Barber, 1942
	19	38	Shindo & Kamemoto, 1963c			36	Kliphuis, 1963
Aer. longicornu	19		Mehra & Vij, 1970			36	Natarajan, 1979
Aer. maculosa		38	Jones, 1967	Ancistrorhynchus cladestinus		48	Ar-rushdi, 1971
Aer. maculosum		38	Kulkarni & Jorapur, 1979	A. recurvus		ca. 50	Jones, 1967
Aer. mitratum		38	Kamemoto et al., 1964	Angraecopsis breviloba		50	Jones, 1967
		38	Tara & Kamemoto, 1970	Angraecum anocentrum		38	Jones, 1967
Aer. multiflorum		40 (22)	Sharma & Chatterji, 1966	Angcm. arachnites		38	Jones, 1967
	19		Arora, 1968	Angcm. bilobum	25	50	Chardard, 1963
		38	Mehra & Kashyap, 1979	Angcm. calceolus		38	Jones, 1967
Aer. odoratum	19	38	Shindo & Kamemoto, 1963a	Angcm. chevalieri		ca. 38	Jones, 1967
		38	Kamemoto et al., 1964	Angcm. compressicaule		42–48	Chardard, 1963
	20	40	Sharma & Chatterji, 1966	Angcm. eburneum		40	Eftimiu-Heim, 1941
		38	Jones, 1967			38	Shindo & Kamemoto, 1963a
	19		Arora, 1968	Angcm. eichlerianum		38	Chardard, 1963
Aer. odoratum var. immaculatum		76	Kamemoto, et al., 1964			38	Jones, 1967

Plant name	Chromosome number n	Chromosome number 2n	Reference
		38	Tara & Kamemoto, 1970
Angcm. erectum		63	Jones, 1967
Angcm. giryamae		38	Jones, 1967
Angcm. guillauminii		50	Chardard, 1963
Angcm. infundibulare		38	Jones, 1967
Angcm. leonis		40	Eftimiu-Heim, 1941
Angcm. multinominatum		42	Jones, 1967
Angcm. sacciferum		ca. 76	Jones, 1967
Angcm. sanderianum	25		Chardard, 1963
Angcm. scottianum		38	Jones, 1967
Angcm. sesquipedale		38	Woodard (in Duncan, 1959)
		42	Chardard, 1963
Anoectochilus brevilabris	20		Mehra & Sehgal, 1974
Anct. formosanus	12		Hsu, 1971
Anct. siamensis		40	Larsen, 1966
Anct. sikkimensis	15		Mehra & Vij, 1970
	15		Mehra & Vij, 1972a
Anct. tetsuoi		40	Tanaka, 1965b
		40	Tanaka, 1971
Ansellia nilotica		42	Tanaka, 1964a
Anthogonium gracile		42	Chatterji, 1968
	20		Mehra & Vij, 1970
	27		Sharma & Sarkar, 1967–1968
		38	Mehra & Sehgal, 1978
Aphyllorchis caudata		ca. 36	Larsen, 1966
A. unguiculata		ca. 40	Larsen, 1966
Arachmanthe clarkei		38	Sharma & Sarkar, 1967–1968
Arachnis flosaeris		38	Shindo & Kamemoto, 1963a
Aranda Hilda Galistan	variable	38	Tanaka & Kamemoto, 1961
Aranthera Mohammed Haniff	15–23	38	Kamemoto & Shindo, 1962
Arundina bambusifolia		40	Sharma & Chatterji, 1966
	21		Mehra & Sehgal, 1975
A. graminifolia		32	Pancho, 1965a
		42	Larsen, 1966
	20		Mehra & Vij, 1970
A. sinensis (= A. chinensis)		40	Tanaka, 1965b
		40	Tanaka, 1971
A. species	16	32	Samphathkumaran & Rangaswamy, 1931
Ascocenda Portia Doolittle	variable	38	Tanaka & Kamemoto, 1961
Ascocentrum ampullaceum		38	Woodard (in Duncan, 1959)
		38	Kamemoto et al., 1964
		38	Tara & Kamemoto, 1970
Asctm. curvifolium		38	Shindo & Kamemoto, 1963a
		38	Kamemoto et al., 1964
		38	Tara & Kamemoto, 1970
Asctm. micranthum		38	Kamemoto et al., 1964
		38	Tara & Kamemoto, 1970
Asctm. miniatum		38	Kamemoto et al., 1964
		38	Pancho, 1965a
		ca. 38	Jones, 1967
		38	Tara & Kamemoto, 1970
Ascofinetia Twinkie	variable	38	Shindo & Kamemoto, 1962
Ascotainia laxiflora		36	Miduno, 1940b
Aspasia epidendroides		60	Charanasri & Kamemoto, 1975
Asp. principissa		58	Sinoto, 1962
		60	Charanasri & Kamemoto, 1975
Asp. pusilla		56	Sinoto, 1962
Aspasium Regal		58	Sinoto, 1962
Aspsm. unnamed (Aspasia principissa × Oncidium sphacelatum)		56	Sinoto, 1962
Barlia robertiana		36	Raynaud, 1971
Biermannia bimaculata	18		Mehra & Sehgal, 1978
Bifrenaria harrisoniae		40	Hoffmann, 1929
		40	Hoffmann, 1930
		38	Tanaka, 1962a
Blephariglottis lacera		42	Löve & Simon, 1968
Bletia rodriguesii		40	Blumenschein, 1960
Bletia verecunda		60	Tanaka, 1965b
Bletilla formosana		36	Miduno, 1939
	18		Miduno, 1940b
		36	Tanaka, 1965b
		36	Tanaka, 1971
		16	Hsu, 1972
Ble. hyacinthia	16		Afzelius, 1943
Ble. striata		32	Miduno, 1939
	16	32	Miduno, 1940b
		32	Mutsuura & Nakahira, 1958
		32	Tanaka, 1962a
		ca. 32	Nakasone & Moromizato, 1964
		32	Tanaka, 1965b
		32	Tan, 1969
		32	Tanaka, 1971

Plant name	Chromosome number n	Chromosome number 2n	Reference
Ble. striata var. albomarginata		32	Miduno, 1939
Ble. striata forma gebina	3–32	32	Miduno, 1939
		16 (haploid)	Miduno, 1940a
		32	Tan, 1969
Ble. unnamed (Ble. striata f. gebina × Eleorchis japonica)		36	Miduno, 1940a
Brachycorythis helferi		ca. 42	Larsen, 1966
B. obcordata		42	Mehra & Kashyap, 1978
Brapasia Serene		58	Sinoto, 1962
Brassavola cucullata		40	Blumenschein, 1960
B. digbyana		40	Chardard, 1963
B. grandiflora (= Laelia grandiflora)	20		Afzelius, 1943
	20		Duncan & MacLeod, 1948b
B. nodosa		40	Kamemoto, 1950
		40	Blumenschein, 1960
B. nodosa 'Gigas'		40	Kamemoto et al., 1961
B. perrinii (= Laelia perrinii)	20		Afzelius, 1943
		40	Blumenschein, 1960
Brassia allenii		50	Charanasri et al., 1973
Brs. caudata		60	Sinoto, 1962
		60	Sinoto, 1969b
		60	Charanasri et al., 1973
		60	Charanasri & Kamemoto, 1975
Brs. chloroleuca		60	Sinoto, 1962
		60	Sinoto, 1969b
Brs. gireoudiana		60	Sinoto, 1962
		60	Sinoto, 1969b
		60	Charanasri et al., 1973
Brs. lawrenceana var. longissima		52–56	Chardard, 1963
Brs. longissima		60	Sinoto, 1962
		60	Sinoto, 1969b
Brs. maculata		60	Sinoto, 1962
		60	Sinoto, 1969b
		60	Charanasri et al., 1973
Brs. pumila		60	Charanasri et al., 1973
Brs. verrucosa		60	Sinoto, 1962
		60	Tanaka, 1962a
		52–58	Chardard, 1963
		60	Sinoto, 1969b
Brs. verrucosa var. grandiflora		56	Dodson, 1957c
Brassidium Betty N. Shiraki		58	Sinoto, 1962
Brsdm. Black Beauty		58	Sinoto, 1962
Brsdm. Isao Nakagawa		60	Sinoto, 1962
Brsdm. Supreme		49	Sinoto, 1962
		49	Sinoto, 1966
Brsdm. unnamed (Brassia gireoudiana × Oncidium isthmi)		58	Sinoto, 1962
Brsdm. unnamed (Oncidium lanceanum × Brassia caudata)		44	Sinoto, 1962
Brassocattleya Akebono		ca. 40, 60	Kamemoto, 1952
Bc. Akebono 'No. 1'		60 ± 1	Kamemoto et al., 1961
Bc. Albion		diploid	de Tomasi, 1954
Bc. Cliftonii 'Magnifica'		60	Kamemoto et al., 1961
Bc. Cornelius		68–103	Kamemoto et al., 1967
Bc. Cytherea		ca. 60	Kamemoto, 1958
Bc. Deése 'French Lace'		60	Tanaka, 1964a
Bc. Empress of Russia 'Ohyamazaki'		ca. 60	Kamemoto, 1959b
Bc. Evelyn Zuck 'Darryl'		80 ± 1	Kamemoto et al., 1967
Bc. Grace S. Weston		40	Kamemoto, 1950
Bc. Hartland		80	Kamemoto et al., 1961
Bc. Hula Girl 'Sunshine'		40	Kamemoto et al., 1961
Bc. Hula Girl 'Sweet Sixteen'		60	Kamemoto et al., 1961
Bc. John Linford 'Symphony'		ca. 60	Kamemoto, 1952
Bc. Imperialis 'Westport'		84	Sagawa, 1962a
Bc. Minerva 'Taiwan'		60	Tanaka, 1966
Bc. Ohyamazaki 'Fine'		ca. 100	Kamemoto, 1959b
Bc. Ohyamazaki 'Hibarigaoka'		ca. 100	Kamemoto, 1959b
Bc. Pei Feng 'Fuji'		80	Tanaka, 1964a
Bc. Princess Patricia		ca. 80	Kamemoto, 1952
		80 ± 2	Kamemoto et al., 1961
Bc. Princess Patricia 'Falstaff'		ca. 80	Kamemoto, 1959b
Bc. unnamed (C. Barbara Dane × Bc. Everest)		60 ± 1	Kamemoto et al., 1961
Brassolaeliocattleya Accolade		tetraploid	Niimoto & Randolph, 1958
Blc. Amber 'Yamazaki's No. 1'		ca. 60	Kamemoto, 1959b
Blc. Aprica		60	Tanaka, 1966
Blc. Ben Kodama		60	Kamemoto et al., 1961
Blc. Bikan		ca. 80	Kamemoto, 1952
Blc. Cathy		81 ± 1	Kamemoto et al., 1961
Blc. Chief Joseph		triploid	de Tomasi, 1954
Blc. C. H. Tanaka		63 ± 1	Kamemoto et al., 1961
Blc. Consul Greig		tetraploid	de Tomasi, 1954
Blc. Daffora		ca. 80	Kamemoto, 1952

Plant name	n	2n	Reference
		80 ± 1	Kamemoto et al., 1961
Blc. Daffora 'Citrina'		ca. 60	Kamemoto, 1952
Blc. Dawn Angela		tetraploid	de Tomasi, 1954
Blc. Dinsmore 'Perfection'		84	Sagawa, 1962a
Blc. Duval 'Maxima'		85	Sagawa, 1962a
Blc. Elliott Markell 'Orchidglade'		101	Sagawa, 1962a
Blc. Eudora		67 ± 1	Kamemoto et al., 1961
Blc. Frank Tatsumura		80 ± 2	Kamemoto et al., 1967
Blc. Frank Tatsumura 'Tomiyasu'		80 ± 2	Kamemoto et al., 1961
Blc. Galatea 'Hozan'		85	Tanaka, 1964a
Blc. Golden Crown 'Excelsior'		60	Kamemoto et al., 1961
Blc. Golden Dawn		ca. 80	Kamemoto, 1959b
Blc. Golden Dome		60	Kamemoto et al., 1961
Blc. Golden Dome 'Chroma'		60	Tanaka, 1964a
Blc. Golden Queen 'Regina'		ca. 80	Kamemoto, 1952
		81 ± 1	Kamemoto et al., 1961
Blc. Goldenthea 'Golden Oriole'		80	Tanaka, 1966
Blc. Helen Fujiwara		80	Kamemoto et al., 1967
Blc. Herons Ghyll 'Ashiya'		80 ± 1	Tanaka, 1964a
Blc. Herons Ghyll 'Firesprite'		80	Tanaka, 1966
Blc. Herons Ghyll 'Nigrescens'		80	Tanaka, 1964a
Blc. Herons Ghyll 'Sensation'		78	Tanaka, 1966
Blc. Herons Ghyll 'Vulcan'		80	Tanaka, 1964a
Blc. Iliad		60 ± 1	Kamemoto et al., 1961
Blc. Ishbel		triploid	de Tomasi, 1954
Blc. Jane Helton		ca. 80	Kamemoto, 1959b
Blc. Llewellyn		ca. 80	Kamemoto, 1952
Blc. Luis H. Yanes, 'Caracas'		40	Kamemoto et al., 1967
Blc. Luis H. Yanes 'No. 1'		40	Kamemoto et al., 1967
Blc. Lyranda		80	Sagawa, 1962a
Blc. Malvern 'Grace'		80	Kamemoto et al., 1961
Blc. Marjorie Frey		92	Kamemoto et al., 1961
Blc. Mark 'Constance'		62 ± 2	Kamemoto et al., 1967
Blc. Matriarch 'Luscious'		80 ± 1	Kamemoto et al., 1961
Blc. Miami Sunset		66	Sagawa, 1962a

Plant name	n	2n	Reference
Blc. Myophia 'Hardesty'		60 ± 2	Kamemoto et al., 1961
Blc. Nai Tong Leng		ca. 60	Kamemoto, 1959b
Blc. Nanette		triploid	de Tomasi, 1954
		ca. 80	Kamemoto, 1959b
		80 ± 2	Kamemoto et al., 1961
Blc. Norman's Bay 'Gothic'		ca. 80	Kamemoto, 1959b
Blc. Norman's Bay 'Lucile'		82	Sagawa, 1962a
Blc. Norman's Bay 'Regal'		80	Tanaka, 1964a
		80	Tanaka, 1966
Blc. Norman's Bay 'Royal Bride'		82	Tanaka, 1964a
Blc. Norman's Bay 'Splendor'		80	Kamemoto et al., 1961
Blc. Norman's Bay 'Stuart Low'		81 ± 1	Kamemoto et al., 1961
Blc. Nugget 'Puritan'		80	Kamemoto et al., 1961
Blc. Oiai 'Tomiyasu'		60 ± 1	Kamemoto et al., 1961
Blc. Paul Nomura		60 ± 2	Kamemoto et al., 1961
Blc. R. Nakayama 'Mammoth'		100	Tanaka, 1964a
Blc. R. Nakayama 'No. 6'		100 ± 1	Tanaka, 1964a
Blc. Tecumseh		ca. 80	Kamemoto, 1952
Blc. The Baroness		79	Tanaka, 1966
Blc. Wake Island 'No. 7'		80	Kamemoto et al., 1961
Blc. Wake Island 'Queen'		ca. 80	Kamemoto, 1952
		80	Kamemoto et al., 1961
Blc. Wake Island 'Victory'		80	Kamemoto et al., 1961
Blc. Wendall Hoshino		ca. 80	Kamemoto, 1952
		83 ± 2	Kamemoto et al., 1961
Blc. Wendiana		69–106	Kamemoto et al., 1967
Blc. Winston Hoshino 'Ruby'		80	Kamemoto et al., 1967
Blc. Zeecrabbe 'Lucile'		80	Sagawa & Niimoto, 1961
Blc. unnamed (Blc. Wake Island × Lc. Emma Matsuguma)		80	Kamemoto et al., 1961
Blc. unnamed (Blc. Wendell Hoshino × Lc. Supervia)		86 ± 2	Kamemoto et al., 1961
Blc. unnamed (C. Albor × Blc. Accolade)		58–66, 81	Niimoto & Randolph, 1958
Blc. unnamed (C. bowringiana 'Splendens' × Blc. Wendell Hoshino)		70; 71 ± 1; 100 ± 1; 79 ± 1	Kamemoto et al., 1961

Plant name	Chromosome number		Reference	Plant name	Chromosome number		Reference
	n	2n			n	2n	
Blc. unnamed (*Lc.* Derrynane × *Blc.* Molfbra) 'S.D.-1'		80	Tanaka, 1966	*Bulb. fuscoides*		ca. 38	Daker, 1970
				Bulb. gamblei	20		Mehra & Vij, 1970
Blc. unnamed (*Lc.* Dinard × *Blc.* Galatea)		ca. 80	Kamemoto, 1952	*Bulb. grandiflorum*		38	Daker, 1970
		82 ± 2	Kamemoto et al., 1961	*Bulb. griffithii*	19		Mehra & Sehgal, 1975
Blc. unnamed (*Lc.* Gatton Glory × *Blc.* Chief Joseph 'Ele')		80 ± 2	Tanaka, 1966	*Bulb. gymnopus*	19		Mehra & Sehgal, 1974
				Bulb. imbricatum		38	Daker, 1970
				Bulb. inconspicuum		38	Tanaka, 1965b
Blc. unnamed (*Lc.* Kaumana × *Blc.* Llewellyn)		80	Kamemoto et al., 1961			38	Tanaka, 1971
				Bulb. intertextum		38	Daker, 1970
Blc. unnamed (*Lc.* Mysedo × *Blc.* Wendell Hoshino)		80 ± 1	Kamemoto et al., 1961	*Bulb. japonicum*		40	Mutsuura & Nakahira, 1960
						40	Tanaka, 1965b
						40	Tanaka, 1971
Broughtonia sanguinea	20		Sagawa & Niimoto, 1961	*Bulb. lacerata*		80 ± 2	Pancho, 1965a
						80 ± 2	Pancho, 1965b
Bulbophyllum adenopetalum		40	Pancho, 1965a	*Bulb. leopardinum*	19		Mehra & Vij, 1970
		40	Pancho, 1965b		18		Mehra & Sehgal, 1975
		38	Daker, 1970				
Bulb. aeolium		40	Pancho, 1965a	*Bulb. levanae* var. *giganteum*		60	Pancho, 1965a
Bulb. affine		36	Sharma & Chatterji, 1966			60	Pancho, 1965b
				Bulb. lobbii		38–42	Chardard, 1963
Bulb. affinii	20		Mehra & Vij, 1970			39	Daker, 1970
Bulb. alagense		40	Pancho, 1965a	*Bulb. lupulinum*		38	Daker, 1970
Bulb. antenniferum		40	Pancho, 1965b			40	Ar-rushdi, 1971
Bulb. apodum		38	Daker, 1970	*Bulb. makinoanum*		38	Tanaka, 1965b
Bulb. auratum	20		Pancho, 1965a	*Bulb. micholitzii*		38	Daker, 1970
	20		Pancho, 1965b				
Bulb. barbigerum		38	Daker, 1970	*Bulb. minutipetalum*		38	Daker, 1970
Bulb. braccatum	20		Pancho, 1965a	*Bulb. neilgherrense*		40	Jorapur & Hedge, 1974
	20		Pancho, 1965b				
Bulb. calamarium	19		Daker, 1970	*Bulb. nutans*		38	Daker, 1970
Bulb. califlorum	21		Mehra & Sehgal, 1978	*Bulb. odoratissimum*		38	Chardard, 1963
Bulb. canlanoense		40	Pancho, 1965a		29		Malla et al., 1977a
		40	Pancho, 1965b	*Bulb. oreonastes*		80	Ar-rushdi, 1971
Bulb. careyanum		38	Sharma & Chatterji, 1966	*Bulb. penicillium*	19		Mehra & Sehgal, 1978
	19 + B		Mehra & Vij, 1970	*Bulb. phaeopogon*		38	Daker, 1970
Bulb. clarkeyanum	19		Daker, 1970	*Bulb. polyrhizum*	19		Arora, 1971
Bulb. cocoinum		38	Daker, 1970	*Bulb. rau*		40	Mehra & Kashyap, 1979
Bulb. congolanum		38	Daker, 1970	*Bulb. refractoides*	19		Arora, 1971
Bulb. cornutum		38	Chardard, 1963	*Bulb. reflexiflorum*		38	Chardard, 1963
Bulb. cumingii		40	Pancho, 1965a	*Bulb. reptans*	19 + 0 – 1B		Mehra & Sehgal, 1975
		40	Pancho, 1965b			38	Mehra & Kashyap, 1978
Bulb. cylindraceum	20		Mehra & Vij, 1970	*Bulb. saurocephalum*	20		Hoffmann, 1929
Bulb. densiflorum	19		Arora, 1971		20		Hoffmann, 1930
Bulb. distans		57	Daker, 1970	*Bulb. secundum*	20		Mehra & Vij, 1970
Bulb. drymoglossum		40	Mutsuura & Nakahira, 1960	*Bulb. sociale*		38	Daker, 1970
Bulb. elatius		38	Daker, 1970	*Bulb. striatum*	19		Mehra & Sehgal, 1974
Bulb. emiliorum		40	Pancho, 1965a	*Bulb. tenuicaule*	19		Chardard, 1963
		40	Pancho, 1965b			38	
Bulb. eublepharum	19		Mehra & Vij, 1970	*Bulb. triste*	19		Arora, 1971
Bulb. evrardii		38–42	Chardard, 1963	*Bulb. umbellatum*		38	Mehra & Kashyap, 1978
Bulb. falcatum		38	Daker, 1970	*Bulb. veluntinum*	19		Daker, 1970
Bulb. flavidum		40	Ar-rushdi, 1971				
Bulb. frostii		38	Daker, 1970				

Plant name	Chromosome number n	Chromosome number 2n	Reference
Bulb. virescens		38	Daker, 1970
Bulb. species		40	Blumenschein, 1960
Calanthe alismaefolia	22	44	Sharma & Sarkar, 1967–1968
Cal. alpina	20		Mehra & Vij, 1970
Cal. aristrifera (= C. kirishimensis)		40	Miduno, 1940b
		40	Ito & Mutsuura, 1958
		40	Mutsuura & Nakahira, 1958
		40	Ito & Mutsuura, 1959
		40	Tanaka, 1965b
Cal. biloba		38	Sharma & Sarkar, 1967–1968
	40		Mehra & Vij, 1970
Cal. brevicornu		38, (57)	Sharma & Chatterji, 1966
	24		Sharma & Sarkar, 1967–1968
	20		Mehra & Vij, 1970
Cal. cardioglossa		ca. 44	Larsen, 1966
Cal. chevalieri	20		Chardard, 1963
Cal. chloroleuca		28	Sharma & Sarkar, 1967–1968
	20		Mehra & Sehgal, 1975
Cal. clavata	20		Mehra & Sehgal, 1974
Cal. discolor		40	Morinaga & Fukushima, 1931
		40	Miduno, 1940b
		40	Ito & Mutuura, 1958
		40	Mutsuura & Nakahira, 1958
		40	Ito & Mutsuura, 1959
		40	Tanaka, 1965b Lee, 1967
Cal. discolor var. kanashiroi		40	Tanaka, 1965b
Cal. fauriei		40	Tanaka, 1965b
Cal. foerstermannii		40	Larsen, 1966
Cal. furcata		40	Miduno, 1940b
		40	Ito & Mutsuura, 1958
		40	Mutsuura & Nakahira, 1958
		40	Ito & Mutsuura, 1959
		40	Nakasone & Moromizato, 1964
		40	Tanaka, 1965b
		40	Tanaka, 1966
Cal. gracilis	20		Mehra & Vij, 1970
Cal. hattorii		40	Ono, 1977
Cal. herbacea		40 + 2B	Mehra & Vij, 1970
Cal. japonica		40	Ito & Mutsuura, 1958
		40	Mutsuura & Nakahira, 1958
		40	Ito & Mutsuura, 1959
		40	Tanaka, 1965b
Cal. kirishimensis (= Cal. aristrifera)		40	Miduno, 1940b
Cal. liukiuensis		40	Nakasone & Moromizato, 1964
		40	Tanaka, 1965b
Cal. longicalcarata		40	Tanaka, 1965b
		20	Hsu, 1972
Cal mannii	20		Mehra & Sehgal, 1974
		40	Mehra & Kashyap, 1979
Cal. masuca		40	Larsen, 1966
		52	Sharma & Sarkar, 1967–1968
	20		Mehra & Vij, 1970
Cal. nipponica		40	Mutsuura & Nakahira, 1958
		40	Ito & Mutsuura, 1959
		38	Tanaka, 1965b
Cal. plantaginea		40	Arora, 1968
Cal. reflexa		40	Miduno, 1940b
		42	Ito & Mutsuura, 1958
		42	Mutsuura & Nakahira, 1958
		42	Ito & Mutsuura, 1959
		42	Mutsuura, 1959
		40	Tanaka, 1965b
		40	Hsu, 1971
Cal. rubens		44	Tanaka, 1965b
Cal. schlechteri		44	Mutsuura & Nakahira, 1958
		44	Ito & Mutsuura, 1959
		44	Mutsuura, 1959
		40	Tanaka, 1965b
Cal. sieboldii		40	Tahara, 1977
Cal. striata		40	Ito & Mutsuura, 1958
		40	Mutsuura & Nakahira, 1958
		40	Ito & Mutsuura, 1959
		40	Tanaka, 1965b
		40	Tanaka, 1974
	20		Terasaka & Tanaka, 1974
Cal. striata var. sieboldii		40	Miduno, 1940b
		40	Ito & Mutsuura, 1958
		40	Mutsuura & Nakahira, 1958
		40	Ito & Mutsuura, 1959
		40	Tanaka, 1965b
Cal. sylvatica	20		Chardard, 1963
Cal. torifera (= Cal. tricarinata)		40	Miduno, 1940b
		40	Tanaka, 1965b

Plant name	Chromosome number		Reference
	n	2n	
Cal. tricarinata		40	Tanaka, 1956b
(*Cal. tori-*		40, 60	Ito & Mutsuura,
fera)			1958
		40, 60	Mutsuura &
			Nakahira,
			1958
		40	Ito & Mutsuura,
			1959
		40	Mutsuura,
			1959
		60 (natural)	
	20		Mehra &
			Bawa, 1962
		42	Sharma & Sar-
			kar, 1967–
			1968
	20		Mehra &
			Bawa, 1970
	20		Mehra & Kash-
			yap, 1979
Cal. trulliformis	20		Mehra & Vij,
			1970
Cal. venusta		40	Ito & Mutsuura,
			1958
		40	Mutsuura &
			Nakahira,
			1958
		40	Ito & Mutsuura,
			1959
		40	Tanaka, 1965b
Cal. veratrifolia		40	Pancho, 1965a
		40	Pancho, 1965b
		40	Larsen, 1966
Cal. vestita	20		Hoffmann,
			1930
Cal. yushuni		20	Hsu, 1972
Cal. species		58	Tanaka, 1965b
(from Thai-			
land)			
Cal. species		40	Hsu, 1971
Cal. species		20	Hsu, 1972
Calopogon		42	Thien, 1973
barbatus			
C. multiflorus		42	Thien, 1973
C. pallidus		42	Thien, 1973
C. pulchellus	ca. 13	ca. 26	Pace, 1909
C. tuberosus		42	Thien, 1973
Calypso		32	Humphrey,
bulbosa			1932a,
			1932b
	14	28	Hagerup,
			1944a
Camarotis		38	Kamemoto *et*
apiculata			*al.*, 1964
C. manii	19		Mehra & Vij,
			1970
C. obtusa	19		Mehra & Vij,
			1970
Catasetum		56	Blumenschein,
atratum			1960
		ca. 108	Jones and
			Daker, 1968
Ctsm. callo-		54	Jones &
sum			Daker, 1968
Ctsm. cassi-		54	Jones &
dum			Daker, 1968
Ctsm. cernuum		56	Blumenschein,
			1960
		54	Jones &
			Daker, 1968
Ctsm. deltoid-		ca. 54	Jones &
eum			Daker, 1968
Ctsm. discolor		108	Jones &
			Daker, 1968
Ctsm. fimbri-		108	Jones &
atum			Daker, 1968
Ctsm. fimbri-		108	Jones &
atum var.			Daker, 1968
inconstans			
Ctsm. fimbri-		ca. 108	Jones &
atum var.			Daker, 1968
morrenianum			

Plant name	Chromosome number		Reference
	n	2n	
Ctsm. hookeri		56	Blumenschein,
			1960
Ctsm. integer-		54	Jones &
rimum			Daker, 1968
Ctsm. luridum		ca. 54	Jones &
			Daker, 1968
Ctsm. macro-		56	Blumenschein,
carpum			1960
		54	Jones &
			Daker, 1968
Ctsm. pileatum		ca. 108	Jones &
			Daker, 1968
Ctsm. plani-		ca. 162	Jones &
ceps			Daker, 1968
Ctsm. plani-		ca. 108	Jones &
ceps (peloric			Daker, 1968
form)			
Ctsm. russelli-		54	Jones &
anum			Daker, 1968
Ctsm. splen-		54	Jones &
dens (*Ctsm.*			Daker, 1968
macro-			
carpum ×			
Ctsm. pile-			
atum)			
Ctsm. thylacio-		54	Jones &
chilum			Daker, 1968
Ctsm. trulla		54	Jones &
			Daker, 1968
Ctsm. viridi-		54	Jones &
flavum			Daker, 1968
Ctsm. warsce-		54	Jones &
wiczii			Daker, 1968
Cattleya Albor		40	Niimoto & Ran-
			dolph, 1958
C. Amabilis	20, 21	40	Kamemoto,
			1950
C. Ashland		ca. 60	Kamemoto,
'Lion'			1952
		60 ± 1	Kamemoto *et*
			al., 1961
C. aurantiaca		40	Kamemoto,
			1950
C. Balmar		60	Kamemoto,
			1950
C. Balmar		41, 75	Niimoto & Ran-
(self)			dolph, 1958
C. Barbara		ca. 60	Kamemoto,
Dane			1952
		61 ± 1	Kamemoto *et*
			al., 1961
C. Barbara		ca. 60	Kamemoto,
Dane 'Per-			1952
fection'		tetraploid	de Tomasi,
			1954
		61 ± 1	Kamemoto *et*
			al., 1961
		62	Sagawa & Nii-
			moto, 1961
		62	Sagawa,
			1962a
C. Barbara		43	Kamemoto *et*
Sander			*al.*, 1967
C. Bengrave		ca. 60	Kamemoto,
			1952
C. Bengrave		60 ± 2	Kamemoto *et*
'No. 2'			*al.*, 1961
C. Bengrave		40	Kamemoto *et*
'No. 3'			*al.*, 1961
C. Ben Nevis		diploid	de Tomasi,
			1954
C. Bertii		40	Kamemoto *et*
			al., 1961
C. bicolor		40	Kamemoto,
			1950
		40, 80	Blumenschein,
			1960
		40	Blumenschein,
			1961

Plant name	Chromosome number n	Chromosome number 2n	Reference	Plant name	Chromosome number n	Chromosome number 2n	Reference
C. bicolor var. measuresiana (= C. measuresiana)		80	Blumenschein, 1961			40	Chardard, 1963
C. Bob Betts		ca. 80	Kamemoto, 1952	C. Claire Ayau 'Mae'		60 ± 1	Kamemoto et al, 1961
C. Bob Betts 'Betty'		83	Kamemoto et al., 1961	C. Clementine Goldfarb 'Purity'		40	Niimoto & Randolph, 1958
C. Bob Betts 'Miami Shores'		80	Sagawa & Niimoto, 1961	C. Cooksonii 'Alba'		tetraploid	de Tomasi, 1954
C. Bob Betts 'No. 1'		82 ± 2	Kamemoto et al., 1961	C. Cynthia alba 'Grandis'		82	Sagawa, 1962a
C. Bob Betts 'No. 2'		80 ± 2	Kamemoto et al., 1961	C. Dinah		ca. 80	Kamemoto, 1952
C. Bob Betts 'No. 3'		80 ± 2	Kamemoto et al., 1961			ca. 80	Kamemoto, 1959b
C. Bob Betts 'No. 10'		80 ± 1	Kamemoto et al., 1961			80 ± 1	Kamemoto et al., 1961
C. Bob Betts 'No. 29'		82 ± 1	Kamemoto et al., 1961	C. dormaniana		40	Blumenschein, 1960
C. Bob Betts 'No. 43'		80 ± 2	Kamemoto et al., 1961	C. Dorothy Mackaill		40–42	Niimoto & Randolph, 1958
C. Bow Bells		60, 61, 62	Kamemoto, 1950	C. dowiana	20	40	Kamemoto, 1950
		40	Kamemoto, 1952	C. dowiana var. aurea		40	Sagawa, 1962a
		triploid	de Tomasi, 1954	C. Edithiae		40	Kamemoto, 1952
		60, 62 ± 2	Niimoto & Randolph, 1958	C. Edithiae 'White Empress'		62	Kamemoto, 1950
C. Bow Bells 'Blue Ribbon'		ca. 80	Kamemoto, 1959b			40	Kamemoto, 1952
C. Bow Bells 'Chattanooga'		61	Niimoto & Randolph, 1958			62	Niimoto & Randolph, 1958
C. Bow Bells 'Elzada'		ca. 60	Kamemoto, 1952			40	Kamemoto et al., 1961
		60	Kamemoto et al., 1961	C. Ellen Beckert		60, 61, 62	Kamemoto, 1950
C. Bow Bells 'Honolulu'		78 ± 2	Niimoto & Randolph, 1958	C. elongata 'No. 1'		80	Kamemoto et al., 1961
C. Bow Bells 'Honolulu' (selfed)		75–86	Niimoto & Randolph, 1958	C. Empress Bells		80 ± 2, 81 ± 1	Kamemoto et al., 1961
C. Bow Bells '170th Anniversary'		ca. 60	Kamemoto, 1959b	C. Enid		84	Kamemoto, 1950
C. Bow Bells 'Maunakea'		ca. 60	Kamemoto, 1959b	C. Enid Alba		diploid	de Tomasi, 1954
C. Bow Bells 'Princess'		80	Tanaka, 1964a			40, 41 ± 1, 42, 44	Niimoto & Randolph, 1958
C. bowringiana		40	Eftimiu-Heim, 1941	C. Enid Alba 'Mandarin'		80	Sagawa, 1962a
	20, 21	41	Kamemoto, 1950	C. Enid Alba 'Ranier'		80	Kamemoto et al., 1967
		40–42	Chardard, 1963	C. Enid Alba 'United Nations'		81	Niimoto & Randolph, 1958
		60	Tanaka, 1964a			60	Kamemoto et al., 1961
C. bowringiana 'Katayama'		40	Tanaka, 1966	C. Enid Alba 'Warne'		60	Kamemoto et al., 1961
C. bowringiana 'Labor Day'		40	Sagawa & Niimoto, 1961	C. Enid 'Orchidhaven'		84	Kamemoto et al., 1961
C. bowringiana 'Splendens'		61 ± 1	Kamemoto et al., 1961	C. Estelle		triploid	de Tomasi, 1954
C. Brussels		80 ± 1	Kamemoto et al., 1961	C. Estelle Alba		ca. 80	Kamemoto, 1952
C. Cargill		40	Tanaka, 1964a	C. Estelle Alba 'Chambers'		40	Kamemoto et al., 1967
C. Celia		tetraploid	Niimoto & Randolph, 1958	C. Estelle Alba 'Cynosure'		80 ± 1	Kamemoto et al., 1961
		80	Kamemoto et al., 1961	C. Estelle Alba 'Makishima'		40	Kamemoto et al., 1967
		60	Sagawa, 1962a	C. Ethel Lederer 'Flat-top'		40	Sagawa, 1962a
C. Charybdis		81	Sagawa & Niimoto, 1961	C. Fabia	20	40	Kamemoto, 1950
C. Charybdis Orchidglade'		81	Sagawa & Niimoto, 1961	C. Fabingiana 'Hibarigaoka'		60 ± 1	Tanaka, 1964a
C. citrina		40	Kamemoto, 1950	C. Fabingiana 'Mikage'		ca. 60	Kamemoto, 1959b
				C. Falco		40	Chardard, 1963

Plant name	n	2n	Reference
C. forbesii		54–60	Chardard, 1963
C. Francis 'T.C. Au'		60 ± 2	Kamemoto et al., 1961
		60	Tanaka, 1964a
C. gaskelliana	20	40	Kamemoto, 1950
C. General Maude 'Victory'		60 ± 2	Kamemoto et al., 1961
C. General Patton		71 ± 2	Kamemoto et al., 1961
C. General Patton		80 ± 1	Tanaka, 1964a
C. General Patton 'Cheer'		80 ± 1	Kamemoto et al., 1961
C. General Patton 'Victory'			
C. George Eastman		40	Kamemoto, 1959b
C. gigas (= *C. warscewiczii*)	20	40	Kamemoto, 1950
		40	Niimoto & Randolph, 1958
		40	Chardard, 1963
C. gigas 'Firmin Lambeau'		40	Kamemoto et al., 1961
C. gigas 'Frau Melanie Beyrodt'		diploid	de Tomasi, 1954
		40	Niimoto & Randolph, 1958
C. Governor Gore		68 ± 1	Kamemoto et al., 1961
C. Gudhard	20	40	Kamemoto, 1950
C. guttata		40	Kamemoto, 1950
		40	Blumenschein, 1960
C. harrisoniana	20	40	Kamemoto, 1950
C. Hesperus	20, 21	40	Kamemoto, 1950
C. intermedia		40	Kamemoto, 1950
C. intermedia var. *alba*		41 ± 1f	Sagawa, 1962a
C. intermedia 'Aquini'		40	Sagawa, 1962a
C. intermedia 'Graham'		40	Kamemoto, 1950
		40	Blumenschein, 1960
		40	Vajrabhaya & Randolph, 1961
C. Intertexta 'Juliettiae'		triploid	de Tomasi, 1954
C. Jean Barrow		ca. 80	Kamemoto, 1952
C. Jean Barrow 'Kodama'		80 ± 1	Kamemoto et al., 1961
C. Jean Faircloth MacArther		ca. 60	Kamemoto, 1959b
C. Joyce Hannington		61	Kamemoto, 1950
		40	Kamemoto, 1952
		tretraploid	de Tomasi, 1954
		60	Kamemoto et al., 1961
C. Joyce Hannington 'September Morn'		81	Sagawa, 1962a
C. Kiwi 'Festival'		67 ± 1	Kamemoto et al., 1961
C. labiata		40	Eftimiu-Heim, 1941
	20	40, 42	Kamemoto, 1950
		diploid	de Tomasi, 1954
		triploid	de Tomasi, 1954
		tetraploid	de Tomasi, 1954
		40	Vajrabhaya & Randolph, 1961
	20	40	Tanaka, 1971
C. labiata 'Alba'		tetraploid	de Tomasi, 1954
C. labiata 'Amesiana'	20, 21	40, 41	Kamemoto, 1950
C. labiata 'Harefield Hall'		tetraploid	de Tomasi, 1954
		40	Sagawa & Niimoto, 1961
C. labiata 'Westonbirt'		40	Kamemoto et al., 1961
C. Leah Adis		58–62	Niimoto & Randolph, 1958
C. leopoldii		40	Blumenschein, 1960
C. lueddemanniana	20	40	Kamemoto, 1950
C. Madeleine Knowlton		100	Zuck, 1957
C. Madeline Knowlton 'G-1'		80	Kamemoto et al., 1961
C. Madeline Knowlton 'No. 1'		85 ± 1	Kamemoto et al., 1961
C. Mantini		40	Chardard, 1963
C. measuresiana (= *C. bicolor* var. *measuresiana*)		80	Blumenschein, 1961
C. Mem. T. Yamada 'Marijo'		78 ± 2	Kamemoto et al., 1961
C. mossiae	20	40	Kamemoto & Randolph, 1949
C. mossiae 'Mrs. Butterworth'		ca. 60	Kamemoto, 1950
C. mossiae var. *reineckiana* 'Youngs'		41	Niimoto & Randolph, 1958
C. mossiae 'Verna'		40	Kamemoto, 1950
C. mossiae 'Wageneri'		41	Niimoto & Randolph, 1958
C. Mrs. Frederick Knollys		40	Niimoto & Randolph, 1958
C. Mrs. James Watson 'Alba'		42	Niimoto & Randolph, 1958
C. Nancy Off		75–86	Niimoto & Randolph, 1958
C. Nigrella 'Jungle Prince'		ca. 80	Kamemoto, 1959b
C. North Star		68–107	Niimoto & Randolph, 1958
C. North Star 'Niimoto'		102	Vajrabhaya & Randolph, 1961
C. North Star (self)		85–103	Vajrabhaya & Randolph, 1961
C. Oboro		ca. 80	Kamemoto, 1959b

Plant name	Chromosome number n	Chromosome number 2n	Reference
C. Old Forester		80	Niimoto & Randolph, 1958
C. Pearl Harbor		80 ± 2	Kamemoto et al., 1961
C. Pearl Harbor 'Rotunda'		100	Sagawa & Niimoto, 1961
C. Pearl Harbor 'Silver Star'		102	Tanaka, 1964a
C. Peetersii		diploid	de Tomasi, 1954
C. Pegeen Fitzgerald		61	Kamemoto, 1950
C. percivaliana		40	Kamemoto & Randolph, 1949
	20	40	Kamemoto, 1950
C. Pink Frosting		40	Niimoto & Randolph, 1958
C. Portia		42	Kamemoto et al., 1961
C. Portia 'Coerulea'		40	Kamemoto, 1950
C. Portia 'Shinjuku'		ca. 60	Kamemoto, 1952
		60	Kamemoto et al., 1961
C. Prima Donna 'Tracy Ann'		80	Tanaka, 1964a
C. Prince Shimazu		ca. 60	Kamemoto, 1959b
C. Priscilla 'Alba'	20, 21	40	Kamemoto, 1950
C. Raphaellaurea		triploid	de Tomasi, 1954
C. Rembrandt		ca. 60	Kamemoto, 1952
		60	Kamemoto et al., 1961
C. Remy Chollet 'Kataoka'		60	Tanaka, 1964a
C. rex		40	Kamemoto, 1950
C. R. Cadwalader		41 ± 1	Niimoto & Randolph, 1958
C. Rodomont		86 ± 2	Kamemoto et al., 1961
C. R. Prowe		40	Kamemoto et al., 1961
C. Silver Swan 'Ogawa No. 8'		60	Tanaka, 1966
C. Silver Swan 'White Dove'		60	Tanaka, 1964a
C. skinneri		40	Kamemoto & Randolph, 1949
	20	40	Kamemoto, 1950
		40	Chardard, 1963
C. Snow Queen		ca. 60	Kamemoto, 1959b
C. Snowdon		triploid	de Tomasi, 1954
C. Souvenir de Louis Sander		61	Kamemoto, 1950
C. Suzanne Hye 'Kato'		40 + 2f.	Tanaka, 1964a
C. Tela 'Orchidglade'		80	Sagawa, 1962a
C. Thebes 'Bronze King'		ca. 80	Kamemoto, 1952
		80 ± 1	Kamemoto et al., 1961
C. Titrianae		80	Zuck, 1957
C. Tityus		40	Kamemoto, 1950
C. Tityus 'Westonbirt'		ca. 80	Kamemoto, 1952
		80 ± 2	Kamemoto et al., 1961
C. trianaei	20		Hoffman, 1930
		40	Eftimiu-Heim, 1941
		40	Kamemoto, 1950
C. trianaei 'Alba'		40	Sagawa & Niimoto, 1961
C. trianaei 'A. C. Burrage'		ca. 60	Kamemoto, 1952
		60 ± 1	Kamemoto et al., 1961
C. trianaei 'Broomhills'		40	Tanaka, 1964a
C. trianaei 'Grand Monarch'		40	Kamemoto, 1959b
C. trianaei 'Joan'		40	Kamemoto, 1950
C. trianaei 'Jungle Queen'		60	Sagawa, 1962a
C. trianaei 'Llewellyn'		83	Kamemoto, 1950
C. trianaei 'Mary Fennell'		60	Sagawa, 1962a
C. trianaei 'Mooreana'		ca. 60	Kamemoto, 1959b
C. trianaei 'Naranja'		59	Sagawa, 1962a
C. Tribells		100	Zuck, 1957
		73–102	Niimoto & Randolph, 1958
C. Trichlotho 'Perfection'		80	Sagawa & Niimoto, 1961
C. Varuna		40	Kamemoto et al., 1961
C. velutina		40	Blumenschein, 1960
C. walkeriana		40	Blumenschein, 1960
C. warneri		40	Kamemoto & Randolph, 1949
		40	Kamemoto, 1950
C. warscewiczii (= C. gigas)	20	40	Kamemoto, 1950
		40	Niimoto & Randolph, 1958
		40	Chardard, 1963
C. warscewiczii 'Firmin Lambeau'		40	Kamemoto, 1952
C. warscewiczii 'Frau Melanie Beyrodt'		diploid	de Tomasi, 1954
		40	Niimoto & Randolph, 1958
C. White Empress		40	Vajrabhaya & Randolph, 1961
C. unnamed (C. Albor × C. Pink Frosting)		40–41, 42, 60	Niimoto & Randolph, 1958
C. unnamed (C. Barbara Billingsley 'No. 299' × C. Edithiae 'White Empress')		83 ± 1	Niimoto & Randolph, 1958
C. unnamed (C. Barbara Billingsley, 2x × C. Edithiae 'White Empress,' 3x)		55, 56, 57, 60	Niimoto & Randolph, 1958

Plant name	Chromosome number n	2n	Reference
C. unnamed (Rivermont 1840) (C. Bow Bells × C. Ethel Bishop)		100 / 58–102	Zuck, 1957 / Niimoto & Randolph, 1958
C. unnamed (C. Bow Bells × C. Everest 'Superbissima')		83–92	Niimoto & Randolph, 1958
C. unnamed (C. Bow Bells 'Athena' × C. Empress Bells 'Eugenia')		79 ± 1	Kamemoto et al., 1961
C. unnamed (C. Bow Bells, 3x × C. trianae Alba 'Broomhill,' 4x)		73–102	Niimoto & Randolph, 1958
C. unnamed (C. Joyce Hannington × C. Bebe White)		75–86	Niimoto & Randolph, 1958
C. unnamed (C. Joyce Hannington × C. Edithae 'White Empress')		ca. 40	Kamemoto, 1952
C. unnamed (C. intermedia [2n = 40] × C. North Star 'Niimoto' [2n = 102])		60–127	Vajrabhaya & Randolph, 1961
C. unnamed (C. Mrs. Frederick Knollys × C. Enid Alba)		40–42	Niimoto & Randolph, 1958
C. unnamed (C. North Star 'B₁' [2n = 71] × C. labiata [2n = 40])		49–71	Vajrabhaya & Randolph, 1961
C. unnamed (C. North Star 'Niimoto,' 5x × C. Bow Bells 'Honolulu,' 4x)		79–91	Vajrabhaya & Randolph, 1961
C. unnamed (C. North Star 'Niimoto' [2n = 102] × C. White Empress [2n = 40])		78–89	Vajrabhaya & Randolph, 1961
C. unnamed (C. Pink Frosting × C. Albor)		40–42	Niimoto & Randolph, 1958
C. unnamed (C. Thebes × C. Aureata)		60	Kamemoto et al., 1961
Cattleytonia Rosy Jewel		82 ± 1	Kamemoto et al., 1967
Caularthron bicornutum	20	40	Adair & Sagawa, 1969
Cephalanthera damasonium		32 / 32	Barber, 1942 / Hagerup, 1947

Plant name	Chromosome number n	2n	Reference
		36	Pogan & Wcislo (in Löve & Löve, 1961)
	18		Kliphuis, 1963
		36	Wegener, 1966
C. ensifolia		34	Mehra & Bawa, 1962
		34	Mehra & Bawa, 1970
		32	Mehra & Vij, 1970
		32	Mehra & Vij, 1972a
		34	Vij & Gupta, 1975
	17		Malla et al., 1978
C. erecta		34	Miduno, 1937
		34	Miduno, 1938
C. falcata		34	Miduno, 1937
		34	Miduno, 1938
		34	Mutsuura & Nakahira, 1959
		34	Tanaka, 1971
C. grandifolia	18		Barber, 1942
C. longibracteata		32	Sokolovskaya, 1966
		42	Ohno, 1971
C. longifolia (=	16		Afzelius, 1943
C. ensifolia)	16	32	Hagerup, 1947
		32	Löve & Kjellquist, 1973
		32	Mehra & Kashyap, 1978
		32	Uhriková & Feráková, 1978
C. rubra	24	48	Titz, 1966
		36	Wegener, 1966
C. shizuoi		32	Miduno, 1937
		32	Miduno, 1938
Chamaeangis odoratissima		50	Jones, 1967
C. vesicata		95–100	Jones, 1967
Chamaeorchis alpina		42	Heusser, 1938
Chamorchis alpina		42	Engelskjoen & Knaben, 1971
Cheirostylis griffithii	13		Mehra & Sehgal, 1975
Chiloschista luniferus		38	Kamemoto et al., 1964
C. usnoides		38	Tara & Kamemoto, 1970
Cirrhopetalum acuminatum		38	Daker, 1970
Cirr. andersonii		38	Daker, 1970
Cirr. boninense		20	Ono, 1977
Cirr. caespitosum	20		Mehra & Vij, 1970
Cirr. caudatum	19		Mehra & Vij, 1970
Cirr. cornutum	19		Arora, 1971
Cirr. cuminghi		38	Chardard, 1963
		38	Daker, 1970
Cirr. gracillimum		ca. 38	Daker, 1970
Cirr. lasiochilum		38	Daker, 1970
Cirr. lepidum		38	Daker, 1970
Cirr. longiflorum		38–40	Chardard, 1963
Cirr. maculosum		38	Chatterji, 1968
Cirr. makayanum		38–40	Chardard, 1963
Cirr. mastersianum		38–40	Chardard, 1963
Cirr. mundulum		38	Daker, 1970
		38	Daker, 1970

Plant name	Chromosome number n	2n	Reference
Cirr. mysorense		ca. 38	Daker, 1970
Cirr. ornatissimum		38–40	Chardard, 1963
		ca. 38	Daker, 1970
Cirr. parvulum	19		Mehra & Vij, 1970
Cirr. picturatum		48	Eftimiu-Heim, 1941
cirr. pulchrum		38	Daker, 1970
Cirr. robustum		38	Daker, 1970
Cirr. stramineum		38–40	Chardard, 1963
Cirr. thouarsii		38	Chardard, 1963
Cirr. umbellatum		38	Daker, 1970
Cirr. vaginatum		38	Daker, 1970
Cirr. viridiflorum	19		Mehra & Vij, 1970
	19 + 0 – 3B		Mehra & Kashyap, 1978
Cirr. wallichii	19		Mehra & Vij, 1970
Cleistes divaricata		18	Baldwin & Speese, 1957
Cleistostoma brevipes	20		Mehra & Vij, 1970
	36		Mehra & Sehgal, 1974
C. gemmatum	20		Mehra & Vij, 1970
C. micranthum	19		Mehra & Vij, 1970
		38	Mehra & Kashyap, 1976
C. striatum	19, 20		Mehra & Sehgal, 1978
Coeloglossum viride (= *Platanthera bracteatum*)	20	40	Richardson, 1935
		40	Heusser, 1938
		40	Sokolovskaja & Strelkova, 1940
	20	40, 80, 85	Afzelius, 1943
		40	Löve & Löve, 1944
		40	Löve & Löve, 1956
		40	Mutsuura & Nakahira, 1960
		40	Sokolovskaya & Strelkova, 1960
		40	Pogan & Wcislo (in Löve & Löve, 1961)
		40	Gadella & Kliphuis, 1963
		40	Kliphuis, 1963
		ca. 40–42	Sokolovskaya, 1963
		40	Knaben & Engelskjön, 1967
		40	Laane, 1967
		40	Zhukova & Tikhonova, 1971
	20		Richards, 1972
		40	Uhríková & Schwarzová, 1976
C. viride ssp. *bracteatum*		40	Löve & Simon, 1968
C. viride ssp. *islandicum*		40	Löve & Löve, 1944
		40	Löve & Löve, 1956
Coelogyne barbata	20		Chardard, 1963

Plant name	Chromosome number n	2n	Reference
	20		Mehra & Vij, 1970
Coel. candoonensis		40	Pancho, 1965a
		40	Pancho, 1965b
Coel. chloroptera		40	Pancho, 1965a
		40	Pancho, 1965b
Coel. corymbosa		38 (22)	Sharma & Chatterji, 1966
	20		Mehra & Vij, 1970
Coel. cristata		40	Tanaka, 1964a
	20		Mehra & Vij, 1970
		40	Tanaka, 1971
		40	Arp, 1973
		40	Mehra & Kashyap, 1978
Coel. eberhardtii		40–44	Chardard, 1963
Coel. elata		44	Sharma & Sarkar, 1967–1968
	20		Mehra & Vij, 1970
	20		Arora, 1971
Coel. elmeri		40	Pancho, 1965a
		40	Pancho, 1965b
Coel. fimbriata	20		Hoffmann, 1929
	20		Hoffmann, 1930
Coel. flaccida	20		Mehra & Vij, 1970
Coel. flavida	20		Mehra & Vij, 1970
Coel. flexuosa	20		Hoffmann, 1929
	20		Hoffmann, 1930
Coel. fuliginosa	20		Hoffmann, 1929
	20		Hoffmann, 1930
Coel. fuscescens	20		Mehra & Vij, 1970
Coel. gardneriana	21		Mehra & Sehgal, 1974
Coel. huettneriana	20		Chardard, 1963
Coel. longipes	20		Mehra & Vij, 1970
Coel. merrittii		40	Pancho, 1965a
		40	Pancho, 1965b
Coel. micranthum	21		Mehra & Sehgal, 1974
Coel. nigrofurfuracea	20		Chardard, 1963
Coel. occultata	20		Mehra & Vij, 1970
		76	Mehra & Sehgal, 1974
		38	Mehra & Sehgal, 1978
Coel. ochracea	20		Mehra & Vij, 1970
Coel. ovalis	20		Mehra & Vij, 1970
Coel. prolifera	20		Mehra & Sehgal, 1974
Coel. punctulata	19 + (0 – 2) B		Mehra & Sehgal, 1974
Coel. stricta		40	Mehra & Kashyap, 1978
Coel. uniflora	20		Mehra & Vij, 1970
Comparettia falcata		42	Sinoto, 1962
		44	Charanasri & Kamemoto, 1975
Comp. speciosa		42	Sinoto, 1962

Plant name	Chromosome number n	Chromosome number 2n	Reference
Corallorhiza innata	21	42	Miduno, 1940b; Hagerup, 1941
C. maculata	42		Löve & Simon, 1968
C. maculata ssp. mertensiana	20		Taylor & Mulligan, 1968
C. striata		42	Löve & Simon, 1968
C. trifida		42	Miduno, 1940
		42	Hagerup, 1941
		42	Sorensen & Westergaad (in Löve & Löve, 1948)
		42	Löve & Löve, 1956
	21		Jørgensen et al. 1958
		ca. 42	Sorsa, 1963
		42	Laane, 1967
C. trifida var. verna		42	Löve, 1956
Coryanthes maculata		40	Daker & Jones, 1970
Corybas purpureus		40	Mehra & Sehgal, 1978
Corymborchis confusa		40	Pancho, 1965a
		40	Pancho, 1965b
Cremastra unguiculata		48	Mutsuura & Nakahira, 1959
		50	Tanaka, 1965b
C. variabilis	24	48	Ono & Hashimoto, 1956
		48	Mutsuura & Nakahira, 1958
(as C. appendiculata)		46	Sinoto & Shoji, 1962
		48	Tanaka, 1965b
C. wallichiana	26		Mehra & Vij, 1970
Cryptochilus lutea	19		Mehra & Vij, 1970
C. sanguinea	19		Mehra & Vij, 1970
Cryptopus elatus		95	Jones, 1967
Cryptostylis arachnites		42	Larsen, 1966
Cycnoches chlorochilon		68	Jones & Daker, 1968
Cyc. egertonianum		ca. 68	Jones & Daker, 1968
Cyc. loddigesii		64	Jones & Daker, 1968
Cyc. ventricosum		68	Jones & Daker, 1968
Cymbidiella rhodochila		54	Wimber, 1957a
Cymbidium Adrienne		diploid	Wells, 1956
Cym. Albanense		40	Mehlquist, 1952
	variable		Yeh, 1962
Cym. Alexanderi		40	Mehlquist, 1952
Cym. Alexanderi 'Album'		40	Mehlquist, 1952
		diploid	Wimber, 1957d
Cym. Alexanderi 'Fine'		40	Tanaka, 1962a
Cym. Alexanderi 'Perfection'		40	Mehlquist, 1952
		diploid	Wells, 1956
Cym. Alexanderi 'Roseum'		40	Mehlquist, 1952
Cym. Alexanderi 'Westonbirt'		tetraploid	Mehlquist, 1949

Plant name	Chromosome number n	Chromosome number 2n	Reference
		80	Mehlquist, 1952
		tetraploid	Menninger, 1954
		tetraploid	Wells, 1956
		tetraploid	Wimber, 1957d
		ca. 80	Kamemoto, 1959b
		80	Tanaka, 1964a
Cym. Alexette		triploid	Wells, 1956
Cym. Alexfrida		triploid	Wells, 1956
Cym. aloifolium	16	32	Sampathkumaran & Rangaswamy, 1931
		40	Mehlquist, 1952
		40	Nakasone & Moromizato, 1964
		40	Pancho, 1965a
		40	Pancho, 1965b
		40	Sharma & Chatterji, 1966
	20		Mehra & Vij, 1970
Cym. Altair 'Luath'		triploid	Wells, 1956
Cym. Amelia		40	Mehlquist, 1952
Cym. Ann Green		80 ± 1	Tanaka, 1962a
Cym. Anthony Evans		triploid	Wells, 1956
Cym. Antigone		ca. 60	Kamemoto, 1959b
Cym. Apollo 'Exbury'		diploid	Wimber, 1957d
Cym. Arabella 'II'		60	Mehlquist, 1952
Cym. Arabella 'Bexley'		triploid	Wells, 1956
Cym. Arabella 'Waverly'		tetraploid	Wells, 1956
Cym. Arabian Nights		triploid	Wells, 1956
Cym. Atlantes		60	Mehlquist, 1952
Cym. Atlantes 'Bellevue'		triploid	Wells, 1956
Cym. atropurpureum		40	Pancho, 1965
Cym. Ayot St. Peter		triploid	Wells, 1956
Cym. Babylon 'Carpentier'		tetraploid	Menninger, 1954
		tetraploid	Wimber, 1957d
Cym. Babylon 'Castle Hill'		tetraploid	Menninger, 1954
		tetraploid	Wimber, 1957d
Cym. Bali		60	Mehlquist & Clovis, 1957
Cym. Balkis		tetraploid	Menninger, 1954
		83 ± 1	Tanaka, 1962a
Cym. Balkis 'Luath'		tetraploid	Wells, 1956
Cym. Balkis 'Perfection'		tetraploid	Wimber, 1957d
Cym. Balkis 'Silver Orb'		tetraploid	Wells, 1956
		tetraploid	Wimber, 1957d
Cym. Beatrice		40	Mehlquist, 1952
Cym. Bengal Bay		60	Mehlquist & Clovis, 1957
Cym. Beryl		40	Mehlquist, 1952
Cym. bicolor	20		Swamy, 1941
Cym. Blue Smoke 'Beverly Glen'		diploid	Wimber, 1957d

Plant name	Chromosome number n	Chromosome number 2n	Reference
Cym. Blue Smoke 'Green Meadow'		diploid	Wimber, 1957d
Cym. Blue Smoke 'Pernod'		diploid	Wimber, 1957d
Cym. Blue Smoke 'Sea Green'		diploid	Wimber, 1957d
Cym. Bodmin Moor		triploid	Mehlquist, 1952
		triploid	Wells, 1956
Cym. Brissie		diploid	Wells, 1956
Cym. Butterfly		40	Mehlquist, 1952
Cym. Butterfly 'Westonbirt'		40	Mehlquist, 1952
Cym. Calcutta		80	Mehlquist & Clovis, 1957
Cym. Carisbrook 'Baxley'		diploid	Wells, 1956
Cym. Carisbrook 'Florence'		diploid	Wells, 1956
Cym. Carisona 'Glendessary'		diploid	Wimber, 1957d
Cym. Cassandra 'Bellevue'		triploid	Wells, 1956
Cym. Cassandra 'Junnifer'		triploid	Wells, 1956
Cym. Cassandra 'Karangah'		triploid	Wells, 1956
Cym. Cassandra 'Pastel Queen'		triploid	Wells, 1956
Cym. Cassandra 'Toxteth'		triploid	Wells, 1956
Cym. Cassandra 'Warringal'		triploid	Wells, 1956
Cym. Cassandra 'Waverly'		triploid	Wells, 1956
Cym. Cerema 'Fine'		ca. 60	Kamemoto, 1959b
Cym. Ceres 'F. J. Hanbury'	variable		Yeh, 1962
Cym. Charm		40	Mehlquist, 1952
Cym. Charmant		60	Mehlquist, 1952
Cym. Charmion		40	Mehlquist, 1952
Cym. Chesham 'Green Valley'		diploid	Wimber, 1957d
Cym. Chloris		40	Mehlquist, 1952
Cym. Chough		triploid	Wells, 1956
Cym. Christmas Cheer		40	Mehlquist, 1952
Cym. Clare Armstrong		60	Mehlquist, 1952
		triploid	Wells, 1956
Cym. Clasina de Wit		triploid	Wells, 1956
Cym. Claudona 'Glendessary'		diploid	Wimber, 1957d
Cym. Cleo Sherman		80	Mehlquist & Clovis, 1957
		80	Tanaka, 1962a
Cym. cochleare		40	Wimber, 1957a
Cym. Coningsbyanum 'Brockhurst'		40	Mehlquist, 1952
		40, 80 (colchiploid)	Menninger, 1963
Cym. Cornelia		40	Mehlquist, 1952
Cym. Corona		40	Mehlquist, 1952
Cym. Cremona 'Black Prince'		diploid	Wimber, 1957d
Cym. Cygnet 'Elfin'		40	Mehlquist, 1952
Cym. Cygnus 'The Bride'		triploid	Wells, 1956
Cym. cyperifolium		42	Mehra & Sehgal, 1978
Cym. Cyzara		40	Mehlquist, 1952
Cym. Dante		diploid	Wimber, 1957d
Cym. dayanum var. austrojaponicum		40	Mutsuura & Nakahira, 1960
		40	Tanaka, 1965b
Cym. December Green 'Early Ireland'		diploid	Wells, 1956
Cym. Dede Hinkson 'Spring Snow'		60	Tanaka, 1962a
Cym. Delysia		40	Mehlquist, 1952
Cym. Desirée Elizabeth A'Logann		80 ± 1	Tanaka, 1962a
Cym. devonianum		40	Wimber, 1957a
	20		Mehra & Vij, 1970
Cym. Diana		40	Mehlquist, 1952
Cym. Dorchester		60	Mehlquist, 1952
		diploid	Wells, 1956
Cym. Dorchester 'Alpha'		triploid	Wimber, 1957d
Cym. Dorchester 'Curragh'		ca. 60	Kamemoto, 1959b
Cym. Dorchester 'Manuka'		66	Wells, 1956
Cym. Doreen		40	Mehlquist, 1952
Cym. Doris		40	Mehlquist, 1952
Cym. Doris Aurea 'F. J. Noonan'		diploid	Wimber, 1957d
Cym. Dryad		40	Tanaka, 1962a
Cym. Dryad 'Westonbirt'		40	Mehlquist, 1952
Cym. Eagle 'Arctic'		triploid	Wells, 1956
Cym. Eagle 'Elizabeth Ann'		triploid	Wells, 1956
Cym. Eagle 'Mt. Shasta'		triploid	Wimber, 1957d
Cym. Eagle 'Rosy Dawn'		triploid	Wells, 1956
Cym. Eagle 'Snow Queen'		triploid	Wells, 1956
Cym. Early Bird 'Pacific'		tetraploid	Mehlquist, 1952
Cym. Eburneo-Lowianum		40	Mehlquist, 1952
Cym. Eburneo-Lowianum 'Concolor'		40	Mehlquist, 1952
		diploid	Wimber, 1957d
Cym. eburneum		40	Mehlquist, 1952
		40	Wimber, 1957a
Cym. Edna Cobb		triploid	Wells, 1956
		60	Mehlquist & Clovis, 1957
Cym. Elouera		tetraploid	Wells, 1956

Plant name	Chromosome number		Reference	Plant name	Chromosome number		Reference
	n	2n			n	2n	
Cym. ensi-folium		40	Wimber, 1957a	*Cym. grandi-florum*		40	Mehlquist, 1952
		40	Tanaka, 1962a			40	Wimber, 1957a
		40	Tanaka, 1965b	*Cym. grandi-florum* 'Westonbirt'		40	Mehlquist, 1952
Cym. Erica Sander		40	Mehlquist, 1952				
		diploid	Wimber, 1957d	*Cym. Guelda*		40	Mehlquist, 1952
Cym. erythrostylum		40	Mehlquist, 1949	*Cym. gyokuchin*		40	Kamemoto, 1959b
		40	Mehlquist, 1952	*Cym. Heathrow* 'Mary Bea'		diploid	Wimber, 1957d
		40	Wimber, 1957a				
Cym. Ethel Ward		triploid	Wells, 1956	*Cym. Hera* 'Giganteum'		75	Wimber & Hernlund, 1955
Cym. Europa 'Wells'		diploid	Wells, 1956				
Cym. faberi		40	Tanaka, 1964a	*Cym. Herod*		diploid	Wells, 1956
		40	Löve & Löve, 1969	*Cym. Historian* 'Linfield'		tetraploid	Wells, 1956
Cym. Felicity		40	Mehlquist, 1952	*Cym. hoosai (Cym. sinense)*		40	Kamemoto, 1959b
Cym. Feronia		40	Mehlquist, 1952	*Cym. Hugh Evans*		40	Mehlquist, 1952
Cym. Fieldfare		diploid	Wells, 1956	*Cym. i'ansoni*		40	Mehlquist, 1952
Cym. finlaysonianum		40	Mehlquist, 1952			40	Wimber, 1957a
		40	Pancho, 1965a	*Cym. Icarus* 'Roberts'		triploid	Wells, 1956
		40	Pancho, 1965b				
Cym. Flamingo		94	Wells, 1956	*Cym. Ilkley Moor*		triploid	Wells, 1956
		pentaploid	Wimber, 1957d			100	Zuck, 1957
Cym. Flamingo 'Allambie'		88	Wells, 1956	*Cym. Imbros*		60	Tanaka, 1962a
Cym. Flamingo 'Nobilior'		ca. 100	Wimber, 1954	*Cym. insigne*		40	Mehlquist, 1952
Cym. Flirtation	variable		Yeh, 1962			40	Wimber, 1957a
		40	Tanaka, 1964a			40	Larsen, 1966
Cym. Floryi		40	Mehlquist, 1952			40	Mehlquist, 1952
				Cym. insigne var. *albens*			
Cym. forrestii		40	Wimber, 1957a	*Cym. insigne* f. *album*	20		Yeh, 1962
Cym. Frivolity		40	Mehlquist, 1952				
Cym. Frivolity 'Alba'		diploid	Wimber, 1957d	*Cym. insigne* var. *album*		40	Mehlquist, 1952
Cym. Garnet		40	Mehlquist, 1952	*Cym. insigne* var. *atrosanguinea*		40	Tanaka, 1962a
		40	Tanaka, 1962a			40, 40	Tanaka, 1964a
Cym. Gattonense		40	Mehlquist, 1952	*Cym. insigne* var. *rodochilum*		40	Mehlquist, 1952
Cym. giganteum		40	Mehlquist, 1952	*Cym. insigne* 'Westonbirt'		40	Mehlquist, 1952
		40	Wimber, 1957a	*Cym. irridifolium*		40	Wimber, 1957a
		40	Sharma & Chatterji, 1966	*Cym. Irina* 'Celestoe'		diploid	Wimber, 1957d
		40	Mehra & Kashyap, 1978	*Cym. Islander* 'Showboat'		60	Tanaka, 1962a
Cym. Girrahween 'Elaine'		64	Wells, 1956	*Cym. Ispahan* 'Mascot'		triploid	Wells, 1956
Cym. Girrahween 'Enid'		76	Wells, 1956	*Cym. Janette*		60	Mehlquist, 1952
		60	Tanaka, 1966	*Cym. Janette* 'A. A. McBean'		triploid	Wells, 1956
						triploid	Wimber, 1957d
Cym. Girrahween 'Gloria'		69	Wells, 1956	*Cym. Janette* 'Golden Crown'		triploid	Wells, 1956
Cym. Girrahween 'Red Star'		68	Wells, 1956	*Cym. Jason* 'Marblethorpe'		triploid	Wells, 1956
Cym. Goldcrest 'Wondabah'		triploid	Wells, 1956	*Cym. Joan of Arc* 'Snowball'		80	Tanaka, 1962a
Cym. Golden Eagle 'Robinson'		triploid	Wells, 1956	*Cym. Jolity*		40	Mehlquist & Clovis, 1957
Cym. Golden Oriole		40	Mehlquist, 1952	*Cym. Joy Sander*		40	Mehlquist, 1952
Cym. Goldstar		ca. 60	Kamemoto, 1959b	*Cym. Jungfrau*		60	Mehlquist, 1952
Cym. Gottianum 'Westonbirt'		40	Mehlquist, 1952	*Cym. Kangar* 'McBean'		diploid	Wimber, 1957d
Cym. Grand Monarch 'Equisitum'		diploid	Wells, 1956	*Cym. kanran*		40	Wimber, 1957a
						40	Tanaka, 1965b

Plant name	Chromosome number n	2n	Reference	Plant name	Chromosome number n	2n	Reference
Cym. Khyber Pass		40	Mehlquist & Clovis, 1957	*Cym.* Midlothian 'Greensleeves'		diploid	Wells, 1956
Cym. Khyber Pass 'Glitter'		40	Tanaka, 1962a	*Cym.* Minstrel 'Oakley Court'		diploid	Wells, 1956
Cym. Kittiwake		40	Mehlquist, 1952	*Cym.* Minuet		40	Mehlquist, 1952
Cym. Laelia Sasso		triploid	Wells, 1956		variable	40	Yeh, 1962
Cym. lancifolium (= *Cym. nagifolium*)	20	40	Wimber, 1957a Chardard, 1963	*Cym.* Minuet 'Maxine'		ca. 60	Kamemoto, 1959b
		38	Mehra & Sehgal, 1978	*Cym.* Miranda		40	Mehlquist, 1952
Cym. Lillian Stewart 'Ebisu'		60	Tanaka, 1962a			ca. 60	Kamemoto, 1959b
Cym. Linnet 'Olive'		40	Mehlquist, 1952	*Cym.* Miretta 'Dos Pueblos'		diploid	Wimber, 1957d
Cym. Louis Sander 'Kirribilli'		triploid	Wells, 1956	*Cym.* Miretta 'Glendessary'		diploid	Wimber, 1957d
Cym. Louis Sander 'Regal'		triploid	Wells, 1956	*Cym.* Moira		40	Mehlquist, 1952
Cym. lowianum	9–10		Suessenguth, 1921	*Cym.* Mondecito		diploid	Wimber, 1957d
	20		Hoffmann, 1929	*Cym. munronianum*		40	Sharma & Chatterji, 1966
	20		Hoffman, 1929	*Cym.* Muse		diploid	Wells, 1956
		diploid	Mehlquist, 1949	*Cym.* Nadina		40	Mehlquist, 1952
		40	Mehlquist, 1952			triploid	Wells, 1956
		40	Wimber, 1957a	*Cym. nagifolium* (= *Cym. lancifolium*)		40	Mutsuura & Nakahira, 1959
		40	Kamemoto, 1959b			38	Tanaka, 1965b
		40	Sharma & Chatterji, 1966	*Cym.* Nam Khan		tetraploid	Wimber, 1957d
	22		Sharma & Sarkar, 1967–1968	*Cym.* Nam Khan (self)		90 ± 1	Tanaka, 1964a
Cym. lowianum var. *concolor*		40	Mehlquist, 1952	*Cym.* Nam Khan 'Verulam'		tetraploid	Menninger, 1954
Cym. lowianum 'Fir Grange'		40	Mehlquist, 1952	*Cym.* Nell Gwynne		40	Mehlquist, 1952
Cym. lowianum 'McBeans'		40	Mehlquist, 1952	*Cym.* Nirvana 'Warringal'		triploid	Wells, 1956
Cym. lowianum 'Pitt's'		40	Mehlquist, 1952	*Cym.* Nitocris		40	Mehlquist, 1952
Cym. lowianum 'St. Denis'		40	Mehlquist, 1952	*Cym.* Northern Lights 'Daybreak'		66	Wells, 1956
		40	Arp, 1973	*Cym.* Nymph		40	Mehlquist, 1952
Cym. Lowio-Grandiflorum		diploid	Mehlquist, 1949	*Cym.* Occident		diploid	Wells, 1956
		40	Mehlquist, 1952	*Cym.* Oiso 'Setonoumi'		40	Tanaka, 1964a
Cym. Lowio-Grandiflorum 'Westonbirt'		40	Mehlquist, 1952	*Cym.* Omega 'Dos Pueblos'		triploid	Wimber, 1957d
		diploid	Wimber, 1957d	*Cym. parishii* var. *sanderae*		40	Mehlquist, 1952
Cym. Lowville		diploid	Wimber, 1957d	*Cym.* Parsifal 'Roseum'		40	Mehlquist, 1952
Cym. Lutescens		40	Mehlquist, 1952	*Cym.* Pauwelsii		40	Mehlquist, 1952
Cym. Lyoth		40	Mehlquist, 1952		variable		Yeh, 1962
Cym. macrorhizon	19		Mehra & Sehgal, 1978	*Cym.* Pauwelsii 'Auriga Brockhurst'		40	Mehlquist, 1952
Cym. Madeleine		40	Mehlquist, 1952	*Cym.* Pauwelsii 'Comte d'Hemptinne'		tetraploid	Mehlquist, 1949
Cym. Madonna		60	Mehlquist, 1952			80	Mehlquist, 1952
Cym. Marmie Kingsford		triploid	Wells, 1956			tetraploid	Menninger, 1954
Cym. Mary Pinches		40	Tanaka, 1964a			tetraploid	Wimber, 1957d
Cym. mastersii		40	Wimber, 1957a	*Cym.* Pauwelsii 'Magnificum'		40	Mehlquist, 1949
Cym. Memoria Albertii 'Albert'		triploid	Wells, 1956			40	Mehlquist, 1952

Plant name	Chromosome number		Reference
	n	2n	
Cym. Pearl 'Magnificum'		40	Mehlquist, 1952
		diploid	Wimber, 1957d
Cym. Pearl 'Mastiff'		40	Mehlquist, 1952
Cym. Pearl-Amber		72	Wells, 1956
Cym. Pedregosa		46, 49, 51, 54	Wimber & Hernlund, 1955
Cym. pendulum		40	Sharma & Sarkar, 1967–1968
	20		Mehra & Vij, 1970
Cym. Peri		57, 58, 60	Mehlquist, 1952
Cym. Peri 'Beefeater'		68	Wells, 1956
Cym. Peri 'Fiesta'		64	Wells, 1956
Cym. Peri 'Imperial'		64	Well, 1956
Cym. Peri 'Ironclad'		66	Wells, 1956
Cym. Peri 'The King'		66	Wells, 1956
Cym. Persian Carpet		60	Mehlquist & Clovis, 1957
Cym. Peter Grimes		40	Mehlquist, 1952
Cym. Plover		40	Mehlquist, 1952
Cym. Plover 'Fuschia'		diploid	Wimber, 1957d
Cym. President Wilson		40	Mehlquist, 1952
Cym. President Wilson 'Concolor'		40	Mehlquist, 1952
Cym. President Wilson 'Democrat'		triploid	Wells, 1956
Cym. President Wilson 'Westonbirt'		40	Mehlquist, 1952
Cym. Priam 'Ada Meech'		diploid	Wells, 1956
Cym. Prince Charles		79 ± 1	Tanaka, 1966
Cym. Prince Charming 'Charmer'		diploid	Wells, 1956
Cym. Princess Astrid		40	Mehlquist, 1952
Cym. Princess Elizabeth 'Iris'		triploid	Wells, 1956
Cym. Princess Elizabeth 'Maisie'		triploid	Wells, 1956
Cym. Princess Elizabeth 'Reece'		triploid	Wells, 1956
Cym. Princess Elizabeth 'Taylor'		triploid	Wells, 1956
Cym. Profusion 'Violaceum'		diploid	Wells, 1956
Cym. Pumander		40	Mehlquist, 1952
	variable		Yeh, 1962
Cym. pumilum		40	Mehlquist, 1952
		40	Wimber, 1957a
		40	Kamemoto, 1959b
		40	Tanaka, 1962a
		40	Tanaka, 1964a
Cym. pumilum 'Folio Albo marginalis'		40	Mehlquist, 1952

Plant name	Chromosome number		Reference
	n	2n	
Cym. pumilum 'Gessho'		40	Tanaka, 1962a
		40	Tanaka, 1964a
Cym. pumilum 'Gesshohen'		80	Tanaka, 1962a
Cym. Ramboda		40	Mehlquist, 1952
Cym. Ramley 'McBean's'		tetraploid	Wells, 1956
Cym. Redstart 'Radiance'		40	Mehlquist, 1952
Cym. Remus 'Vivid'		diploid	Wimber, 1957d
Cym. Riga		40	Mehlquist, 1952
Cym. Roger Sander		40	Mehlquist, 1952
Cym. Romeo		diploid	Wimber, 1957d
Cym. Rosa Vellie		60	Tanaka, 1966
Cym. Rosalita 'Dos Pueblos'		diploid	Wimber, 1957d
Cym. Rosanna		60	Mehlquist, 1952
Cym. Rosanna 'Pinkie'		tetraploid	Wimber, 1957d
Cym. Rosanna 'Warringal'		tetraploid	Mehlquist, 1952
		tetraploid	Wells, 1956
Cym. Rosefieldense		40	Mehlquist, 1952
Cym. Roxette		triploid	Wells, 1956
Cym. Ruanda 'The Finest'		diploid	Wells, 1956
Cym. Samarkand		triploid	Wells, 1956
Cym. Sandpiper 'Dorothy'		triploid	Wells, 1956
Cym. Sanrita		diploid	Wells, 1956
Cym. Seamew		40	Mehlquist, 1952
Cym. schroederi		40	Mehlquist, 1952
		40	Wimber, 1957a
Cym. Shina Black		diploid	Wimber, 1957d
Cym. Shiraz		tetraploid	Wells, 1956
Cym. Shiraz 'Mary Bea'		tetraploid	Wimber, 1957d
Cym. Shirley		tetraploid	Mehlquist, 1952
Cym. Sierra		60	Mehlquist & Clovis, 1957
Cym. sikkhinense	19		Chardard, 1963
Cym. simonsianum (= Cym. dayanum)		40	Wimber, 1957a
Cym. sinense (= Cym. hoosai)		40	Sugiura, 1939
		40	Wimber, 1957a
		40	Tanaka, 1964b
		40	Tanaka, 1965b
		40	Sharma & Chatterji, 1966
Cym. Solent		40	Mehlquist, 1952
Cym. Solon		40	Mehlquist, 1952
Cym. Spartan Queen 'Mrs. Ireland'		diploid	Wimber, 1957d
Cym. Sussex		40	Mehlquist, 1952
		tetraploid	Wells, 1956
Cym. Swallow		80	Mehlquist, 1949
		40, 60	Mehlquist, 1952
		tetraploid	Menninger, 1954

Plant name	Chromosome number		Reference	Plant name	Chromosome number		Reference
	n	2n			n	2n	
Cym. Swallow		triploid ca. 80	Wells, 1956 Kamemoto, 1959b	*Cym.* unnamed (*Cym.* Alexanderi 'Westonbirt' × *Cym.* Sussex 'Laelia Sasso')		ca. 60	Kamemoto, 1959b
Cym. Swallow 'Charm'		60	Tanaka, 1962a				
Cym. Swallow 'Gold Wing'		ca. 60	Kamemoto, 1959b				
Cym. Swallow 'Golden Glory'		triploid	Wells, 1956	*Cym.* unnamed, Stewart 1480 (*Cym.* Balkis 'Silver Orb' × *Cym.* Carisona 'Glendessary')		60	Mehlquist & Clovis, 1957
Cym. Swallow 'Hebe'		triploid	Wells, 1956				
Cym. Swallow 'Jill'		triploid	Wells, 1956				
Cym. Swallow 'Magnolia'		triploid	Wells, 1956				
Cym. Swallow 'Pastel'		triploid	Wells, 1956	*Cym.* unnamed, Stewart 1477 (*Cym.* Balkis 'Silver Orb' × *Cym.* Swallow 'Green Mist')		80	Mehlquist & Clovis, 1957
Cym. Swallow 'Pink'		40	Tanaka, 1962a				
Cym. Swallow 'Rainbow'		tetraploid	Wells, 1956				
Cym. Swallow 'Ronnoc'		tetraploid	Wells, 1956	*Cym.* unnamed, Stewart 1506 (*Cym.* Carisona 'Abundance' × *Cym.* Balkis 'Silver Orb')		60	Mehlquist & Clovis, 1957
Cym. Swallow 'Soulangeana'		tetraploid	Wells, 1956				
Cym. Swallow 'Takarazuka'		ca. 60	Kamemoto, 1959b				
Cym. Thelma		60 ca. 60	Mehlquist, 1952 Kamemoto, 1959b	*Cym.* unnamed, Stewart 1400 (*Cym.* Esmeralda × Cym. Apollo 'Exbury')		40	Melquist & Clovis, 1957
Cym. Tinsel 'Fine'		triploid	Wells, 1956				
Cym. Tityus		40	Mehlquist, 1952				
Cym. tracyanum		diploid 40 40	Mehlquist, 1949 Mehlquist, 1952 Wimber, 1957a	*Cym.* unnamed (*Cym.* Lowio-Grandiflorum × *Cym.* Claudona)		40	Tanaka, 1962a
Cym. Vashti		40	Mehlquist, 1952				
Cym. virescens (= *Cym. goeringii*)		40 40 40 40	Mutsuura & Nakahira, 1958 Kamemoto, 1959b Mutsuura, 1959 Tanaka, 1965b	*Cym.* unnamed, Stewart, 1492 (*Cym.* Nell Gwynne 'White Throat' × *Cym.* Esmeralda)		40	Mehlquist & Clovis, 1957
Cym. virescens 'Aneuploid'		46	Mutsuura & Nakahira, 1960				
Cym. whiteae		40	Wimber, 1957a	*Cym.* unnamed (*Cym.* Northern Lights × *Cym.* Rosanna 'Pinkie')		triploid	Wells, 1956
Cym. Wiganianum		40	Mehlquist, 1952				
Cym. Windsor 'Christmas Star'		40	Mehlquist, 1952				
Cym. Woodpigeon 'Yellow Gem'		diploid	Wells, 1956	*Cym.* unnamed (*Cym.* Orcades × *Cym.* Tinsel)		triploid	Wells, 1956
Cym. York		triploid	Wells, 1956	*Cym.* unnamed (*Cym.* Pauwelsii × *Cym.* Babylon 'Castle Hill')		60 ± 1	Tanaka, 1964a
Cym. York 'Carpentier'		66	Wells, 1956				
Cym. Zebra		40	Mehlquist, 1952				
Cym. unnamed, Stewart 1383 (*Cym.* Alexanderi 'Westonbirt' × Cym. Eagle 'Heritage')		60	Mehlquist & Clovis, 1957	*Cym.* unnamed (*Cym.* Pauwelsii 'Comte d'Hemptinne' × *Cym.* President Wilson 'Westonbirt')		triploid	Mehlquist, 1949

Plant name	Chromosome number		Reference
	n	2n	
Cym. unnamed (Cym. President Wilson × Cym. Pauwelsii 'Comte d'Hemptinne')		65, 70, 80, 81, 85	Wimber & Hernlund, 1955
Cym. unnamed (Cym. pumilum × Cym. Sumida)		40	Tanaka, 1966
Cym. unnamed (Cym. Shirley × Cym. Alexanderi 'Westonbirt')		tetraploid	Menninger, 1954
Cym. unnamed (Cym. Sussex 'Laelia Sasso' × Cym. Remus)		40	Tanaka, 1966
Cym. unnamed (Cym. Sweetheart × Cym. Alexanderi 'Hamilton Smith')		60, 61	Tanaka, 1964a
Cym. unnamed (Cym. Sweetheart 'Radiance' × Cym. Alexanderi 'Westonbirt')		82	Tanaka, 1964a
Cym. unnamed, Stewart 1501 (Cym. Verona 'Ruby' × Cym. Alexanderi 'Westonbirt')		60	Mehlquist & Clovis, 1957
Cym. unnamed, Stewart 1994 (Cym. Zebra [#235] × Cym. pumilum)		40	Mehlquist & Clovis, 1957
Cynorkis anacamptoides		14	Thulin, 1970
Cyperorchis cochleare	20		Mehra & Vij, 1970
C. elegans	20		Mehra & Vij, 1970
C. eubernea	20		Mehra & Vij, 1970
C. grandiflora	20		Mehra & Vij, 1970
	20		Mehra & Sehgal, 1978
C. longifolia	20		Mehra & Vij, 1970
C. mastersii	20		Mehra & Vij, 1970
Cypripedium acaule	10	20	Belling, 1924
	10	20	Belling, 1926b
	10	20	Humphrey, 1932a
	10	20	Humphrey, 1932b
		20	Löve & Simon, 1968
Cyp. Andrewsii	10		Duncan, 1959

Plant name	Chromosome number		Reference
	n	2n	
Cyp. arietinum		20	Löve & Simon, 1968
Cyp. calceolus		22	Francini, 1931
		20	Humphrey, 1932a
		20	Humphrey, 1932b
		20	Löve & Löve, 1954
		20	Pogan & Wcislo (in Löve & Löve, 1961)
		20	Sokolovskaya, 1966
Cyp. candidum	11	22	Pace, 1907
		20	Humphrey, 1932a
		20	Humphrey, 1932b
		20	Löve & Simon, 1968
Cyp. cordigerum		20	Mehra & Bawa, 1962
		20	Mehra & Bawa, 1970
	10		Mehra & Vij, 1970
	10	20	Vij & Mehra, 1974
	10	20	Vij & Gupta, 1975
		20	Mehra & Kashyap, 1978
		20	Mehra & Pandita, 1979
Cyp. debile	10	20	Miduno, 1955
		20	Mutsuura & Nakahira, 1958
	10	20	Yamasaki, 1959
Cyp. fasciculatum		20	Löve & Simon, 1968
Cyp. guttatum		20	Sokolovskaya, 1966
		20, 30	Balaeva & Siplivinski, 1976
Cyp. himalaicum	10	20	Vij & Mehra, 1974
		20	Mehra & Kashyap, 1978
Cyp. hirsutum	10	20	Humphrey, 1933
Cyp. japonicum	10		Ohno, 1954
		20	Mutsuura & Nakahira, 1958
		20	Tanaka, 1965b
		20	Tanaka, 1971
Cyp. jatabeanum		20	Sokolovskaya, 1963
Cyp. marcanthum		20	Sokolovskaya, 1966
		20	Balaeva & Siplivinski, 1976
Cyp. marcanthum var. rebunense		20	Mutsuura & Nakahira, 1958
		20	Mutsuura, 1959
Cyp. parviflorum	11		Pace, 1907
		20	Carlson, 1945
		20	Löve & Ritchie, 1966
Cyp. passerinum		20	Löve & Löve, 1965
		20	Löve & Ritchie, 1966
		20	Löve & Simon, 1968

Plant name	Chromosome number		Reference
	n	2n	
Cyp. pubescens	11	22	Pace, 1907
	10		Belling, 1926b
		20	Humphrey, 1932a,b
		20	Löve & Simon, 1968
Cyp. reginae (= Cyp. spectabile)		20	Humphrey, 1933
		20	Humphrey, 1934
	10		Chouinard (from Duncan, 1959)
		20	Löve & Löve, 1961
		20	Löve & Simon, 1968
Cyp. spectabile (= Cyp. reginae)	11	22	Pace, 1907
	11		Hoffmann, 1929
		22	Hoffmann, 1930
	10		Duncan, 1959b
Cyrtorchis arcuata ssp. variabilis		ca. 150	Jones, 1967
Cyrtcs. chailluana	22–23		Chardard, 1963
Cyrtcs. species		46, 50	Jones, 1967
Dactylorchis cordigera		80	Vermeulen, 1947
D. cruenta (= Orchis cruenta)		40	Heusser, 1938
		40	Löve & Löve, 1944
		40	Vermeulen, 1947
		40	Heslop-Harrison, 1950
		40	Engelskjoen & Knaben, 1971
D. foliosa		40	Vermeulen, 1938
		40	Vermeulen, 1947
D. fuchsii (= Orchis maculata var. meyeri)	20		Hagerup, 1938
		40	Barber, 1942
		20, 40	Hagerup, 1944b
		20, 40	Vermeulen, 1947
		40	Heslop-Harrison, 1951
		40	Löve, 1951
		40	Löve & Löve, 1956
		40	Afzelius, 1958
		40	Pogan & Wcislo (in Löve & Löve, 1961)
	20	40	Kliphuis, 1963
		40	Knaben & Engelskjön, 1967
D. fuchsii ssp. hebridensis		40	Heslop-Harrison, 1948
D. fuchsii var. meyeri	20	40	Vaucher, 1966
D. fuchsii ssp. okellyi		40	Heslop-Harrison (in Löve & Löve, 1961)
D. fuchsii ssp. psychrophila		80	Wegener, 1966
D. fuchsii ssp. rhemensis		40	Heslop-Harrison, 1951
D. fuchsii ssp. typica		40	Vermeulen, 1947
D. hybrid (intergeneric) (as Orchis maculata × Gymnadenia odorata)	12	36	Fuchs & Ziegenspeck, 1924
D. incarnata (= Orchis latifolia) (= Orchis elodes) (= Orchis incarnata)	10	20	Fuchs & Ziegenspeck, 1923
		40	Heusser, 1938
		40	Hagerup, 1938
		79, 80	Maude, 1939
		40	Sokolovskaya & Strelkova, 1940
	20	40	Vermeulen, 1947
		40	Heslop-Harrison, 1948
		40	Holmen & Kaad, 1956
	20		Sorsa, 1963
	20	40	Kliphuis, 1963
		40	Vaucher, 1966
D. latifolia (= D. majalis)		80	Vaucher, 1966
D. maculata		40, 80	Titz, 1965
		40, 60, 80	Groll, 1965
	40	ca. 80	Vaucher, 1966
		80	Knaben & Engelskjön, 1967
		40	van Loon & de Jong, 1978
D. maculata ssp. maculata (= Orchis maculata)	16		Strasburger, 1888
	10	20	Fuchs & Ziegenspeck, 1923
		40, 80	Heusser, 1938
		40, 42, 80	Hagerup, 1938
	20		Barber, 1942
		40, 42, 80	Hagerup, 1944b
		40	Löve & Löve, 1944
		80	Vermeulen, 1947
		80	Diannelidis, 1948
		80	Fernandes, 1950
		80	Heslop-Harrison, 1951
		80	Diannelidis, 1955
		80	Holmen & Kaad, 1956
		ca. 80	Sorsa, 1962
		80	Sorsa, 1963
D. maculata ssp. elodes (= Orchis maculata ssp. elodes)	40		Hagerup, 1938
	40		Hagerup, 1944b
		80	Vermeulen, 1947
		80	Fernandes, 1950
		80	Heslop-Harrison, 1951
		80	Löve, 1951
		80	Heslop-Harrison, 1951
		80	Löve & Löve, 1956
	40	80, 100, 120	Kliphuis, 1963
D. maculata ssp. ericetorum (= Orchis maculata var. meyeri) (= Orchis maculata var. ericetorum)	20		Hagerup, 1938
		80 (40)	Hagerup, 1944b
		80	Vermeulen, 1947
		80	Heslop-Harrison, 1948
		80	Heslop-Harrison, 1951
D. maculata var. genuina (= Orchis maculata var. genuina)		40	Hagerup, 1938

Plant name	Chromosome number		Reference	Plant name	Chromosome number		Reference
	n	2n			n	2n	
D. maculata		80	Löve, 1951			80	Holmen &
ssp. *islan-*		80	Löve & Löve,				Kaad, 1956
dica			1956			80	Sokolovskaya
D. maculata		80	Richardson (in				& Strelkova,
var. *o'kelly*			Maude,				1960
			1939)	*D. traunsteineri*	20		Fuchs & Zie-
D. maculata		80	Vermeulen,	var. *gigas*			genspeck,
ssp. *typica*			1947	(= *Orchis*			1923
D. majalis (=		80	Hagerup, 1938	*traunsteineri*			
D. latifolia)		80	Heusser, 1938	var. *gigas*)			
(= *Orchis*		80	Vermeulen,	*D. traunsteineri*		122	Vermeulen,
majalis)			1938	ssp. *russowii*			1938
		80	Eftimiu-Heim,	*D. traunsteineri*		80	Zeylemaher (in
			1941	ssp. *typica*			Vermeulen,
		80	Pogan & Wcis-				1949)
			lo (in Löve &	*D. unnamed*	sterile	60	Heslop-Harri-
			Löve, 1961)	(*D. fuchsii* ×			son, 1953
	40	80	Kliphuis, 1963	*D. praeter-*			
D. majalis ssp.		80	Vermeulen,	*missa*)			
occidentalis			1938	*D. unnamed*		60	Vermeulen,
		80	Vermeulen,	(*D. fuchsii* ×			1938
			1947	*D. purpur-*			
		80	Heslop-Harri-	*ella*)			
			son (in Löve	*D. unnamed*		60	Heusser, 1938
			& Löve,	(*D. maculata*			
			1961)	× *D. incar-*			
D. munbyana		80	Vermeulen,	*nata*)			
(= *Orchis*			1938	*D. unnamed*		60	Holmen &
munbyana)		80	Vermeulen,	(*D. traun-*			Kaad, 1956
			1947	*steineri* × *D.*			
D. praeter-		80	Vermeulen,	*incarnata*)			
missa (= *Or-*			1938	(natural			
chis praeter-		80, 82	Maude, 1939	hybrid)			
missa)		80	Vermeulen,	*D. unnamed*		80	Holmen &
			1947	(*D. traun-*			Kaad, 1956
		80	Heslop-Harri-	*steineri* × *D.*			
			son (in Löve	*maculata*)			
			& Löve,	(natural			
			1961)	hybrid)			
	40	80	Kliphuis, 1963	*Dactylostalix*		42	Shoji, 1963
D. praeter-		80	Vermeulen,	*ringens*			
missa ssp.			1938	*Dactylorhiza*		42	Löve & Simon,
junialis	40	80	Kliphuis, 1963	*aristata*			1968
D. praeter-		80, 82	Richardson (in	*D. fuchsii*		40	Lovka *et al.*,
missa var.			Maude,				1971
pulchella (=			1939)			40	Speta & Voeth,
Orchis prae-							1972
termissa var.				*D. fuchsii* ssp.	20		Richards, 1972
pulchella)				*o'kellyi*			
D. pseudo-	variable	variable	Fuchs & Zie-	*D. hatagirea*		40, 80	Mehra & Pan-
traunsteineri	6–15	16–28	genspeck,				dita, 1978
(= *Orchis*			1924	*D. traunsteineri*		80	Löve & Kjell-
traunsteineri)							quist, 1973
D. purpurella		80	Maude, 1939	*Dendrobium*	19		Mehra & Seh-
(= *Orchis*		80	Richardson (in	*acinaciforme*			gal, 1975
purpurella)			Maude,	*Den. acumina-*		40	Pancho, 1965a
			1939)	*tissimum*		40	Pancho, 1965b
		80	Vermeulen,	*Den. acumina-*		40	Kosaki &
			1947	*tum* (= *Den.*			Kamemoto,
		80	Heslop-Harri-	*lyonii*)			1961
			son, 1948	*Den. aggrega-*	19	38	Vajrabhaya &
D. russovii		120, 122	Vermeulen,	*tum*			Randolph,
			1938				1960
		120, 122	Vermeulen,		19	38	Kosaki &
			1947				Kamemoto,
D. saccifera		80	Vermeulen,				1961
			1947			32–35	Chardard,
D. sambucina	20	40	Heusser, 1938				1963
(*Orchis sam-*	21		Hagerup, 1938			38	Kamemoto &
bucina)		40	Vermeulen,				Sagarik,
			1947				1967
		40	Vermeulen,			38	Wilfret &
			1949				Kamemoto,
		42	Sorsa, 1963				1971
D. sesqui-		80	Vermeulen,	*Den. aggrega-*		38	Kosaki, 1958
pedale			1938	*tum* var.			
		80	Vermeulen,	*majus*			
			1947	*Den. Agnes*		57 ± 1	Kosaki &
D. traunsteineri	variable	variable	Fuchs & Zie-	Cheok			Kamemoto,
(= *Orchis*	9–22	16–24	genspeck,				1961
traunsteineri)			1924			57 ± 1	Kamemoto *et*
		80	Heusser, 1938				*al.*, 1961
		40, 80, 120	Vermeulen,	*Den. Ains-*		38	Ito & Mutsuura,
			1947	*worthii*			1957

Plant name	Chromosome number n	Chromosome number 2n	Reference
Den. Ainsworthii 'Armstrongii'		38	Ito & Mutsuura, 1957
Den. Albanense		38	Vajrabhaya & Randolph, 1960
Den. albayense		40	Pancho, 1965a
		40	Pancho, 1965b
Den. Alex C. Chang		38	Vajrabhaya & Randolph, 1960
Den. Alice Cummins		38	Vajrabhaya & Randolph, 1960
Den. Alpestre	20		Arora, 1968
	20		Mehra & Kashyap, 1976
Den. amoenum		38	Jones, 1963
	20		Mehra & Vij, 1970
	20		Arora, 1971
Den. amplum		38	Banerji & Chaudhuri, 1972
Den. ampulum	20		Mehra & Vij, 1970
Den. anceps	19 + (0 − 2B)		Mehra & Vij, 1970
Den. anosmum (= *Den. superbum*)		40	Eftimiu-Heim, 1941
		40	Ito & Mutsuura, 1957
	19		Kosaki, 1958
	19		Vajrabhaya & Randolph, 1960
	19		Kosaki & Kamemoto, 1961
		38	Wilfret & Kamemoto, 1971
Den. Anouk		38	Vajrabhaya & Randolph, 1960
		57	Kosaki & Kamemoto, 1961
		57	Kamemoto et al., 1961
Den. aphyllum		38	Jones, 1963
	19		Mehra & Kashyap, 1979
Den. aporoides		38 ± 2	Pancho, 1965a
		38 ± 2	Pancho, 1965b
Den. aqueum		38	Jones, 1963
		38	Hedge & Boraiah, 1973
Den. arachnites		38	Pancho, 1965a
		38	Pancho, 1965b
Den. atroviolaceum		38	Wilfret & Kamemoto, 1971
Den. aurantiacum		38	Banerji & Chaudhuri, 1972
Den. bicallosum		40	Pancho, 1965a
		40	Pancho, 1965b
Den. bicameratum		38	Jones, 1963
		40	Arora, 1968
		38	Mehra & Kashyap, 1978
Den. bigibbum		38	Jones, 1963
(as var. *bigibbum*)		38	Wilfret & Kamemoto, 1971
Den. bigibbum var. *compactum*		38, ca. 57	Jones, 1963
Den. bronckartii		40	Eftimiu-Heim, 1941
		40	Ito & Mutsuura, 1957
Den brymerianum		40	Ito & Mutsuura, 1957
		38	Jones, 1963
Den. bullenianum		38	Wilfret & Kamemoto, 1971
Den. Caesar		57	Kosaki, 1958
	19, 38	38	Vajrabhaya & Randolph, 1960
		38, 57	Kosaki & Kamemoto, 1961
		38, 40	Dorn & Kamemoto, 1962
Den. canaliculatum		2x	Jones, 1963
		38	Wilfret & Kamemoto, 1971
Den. candidum		38	Jones, 1963
Den. capillipes	19		Malla et al., 1977a
Den. capituliflorum		38	Jones, 1963
Den. cariniferum		38	Kosaki & Kamemoto, 1961
		38	Kamemoto & Sagarik, 1967
Den. Cassiope		38	Miduno, 1940b
		40	Ito & Mutsuura, 1957
Den. Cassiope 'Miss Biwako'		38	Tanaka, 1962a
Den. cathcartii	19		Mehra & Vij, 1970
Den. chameleon		38	Pancho, 1965a
		38	Pancho, 1965b
Den. Chlorostele 'Chlorostele'		38	Ito & Mutsuura, 1957
		60	Vajrabhaya & Randolph, 1960
Den. Chlorostele 'Xanthocentrum'	19	38	Vajrabhaya & Randolph, 1960
Den. chrysanthum	19	38	Vajrabhaya & Randolph, 1960
		38	Kosaki & Kamemoto, 1961
		38	Jones, 1963
		38	Kamemoto & Sagarik, 1967
		40	Mehra & Kashyap, 1978
Den. chrysocrepis		ca. 76	Jones, 1963
Den. chrysotoxum	20		Hoffmann, 1929
	20		Hoffmann, 1930
		40	Ito & Mutsuura, 1957
		38	Kosaki & Kamemoto, 1961
		40	Chardard, 1963
(as var. *chrysotoxum*)		38	Jones, 1963
		38	Tanaka, 1964a
		38	Kamemoto & Sagarik, 1967

Plant name	Chromosome number		Reference	Plant name	Chromosome number		Reference
	n	2n			n	2n	
		38	Wilfret & Kamemoto, 1971	Den. Diamond Head Beauty		ca. 76	Kosaki & Kamemoto, 1961
Den. chryso-toxum var. suavissimum		38	Jones, 1963			76 ± 2	Kamemoto et al., 1961
Den. chryso-tropis		38	Jones, 1963	Den. di-cuphum		38	Jones, 1963
Den. clavatum	19		Mehra & Vij, 1970	Den. distichum		57	Vajrabhaya & Randolph, 1960
Den. Cleopatra		57	Kosaki, 1958			38	Pancho, 1965a
		57	Kosaki & Kamemoto, 1961			38	Pancho, 1965b
						38	Wilfret & Kamemoto, 1971
		57	Kamemoto et al., 1961	Den. dixan-thum		41	Jones, 1963
Den. Cleopatra 'Cleo'		58	Kamemoto et al., 1967			40	Kamemoto & Sagarik, 1967
Den. cobbi-anum		38	Pancho, 1965a			40	Wilfret & Kamemoto, 1971
		38	Pancho, 1965b				
Den. Concert		74 ± 1	Kosaki & Kamemoto, 1961	Den. draconis		38	Shindo & Kamemoto, 1963b
		74 ± 2	Kamemoto et al., 1961			38	Kamemoto & Sagarik, 1967
Den. crassi-node		38	Kamemoto & Sagarik, 1967			38	Wilfret & Kamemoto, 1971
Den. crepi-datum		38	Jones, 1963				
		38	Kamemoto & Sagarik, 1967	Den. Esther Moriguchi		55 ± 2	Kosaki & Kamemoto, 1961
		38	Hedge & Boraiah, 1973			55 ± 2	Kamemoto et al., 1961
Den. creta-ceum		38 ± 1f	Jones, 1963	Den. Ethel Kawamoto		57	Vajrabhaya & Randolph, 1960
Den. cruentum		40	Kamemoto & Sagarik, 1967	Den. falconeri		2x	Jones, 1963
Den. crumena-tum		38 ± 1f	Jones, 1963	Den. farmeri		40	Kamemoto & Sagarik, 1967
		40	Pancho, 1965a				
		38	Kamemoto & Sagarik, 1967			40	Banerji & Chaudhuri, 1972
		40	Pancho, 1965b	Den. farmeri var. aureo-flava		40	Kamemoto & Sagarik, 1967
		38	Wilfret & Kamemoto, 1971				
Den. crystal-linum		38	Jones, 1963	Den. fimbriato-labellum		18	Hsu, 1972
		38	Kamemoto & Sagarik, 1967	Den. fimbri-atum		38	Ito & Mutsuura, 1957
Den. curranii		38	Pancho, 1965a			38	Jones, 1963
		38	Pancho, 1965b			38	Kamemoto & Sagarik, 1967
Den. d'albertsii	19	38	Kosaki & Kamemoto, 1961		20		Arora, 1971
		38	Wilfret & Kamemoto, 1971	Den. fimbri-atum var. oculatum		38	Ito & Mutsuura, 1957
						38	Kosaki & Kamemoto, 1961
Den. Dark Victory		38	Vajrabhaya & Randolph, 1960	Den. findlay-anum		38	Jones, 1963
Den. delacourii (= Den. cili-atum)		38	Kamemoto & Sagarik, 1967			38	Kamemoto & Sagarik, 1967
		38	Wilfret & Kamemoto, 1971	Den. flammula		38	Jones, 1963
				Den. flavi-florum		38	Hsu, 1972
Den. delicatum		ca. 57	Jones, 1963	Den. formo-sanum		38	Banerji & Chaudhuri, 1972
Den. densi-florum (= Den. densi-forme)	20 + (1 − 2B)	40 + 2f	Kosaki, 1958 Mehra & Vij, 1970	Den. formosum		38	Ito & Mutsuura, 1957
Den. de-nudans		40	Jones, 1963			38	Shindo & Kamemoto, 1963b
Den. devoni-anum	19		Chardard, 1963	Den. formosum var. gigan-teum		38	Kosaki & Kamemoto, 1961
		38	Banerji & Chaudhuri, 1972			38	Kamemoto & Sagarik, 1967

Plant name	Chromosome number		Reference	Plant name	Chromosome number		Reference
	n	2n			n	2n	
		38	Wilfret & Kamemoto, 1971	Den. heishana-ense		38	Hsu, 1972
Den. frieder-icksianum		38	Jones, 1963	Den. Helen Fukumura		66	Vajrabhaya & Randolph, 1960
		38	Chardard, 1963			variable	Kamemoto et al., 1961
		38	Kamemoto & Sagarik, 1967	Den. hender-sonii		38	Jones, 1963
Den. fusiforme		38	Kosaki, 1958	Den. hetero-carpum (=		38	Kosaki, 1958
Den. gamblei		2x	Jones, 1963			38	Kosaki & Kamemoto, 1961
Den. Gatton Monarch		57	Ito & Mutsuura, 1957	Den. au-reum)			
Den. Gatton Monarch 'Black and Flory'		57	Tanaka, 1964a			38	Jones, 1963
						38	Pancho, 1965a
						38	Pancho, 1965b
						38	Kamemoto & Sagarik, 1967
Den. Gatton Monarch 'Grace'		57	Ito & Mutsuura, 1957			38	Wilfret & Kamemoto, 1971
Den. Gatton Sunray		57	Ito & Mutsuura, 1957			38	Banerji & Chaudhuri, 1972
	19		Vajrabhaya & Randolph, 1960	Den. hilde-brandii		38, 38 + 1f.	Kosaki, 1958
Den. gibsonii		38	Vajrabhaya & Randolph, 1960			38, 38 + 1f.	Kosaki & Kamemoto, 1961
Den. gordonii		38	Kosaki & Kamemoto, 1961			38	Jones, 1963
Den. gouldii		38	Kosaki, 1958			38	Kamemoto & Sagarik, 1967
		38	Kosaki & Kamemoto, 1961	Den. hookeri-anum		40	Jones, 1963
		38	Wilfret & Kamemoto, 1971	Den. Hula Girl		38	Kamemoto et al., 1961
Den. Grace (var. of Gatton Monarch)		57	Ito & Mutsuura, 1957	Den. Illustre		38	Ito & Mutsuura, 1957
						57	Kamemoto et al., 1967
Den. gracili-caule (as. var. gracili-caule)		38	Jones, 1963	Den. infundi-bulum	20		Hoffman, 1929
						40	Hoffman, 1930
						38	Tanaka, 1964a
						38	Kamemoto & Sagarik, 1967
Den. gracili-caule var. howeanum		38	Jones, 1963	Den. infundi-bulum var. jamesianum		38	Jones, 1963
Den. gramini-folium		38	Pancho, 1965a	Den. jamesi-anum		38	Tanaka, 1964a
		38	Pancho, 1965b				
Den. grantii		38	Kosaki, 1958	Den. Jaquelyn Thomas		38	Sagawa & Nii-moto, 1961
		38	Kosaki & Kamemoto, 1961			38–44, 76	Dorn & Kame-moto, 1962
		38	Wilfret & Kamemoto, 1971	Den. jenkinsii		38	Jones, 1963
				Den. Joanne Sawyer		ca. 38	Vajrabhaya & Randolph, 1960
Den. gratiosis-simum		38	Jones, 1963				
Den. Harmony 'Kubo'		38	Tanaka, 1962	Den. johannis	19		Kosaki & Kamemoto, 1961
Den. Harmony 'Tomy'		76	Tanaka, 1962	Den. Jungfrau		38	Ito & Mutsuura, 1957
Den. Hawaii		57 ± 1	Kosaki, 1958	Den. kingi-anum		76	Vajrabhaya & Randolph, 1961
		57	Vajrabhaya & Randolph, 1960	(as var. kingi-anum)		38, 112–114	Jones, 1963
		57 ± 1	Kosaki & Kamemoto, 1961			76	Tanaka, 1964a
		57 ± 1	Kamemoto et al., 1961			38, 57, 76	Maxwell, 1967
						38, 57, 76	Maxwell, 1971
		57	Dorn & Kame-moto, 1962	Den. kingi-anum var. album		ca. 57, 76	Jones, 1963
						ca. 57, 76	Maxwell, 1967
Den. Hawaii Nui		38–57	Vajrabhaya & Randolph, 1960	Den. kingi-anum var. silcockii		ca. 76	Jones, 1963
						ca. 76	Maxwell, 1967
Den. Hawaiian Beauty		75 ± 2	Kosaki & Kamemoto, 1961	Den. King of Lake		57	Tanaka, 1964a
		75 ± 2	Kamemoto et al., 1961	Den. kwasho-tense		38	Tanaka, 1965b
						38	Hsu, 1972

Plant name	Chromosome number		Reference
	n	2n	
Den. Lady Constance		57 ± 1	Kosaki, 1958
		57 ± 1	Kosaki & Kamemoto, 1961
		57 ± 1	Kamemoto et al., 1961
Den. Lady Constance 'Carol'		76	Kamemoto et al., 1967
Den. Lady Fay		66	Kosaki & Kamemoto, 1961
		variable	Kamemoto et al., 1961
Den. Lady Hamilton		76	Kosaki, 1958
		76	Kosaki & Kamemoto, 1961
		76	Kamemoto et al., 1961
Den. Lady Hamilton 'Fay'		56	Kamemoto et al., 1967
Den. lawianum		38	Hedge & Boraiah, 1973
Den. leonis		40	Wilfret & Kamemoto, 1971
Den. leucorhodum		38	Jones, 1963
Den. Liliha		38	Vajrabhaya & Randolph, 1960
Den. Lim Chong Min		63–81	Dorn & Kamemoto, 1962
Den. lindleyi		38	Jones, 1963
Den. linguella (= Den. hercoglossum)		38	Kamemoto & Sagarik, 1967
		38	Wilfret & Kamemoto, 1971
Den. linguiforme		38	Jones, 1963
Den. lituiflorum		38	Jones, 1963
		38	Kamemoto & Sagarik, 1967
Den. loddigesii		38	Jones, 1963
		40	Ito & Mutsuura, 1957
		38	Chardard, 1963
Den. Lois Anderson		38–152	Vajrabhaya & Randolph, 1960
Den. longicalcaratum		38	Hsu, 1972
Den. longicornu		38	Jones, 1963
	19		Malla, 1977a
Den. longispicatum		38	Pancho, 1965a
		38	Pancho, 1965b
Den. Louis Bleriot		57	Kamemoto et al., 1967
Den. Louis Bleriot 'Mrs. Dupont'		57	Vajrabhaya & Randolph, 1960
Den. macraei	19		Mehra & Vij, 1970
Den. macrophyllum		38	Kosaki, 1958
		38	Kosaki & Kamemoto, 1961
Den. macrostachyum	20	38	Jones, 1963 Arora, 1971
		38	Hedge & Boraiah, 1973
Den. Magda 'Special'		60	Ito & Mutsuura, 1957
Den. Maui Beauty		75 ± 2	Kosaki & Kamemoto, 1961
		75 ± 2	Kamemoto et al., 1961
Den. May Neal		ca. 38	Vajrabhaya & Randolph, 1960
Den. Melondiscus		76	Vajrabhaya & Randolph, 1960
Den. Merlin		57	Ito & Mutsuura, 1957
		57	Tanaka, 1962a
Den. Merlin 'Shinjuku'		57	Tanaka, 1962a
Den. microchilum		38	Pancho, 1965a
		38	Pancho, 1965b
Den. mirbelianum		38	Wilfret & Kamemoto, 1971
Den. Miss Kobayashi		76	Tanaka, 1962a
Den. miyakei		38	Hsu, 1972
Den. Moluccas		38	Vajrabhaya & Randolph, 1960
Den. Momi Cummins		56 ± 2	Kosaki & Kamemoto, 1961
		56 ± 2	Kamemoto et al., 1961
Den. Momi Fujimoto		38–49	Vajrabhaya & Randolph, 1960
Den. moniliforme		38	Miduno, 1940b
		38	Ito & Mutsuura, 1957
		38	Mutsuura & Nakahira, 1958a
		38	Kosaki & Kamemoto, 1961
		38; 38 + 1 ~ 3f.	Jones, 1963
		ca. 38	Nakasone & Moromizato, 1964
		38	Tanaka, 1965b
		38	Wilfret & Kamemoto, 1971
		38	Tanaka, 1971
		38	Hsu, 1972
Den. moniliforme 'Pink Flower'		48	Mutsuura & Nakahira, 1960
Den. moniliforme 'Ginryu'		38	Tanaka, 1962a
Den. moschatum		40	Jones, 1963
		38	Chardard, 1963
		38, 39	Kamemoto & Sagarik, 1967
		38	Wilfret & Kamemoto, 1971
Den. moschatum var. cupreum		38 + 3f.	Kosaki, 1958
		38	Kosaki & Kamemoto, 1961
Den. mutabile		2x	Jones, 1963
Den. nakaharai		30	Hsu, 1972
Den. Neo Hawaii		38–40; 56–57 (reciprocal cross)	Dorn & Kamemoto, 1962
Den. nobile		ca. 20	Hoffmann, 1929
		ca. 20	Hoffmann, 1930
	19	38	Miduno, 1940b
		40	Eftimiu-Heim, 1941
	19	38	Ito & Mutsuura, 1957

Plant name	Chromosome number		Reference	Plant name	Chromosome number		Reference
	n	2n			n	2n	
	19	38	Vajrabhaya & Randolph, 1960			76 ± 1	Kamemoto et al., 1961
(as var. nobile)		38, 57	Jones, 1963	Den. phalaenopsis 'Hololeucum'		38	Vajrabhaya & Randolph, 1960
		19	Chardard, 1963	Den. phalaenopsis 'Lyon's Light No. 1'	19, 38	38	Kosaki & Kamemoto, 1961
		38	Kamemoto & Sagarik, 1967			38	Kamemoto et al., 1961
		38	Tanaka, 1971		variable	38	Dorn & Kamemoto, 1962
Den. nobile var. cooksonianum	19	38	Ito & Mutsuura, 1957			38	Kamemoto & Tara, 1968
		38	Jones, 1963	Den. phalaenopsis 'Lyon's Light No. 1' (self)		56, 57, 58, 59	Kamemoto & Tara, 1968
Den. nobile 'King George'	38	76	Ito & Mutsuura, 1957	Den. phalaenopsis ('Lyon's Light No. 1' × 'Lyon's Light No. 2')		38, 39	Kamemoto & Tara, 1968
		76	Tanaka, 1962a	Den. phalaenopsis ('Lyon's Light No. 2' × 'Lyon's Light No. 1')		57	Kamemoto & Tara, 1968
Den. nobile var. nobilius		ca. 57	Jones, 1963	Den. phalaenopsis 'Ruby'		ca. 76	Kosaki, 1958
Den. nobile var. pendulum		38	Banerji & Chaudhuri, 1972			ca. 76	Kosaki & Kamemoto, 1961
Den. nobile var. sanderianum		38–40	Chardard, 1963			76	Kamemoto et al., 1961
Den. nobile var. virginale		57	Jones, 1963	Den. phalaenopsis var. schroederianum	19	38	Vajrabhaya & Randolph, 1960
Den. nobile var. wallichianum		38	Jones, 1963	Den. phalaenopsis 'Shibata'		38	Kamemoto et al., 1961
Den. ochreatum		2x	Jones, 1963	Den. philippinensis		38	Kosaki & Kamemoto, 1961
Den. Orchidwood		57 ± 2	Kosaki & Kamemoto, 1961	Den. pierardii	19		Kosaki, 1958
		57 ± 2	Kamemoto et al., 1961			38	Vajrabhaya & Randolph, 1960
Den. ovatum		40	Jones, 1963		19		Kosaki & Kamemoto, 1961
Den. Owen		38	Kosaki & Kamemoto, 1961		19–20		Chardard, 1963
Den. palpebrae		40	Jones, 1963		19	38, 57	Sharma & Chatterji, 1966
Den. paranalum		38	Pancho, 1965a			38	Kamemoto & Sagarik, 1967
		38	Pancho, 1965b			38	Sarkar et al., 1978
Den. parcoides	20		Chardard, 1963	Den. pitcherianum		2x	Jones, 1963
Den. parishii		40	Ito & Mutsuura, 1957	Den. platycaulon		38	Pancho, 1965a
		38	Jones, 1963			38	Pancho, 1965b
		38	Kamemoto & Sagarik, 1967	Den. Pompadour (= Den. Mme. Pompadour)		38–55	Vajrabhaya & Randolph, 1960
Den. Pauline		38	Vajrabhaya & Randolph, 1960	Den. porphyrochilum	19		Mehra & Sehgal, 1975
Den. pendulum		2x	Jones, 1963	Den. porphyrophyllum	19		Chardard, 1963
Den. Perfection		40	Ito & Mutsuura, 1957	Den. primulinum		38	Ito & Mutsuura, 1957
Den. Permer 'Mikage'		78	Tanaka, 1962a			38	Jones, 1963
Den. Permer 'Kobe'		76	Tanaka, 1964a			38	Kamemoto & Sagarik, 1967
Den. Permer 'Okubo'		76, 73 ± 1	Tanaka, 1962a		19		Mehra & Vij, 1970
Den. Permoth 'No. 1'		79	Tanaka, 1964a				
Den. phalaenopsis	19	38	Kosaki, 1958				
		38	Kosaki & Kamemoto, 1961				
		38	Wilfret & Kamemoto, 1971				
		38	Tanaka, 1971				
Den. phalaenopsis 'Extra'		76	Kamemoto et al., 1961				
Den. phalaenopsis 'Giganteum'		ca. 76	Kosaki, 1958				
		ca. 76	Kosaki & Kamemoto, 1961				

Plant name	Chromosome number n	2n	Reference
		38	Mehra & Kashyap, 1976
Den. prostratum		2x	Jones, 1963
Den. pulchellum (= Den. dalhausieanum)		38	Kosaki & Kamemoto, 1961
		2x	Jones, 1963
		40	Kamemoto & Sagarik, 1967
Den. ramosum		40	Jones, 1963
Den. regium		38	Jones, 1963
Den. revolutum		40	Kamemoto & Sagarik, 1967
Den. Rickie Cornetti		38	Vajrabhaya & Randolph, 1960
Den. rotundatum	20		Mehra & Vij, 1970
Den. Ruby King		75 ± 1	Kosaki, 1958
		75 ± 1	Kosaki & Kamemoto, 1961
		75 ± 1	Kamemoto et al., 1961
Den. Salak 'Beaumont'		76	Kamemoto et al., 1967
Den. sanderae	20	40	Shindo & Kamemoto, 1963d
Den. scabrilingue		38	Kamemoto & Sagarik, 1967
Den. schuetzei	20	40	Shindo & Kamemoto, 1963d
Den. schulleri		38	Vajrabhaya & Randolph, 1960
Den. secundum		40	Jones, 1963 Chardard, 1963
dum	20		
		40	Kamemoto & Sagarik, 1967
Den. senile		38	Kamemoto & Sagarik, 1967
		38	Wilfret & Kamemoto, 1971
Den. signatum		2x	Jones, 1963
Den. smilliae		38	Jones, 1963
Den. Sohma		80	Ito & Mutsuura, 1957
		85	Tanaka, 1962
Den. sophronites		ca. 80	Jones, 1963
Den. speciosum		38	Blumenschein, 1960
Den. speciosum var. fusiforme		38	Kosaki & Kamemoto, 1961
Den. speciosum var. hillii		38	Jones, 1963
Den. spectabile		38	Kosaki, 1958
		38	Kosaki & Kamemoto, 1961
		38	Wilfret & Kamemoto, 1971
Den. spurium		40	Pancho, 1965a
		40	Pancho, 1965b
Den. stratiotes		38	Kosaki, 1958
		38	Vajrabhaya & Randolph, 1960
		38	Kosaki & Kamemoto, 1961

Plant name	Chromosome number n	2n	Reference
Den. stratiotes var. giganteum		38	Jones, 1963
		38	Wilfret & Kamemoto, 1971
Den. strebloceras		38	Jones, 1963
		38	Wilfret & Kamemoto, 1971
Den. superbiens	19	38	Vajrabhaya & Randolph, 1960
		38	Jones, 1963
Den. superbiens 'Daeng Yai'		38	Vajrabhaya & Randolph, 1960
Den. sutepense		2x	Jones, 1963
		38	Wilfret & Kamemoto, 1971
Den. taurinum		38	Kosaki, 1958
		38	Kosaki & Kamemoto, 1961
Den. teretifolium		2x	Jones, 1963
Den. Thomas Warne	20	40	Shindo & Kamemoto, 1963
Den. Thwaitesiae		38	Vajrabhaya & Randolph, 1960
Den. Thwaitesiae 'Veitchi's'		38	Tanaka, 1962a
Den. thyrsiflorum	20		Hoffmann, 1929
	20		Hoffmann, 1930
		40	Vajrabhaya & Randolph, 1960
		40	Kosaki & Kamemoto, 1961
		40	Kamemoto & Sagarik, 1967
Den. toftii		38	Vajrabhaya & Randolph, 1960
		38	Kosaki & Kamemoto, 1961
Den. tokai		38	Vajrabhaya & Randolph, 1960
	19		Kosaki & Kamemoto, 1961
		38	Jones, 1963
Den. topaziacum		38	Pancho, 1965a
		38	Pancho, 1965b
Den tortile		38	Kosaki & Kamemoto, 1961
		38	Jones, 1963
		38	Kamemoto & Sagarik, 1967
		38	Wilfret & Kamemoto, 1971
Den. tosaense		40	Mutsuura & Nakahira, 1959
		38	Tanaka, 1965b
		38	Tanaka, 1971
Den. transparens		38	Jones, 1963
parens	20	40 (30)	Sharma & Chatterji, 1966
	20		Mehra & Vij, 1970

Plant name	Chromosome number n	2n	Reference	Plant name	Chromosome number n	2n	Reference
Den. trigonopus		38	Wilfret & Kamemoto, 1971	*Den.* unnamed (*Den.* Cassiope × *Den. nobile*)		38	Miduno, 1940b
Den. undulatum	19	38	Kosaki & Kamemoto, 1961	*Den.* unnamed (*Den. d'albertsii* × *Den. canaliculatum*)		38	Wilfret *et al.*, 1979
		38	Jones, 1963				
		38	Wilfret & Kamemoto, 1971	*Den.* unnamed (*Den. d'albertsii* × *Den. mirbelianum*)		38	Wilfret *et al.*, 1979
Den. undulatum var. *broomfieldii*	19		Kosaki & Kamemoto, 1961				
Den. Variabilis		57	Ito & Mutsuura, 1957	*Den.* unnamed (*Den. d'albertsii* × *Den. phalaenopsis*)		38	Wilfret *et al.*, 1979
Den. Variabilis 'Yellow Queen'		57	Tanaka, 1964a				
Den. Veitchii		92	Vajrabhaya & Randolph, 1960	*Den.* unnamed (*Den. d'albertsii* × *Den. phalaenopsis* 'Lyon's Light No. 1')		56, 57, 58	Kamemoto & Tara, 1968
Den. ventricosum		38	Pancho, 1965a				
		38	Pancho, 1965b				
		20	Hsu, 1972	*Den.* unnamed (*Den. d'albertsii* × *Den. undulatum*)		38	Wilfret *et al.*, 1979
Den. veratrifolium		38	Kosaki, 1958				
		38	Vajrabhaya & Randolph, 1960				
		38	Kosaki & Kamemoto, 1961	*Den.* unnamed (*Den. dearei* × *Den. formosum*)	variable	39	Shindo & Kamemoto, 1963
		38	Jones, 1963				
Den. victoriae-reginae		38	Jones, 1963	*Den.* unnamed (*Den. dicuphum* × *Den. gouldii*)		38	Wilfret *et al.*, 1979
		38	Wilfret & Kamemoto, 1971				
Den. Waialua		57	Vajrabhaya & Randolph, 1960	*Den.* unnamed (*Den. gouldii* × *Den. strebloceras*)		38	Wilfret *et al.*, 1979
Den. Waikiki Beauty		66 ± 2	Kosaki & Kamemoto, 1961				
		66 ± 2	Kamemoto et al., 1961	*Den.* unnamed (*Den.* Hawaii Nui × *Den.* Anouk)		38–152	Vajrabhaya & Randolph, 1960
Den. wardianum (as var. *wardianum*)		2x	Jones, 1963	*Den.* unnamed (*Den.* Hercules × *Den.* Thwaitesiae)		76	Tanaka, 1962a
Den. wardianum var. *album*		ca. 57	Jones, 1963	*Den.* unnamed [(*Den.* Iris × *Den.* Gatton Prince) × *Den.* Mont Blanc]		38, 76	Tanaka, 1962a
Den. wardianum var. *giganteum*		40	Hoffmann, 1929				
		40	Hoffmann, 1930				
Den. Yamazaki 'Shoten'		78 ± 1	Tanaka, 1964a	*Den.* unnamed [(*Den.* Iris × *Den.* Gatton Prince) × *Den.* Thwaitesiae 'Veitchi's']		38	Tanaka, 1964a
Den. Yamazaki 'Zenihara'		81	Tanaka, 1964a				
Den. unnamed (*Den.* Alice Spalding × *Den. stratiotes* 'UF#1')		38	Sagawa & Niimoto, 1961	*Den.* unnamed (*Den.* Lady Constance × *Den.* Lady Hamilton)		65–70	Kosaki & Kamemoto, 1961
Den. unnamed (*Den.* Beach Girl × *Den.* Takami Kodama)		38	Vajrabhaya & Randolph, 1960	*Den.* unnamed (*Den.* Lady Constance × *Den. phalaenopsis*)		38, 42, 46, 51, 52, 57, 75	Kosaki & Kamemoto, 1961
Den. unnamed (*Den.* Betty Potter × *Den. phalaenopsis* 'Dixon')		ca. 57	Vajrabhaya & Randolph, 1960				
Den. unnamed (*Den. bigibbum* × *Den. d'albertsii*)		38	Wilfret *et al.*, 1979	*Den.* unnamed (*Den.* Lady Hamilton × *Den. phalaenopsis*)		76 ± 1	Kamemoto et al., 1961

Plant name	Chromosome number		Reference	Plant name	Chromosome number		Reference
	n	2n			n	2n	
Den. unnamed [(*Den.* Lady Hamilton × *Den.* Top Hat) × (*Den.* Lady Hamilton × *Den.* Lady Constance)]		43 ± 1, 57 ± 1, 133 ± 2	Tanaka, 1964a	*Den.* unnamed (*Den. ostrinoglossum* × *Den. phalaenopsis*)		38	Wilfret *et al.*, 1979
Den. unnamed (*Den. macrophyllum* × *Den. bigibbum*)		38	Wilfret *et al.*, 1979	*Den.* unnamed (*Den.* Pauline × *Den. undulatum*)		38, 57	Vajrabhaya & Randolph, 1960
Den. unnamed (*Den. macrophyllum* × *Den. phalaenopsis*)		38	Wilfret *et al.*, 1979	*Den.* unnamed (*Den.* Perfection × *Den.* Merlin)		74	Ito & Mutsuura, 1957
Den. unnamed (*Den. macrophyllum* × *Den. undulatum*)		38	Wilfret *et al.*, 1979	*Den.* unnamed (*Den. phalaenopsis* × *Den. caniculatum*)		38	Wilfret *et al.*, 1979
Den. unnamed (*Den.* Mary Cane × *Den.* Sohma)		57	Tanaka, 1964a	*Den.* unnamed (*Den. phalaenopsis* × *Den. d'albertsii*)		38	Wilfret *et al.*, 1979
Den. unnamed (*Den.* Merlin × *Den. nobile*)		76	Ito & Mutsuura, 1957	*Den.* unnamed (*Den. phalaenopsis* × *Den. draconis*)		38	Wilfret *et al.*, 1979
Den. unnamed [*Den.* Merlin × (*Den.* Thwaitesiae 'Veichi's' × *Den. virginalis*)]		76	Ito & Mutsuura, 1957	*Den.* unnamed (*Den. phalaenopsis* × *Den. gouldii*)		38	Wilfret *et al.*, 1979
Den. unnamed [(*Den.* Merlin 'Dark' × *Den.* Queen of Gatton) × (*Den.* Hercules × *Den.* Thwaitesiae)]		54 ± 1	Tanaka, 1964a	*Den.* unnamed (*Den. phalaenopsis* × *Den. grantii*)		38	Wilfret *et al.*, 1979
Den. unnamed [*Den.* Merlin 'Shinjuku' × (*Den.* Reagal × *Den.* Gatton Monarch)]		74, 76	Tanaka, 1962a	*Den.* unnamed (*Den. phalaenopsis* × *Den. primulinum*)		38	Wilfret *et al.*, 1979
Den. unnamed (*Den.* Merlin 'Shinjuku' × *Den.* Sohma)		76	Tanaka, 1964a	*Den.* unnamed (*Den. phalaenopsis* × *Den. stratiotes*)		38	Wilfret *et al.*, 1979
Den. unnamed (*Den. mirbelianum* × *Den. johannis*)		38	Wilfret *et al.*, 1979	*Den.* unnamed (*Den. phalaenopsis* × *Den. strebloceras*)		38	Wilfret *et al.*, 1979
Den. unnamed (*Den.* Montrose × *Den.* Melpomene)		38	Tanaka, 1964a	*Den.* unnamed (*Den. phalaenopsis* × *Den. undulatum*)		38	Wilfret *et al.*, 1979
Den. unnamed (*Den. ostrinoglossum* × *Den. gouldii*)		38	Wilfret *et al.*, 1979	*Den.* unnamed (*Den. phalaenopsis* 'Hololeucum' × *Den. chrysanthum*)		38	Vajrabhaya & Randolph, 1960
				Den. unnamed (*Den.* Renown × *Den.* Kobe)		76 ± 1	Tanaka, 1964
				Den. unnamed (*Den.* Ronaele × *Den.* Merlin)		77	Vajrabhaya & Randolph, 1960
				Den. unnamed (*Den. sanderae* × *Den. dearei*)	variable	60	Shindo & Kamemoto, 1963
				Den. unnamed (*Den. schuetzei* × *Den. dearei*)	20	40	Shindo & Kamemoto, 1963

Plant name	Chromosome number n	Chromosome number 2n	Reference	Plant name	Chromosome number n	Chromosome number 2n	Reference
Den. unnamed (*Den. spectabile* × *Den. undulatum*)		38	Wilfret *et al.*, 1979	*Den.* unnamed (*Den. xanthocentrum* × *Den.* Gatton Monarch 'Black and Flory')		57	Tanaka, 1964a
Den. unnamed (*Den. stratiotes* × *Den. d'albertsii*)		38	Wilfret *et al.*, 1979	*Dendrochilum cobbianum*		40	Pancho, 1965a
Den. unnamed (*Den. stratiotes* × *Den. phalaenopsis*)		38	Wilfret *et al.*, 1979			40	Pancho, 1965b
				D. filiforme		40	Pancho, 1965a
						40	Pancho, 1965b
Den. unnamed (*Den. stratiotes* × *Den. phalaenopsis* 'Lyon's Light No. 1')		57	Kamemoto & Tara, 1968	*D. formosanum*		30	Hsu, 1972
				D. glumaceum (= *Platyclinis glumaceum*)	20		Hoffmann, 1929
					20		Hoffmann, 1930
Den. unnamed (*Den. strebloceras* × *Den. bigibbum*)		38	Wilfret *et al.*, 1979	*D. pumilum*		40	Pancho, 1965a
						40	Pancho, 1965b
				D. tenellum		40	Pancho, 1965a
Den. unnamed (*Den. strebloceras* × *Den. canaliculatum*)		38	Wilfret *et al.*, 1979			40	Pancho, 1965b
				Dendrophylax funalis		42	Shindo & Kamemoto, 1963d
Den. unnamed (*Den. strebloceras* × *Den. d'albertsii*)		38	Wilfret *et al.*, 1979	*Diacrium bilamelatum*		40	Blumenschein, 1960
				Diaphananthe cuneata		ca. 50	Jones, 1967
Den. unnamed (*Den. strebloceras* × *Den. undulatum*)		38	Wilfret *et al.*, 1979	*D. densiflora*		50	Jones, 1967
				D. plehniana		50	Jones, 1967
				D. rutila		100	Jones, 1967
Den. unnamed (*Den. undulatum* × *Den. d'albertsii*)		38	Wilfret *et al.*, 1979			50, 100	Ar-rushdi, 1971
				D. species		ca. 50	Jones, 1967
Den. unnamed (*Den. undulatum* × *Den. gouldii*)	19	38	Vajrabhaya & Randolph, 1960	*Dichaea muricata* var. *neglecta*		52	Woodard (from Duncan, 1959)
				Dilomilis montana	21		Nevling, 1969
Den. unnamed (*Den. undulatum* × *Den. phalaenopsis*)		38	Wilfret *et al.*, 1979	*Dimerandra stenopetala*		40	Blumenschein, 1960
				Diplocentrum congestum		38	Kulkarni & Jorapur, 1979
Den. unnamed (*Den. undulatum* × *Den. spectabile*)		38	Wilfret *et al.*, 1979	*D. recurvum*		38	Kulkarni & Jorapur, 1979
Den. unnamed (*Den. undulatum* × *Den. stratiotes*)		38	Wilfret *et al.*, 1979	*Diplomeris hirsuta*	21		Mehra & Kashyap, 1976
				Diploprora championi		38	Kamemoto *et al.*, 1964
Den. unnamed (*Den. undulatum* × *Den. strebloceras*)		38	Wilfret *et al.*, 1979	*D. uraiense*		16	Hsu, 1972
				Doritis buyssoniana (= *phalaenopsis buyssoniana*)		76	Woodard, 1951 (in Duncan, 1959)
Den. unnamed (*Den.* Veitchii × *Den. nobile*)		57–67	Vajrabhaya & Randolph, 1960	*Dor. pulcherrima* (= *Phalaenopsis esmeralda*), (= *Phal. pulcerrima*)		38	Woodard, 1951
					19	38	Sagawa & Niimoto, 1961
Den. unnamed (*Den. xanthocentrum* × *Den.* Gatton Monarch)		38	Tanaka, 1962a			38	Shindo & Kamemoto, 1963e
					19		Chardard, 1963
						38	Kamemoto *et al.*, 1964
				Dor. pulcherrima var. *buyssonniana* (= *Dor. buyssoniana*)		76	Kamemoto *et al.*, 1964
				Dor. taenialis		40	Sharma & Sarkar, 1967–1968
				Dor. wightii	19		Mehra & Vij, 1970
				Eleorchis conformis		40	Miduno, 1939
						40	Mutsuura & Nakahira, 1958

Plant name	n	2n	Reference
E. japonica		40	Miduno, 1939
		40	Mutsuura & Nakahira, 1958
		40	Tanaka, 1965b
		40	Tanaka, 1971
Encyclia odoratissima		40	Blumenschein, 1960
E. odoratissima var. serroniana		40	Blumenschein, 1960
Ephippianthus schmidtii		40	Mutsuura & Nakahira, 1960
		42	Shoji, 1963
		36	Tanaka, 1965b
Epidendrum atropurpureum	20	40	Kamemoto, 1950
		80–90	Chardard, 1963
Epi. brachyphyllum	30		Huynh, 1965
Epi. brachyphyllum aff. brachyphyllum	14		Huynh, 1965
Epi. brassavolae	20	40	Kamemoto, 1950
Epi. Burtonii		80	Kamemoto, 1950
Epi. campylostalix	20	40	Kamemoto & Randolph, 1949
		40	Kamemoto, 1950
Epi. ciliare	20	40, 80, 160	Geitler, 1940
		40	Eftimiu-Heim, 1941
	20	40	Kamemoto, 1950
		40	Blumenschein, 1960
Epi. cochleatum	20	40	Kamemoto, 1950
Epi. conopseum	20	40	Kamemoto, 1950
		40	Chardard, 1963
Epi. denticulatum		40	Blumenschein, 1960
Epi. difforme		39–40	Chardard, 1963
Epi. diffusum	20	40	Kamemoto, 1950
Epi. ellipticum		56	Blumenschein, 1960
Epi. elongatum		56	Blumenschein, 1960
Epi. floribundum		40	Blumenschein, 1960
Epi. lindenii		56	Blumenschein, 1960
Epi. linkianum	ca. 20		Hoffmann, 1930
	20	40	Kamemoto, 1950
Epi. loefgrenii		40	Blumenschein, 1960
Epi. longisphatum		40	Blumenschein, 1960
Epi. mariae		40	Tanaka, 1964a
Epi. mosenii		24	Blumenschein, 1960
Epi. munroeanum		40	Eftimiu-Heim, 1941
Epi. nocturnum	20		Hoffmann, 1929
	20		Hoffmann, 1930
		ca. 80	Kamemoto, 1950
		40, 80	Blumenschein, 1960
		74–85	Chardard, 1963
Epi. nocturnum var. guadetoupense		42–48	Chardard, 1963
Epi. obrienianum		40	Malla et al., 1977b
Epi. ochraceum	20	40	Kamemoto & Randolph, 1949
	20	40	Kamemoto, 1950
Epi. patens		40	Chardard, 1963
Epi. prismatocarpum		40	Blumenschein, 1960
Epi. propinguum		40	Kamemoto, 1950
Epi. purpureum		56	Blumenschein, 1960
Epi. radicans		40, 70	Kamemoto, 1950
		48–57	Chardard, 1963
	19		Mehra & Vij, 1970
Epi. raniferum	20		Hoffmann, 1929
	20		Hoffmann, 1930
		40	Blumenschein, 1960
Epi. rigidum		40	Blumenschein, 1960
Epi. tampense	20	40	Kamemoto & Randolph, 1949
	20	40	Kamemoto, 1950
Epi. xanthium		ca. 80	Kamemoto, 1950
Epilaelia unnamed (Epidendrum xanthinum × Laelia flava)		60	Kamemoto, 1950
Epilaeliopsis unnamed (Laeliopsis domingaiensis × Epidendrum mariae)		40	Tanaka, 1964
Epipactis atropurpurea	20		Hagerup, 1947
E. atrorubens		40	Löve & Löve, 1944
		40	Hagerup, 1944a
		40	Hagerup, 1947
		40	Pogan & Wcislo (in Löve & Löve, 1961)
		40	Kliphuis, 1963
		40	Knaben & Engelskjön, 1967
E. confusa		40	Hagerup, 1945
		40	Hagerup, 1947
E. consimilis	20	20, 40	Mehra & Vij, 1972a
		40	Mehra & Kashyap, 1979
E. falcata (= Cephalanthera falcata)		24	Sugiura, 1928

Plant name	Chromosome number n	Chromosome number 2n	Reference
E. gigantea	20		Raven et al., 1965
	30		Niehaus & Wong, 1971
		40	Vij & Gupta, 1975
E. helleborine	19		Barber, 1942
		38	Barber, 1942
	19, 20	40	Hagerup, 1945
	19, 20	38, 40	Hagerup, 1947
		40 (20)	Weijer, 1952
		38, 40	Pogan & Wcislo (in Löve & Löve, 1961)
		38	Gadella & Kliphuis, 1963
	19	38	Kliphuis, 1963
		38	Löve & Löve, 1969
	19	38	Mehra & Bawa, 1970
		40	Uhriková & Feráková, 1978
		40	Mehra & Pandita, 1978
E. latifolia		38	Barber, 1942
	20	40 (20)	Hagerup, 1945
	19, 20		Hagerup, 1947
		40	Skalinska et al., 1961
		36, 44	Leveque & Gorenflot, 1969
		40	Mehra & Vij, 1970
	20	40	Mehra & Vij, 1972a
	20 (40)		Vij & Gupta, 1975
		38, 40, 38–40	Balaeva & Siplivinski, 1976
		40	Mehra & Kashyap, 1979
E. leptochila		36	Hagerup, 1947
E. microphylla		40	Hagerup, 1947
E. palustris	12		Friemann, 1910
	12		Müller, 1912
	20	40	Hagerup, 1944a
	20	40	Löve & Löve, 1944
		38	Hagerup, 1947
		40	Gadella & Kliphuis, 1963
	20	40	Kliphuis, 1963
		40	Skalinska et al., 1966
		40, 44, 46, 48	Leveque & Gorenflot, 1969
		40	Uhrikova & Schwarzova, 1976
E. papillosa	20		Matsuura & Suto, 1935
		38–40	Sokolovskaya, 1963
E. persica	20	40	Hagerup, 1947
E. phyllanthes		36	Hagerup, 1947
E. royleana		40	Mehra & Pandita, 1978
E. sayekiana (= E. papillosa var. sayekiana)		40	Miduno, 1937
		40	Miduno, 1938
		40	Shoji, 1963
E. thunbergii		40	Miduno, 1937
		40	Miduno, 1938
		40	Mutsuura, 1959

Plant name	Chromosome number n	Chromosome number 2n	Reference
		40	Mutsuura & Nakahira, 1959
		40	Tanaka, 1965b
		40	Tanaka, 1971
		40	Tanaka, 1974
	20		Terasaka & Tanaka, 1974
E. veratrifolia		40	Arora, 1968
Epipogium aphyllum	34		Francini, 1930
	34		Afzelius, 1954
Eria acervata	20		Mehra & Sehgal, 1975
E. alba		34	Mehra & Sehgal, 1974
E. arisanensis		40	Tanaka, 1965b
E. brachystachya		44	Pancho, 1965a
		44	Pancho, 1965b
E. bractescens		40	Sharma & Chatterji, 1966
E. clemensiae		44	Pancho, 1965a
		44	Pancho, 1965b
E. confusa	20		Mehra & Sehgal, 1974
E. convallarioides	19		Chardard, 1963
	20		Mehra & Vij, 1970
E. corneri		36	Tanaka, 1965b
E. coronaria	18		Mehra & Vij, 1970
E. cymbiformis		42 ± 2	Pancho, 1965a
		42 ± 2	Pancho, 1965b
E. dalzellii		24 + 5 − 7B	Jorapur & Kulkarni, 1979
E. excavata	20		Mehra & Vij, 1970
E. exilis		38	Jorapur & Kulkarni, 1979
E. floribunda		44	Pancho, 1965a
		44	Pancho, 1965b
E. gigantea		66	Pancho, 1965
E. giungii	20		Chardard, 1963
E. graminifolia	19		Mehra & Vij, 1970
E. lagunensis		44	Pancho, 1965a
		44	Pancho, 1965b
E. luchuensis		36	Tanaka, 1965b
	18		Terasaka & Tanaka, 1974
E. microchilos		24 + 9 − 11B	Jorapur & Kulkarni, 1979
E. mysorensis		38	Jorapur & Kulkarni, 1979
E. noodiana		44	Pancho, 1965
E. nudicaulis		40	Tanaka, 1965b
E. ovata		44	Pancho, 1965a
		44	Pancho, 1965b
E. paniculata	19		Chardard, 1963
E. pannea	18		Mehra & Vij, 1970
E. philippinensis		44	Pancho, 1965a
		44	Pancho, 1965b
E. reptans		40	Mutsuura & Nakahira, 1958
		38	Tanaka, 1965b
E. reticosa		42	Jorapur & Kulkarni, 1979
E. ringens		44	Pancho, 1965a
		44	Pancho, 1965b
E. spicata		38	Mehra & Kashyap, 1978
E. woodiana		44	Pancho, 1965a
		44	Pancho, 1965b
E. yakushimensis		36	Tanaka, 1965b

Plant name	Chromosome number		Reference	Plant name	Chromosome number		Reference
	n	2n			n	2n	
Eriopsis biloba		40	Daker & Jones, 1970		19		Mehra & Sehgal, 1978
E. rutidobulbon		40	Daker & Jones, 1970			38	Mehra & Kashyap, 1979
Erycina diaphana		52	Sinoto, 1962	*G. dasypogon*		38	Tara & Kamemoto, 1970
		56	Sinoto, 1969a			38	Mehra & Sehgal, 1978
Eulophia aculeata ssp. *huttonii*	27		Hall, 1965	*G. japonicus*		40	Mutsuura & Nakahira, 1960
E. angolensis	34, 35, 36, 37, 38		Hall, 1965			38	Tanaka, 1965b
E. clavicornis var. *clavicornis*	50		Hall, 1965	*G. matsuran* (= *Saccolabium matsuran*)		34	Mutsuura & Nakahira, 1959
E. clavicornis var. *nutans*	25, 47		Hall, 1965				
E. cristata		46	Ar-rushdi, 1971	*G. somai*		30	Hsu, 1972
E. ensata	27		Hall, 1965	*Gastrodia elata*	8, 9	16, 18	Kusano, 1915
E. euglossa		40, 41	Ar-rushdi, 1971		12		Hsu, 1972
E. foliosa	27		Hall, 1965		18	36	Tanaka & Kamemoto, 1974
E. fridericii	24		Hall, 1965				
E. geniculata	19	38	Chatterji, 1965	*G. galeata*	20		Hoffmann, 1930
E. gracilis		44, 66	Ar-rushdi, 1971				
E. graminea	27		Mehra & Sehgal, 1975	*Geodorum densiflorum*	26		Mehra & Sehgal, 1978
E. gusukumai		56	Tanaka, 1965b			54	Kulkarni & Jorapur, 1979
E. hormusfii	27		Mehra & Vij, 1970				
E. horsfallii		62	Ar-rushdi, 1971	*G. nutans*		36	Pancho, 1965a
E. leachii	26		Hall, 1965			36	Pancho, 1965b
E. leontoglossa	27		Hall, 1965	*Gomesa crispa*		56	Charanasri et al., 1973
E. macowanii	28		Hall, 1965				
E. macrostachya		32	Pancho, 1965a	*Gom. recurva*		56	Sinoto, 1962
		32	Pancho, 1965b			56	Sinoto, 1969b
E. nuda		54	Chatterji, 1965			56	Charanasri & Kamemoto, 1975
E. ovalis ssp. *bainesii*		42	Hall, 1965				
E. ovalis ssp. *ovalis*	21, 40		Hall, 1965	*Gongora galeata*	20		Hoffmann, 1930
E. parviflora	25		Hall, 1965	*G. quinquenervis*		38, 40, 42	Daker & Jones, 1970
E. petersii	24		Hall, 1965				
E. quartiniana		96	Ar-rushdi, 1971	*G. tricolor*		40	Arp, 1973
E. ramentacea		54	Kulkarni & Jorapur, 1979	*G. truncata*		ca. 38	Daker & Jones, 1970
E. speciosa	27		Hall, 1965	*Goodyera biflora*	16 + 2B		Mehra & Kashyap, 1979
E. squalida		32	Pancho, 1965a	*G. boninensis*		28	Tanaka, 1965b
		32	Pancho, 1965b			28	Ono, 1977
E. streptopetala	20	40	Hall, 1965	*G. hachijoensis*		28	Miduno, 1939
						28	Tanaka, 1965b
E. stricta		32	Pancho, 1965a	*G. hachijoensis* var. *leuconeura*		28	Tanaka, 1965b
		32	Pancho, 1965b				
E. tenella	60		Hall, 1965	*G. hachijoensis* var. *yakushimensis*		28	Tanaka, 1965b
E. tuberculata	50		Hall, 1965				
E. welwitschii	27		Hall, 1965	*G. macrantha*		30	Miduno, 1939
E. zeyheriana	56		Hall, 1965			30	Mutsuura & Nakahira, 1958
E. species	16	32	Sampathkumaran & Rangaswamy, 1931			30	Tanaka, 1965b
						30	Tanaka, 1971
E. species		82	Ar-rushdi, 1971	*G. matsumurana*		28	Miduno, 1939
Eulophidium saundersianum		58	Ar-rushdi, 1971			28	Tanaka, 1965b
				G. maximowicziana		42	Miduno, 1939
Eurychone rothschildiana		50	Jones, 1967			56	Mutsuura, 1959
Galaearis spectabilis		42	Löve & Simon, 1968			56	Mutsuura & Nakahira, 1959
Galeola falconeri	15		Mehra & Vij, 1970			28, 56	Tanaka, 1965a
G. nana		28	Larsen, 1966			28, 56	Tanaka, 1971
G. septentrionalis	14	28	Tanaka, 1975	*G. oblongifolia*	15		Taylor & Mulligan, 1968
Galeorchis spectabilis		42	Humphrey, 1932a			22	Löve & Simon, 1968
(= *Orchis spectabilis*)		42	Humphrey, 1932b		15		Pojar, 1973
Gastrochilus calceolaris		38	Kamemoto et al., 1964	*G. ogatai*		22	Tanaka, 1965b
		38	Jones, 1967	*G. ophioides*		30	Löve & Löve, 1954
	19		Arora, 1971				

Plant name	Chromosome number n	2n	Reference	Plant name	Chromosome number n	2n	Reference
G. pendula		28	Mutsuura & Nakahira, 1960			40, 80	Heusser, 1938
						40, 80	Sokolovskaya & Strelkova, 1940
		30	Tanaka, 1965b				
G. procera		42	Miduno, 1939		20	40	Frahm-Leliveld, 1941
	11		Afzelius, 1943				
		42	Tanaka, 1965b		20		Barber, 1942
		42	Tanaka, 1971		18, 19, 20		Afzelius, 1943
G. pubescens	13		Bostick, 1965			40	Diannelidis, 1948
G. recurva	16		Mehra & Sehgal, 1978			40	Diannelidis, 1955
G. repens	15	30	Richardson, 1935			40	Mutsuura & Nakahira, 1958
		28, 32	Eftimiu-Heim, 1941			40	Sokolovskaya & Strelkova, 1960
		30	Löve & Löve, 1944			40	Pogan & Wcislo (in Löve & Löve, 1961)
		30	Löve & Löve, 1954				
		30	Mutsuura & Nakahira, 1959			38	Sinoto & Shoji, 1962
		30	Gadella & Kliphuis, 1963			40	Gadella & Kliphuis, 1963
	15	30	Kliphuis, 1963		20	40	Kliphuis, 1963
		32	Tanaka, 1965b			40, 80, 100, 120	Groll, 1965
	15		Mehra & Bawa, 1970			ca. 40	Laane, 1965
		32	Tanaka, 1971			80	Wegener, 1966
	15		Mehra & Vij, 1972a			40	Knaven & Engelskjön, 1967
		32	Schotsman, 1970a			40	Zhukova, 1967
	15, 16	30	Vij & Gupta, 1975			20, 40, 80	Balaeva & Siplivinski, 1976
		30	Mehra & Pandita, 1979	G. conopsea ssp. conopsea		40	Leveque & Gorenflot, 1969
G. repens ssp. ophioides		30	Löve & Simon, 1968	G. conopsea ssp. montana		40	Majovsky et al., 1974
G. schlechtendaliana		30	Mutsuura & Nakahira, 1958	G. conopsea ssp. serotina		40	Heusser, 1938
		30	Shoji, 1963	G. conopsea var. cissuriensis		40	Sokolovskaya, 1966
		30	Tanaka, 1965b				
G. secundiflora	15		Mehra & Sehgal, 1974	G. cuculata		42	Tanaka, 1965b
G. velutina		28	Miduno, 1939	G. odoratissima	10	20	Fuchs & Ziegenspeck, 1923
		28	Mutsuura, 1959				
		28	Mutsuura & Nakahira, 1960		20	40	Heusser, 1938
						40	Pogan & Wcislo (in Löve & Löve, 1961)
		28	Tanaka, 1965b				
G. yaeyamae		44	Tanaka, 1965b			40	Susnik & Lovka, 1973
Grammangis ellisii		54	Chardard, 1963				
Grammatophyllum scriptum		40	Wimber, 1957a	G. unnamed (intergeneric hybrid) (Gymnadenia × Anacamptis)		20	Fuchs & Ziegenspeck, 1924
		40	Pancho, 1965a				
		40	Pancho, 1965b				
Gram. speciosum		40	Wimber, 1957a	G. unnamed (G. odoratissima × G. conopsea)		40	Heusser, 1938
		40	Pancho, 1965a				
		40	Pancho, 1965b				
Grobya galeata		56	Blumenschein, 1960	Gyrostachys cernua (= Spiranthes cernua)	30		Pace, 1914
Gymnadenia camtschatica		40	Mutsuura & Nakahira, 1958				
		40	Mutsuura, 1959	G. gracilis (= Spiranthes gracilis)	15	30	Pace, 1914
G. chidori (= Orchis chidori)		42	Miduno, 1940b	Habenaria acuifera		42	Mehra & Sehgal, 1974
G. clavellata		40	Löve & Simon, 1968	Hab. aitchisonii	21		Mehra & Vij, 1970
G. conopsea (= G. densiflora)	16		Strasburger, 1888		21		Mehra & Vij, 1972b
	10	20	Fuchs & Ziegenspeck, 1923	Hab. albida (= Leucorchis albida)		42	Harmsen, 1943
	8		Chodat, 1924				
	20	40	Richardson, 1935				

Plant name	n	2n	Reference
Hab. andrewsii		42	Bent, 1969
Hab. arietina	21		Mehra & Bawa, 1962
		28	Sharma & Sarkar, 1967–1968
	21		Mehra & Bawa, 1970
	21		Mehra & Vij, 1972b
Hab. aristata	21		Mehra & Vij, 1970
	21		Mehra & Vij, 1972b
	61		Mehra & Sehgal, 1974
Hab. biermanniana	21		Mehra & Vij, 1970
	21		Mehra & Vij, 1972b
Hab. blephariglottis		42	Humphrey, 1933
		42	Bent, 1969
Hab. bracteata		42	Humphrey, 1932a
		42	Humphrey, 1932b
Hab. chorisiana	21	42	Taylor & Mulligan, 1968
Hab. ciliaris (= Platanthera ciliaris)	16		Brown, 1909
		16	Richardson, 1935
Hab. clavellata		42	Humphrey, 1933
		42	Bent, 1969
Hab. commelinifolia		42	Mehra & Kashyap, 1978
		42	Kulkarni & Jorapur, 1979
Hab. constricta	21		Arora, 1971
Hab. copelandii		42	Pancho, 1965a
		42	Pancho, 1965b
Hab. crenifera		42	Kulkarni & Jorapur, 1979
Hab. densa	23		Mehra & Vij, 1970
	23, 24		Mehra & Vij, 1972b
	22		Mehra & Kashyap, 1979
Hab. digitata	21		Vij & Gupta, 1975
Hab. dilatata (= Platanthera dilatata)		42	Humphrey, 1933
	21	42	Taylor & Mulligan, 1968
		42	Bent, 1969
Hab. dilatata var. leucostachys	21		Raven et al., 1965
Hab. edgeworthii	21		Arora, 1968
	21	42	Mehra & Bawa, 1970
	21		Mehra & Vij, 1972b
	42		Vij & Gupta, 1975
	42		Mehra & Kashyap, 1976
Hab. elegans	21		Raven et al., 1965
Hab. elegans var. maritima	21		Niehaus & Wong, 1971
Hab. elisbethae		42	Mehra & Bawa, 1962
Hab. ensifolia	21		Mehra & Bawa, 1962
	21		Mehra & Bawa, 1970
		42	Mehra & Kashyap, 1979
Hab. fallax	21		Mehra & Vij, 1970
		30	Mehra & Kashyap, 1978
Hab. fimbriata		42	Bent, 1969
Hab. flava		42	Bent, 1969
Hab. galeandra	21		Mehra & Bawa, 1962
	ca. 21		Mehra & Bawa, 1970
Hab. geniculata		62	Miduno, 1939
	42		Mehra & Vij, 1970
	21		Mehra & Vij, 1972b
		84	Mehra & Sehgal, 1974
Hab. goodyeroides	23		Mehra & Vij, 1970
	21		Mehra & Vij, 1972b
Hab. graveolens		42	Arora, 1968
Hab. hookeri		42	Humphrey, 1933
		42	Bent, 1969
		42	Humphrey, 1933
Hab. hyperborea (= Platanthera hyperborea)	42	84	Harmsen, 1943
Hab. hyperborea var. huronensis		84	Bent, 1969
Hab. hystrix		42	Pancho, 1965a
		42	Pancho, 1965b
Hab. intermedia		42	Arora, 1968
	21		Mehra & Bawa, 1970
	21		Mehra & Vij, 1972b
		42	Mehra & Kashyap, 1979
Hab. josephii		40	Mehra & Kashyap, 1978
Hab. khasiana		42	Mehra & Sehgal, 1974
Hab. lacera		42	Bent, 1969
Hab. lacertifera	22		Mehra & Sehgal, 1974
Hab. lawii		42	Mehra & Kashyap, 1978
Hab. longicorniculata		40	Kulkarni & Jorapur, 1979
Hab. longitentaculata		42	Hsu, 1972
Hab. marginata	21		Arora, 1971
	21		Vij & Gupta, 1975
		42	Mehra & Kashyap, 1976
Hab. miersiana		62	Miduno, 1939
		64	Mutsuura & Nakahira, 1960
Hab. mullaeformis	24	48	Sharma & Sarkar, 1967–1968
Hab. obtusata		42	Humphrey, 1933
Hab. oldhami (= Hab. sagittifera)		28	Miduno, 1940b
Hab. orbiculata		42	Humphrey, 1932
		42	Bent, 1969
Hab. pectinata	21		Mehra & Bawa, 1962
		42	Arora, 1968
	21		Mehra & Bawa, 1970
	21		Mehra & Vij, 1972b

Plant name	Chromosome number		Reference
	n	2n	
	21 + 0 – 2B		Mehra & Kashyap, 1976
		42	Mehra & Kashyap, 1979
Hab. plantaginea	21		Arora, 1968
nea	63		Mehra & Vij, 1970
		126	Mehra & Vij, 1972b
	21		Mehra & Kashyap, 1976
Hab. psycodes		42	Bent, 1969
Hab. radiata		32	Miduno, 1939
(= Pecteilis radiata)		32	Mutsuura & Nakahira, 1958
		32	Mutsuura, 1959
		32	Sinoto & Shoji, 1962
		32	Tanaka, 1965b
		32	Tanaka, 1971
		32	Tanaka, 1974
	16		Terasaka & Tanaka, 1974
Hab. rhodocheila	19		Chardard, 1963
Hab. robinsonii		42	Pancho, 1965a
		42	Pancho, 1965b
Hab. saccata	21	42	Taylor & Mulligan, 1968
	21		Niehaus & Wong, 1971
	21		Pojar, 1973
Hab. sagittifera		28	Miduno, 1939
		28	Mutsuura & Nakahira, 1958
		28	Mutsuura, 1959
		28	Tanaka, 1971
Hab. sparsiflora	21		Niehaus & Wong, 1971
Hab. stenostychya		42 + 2B, 46	Mehra & Sehgal, 1974
Hab. straminea (= Leucorchis straminea)	21	42	Harmsen, 1943
Hab. susanne	21		Mehra & Bawa, 1962
	21		Mehra & Bawa, 1970
	21		Mehra & Vij, 1972b
	21		Mehra & Kashyap, 1979
Hab. sutepensis		40	Larsen, 1966
Hab. tridactylites	21		Mehra & Vij, 1970
Hab. triflora		42	Mehra & Kashyap, 1978
Hab. unalascensis ssp. maritima	21		Taylor & Mulligan, 1968
Hab. viridis	21		Mehra & Vij, 1970
	21		Mehra & Vij, 1972b
	21		Vij & Gupta, 1975
Hab. viridis var. bracteata		42	Bent, 1969
Hab. species	16	32	Sampathkumaran & Rangaswamy, 1931
Haemaria discolor var. dowsoniana		44	Tanaka, 1965b
Hammarbya puludosa	14		Hagerup, 1944a
	14		Kliphuis, 1963
Hemipilia cordifolia		44	Mehra & Bawa, 1970
Herminium angustifolium	20		Mehra & Bawa, 1962
folium	19	38	Mehra & Bawa, 1970
	19, 38		Mehra & Vij, 1970
	19, 38		Mehra & Vij, 1972b
		38	Vij & Gupta, 1975
H. duthiei	20		Mehra & Kashyap, 1976
H. elisabethae		42	Mehra & Bawa, 1970
H. fallax	17		Mehra & Sehgal, 1974
H. gramineum	20		Arora, 1968
	20		Mehra & Vij, 1972b
		36	Mehra & Kashyap, 1978
H. jaffereyanum	19		Mehra & Bawa, 1970
	19		Mehra & Vij, 1972b
H. josephii	19		Mehra & Bawa, 1970
	19		Mehra & Vij, 1972b
H. lanceum	21		Arora, 1971
H. monorchis	12–13		Baranow, 1925
	20	40	Heusser, 1938
		40	Gadella & Kliphuis, 1963
	20	40	Kliphuis, 1963
		40	Mehra & Bawa, 1970
	20	40	Mehra & Vij, 1972b
	19		Vij & Gupta, 1975
H. quinguilobium	19		Mehra & Bawa, 1970
	19		Mehra & Vij, 1972b
Hetaeria rubens	21		Mehra & Bawa, 1970
	21		Mehra & Vij, 1972a
		22	Mehra & Sehgal, 1974
H. yakushimensis		42	Tanaka, 1965b
H. xenantha		20	Tanaka, 1965b
Himantoglossum hircinum (=	16		Strasburger, 1888
	12		Heusser, 1915
Loroglossum hircinum)	18	36	Heusser, 1938
		36	Déliot, 1955
	18		Kliphuis, 1963
		36	Susnik & Lovka, 1973
		36	Murín & Majovský, 1976
		36	Natarajan, 1979
H. longibracteatum		36	Natarajan, 1979
Hormidium calamarium		40	Blumenschein, 1960
H. fragans		40	Blumenschein, 1960
H. glumaceum		40	Blumenschein, 1960
H. variegatum		40	Blumenschein, 1960
Ione bicolor	20		Mehra & Sehgal, 1974

Plant name	Chromosome number n	Chromosome number 2n	Reference
I. candida	20		Mehra & Sehgal, 1974
Ionopsis paniculata		46	Blumenschein, 1960
Inps. utricularioides		46	Sinoto, 1962
Isotria medeoloides		18	Baldwin & Speese, 1957
I. verticillata		18	Baldwin & Speese, 1957
Jumellea filicornoides		38–40	Jones, 1967
Katherinea fuscescens		ca. 76	Mehra & Sehgal, 1978
Kingidium taenialis		38	Mehra & Kashyap, 1978
Koellensteinia graminea	ca. 48		Hoffmann, 1929
Laelia albida		42, ca. 63	Kamemoto, 1950
L. anceps		40	Blumenschein, 1960
L. anceps 'Brilliant'		40	Kamemoto, 1950
L. anceps var. *sanderiana*		40	Kamemoto, 1950
L. anceps 'Stella'		40	Kamemoto, 1950
L. autumnalis		41, 42	Kamemoto, 1950
L. briegeri		80	Blumenschein, 1960
L. caulescens		80	Blumenschein, 1960
L. cinnabarina		40	Blumenschein, 1960
		40	Chardard, 1963
L. crispilabia		80	Blumenschein, 1960
L. esalqueana		40	Blumenschein, 1960
L. flava		40	Blumenschein, 1960
L. gouldiana		40, 60	Kamemoto, 1950
L. grandiflora (= *Brassavola grandiflora*)	20		Afzelius, 1943
L. harpophylla		40	Blumenschein, 1960
L. longipes		40, 60, 80	Blumenschein, 1960
L. milleri		40	Blumenschein, 1960
L. mixta		40	Blumenschein, 1960
L. ostermayerii		40	Blumenschein, 1960
L. peduncularis		40–44	Chardard, 1963
L. perrinii (= *Brassavola perrinii*)	20		Afzelius, 1943
L. pumila		40	Blumenschein, 1960
		40	Chardard, 1963
L. purpurata		40	Kamemoto, 1950
		40	Blumenschein, 1960
		40	Arp, 1973
L. purpurata 'Semi-alba'		40 ± 1	Kamemoto et al., 1961
L. rubescens	20	40	Kamemoto & Randolph, 1949
	20	40	Kamemoto, 1950
L. rupestris		80	Blumenschein, 1960
L. tereticaulis		80	Blumenschein, 1960
Laeliocattleya Albata	20, 21, 22, 23	43	Kamemoto, 1950
Lc. Albura 'Monica'		ca. 60	Kamemoto, 1959b
Lc. Alfred J. Proebstle		100	Zuck, 1957
Lc. Alma 'Glory'		60	Tanaka, 1964a
Lc. Alma 'Oda's No. 1'		62	Tanaka, 1964a
Lc. Amber Glow 'Splendens'		80	Tanaka, 1964a
Lc. Aquitania 'AA'		60	Sagawa, 1962a
Lc. Areca 'Grand'		ca. 80	Kamemoto, 1959b
Lc. Areca 'Model'		ca. 80	Kamemoto, 1959b
Lc. Autumn Symphony 'Medon Cardinal'		60 ± 1	Tanaka, 1964a
Lc. Avalanche 'Shigedonia'		82	Tanaka, 1966
Lc. Bikan		80 ± 1	Kamemoto et al., 1961
Lc. Bonanza 'Champion'		80	Tanaka, 1964a
Lc. Bonanza 'Kahu'		80	Kamemoto et al., 1961
Lc. Bonanza 'Trade Winds'		80	Tanaka, 1966
Lc. Braceyana 'Hercules'		ca. 60	Kamemoto, 1952
		60	Kamemoto et al., 1961
Lc. Brightling 'Nakayama'		ca. 60	Kamemoto, 1959b
Lc. Brightling 'No. 1 of Formosa'		ca. 60	Kamemoto, 1959b
Lc. Canberra 'Stonehurst'		ca. 80	Kamemoto, 1952
		80 ± 2	Kamemoto et al., 1961
Lc. Canhamiana	19–21	40	Kamemoto, 1950
Lc. Canhamiana 'Albert's'		80	Sagawa, 1962a
Lc. Cantabile 'Alba'		40	Kamemoto, 1952
Lc. Cantabile 'Alba No. 1'		40	Kamemoto et al., 1961
Lc. Cantabile 'Alba Doris Bush'		ca. 80	Kamemoto, 1952
		80	Kamemoto et al., 1961
Lc. Cardinal 'UF#1'		40	Sagawa, 1962a
Lc. Carmanae 'Goraiko'		40	Kamemoto, 1959b
Lc. Ceylon Topaz	triploid		de Tomasi, 1954
		ca. 60	Kamemoto, 1959b
Lc. Charles Futterman		40	Kamemoto, 1950
Lc. Chitose Kodama		60	Tanaka, 1966
Lc. Choton		ca. 80	Kamemoto, 1959b
Lc. Clara Hashimoto		ca. 60	Kamemoto, 1952
Lc. Clara Hoshino		60 ± 1	Kamemoto et al., 1961
Lc. Clara Hoshino 'Exotica'		60 ± 1	Kamemoto et al., 1961

Plant name	Chromosome number		Reference
	n	2n	
		60	Kamemoto, et al., 1967
Lc. Copper Charm		40	Kamemoto et al., 1961
Lc. Cuesta		triploid	de Tomasi, 1954
Lc. Cynthia 'Majestica'		ca. 60	Kamemoto, 1959b
Lc. Derrynane 'Field's #7'		82	Sagawa, 1962a
Lc. Edger Omura 'Hoshi'		ca. 80	Kamemoto, 1959b
Lc. Edger Omura 'No. 9'		80 ± 1	Kamemoto et al., 1967
Lc. Edgar Omura 'No. 8'		80 ± 1	Kamemoto et al., 1967
Lc. Elizabeth Off		triploid	de Tomasi, 1954
Lc. Ennerdale 'Meteor'		ca. 80	Kamemoto, 1959b
Lc. Erick		40	Kamemoto, 1950
Lc. Estella Jewell 'Kazumura'		60 ± 1	Kamemoto et al., 1967
Lc. Eva Robinson		ca. 60	Kamemoto, 1952
		62 ± 2	Kamemoto et al., 1961
Lc. Eva Robinson 'Nelson's'		60	Sagawa & Niimoto, 1961
Lc. Evelyn Mountain 'Ohbayashi'		ca. 60	Kamemoto, 1959b
Lc. Evelyn Mountain 'Ri'		ca. 60	Kamemoto, 1959b
Lc. Fabrion 'Keiji Takeda'		102	Tanaka, 1966
Lc. Fabrion 'Sumiyoshi'		108 ± 1	Tanaka, 1966
Lc. Fabrion 'Vela Caslavska'		114	Tanaka, 1966
Lc. Fantasia		62	Kamemoto, 1950
Lc. Fedora 'Everest'		40	Kamemoto et al., 1961
Lc. Firebon		81	Kamemoto et al., 1967
Lc. Flora C. Loo		94 ± 1	Kamemoto et al., 1967
Lc. Florida 'Gold Star'		86	Sagawa, 1962a
Lc. Frank Lind 'No. 2'		ca. 80	Kamemoto, 1959b
Lc. Freya		ca. 60	Kamemoto, 1952
		64 ± 2, 82 ± 2	Niimoto & Randolph, 1958
Lc. General Maude 'Victory'		ca. 60	Kamemoto, 1952
Lc. George Baldwin		60, 61, 62	Kamemoto, 1950
Lc. George Baldwin 'UF#1'		62	Sagawa & Niimoto, 1961
Lc. Gertrude Hampton		triploid	de Tomasi, 1954
Lc. Gitche Manito 'Splendor'		ca. 80	Kamemoto, 1952
		80 ± 2	Kamemoto et al., 1961
Lc. Governor Gore 'Miya'		60	Tanaka, 1964a
Lc. Grandee 'Jules Furthman'		80	Kamemoto et al., 1961

Plant name	Chromosome number		Reference
	n	2n	
Lc. Hajime 'Kako'		81	Tanaka, 1966
Lc. Hajime 'Kinotomi'		90	Tanaka, 1966
Lc. Hardyano-Prudence		ca. 60	Kamemoto, 1959b
Lc. Harriet Yin		60 ± 2	Kamemoto et al., 1961
Lc. Harriet Yin 'No. 1'		61	Kamemoto et al., 1967
Lc. Hawaiian Sun 'Vicki Ann'		61	Kamemoto et al., 1967
Lc. Hecubazon 'Hilo Queen'		82 ± 2	Tanaka, 1966
Lc. Hecubazon 'Takeji'		83 ± 1	Tanaka, 1966
Lc. Hecuva		80 ± 2	Kamemoto et al., 1961
Lc. Hecuva 'Ogawa'		80 ± 1	Tanaka, 1964a
Lc. Helen Wilmer 'Shigeko Takeda'		80	Tanaka, 1964a
Lc. Hertha		ca. 100	Kamemoto, 1959b
Lc. Hertha 'Perfecta'		ca. 80	Kamemoto, 1952
Lc. H. G. Alexander		100 ± 2	Kamemoto et al., 1961
Lc. Hilary		tetraploid	de Tomasi, 1954
Lc. Huapala		87 ± 1	Kamemoto et al., 1967
Lc. Hyperion		tetraploid	Zuck, 1957
		ca. 80	Kamemoto, 1959b
		80 ± 2	Kamemoto et al., 1961
Lc. Indra 'Kahu'		80 ± 2	Kamemoto et al., 1961
Lc. Invicta		ca. 80	Kamemoto, 1952
		triploid	de Tomasi, 1954
		82 ± 2	Kamemoto et al., 1961
Lc. Jane Warne 'Alii'		40 ± 2	Kamemoto et al., 1961
Lc. Jay Markell 'Sam Sharpe'		61	Sagawa & Niimoto, 1961
Lc. J. K. Butler 'Wooley'		ca. 60	Kamemoto, 1952
		61 ± 1	Kamemoto et al., 1961
Lc. Jocelyn		64 ± 2	Kamemoto et al., 1961
Lc. Jocelyn 'Alcaza'		62	Kamemoto et al., 1967
Lc. Joseph Hampton 'Roslyn'		tetraploid	de Tomasi, 1954
Lc. Kismet Queen 'Benji'		80 ± 1	Tanaka, 1964a
Lc. Kyoko Takeda 'Konan'		80	Tanaka, 1966
Lc. Kyoko Takeda 'Sumiyoshi'		80	Tanaka, 1966
Lc. Liliha		ca. 80	Kamemoto, 1952
		82 ± 2	Kamemoto et al., 1961
Lc. Lunain 'Invicta'		ca. 60	Kamemoto, 1959b
Lc. Majestical 'Magenta'		82 ± 1	Tanaka, 1964a
Lc. Mark Hoshino		80 ± 1	Kamemoto et al., 1961

Plant name	Chromosome number		Reference	Plant name	Chromosome number		Reference
	n	2n			n	2n	
Lc. Mercia		40	Kamemoto et al., 1961	Lc. Sunburn 'No. 1'		ca. 60	Kamemoto, 1959b
Lc. Miami 'Glory'		86	Sagawa, 1962a	Lc. Supervia		85 ± 2	Kamemoto et al., 1961
Lc. Mme. Chiang Kai Shih 'No. 15'		80	Tanaka, 1964a			85	Kamemoto et al., 1967
Lc. Momus 'Bryndir'		ca. 60	Kamemoto, 1959b	Lc. Supervia 'Hoshino'		85	Kamemoto et al., 1961
Lc. Momus 'Orchidhurst'		ca. 60	Kamemoto, 1959b	Lc. Supervia 'Painting'		82 ± 1	Tanaka, 1964a
Lc. Mullion 'Sumiyoshi'		63	Tanaka, 1966	Lc. Ted Trimble 'Walder'		81 ± 1	Kamemoto et al., 1961
Lc. Mysedo		ca. 80	Kamemoto, 1952	Lc. Tiberta		ca. 60	Kamemoto, 1950
		80 ± 2	Kamemoto et al, 1961	Lc. Titymoma 'Toanohana'		ca. 100	Kamemoto, 1959b
Lc. Navalange		ca. 80	Kamemoto, 1959b	Lc. Titymoma 'Very Fine'		ca. 100	Kamemoto, 1959b
Lc. Ormsby		60	Kamemoto et al., 1961	Lc. Trail's End		triploid	de Tomasi, 1954
Lc. Pasadena		tetraploid	Zuck, 1957	Lc. Twinkle 'No. 6'		40	Kamemoto et al., 1961
		81 ± 2	Kamemoto et al., 1961	Lc. Twinkle Star 'Midnight'		40	Kamemoto et al., 1961
Lc. Prince Kuni		ca. 60	Kamemoto, 1959b	Lc. Valencia 'Perfection'		ca. 100	Kamemoto, 1959b
Lc. Princess Margaret		ca. 80	Kamemoto, 1952	Lc. Valencia 'Yamaoka'		ca. 100	Kamemoto, 1959b
		80 ± 1	Kamemoto et al., 1961	Lc. Venetia		ca. 80	Kamemoto, 1950
Lc. Princess Margaret 'Bonnycrest'		tetraploid	de Tomasi, 1954	Lc. Waianae Sunset 'Pokai'		80	Tanaka, 1964a
Lc. Princess Margaret 'Excelsior'		ca. 80	Kamemoto, 1959b	Lc. Windermere		60	Zuck, 1957
						ca. 80	Kamemoto, 1959b
Lc. Princess Margaret 'No. 2'		80	Zuck, 1957	Lc. Windermere 'Clovelly'		ca. 80	Kamemoto, 1952
Lc. Princess Margaret 'Stonehurst'		tetraploid	de Tomasi, 1954			80 ± 2	Kamemoto et al., 1961
Lc. Princess Pauahi		91 ± 1	Kamemoto et al., 1967	Lc. unnamed (C. Balmar × Lc. Freya)		40–82	Niimoto & Randolph, 1958
Lc. Redskin		tetraploid	de Tomasi, 1954	Lc. unnamed (Lc. Freya × C. Balmer)		40–72	Niimoto & Randolph, 1958
Lc. Roberta Off		65	Kamemoto et al., 1961	Lc. unnamed (C. Dupreana × Lc. Canada)		ca. 80	Kamemoto, 1950
Lc. Roberta Off 'Ginza'		64 ± 1	Kamemoto et al., 1961	Lc. unnamed (C. Magdola × Lc. Rasamunda)		80 ± 2	Kamemoto et al., 1961
Lc. Rosa Kirsch		pentaploid 100 ± 2	Zuck, 1957 Kamemoto et al., 1961	Lc. unnamed (C. Princess Royal × Lc. Canhamiana)		60	Kamemoto, 1950
Lc. Rosa Kirsch 'Kuhina Nui'		100 ± 1	Tanaka, 1966	Lc. unnamed (C. R. N. Cadwalader Jr. × Lc. Princess Margaret)		58–66	Niimoto & Randolph, 1958
Lc. Sam W. Soysa 'Bonfire'		ca. 60	Kamemoto, 1959b				
Lc. Sam W. Soysa 'Noel'		62	Tanaka, 1966	Lc. unnamed (C. Rembrandt × Lc. Cuesta)		100 ± 1	Kamemoto et al., 1961
Lc. Sargon 'Holford'		60	Kamemoto et al., 1961				
Lc. Sargon 'Magnifica'		ca. 80	Kamemoto, 1950	Lc. unnamed (C. trianaei × Lc. Marie Dobrotte)		69 ± 1	Kamemoto et al., 1961
		82 ± 2	Kamemoto et al., 1961	Lc. unnamed (C. trianaei 'Coerulea' × L. pumila 'Coerulea')		40	Kamemoto, 1959b
Lc. Schroderae 'The King'		tetraploid	de Tomasi, 1954				
Lc. Seaforth 'Duke'		60 ± 1	Kamemoto et al., 1967	Lc. unnamed (C. Triclotho × Lc. Cassiopeia)		100	Zuck, 1957
Lc. Senator		63	Kamemoto, 1950				
Lc. Serbia 'Belyta'		100	Tanaka, 1966				
Lc. Snowdrift 'Doris'		59 ± 1	Kamemoto et al., 1961				
Lc. Soulange 'St. Albans'		ca. 60	Kamemoto, 1959b				
Lc. South Esk		80	Kamemoto, 1950				
Lc. Springtide 'Magnifica'		60	Sagawa, 1962a				

Plant name	Chromosome number		Reference
	n	2n	
Lc. unnamed (*Lc.* Canhamiana × *L. tenebrosa* 'Superba')		20	Hoffmann, 1929
Lc. unnamed (*Lc.* Dorothy Fried 'Compacta' × *Lc.* Mysedo 'Miya')		80 ± 2	Kamemoto *et al.*, 1961
Lc. unnamed (*Lc.* Ernest B. Dane × *Lc.* Hyperion)		97	Zuck, 1957
Lc. unnamed (*Lc.* Gorse × *Lc.* Mysedo)		61 ± 2	Kamemoto *et al.*, 1961
Lc. unnamed (*Lc.* Ishtar × *Lc.* Valencia)		80	Kamemoto *et al.*, 1961
Lc. unnamed (*Lc.* Princess Margaret × *C.* Enid 'Orchidhaven')		75–86	Niimoto & Randolph, 1958
Lc. unnamed (*Lc.* Princess Margaret × *Lc.* Profusion)		82 ± 2	Kamemoto *et al.*, 1961
Lc. unnamed (*Lc.* Red Oak × *C.* bowringiana 'UF#1')		62	Sagawa & Niimoto, 1961
Lanium avicula		40	Blumenschein, 1960
Leptotes unicolor		40	Blumenschein, 1960
Leucolaena siamensis		ca. 36, ca. 150	Larsen, 1966
Leucorchis albida (= *Habenaria albida*)		42	Heusser, 1938
		42	Harmsen, 1943
		42	Löve & Löve, 1944
		42	Knaben, 1950
		40	Sokolovskaya & Strelkova, 1960
		40	Pogan & Wcislo (in Löve & Löve, 1961)
L. straminea (= *Habenaria straminea*)	21	42	Harmsen, 1943
		42	Löve & Löve, 1954
		42	Löve & Löve, 1956
Limnorchis convallariaefolius		80	Sokolovskaya, 1963
L. dilatata		42	Taylor & Mulligan, 1968
L. dilatata ssp. *albiflora*		42	Taylor & Mulligan, 1968
L. hyperborea		84	Taylor & Mulligan, 1968
L. saccata		42	Taylor & Mulligan, 1968
Limodorum abortivum		64	Malvesin-Fabre & Eyme, 1949
		56	Coutinho, 1957
Liparis amesiana		30	Pancho, 1965a
		30	Pancho, 1965b
L. bootanensis	19		Mehra & Sehgal, 1974
L. confusa		30	Pancho, 1965a
		30	Pancho, 1965b

Plant name	Chromosome number		Reference
	n	2n	
L. cordifolia	10		Mehra & Kashyap, 1979
L. deflexa	21		Mehra & Kashyap, 1979
L. duthiei	15		Arora, 1968
	15		Mehra & Vij, 1970
L. ferruginea		42	Larsen, 1966
L. fimbriata		42	Larsen, 1966
L. formosana		42	Tanaka, 1965b
		42	Mitsukuri & Hayashi, 1967
L. formosana var. *hachijoensis*		42	Mitsukuri & Hayashi, 1967
L. ganblei	18		Mehra & Vij, 1970
L. glossula	10		Mehra & Vij, 1970
	10		Mehra & Kashyap, 1978
L. japonica		30	Tanaka, 1965b
L. keitaoensis		30	Hsu, 1972
L. krameri		30	Miduno, 1939
		30	Mutsuura & Nakahira, 1958
		30	Mutsuura, 1959
		30	Tanaka, 1965b
		30	Mitsukuri & Hayashi, 1967
L. kumokiri		30	Miduno, 1939
	13		Ohno & Hashimoto, 1956
		30	Mutsuura & Nakahira, 1958
		30	Tanaka, 1956b
		30	Mitsukuri & Hayashi, 1967
L. loeselii		32	Hagerup, 1941
	26		Gadella & Kliphuis, 1963
		26	Kliphuis, 1963
L. longipes		42	Mitsukuri & Hayashi, 1967
L. longipes var. *spathulata*	15		Arora, 1968
L. luteola	19		Mehra & Sehgal, 1975
L. makinoana		30	Miduno, 1939
		30	Mutsuura & Nakahira, 1958
		30	Mutsuura, 1959
		30	Tanaka, 1965b
		30	Sokolovskaya, 1966
L. nepalensis	18		Mehra & Vij, 1970
L. nervosa	21	42	Miduno, 1940b
		42	Mutsuura & Nakahira, 1958
		42	Mutsuura, 1959
		42	Tanaka, 1965b
		42	Mitsukuri & Hayashi, 1967
L. paradoxa	18		Mehra & Vij, 1970
	21		Mehra & Sehgal, 1975
	21		Mehra & Kashyap, 1979

Plant name	Chromosome number n	2n	Reference
L. perpusilla	15		Mehra & Vij, 1970
L. plantaginea	19		Mehra & Sehgal, 1978
L. plicata		42	Mutsuura & Nakahira, 1960
		38	Tanaka, 1965b
		38	Mitsukuri & Hayashi, 1967
L. pulchella	15		Mehra & Sehgal, 1974
L. pulverulenta	40		Chardard, 1963
L. pusila		40	Chatterji, 1968
L. resupinata	14		Mehra & Vij, 1970
	28		Mehra & Sehgal, 1974
L. rostrata	15		Arora, 1968
	14	28	Mehra & Bawa, 1962
		28	Mehra & Kashyap, 1979
L. siamensis		ca. 42	Larsen, 1966
L. taiwaniana		38	Tanaka, 1965b
L. viridiflora	15		Arora, 1971
	15		Mehra & Sehgal, 1974
Listera borealis		56, 56 + B (triploid) (apomictic)	Simon, 1968
L. caurina	17	34	Taylor & Mulligan, 1968
L. convallarioides	18		Taylor & Brockman, 1966
		36	Simon, 1968
L. cordata		42	Harding (in Tischler, 1935–1936)
		42	Blackburn (in Maude, 1939)
		38	Sokolovskaya & Strelkova, 1940
		36–38	Löve & Löve, 1956
		38	Sokolovskaya & Strelkova, 1960
		38	Skalinska et al., 1961
		38	Pogan & Wcislo (in Löve & Löve, 1961)
		40	Kliphuis, 1963
		40	Gadella & Kliphuis, 1963
		36	Löve & Löve, 1966
	19		Taylor, 1967
		40	Knaben & Engelskjön, 1967
		38	Taylor & Mulligan, 1968
		42	Laane, 1969
L. cordata var. japonica		42	Sinoto & Shoji, 1962
L. cordata ssp. nephrophylla		36–38	Simon, 1968
L. kashmeriana		42	Vij & Gupta, 1975
L. makinoana		42	Shoji, 1963
		38	Tanaka, 1965b
		38	Tanaka, 1971
L. nipponica		38	Mutsuura & Nakahira, 1960
L. ovata	16		Guignard, 1884

Plant name	Chromosome number n	2n	Reference
	16		Guignard, 1886
	16		Guignard, 1891
	16		Rosenberg, 1905
		32–34	Müller, 1912
	16, 17, 18	32, 34, 36	Tuschnjakova, 1929
	17		Staner, 1929
	17		Hoffmann, 1929
	17		Hoffmann, 1930
	17, 18	34, 35	Richardson, 1933
		34, 34 + f.	MacMahon, 1936
	17		Barber, 1942
	17, 18	34, 36 (17)	Hagerup, 1947
		34, 36, 38	Nygren (in Löve & Löve, 1948)
		34–40	Löve & Löve, 1956
		42	Harding (in Duncan, 1959)
		38	Skalinska et al., 1961
		34	Pogan & Wcislo (in Löve & Löve, 1961)
		ca. 38	Sorsa, 1962
	19		Sorsa, 1963
	17	34, 35, 36	Kliphuis, 1963
		34, 35, 36, 37, 38	Gadella & Kliphuis, 1963
		34	Knaben & Engelskjön, 1967
		34	Leveque & Gorenflot, 1969
		34, 37, 39	Schotsman, 1970b
		34, 34 + (2 – 3B)	Garabari, 1971
	17 + (0 – 5B)		Vosa & Barlow, 1972
L. pinetorum	20		Mehra & Vij, 1970
	20		Mehra & Vij, 1972a
L. sikokiana		38	Mutsuura & Nakahira, 1958
L. smallii	19		Kondo, 1972
L. tenuis		40	Mehra & Kashyap, 1978
Lockhartia oerstedii		14	Garay, 1963
L. micrantha		56	Charanasri & Kamemoto, 1975
Loroglossum hircinum (Himantoglossum hircinum)	12		Heusser, 1915
Luisanda Uniwai	19 (15–23)	38	Tanaka & Kamemoto, 1961
Luisia boninensis		40	Miduno, 1940b
Lsa. brachystachys	20		Arora, 1971
Lsa. inconspicua	19		Mehra & Vij, 1970
	19		Mehra & Kashyap, 1979
Lsa. liukiuensis		38	Nakasone & Moromizato, 1964

Plant name	Chromosome number n	2n	Reference
Lsa. macrantha		38	Kulkarni & Jorapur, 1979
Lsa. tenuifolia		38	Kulkarni & Jorapur, 1979
Lsa teres (= *Lsa. teretifolia*)		40	Mutsuura & Nakahira, 1960
		38	Shindo & Kamemoto, 1963a
Lsa. teretifolia (= *Lsa. teres*)		38	Pancho, 1965a
		38	Pancho, 1965b
	19	38	Chatterji, 1965
		ca. 38	Jones, 1967
		38	Tara & Kamemoto, 1970
	19		Mehra & Vij, 1970
		38	Kulkarni & Jorapur, 1979
Lsa. trichorhiza		38	Jones, 1967
	20		Arora, 1968
	19		Mehra & Kashyap, 1978
Lycaste aromatica	20		Hoffmann, 1929
	20		Hoffmann, 1930
Lysiella obtusata		42	Löve & Löve, 1965
		42	Löve & Simon, 1968
Macradenia brassavolae		48	Sinoto, 1962
Mcdn. paraensis		52	Blumenschein, 1960
Malaxis acuminata	15		Arora, 1971
M. boninensis		36	Ono, 1977
M. monophylla (= *Acroanthes monophyllos*)	15–17		Stenar, 1937
	15	30	Hagerup, 1944a
M. monophylla ssp. *brachypoda*		28	Löve & Löve, 1969
M. muscifera	30		Mehra & Kashyap, 1979
M. orbicularis		ca. 40	Larsen, 1966
M. paludosa		28	Tanaka, 1965b
	14		Taylor & Mulligan, 1968
		28	Tanaka, 1971
M. parviflora		44	Tanaka, 1971
M. siamensis		ca. 42	Larsen, 1966
Masdevallia coccinea 'Lindenii'		44	Tanaka, 1964a
Masd. ochthoides		64	Tanaka, 1964a
Maxillaria picta		40	Blumenschein, 1960
Max. tenuifolia		40	Tanaka, 1966
Microstylis biloba	18		Mehra & Vij, 1970
M. commelinifolia	19–21		Chardard, 1963
M. congesta	21		Mehra & Vij, 1970
M. cylindrostachya	15		Mehra & Bawa, 1962
	15		Mehra & Vij, 1970
	15 + (0 − 2)B		Mehra & Kashyap, 1976
M. iriomotensis		44	Tanaka, 1965b
M. latifolia		26	Hsu, 1972

Plant name	Chromosome number n	2n	Reference
M. maximowicziana	21		Mehra & Vij, 1970
M. muscifera	15		Mehra & Vij, 1970
M. saprophyta	21		Mehra & Vij, 1970
M. wallichii	18		Mehra & Vij, 1970
	21		Mehra & Kashyap, 1976
M. species	ca. 20		Hoffmann, 1930
Microtis parviflora (= *M. formosana*)		44	Tanaka, 1965b
Milpilia Magic		58	Sinoto, 1962
Miltassia Ballet		59, 60	Sinoto, 1962
Mtssa. unnamed (*Brassia maculata* × *Miltonia festiva*)		60	Sinoto, 1962
Mtssa. unnamed (*Miltonia flavescens* × *Brassia maculata*)		58	Sinoto, 1962
Miltonia bluntii		60	Sinoto, 1962
		60	Sinoto, 1969b
Milt. festiva		59	Sinoto, 1962
		59	Sinoto, 1969b
Milt. flavescens		56	Blumenschein, 1960
		60	Sinoto, 1962
		60	Sinoto, 1969b
		60	Charanasri *et al.*, 1973
Milt. regnellii		60	Sinoto, 1962
		60	Sinoto, 1969b
Milt. roezlii var. *alba*		56	Sinoto, 1962
		60	Sinoto, 1969b
		56	Charanasri & Kamemoto, 1975
Milt. spectabilis		60	Sinoto, 1962
		60	Sinoto, 1969b
		60	Charanasri & Kamemoto, 1975
Milt. spectabilis var. *lineata*		56	Sinoto, 1962
		56	Sinoto, 1969b
Milt. spectabilis var. *moleriana* subvar. *rosea*		86	Sinoto, 1962
		86	Sinoto, 1969b
Milt. vexillaria		60	Sinoto, 1962
		60	Sinoto, 1969b
		56	Sinoto, 1962
Milt. warscewiczii		56	Sinoto, 1969b
Milt. warscewiczii var. *panamense*		56	Sinoto, 1969b
Milt. unnamed (*Milt.* Emory 'No. 6' × *Milt.* Edwige Sabourin)		98	Tanaka, 1966
Milt. unnamed (*Milt.* Lingwood × *Milt.* Piccadilly)		112	Tanaka, 1966
Milt. unnamed (*Milt. warscewiczii* var. *panamense* × *Milt. regnellii*)		60	Sinoto, 1962

Plant name	Chromosome number n	2n	Reference	Plant name	Chromosome number n	2n	Reference
Miltonidium Jack Pot		84	Sinoto, 1962	*Nigritella apo-mictica*		32	Afzelius, 1932
Mormodes buccinator		54	Jones & Daker, 1968	*N. nigra*	19	40	Heusser, 1938
Morm. bucci-nator var. *citrinum*		54	Jones & Daker, 1968		20	38	Chiarugi, 1929
						32	Vis, 1933
						40	Heusser, 1938
					32		Afzelius, 1943
Morm. histrio		54	Jones & Daker, 1968			64	Knaben, 1950
Neofinetia falcata		38	Mutsuura & Nakahira, 1958			64	Knaben & Engelskjön, 1967
		38	Kamemoto, 1959b			64	Lovka et al., 1972
		38	Shindo & Kamemoto, 1963a	*N. nigra* var. *apomictica*	32		Afzelius, 1932
		38	Nakasone & Moromizato, 1964	*N. rubra* (= *N. miniata*)	19		Chiarugi, 1929
		38	Tanaka, 1965b			80	Heusser, 1938
Neotinea intac-ta		40	Borgen, 1969	*N.* unnamed (bigeneric hybrid) (*N. nigra* × *Gymnadenia conopsea*)		40	Heusser, 1938
Neottia asia-tica		36	Sokolovskaya, 1966				
N. inayatii		42	Mehra & Pan-dita, 1979				
N. listeroides	20	40	Mehra & Bawa, 1962	*N.* unnamed (bigeneric hybrid) (*N. nigra* × *Gymnadenia odoratis-sima*)		40	Heusser, 1938
	20		Mehra & Vij, 1970				
	20	40	Mehra & Bawa, 1970	*Notylia bicolor*		42	Sinoto, 1962
	20		Mehra & Vij, 1972a	*N. panamensis*		42	Sinoto, 1962
	20	40 (36)	Vij & Gupta, 1975	*Oberonia auri-culata*	15		Mehra & Kash-yap, 1979
		40	Mehra & Pan-dita, 1979	*O. brunoniana*		30	Jorapur & Hegde, 1975
		40	Mehra & Kash-yap, 1979	*O. caulescens*	13		Mehra & Vij, 1970
N. nidus-avis	16		Guignard, 1891	*O. ensiformis*		30	Jorapur & Hegde, 1975
	18		Modilewski, 1918	*O. falconeri*		30	Jorapur & Hegde, 1975
	18		Modilewski, 1936		15		Mehra & Kash-yap, 1976
		36	Eftimiu-Heim, 1941	*O. integerrima*		30	Chardard, 1963
	18		Barber, 1942	*O. iridifolia*	15		Mehra & Seh-gal, 1975
		36	Pogan & Wcis-lo (in Löve & Löve, 1961)	*O. japonica*		30	Tanaka, 1965b
	18		Kliphuis, 1963			30	Tanaka, 1971
		36	Lovka et al., 1971	*O. mannii*	15		Mehra & Seh-gal, 1978
		36	Majovsky et al., 1974	*O. myriantha*	ca. 36		Arora, 1971
					15		Mehra & Seh-gal, 1978
Nervilia arago-ana		72	Chennaveer-aiah & Jora-pur, 1966	*O. obcordata*	15		Mehra & Vij, 1970
N. discolor		20	Pancho, 1965a	*O. pachyrachis*	15		Mehra & Seh-gal, 1975
		20	Pancho, 1965b			30	Mehra & Kash-yap, 1979
		72	Chennaveer-aiah & Jora-pur, 1966	*O. prainiana*	15		Mehra & Vij, 1970
N. infundibuli-folia		54	Chennaveer-aiah & Jora-pur, 1966	*O. santapaui*		30	Jorapur & Hegde, 1975
N. juliana		54	Kulkarni & Jorapur, 1979	*O. verticilla*		30	Jorapur & Hegde, 1975
N. monantha		144	Chennaveer-aiah & Jora-pur, 1966	*Odontioda* unnamed (*Odonto-glossum incana* 'Fine var.' × *Oda. Gera* 'Fine var.')		112	Tanaka, 1964a
N. plicata		108	Chennaveer-aiah & Jora-pur, 1966	*Odontocidium* unnamed (*Odtcdm. Anzia Argus* × *Odtcdm. Aysha*)		110	Tanaka, 1964a
Neuwiedea singapure-ana		ca. 144	Larsen, 1968				

Plant name	n	2n	Reference
Odontoglossum cariniferum		56	Charanasri et al., 1973
Odm. citrosmum		44–48	Chardard, 1963
		44	Charanasri & Kamemoto, 1975
Odm. cordatum		56	Sinoto, 1962
		56	Sinoto, 1969b
Odm. crispum		56	Hoffmann, 1930
Odm. grande		44	Dodson, 1958
		60?	Sinoto, 1962
		60?	Sinoto, 1969b
		44	Charanasri et al., 1973
Odm. insleayi		44	Dodson, 1958
Odm. kegeljani		56	Dodson, 1958
Odm. pendulum		44	Dodson, 1958
Odm. schlieperianum		44	Dodson, 1958
Odm. stenoglossum		56	Charanasri et al., 1973
Odontonia Debutante		56	Sinoto, 1962
Oeoniella polystachys		38	Tanaka, 1966
Oncidium altissimum		56	Sinoto, 1962
		56	Sinoto, 1969a
Onc. ampliatum		44	Dodson, 1957c
		44	Sagawa & Niimoto, 1961
		44	Sinoto, 1962
		44	Sinoto, 1969a
		44	Charanasri et al., 1973
		44	Charanasri & Kamemoto, 1975
Onc. anciferum		56	Sinoto, 1962
		56	Chardard, 1963
		56	Sinoto, 1969a
		56	Charanasri et al., 1973
Onc. annhadderiae		42	Charanasri & Kamemoto, 1975
Onc. anthocrene		56	Sinoto, 1962
		56	Sinoto, 1969a
Onc. aurosum		54	Chardard, 1963
Onc. bahamense		84	Sinoto, 1962
		84	Charanasri et al., 1973
		84	Charanasri & Kamemoto, 1975
Onc. barbatum		56	Blumenschein, 1960
Onc. baueri		ca. 52	Dodson, 1957c
		56	Sinoto, 1962
		56	Sinoto, 1969a
		56	Charanasri et al., 1973
		56	Charanasri & Kamemoto, 1975
Onc. bicallosum	14		Hoffmann, 1929
	14		Hoffmann, 1930
		28	Dodson, 1957c
		28	Charanasri et al., 1973
		28	Charanasri & Kamemoto, 1975
Onc. brachyandrum		56	Sinoto, 1962
		56	Sinoto, 1969a
Onc. brunleesianum		56	Kugust, 1966
Onc. calochilum		42	Charanasri & Kamemoto, 1975
Onc. carthagenense		28	Dodson, 1957c
		30	Sinoto, 1962
		30	Kugust, 1966
		30	Sinoto, 1969a
		30	Charanasri et al., 1973
		30	Charanasri & Kamemoto, 1975
Onc. carthagenense var. roseum		30	Sinoto, 1962
Onc. cavendishianum		28	Dodson, 1957c
		28	Blumenschein, 1960
Onc. cebolleta (as Onc. ceboretum)		36	Blumenschein, 1960
		34	Sinoto, 1962
		34	Sinoto, 1969a
		36, 72	Charanasri et al., 1973
		36	Phang et al., 1979
Onc. cheirophorum		ca. 48	Dodson, 1957c
		56	Sinoto, 1962
		56	Tanaka, 1964a
		56	Sinoto, 1969a
Onc. cordatum		56	Dodson, 1957c
Onc. crispum		56	Dodson, 1957c
		56	Chardard, 1963
Onc. cubense		42	Charanasri & Kamemoto, 1975
Onc. cucullatum		54	Kugust, 1966
Onc. curtum		52	Chardard, 1963
Onc. Delight		41	Sinoto, 1962
Onc. desertorum (= Onc. intermedium)		40	Sinoto, 1962
		40	Kugust, 1966
		40	Sinoto, 1969a
		40	Charanasri et al., 1973
		40	Charanasri & Kamemoto, 1975
Onc. desertorum 'Gigas'		40	Sinoto, 1969a
Onc. Dr. Schragen		32	Sinoto, 1962
Onc. ebrachiatum		28	Dodson, 1957c
Onc. ensatum		56	Charanasri et al., 1973
Onc. excavatum		56	Eftimiu-Heim, 1941
		56	Sinoto, 1962
		56	Sinoto, 1969a
Onc. Fantastic		76	Sinoto, 1962
Onc. flexuosum		56	Hoffmann, 1929
		56	Hoffmann, 1930
		56	Dodson, 1957c
		56	Charanasri & Kamemoto, 1975
		56	Phang et al., 1979
Onc. floridanum		56	Charanasri et al., 1973
		56	Phang et al., 1979
Onc. floridephillipsiae		126	Charanasri & Kamemoto, 1975

Plant name	Chromosome number		Reference	Plant name	Chromosome number		Reference
	n	2n			n	2n	
Onc. globuli-		56	Sinoto, 1962	Onc. lieboldii		40–42	Kugust, 1966
ferum		56	Sinoto, 1969a	'Alba'			
		56	Charanasri &	Onc. lieboldii f.		42	Sinoto, 1962
			Kamemoto,	album			
			1975	Onc. limmin-		56	Charanasri &
Onc. glosso-		14	Kugust, 1966	gheri			Kamemoto,
mystax							1975
Onc. guttatum		28	Dodson, 1957c	Onc. longi-		28	Dodson, 1957c
Onc. guttatum		32	Sinoto, 1962	folium			
var. oliva-		32	Sinoto, 1969a	Onc. longipes		56	Blumenschein,
ceum							1960
Onc. haemato-		28, ca. 40	Sinoto, 1962			56	Kugust, 1966
chilum		28	Charanasri et	Onc. loxense		56?	Kugust, 1966
			al., 1973	Onc. lucay-		40	Sinoto, 1962
Onc. harrisoni-		42	Sinoto, 1962	anum		40	Kugust, 1966
anum		42	Sinoto, 1969a			40	Charanasri et
		42	Charanasri &				al., 1973
			Kamemoto,			40	Charanasri &
			1975				Kamemoto,
Onc. hastatum		56	Sinoto, 1962				1975
		56	Sinoto, 1969a	Onc. luridum		28	Dodson, 1957
Onc. Helen		40, 42	Sinoto, 1962			32	Sinoto, 1962
Brown						28 + 2f.	Sharma &
Onc. henekenii		40	Sinoto, 1962				Chatterji,
		40	Sinoto, 1969a				1966
		40	Charanasri et			32	Kugust, 1966
			al., 1975			32	Sinoto, 1969a
		40	Charanasri &			30	Charanasri et
			Kamemoto,				al., 1973
			1975			30	Charanasri &
Onc. hiero-		56	Kugust, 1966				Kamemoto,
glyphicum							1975
Onc. Hispaniola		56	Sinoto, 1962	Onc. macran-		56	Dodson, 1957c
Onc. hyphae-		56	Sinoto, 1962	thum		50–57	Kugust, 1966
macticum		56	Sinoto, 1969a	Onc. macula-		56	Sinoto, 1962
Onc. incurvum		56	Sinoto, 1962	tum		56	Sinoto, 1969a
		56	Sinoto, 1969a	Onc. marshalli-		58	Kugust, 1966
Onc. inter-		40	Sinoto, 1962	anum		56	Charanasri &
medium							Kamemoto,
Onc. inter-		40	Sinoto, 1969a				1975
medium				Onc. Memoria		34	Sinoto, 1962
'Gigas'				Pepita de			
Onc. isthmi		56	Sinoto, 1962	Restorepa			
		56	Sinoto, 1969a	Onc. 'Miami'		84	Sinoto, 1962
		56	Charanasri &			84	Sinoto, 1969a
			Kamemoto,	Onc. micro-		36	Dodson, 1957c
			1975	chilum		36, 37	Sinoto, 1962
Onc. jimenezii		42	Charanasri &			36	Kugust, 1966
			Kamemoto,			36, 37	Sinoto, 1969a
			1975			36, 37	Charanasri et
Onc. jonesi-		30	Kugust, 1966				al., 1973
anum		30	Charanasri &	Onc. micro-		56	Charanasri &
			Kamemoto,	pogon			Kamemoto,
			1975				1975
Onc. kenscoffii		84	Sinoto, 1962	Onc. nanum		26	Sinoto, 1962
		84	Sinoto, 1969a			26	Sinoto, 1964
Onc. krameri-		38	Dodson,			26	Sinoto, 1969a
anum			1957b,c	Onc. nebulo-		56	Kugust, 1966
Onc. lammeli-		55–57	Kugust, 1966	sum			
gerum				Onc. nigratum		56	Charanasri &
Onc. lance-		28	Dodson, 1957c				Kamemoto,
anum		28	Sinoto, 1962				1975
	13	26 (24)	Sharma &	Onc. nudum		36	Charanasri et
			Chatterji,				al., 1973
			1966	Onc. obryza-		56	Sinoto, 1962
		28	Sinoto, 1969a	toides		56	Sinoto, 1969a
		26	Charanasri et	Onc. obryza-		56	Sinoto, 1962
			al., 1973	tum		56	Sinoto, 1969a
		26	Charanasri &	Onc. oestlundi-		28	Dodson, 1957c
			Kamemoto,	anum			
			1975	Onc. onustum		56	Sinoto, 1962
Onc. lemoni-		42	Charanasri &			56	Sinoto, 1969a
anum			Kamemoto,			56	Charanasri et
			1975				al., 1973
Onc. leuco-		56	Dodson, 1957c			56	Phang et al.,
chilum		56	Charanasri &				1979
			Kamemoto,	Onc. ornitho-		56	Dodson, 1957c
			1975	rhynchum		56	Sinoto, 1962
Onc. lieboldii		42	Dodson, 1958		28		Chardard,
		42	Sinoto, 1969a				1963
		42	Charanasri &			56	Sinoto, 1969a
			Kamemoto,	Onc. pana-		56	Sinoto, 1962
			1975	mense		56	Sinoto, 1969a

Plant name	Chromosome number n	Chromosome number 2n	Reference
Onc. papilio		38	Dodson, 1957b,c
		38	Sinoto, 1962
		38	Sinoto, 1969a
		38	Charanasri et al., 1973
Onc. papilio 'Latour's var.'		38	Sinoto, 1962
		38	Sinoto, 1969a
Onc. parviflorum		56	Dodson, 1957c
Onc. pentadactylon		40–42	Kugust, 1966
Onc. phalaenopsis		56	Kugust, 1966
Onc. phymatochilum		56	Sinoto, 1962
		56	Sinoto, 1969a
Onc. polyandenium		56	Sinoto, 1962
		56	Kugust, 1966
		56	Sinoto, 1969a
Onc. powellii		56	Dodson, 1957c
		56	Sinoto, 1962
		56	Sinoto, 1969a
Onc. praetextum	28		Afzelius, 1916
Onc. pulchellum		42	Dodson, 1958
		42	Sinoto, 1962
		42	Kugust, 1966
		42	Sinoto, 1969a
		42	Charanasri et al., 1973
Onc. pulvinatum		42	Charanasri et al., 1973
Onc. pumilum		30	Kugust, 1966
Onc. pusillum		10	Dodson, 1957a,c
		10	Sinoto, 1962
		10, 14	Kugust, 1966
		10	Sinoto, 1969a
Onc. quadrilobum		40	Charanasri & Kamemoto, 1975
Onc. robustissimum		44	Dodson, 1957a,c
Onc. sarcodes		56	Dodson, 1957c
		56	Charanasri et al., 1973
Onc. scandens		84	Sinoto, 1962
		84	Charanasri & Kamemoto, 1975
Onc. sphacelatum		56	Sinoto, 1962
		56	Chardard, 1963
		56	Sinoto, 1969a
Onc. splendidum		34	Dodson, 1957c
		36	Sinoto, 1962
		36	Chardard, 1963
		36	Kugust, 1966
		36	Sinoto, 1969a
		36	Charanasri et al., 1973
		36	Charanasri & Kamemoto, 1975
		36	Phang et al., 1978
		36	Phang et al., 1979
Onc. stenotis		56	Sinoto, 1962
		56, 105–111	Chardard, 1963
		56	Sinoto, 1969a
		56	Charanasri et al., 1973
Onc. stipitatum		28	Dodson, 1957c
		36	Charanasri et al., 1973
Onc. stamineum		28	Sinoto, 1962
		30	Kugust, 1966
		28	Sinoto, 1969a
		30	Charanasri et al., 1973
		30	Charanasri & Kamemoto, 1975
Onc. sylvestre		84	Sinoto, 1962
		84	Sinoto, 1969a
		126	Charanasri & Kamemoto, 1975
Onc. teres		28	Dodson, 1957c
Onc. tetrapetalum		42	Dodson, 1958
Onc. tetraskelidon	28		Chardard, 1963
Onc. tigrinum		54	Kugust, 1966
		56	Charanasri et al., 1973
Onc. triquetrum		42	Dodson, 1958
		42	Sinoto, 1962
		42	Sinoto, 1969a
		42	Charanasri et al., 1973
		42	Phang et al., 1978
		42	Phang et al., 1979
Onc. urophyllum		84	Sinoto, 1962
		84	Sinoto, 1969a
		84	Charanasri & Kamemoto, 1975
Onc. varicosum	28		Hoffmann, 1929
	28		Hoffmann, 1930
		56	Dodson, 1957c
		112, 168	Sinoto, 1962
		112, 168	Sinoto, 1969a
Onc. varicosum var. rogersii		56	Chardard, 1963
Onc. variegatum		42	Dodson, 1958
		40	Sinoto, 1962
		40	Sinoto, 1969a
		42	Charanasri et al., 1973
		42	Charanasri & Kamemoto, 1975
		42	Phang et al., 1979
Onc. variegatum cv. roseum		42	Charanasri et al., 1973
Onc. varvelum		63	Charanasri & Kamemoto, 1975
Onc. velutinum		84	Charanasri & Kamemoto, 1975
Onc. volvox	28		Chardard, 1963
Onc. warmengii		140–150	Kugust, 1966
Onc. wentworthianum		56	Sinoto, 1962
		56	Sinoto, 1969a
		56	Charanasri & Kamemoto, 1975
Onc. sp. from Abaco		40	Sinoto, 1962
		40	Sinoto, 1969a
Onc. sp. from Bahama		40	Sinoto, 1962
		40	Sinoto, 1969a
Onc. sp. from Cuba		133	Sinoto, 1962
		133	Sinoto, 1969a
Onc. unnamed (Onc. Brasil × Onc. montanum)		112	Sinoto, 1962

Plant name	Chromosome number n	2n	Reference
Onc. unnamed (Onc. carthagenense × Onc. guttatum)		28	Dodson, 1957c
Onc. unnamed (Onc. carthagenense × Onc. luridum)		30	Charanasri & Kamemoto, 1978
Onc. unnamed (Onc. carthagenense × Onc. stramineum)		30	Charanasri & Kamemoto, 1978
Onc. unnamed (Onc. cebolleta × Onc. nudum)		36	Charanasri & Kamemoto, 1978
Onc. unnamed (Onc. cebolleta × Onc. stipitatum)		36	Charanasri & Kamemoto, 1978
Onc. unnamed (Onc. luridum × Onc. cebolleta)		33	Charanasri & Kamemoto, 1978
Onc. unnamed (Onc. luridum × Onc. lanceanum)		28	Charanasri & Kamemoto, 1978
Onc. unnamed (Onc. luridum × Onc. nudum)		33	Charanasri & Kamemoto, 1978
Onc. unnamed (Onc. maculatum × Onc. sarcodes)		56	Sinoto, 1962
Onc. unnamed (Onc. microchilum × Onc. carthagenense)		33	Charanasri & Kamemoto, 1978
Onc. unnamed (Onc. microchilum × Onc. luridum)		33	Charanasri & Kamemoto, 1978
Onc. unnamed (Onc. microchilum × Onc. nudum)		36	Charanasri & Kamemoto, 1978
Onc. unnamed (Onc. nudum × Onc. carthagenense)		33	Charanasri & Kamemoto, 1978
Onc. unnamed (Onc. obryzatum × Onc. obryzatoides)		56	Sinoto, 1962
Onc. unnamed (Onc. pulchellum × Onc. variegatum)		42, 61	Sinoto, 1962
Onc. unnamed (Onc. splendidum × Onc. cavendishianum)		31	Dodson, 1958
Onc. unnamed (Onc. splendidum × Onc. lanceanum)		31	Charanasri & Kamemoto, 1978

Plant name	Chromosome number n	2n	Reference
Onc. unnamed (Onc. splendidum × Onc. nudum)		36	Charanasri & Kamemoto, 1978
Onc. unnamed (Onc. stipitatum × Onc. nudum)		36	Charanasri & Kamemoto, 1978
Onc. unnamed (Onc. stipitatum × Onc. sprucei)		58	Sinoto, 1962
Onc. unnamed (Onc. stramineum × Onc. carthagenense)		30	Charanasri & Kamemoto, 1978
Onc. unnamed (Onc. stramineum × Onc. luridum)		30	Charanasri & Kamemoto, 1978
Onc. unnamed (Onc. triquetrum × Onc. barbatum)		50	Sinoto, 1962
Onc. unnamed (Onc. triquetrum × Onc. cebolleta)		39	Phang et al., 1979
Onc. unnamed (Onc. triquetrum × Onc. flexuosum)		49	Phang et al., 1979
Onc. unnamed (Onc. triquetrum × Onc. floridanum)		49	Phang et al., 1979
Onc. unnamed (Onc. triquetrum × Onc. henekenii)		41	Sinoto, 1962
Onc. unnamed (Onc. triquetrum × Onc. onustrum)		49	Phang et al., 1979
Onc. unnamed (Onc. triquetrum × Onc. splendidum)		39	Phang et al., 1978
		39	Phang et al., 1979
Onc. unnamed (Onc. triquetrum × Onc. variegatum)		42	Phang et al., 1979
Ophrys apifera	18	36	Heusser, 1938
		36	Barber, 1942
	18	36	Kliphuis, 1963
		36	Gadella & Kliphuis, 1963
		36	Löve & Kjellquist, 1973
O. aranifera (= O. sphegodes)	18	36	Heusser, 1938
		36	Susnik & Lovka, 1973
O. bertolonii		36	Susnik & Lovka, 1973
O. cornuta		36	Susnik & Lovka, 1973
O. fuciflora	18	36	Heusser, 1938
O. fusca		ca. 73	Dahlgren et al., 1971
O. insectifera (= O. muscifera)		36	Heusser, 1938
		36	Barber, 1942
	18	36	Afzelius, 1943
	18	36, 38	Kliphuis, 1963
O. lutea		36	Löve & Kjellquist, 1973
O. muscifera (= O. insectifera)	11–12		Senianinova, 1925
		36	Heusser, 1938

Plant name	Chromosome number n	Chromosome number 2n	Reference
		36	Barber, 1942
O. sphegodes		36	Barber, 1942
(= O. aranifera)		36	Shimoya & Ferlan, 1952
		36	Natarajan, 1979
O. sphegodes ssp. litigiosa (= ssp. pseudospeculum)		36	Heusser, 1938
		36	Shimoya & Ferlan, 1952
Opsisandra Helen Miyamoto	16–22 (38)	38	Tanaka & Kamemoto, 1961
Opsis. May Kawanishi	16–22 (38)	38	Tanaka & Kamemoto, 1961
Opsis. unnamed (Vanda tricolor × Vandopsis lissochiloides)	16–22 (38)	38	Tanaka & Kamemoto, 1961
Orchis aristata		40	Miduno, 1939
		40–42	Sokolovskaya, 1963
Orchis aristata var. immaculata		38	Sinoto & Shoji, 1962
Orchis caucasia		40	Sokolovskaja & Strelkova, 1940
Orchis chidori		42	Miduno, 1940b
		42	Mutsuura & Nakahira, 1959
Orchis coriophora	10	20	Fuchs & Ziegenspeck, 1923
	19	38	Heusser, 1938
		38	Vermeulen, 1949
		36	Susnik & Lovka, 1973
Orchis coriophora ssp. fragrans		38	Löve & Kjellquist, 1973
Orchis cruenta (= Dactylorchis cruenta)		40	Vermeulen, 1947
		40	Heslop-Harrison, 1950
Orchis drudei	7	14	Fuchs & Ziegenspeck, 1924
Orchis elodes (= Dactylorchis incarnata)		79, 80	Maude, 1939
Orchis fauriei		21	Matsuura & Suto, 1935
		42	Mutsuura & Nakahira, 1959
Orchis foliosa (= Orchis maderensis)		40	Vermeulen, 1947
Orchis fuchsii (= Orchis maculata)		40	Vermeulen, 1947
		40, 80	Balaeva & Siplivinski, 1975
Orchis globosa (= Traunsteinera globosa)	21	42	Heusser, 1938
		42	Diannelidis, 1948
Orchis graminifolia		42	Tanaka, 1965b
		42	Tanaka, 1971
Orchis habenarioides	20		Mehra & Vij, 1970
	20		Mehra & Vij, 1972b
		40	Mehra & Kashyap, 1979
Orchis incarnata (= Dactylorchis incarnata)	10		Fuchs & Ziegenspeck, 1923
		40	Hagerup, 1938
Orchis latifolia (= Dactylorchis incarnata) (= Orchis strictifolia)	10	20	Fuchs & Ziegenspeck, 1923
		80	Vermeulen, 1938
		80	Heusser, 1938
		80	Hagerup, 1938
		40, 80	Richardson (in Maude, 1939)
		40	Eftimiu-Heim, 1941
(as Dactylorchis incarnata)		40	Heslop-Harrison, 1948
	40		Vij & Gupta, 1975
Orchis latifolia var. duensis		40	Richardson (in Maude, 1939)
Orchis laxiflora		42	Vermeulen, 1947
		42	Vermeulen, 1949
Orchis maculata (= Dactylorchis maculata) (= Orchis fuchsii)	16		Strasburger, 1888
	10		Fuchs & Ziegenspeck, 1923
		40	Löve & Löve, 1944
		40	Vermeulen, 1947
Orchis maculata ssp. elodes (= Dactylorchis maculata ssp. elodes)		80	Heslop-Harrison, 1951
Orchis maculata var. ericetorum (= Dactylorchis maculata ssp. ericetorum)		80 (40)	Hagerup, 1944b
Orchis maculata var. genuina (= Dactylorchis maculata var. genuina)		40	Hagerup, 1938
Orchis maculata var. meyeri (= Dactylorchis maculata ssp. ericetorum)	20		Hagerup, 1938
Orchis maculata var. meyeri (= Dactylorchis fuchsii)		20	Hagerup, 1944b
Orchis maderensis (= Orchis foliosa)		40	Vermeulen, 1947
Orchis majalis (= Dactylorchis majalis)		80	Vermeulen, 1947
		80	Majovsky et al., 1974
Orchis mascula	21		Heusser, 1938
	21	42	Hagerup, 1938

Plant name	n	2n	Reference	Plant name	n	2n	Reference
		42	Vermeulen, 1947	Orchis praeter-missa var. pulchella (= Dactylorchis praetermissa var. pul-chella)		80, 82	Richardson (in Maude, 1939)
		42	Vermeulen, 1949				
		42	Pogan & Wcis-lo (in Löve & Löve, 1961)				
		42	Gadella & Klip-huis, 1963	Orchis provin-cialis		42	Heusser, 1938
		42	Kliphuis, 1963	Orchis pur-purea	21	42	Heusser, 1938
		42	Löve & Kjell-quist, 1973		21	42	Hagerup, 1938
						40	Eftimiu-Heim, 1941
		42	Uhriková & Schwarzová, 1978			42	Vermeulen, 1947
Orchis militaris	10	20	Fuchs & Zie-genspeck, 1923			42	Vermeulen, 1949
	21	42	Heusser, 1938		21	42	Kliphuis, 1963
	21		Hagerup, 1938			42	Gadella & Klip-huis, 1963
		42	Vermeulen, 1947			42	Corrias & Villa, 1973
		42	Pogan & Wcis-lo (in Löve & Löve, 1961)	Orchis purpur-ella (= Dac-tylorchis pur-purella)		80	Heslop-Harri-son, 1948
	21	42	Kliphuis, 1963	Orchis rotundi-folia		42	Humphrey, 1932a
		42	Gadella & Klip-huis, 1963			42	Humphrey, 1932b
Orchis morio	10	20	Fuchs & Zie-genspeck, 1923	Orchis sambu-cina (= Dactylorchis sambucina)	21		Hagerup, 1938
	18	36	Heusser, 1928			40	Vermeulen, 1947
	18		Hagerup, 1938				
		36	Vermeulen, 1947	Orchis salina		40	Balaeva & Sip-livinski, 1975
		36	Diannelidis, 1948	Orchis sesqui-pedalis		80	Vermeulen, 1947
		36	Vermeulen, 1949	Orchis simia	21	42	Heusser, 1938
		36	Diannelidis, 1955			42	Vermeulen, 1949
		36	Pogan & Wcis-lo (in Löve & Löve, 1961)			42	Kliphuis, 1963
		36, 38	Kliphuis, 1963	Orchis specta-bilis (= Galeorchis spectabilis)		42	Humphrey, 1932a
		36	Gadella & Klip-huis, 1963			42	Humphrey, 1932b
		36	Susnik & Lovka, 1973	Orchis sphae-rica		42	Sokolovskaja & Strelkova, 1940
		36	Majovsky et al., 1974	Orchis stricti-folia (= Or-chis latifolia)	20		Hagerup, 1938
Orchis morio ssp. picta		36	Vermeulen (in Löve & Löve, 1961)	Orchis traun-steineri (= Dactylorchis pseudo-traunsteineri)	variable 6–15	variable 16–28	Fuchs & Zie-genspeck, 1924
		36	Löve & Kjell-quist, 1973			40, 80, 120, 122	Vermeulen, 1947
Orchis mun-byana (= Dactylorchis munbyana)		80	Vermeulen, 1947	Orchis traun-steineri (= Dactylorchis traunsteineri)	10	20	Fuchs & Zie-genspeck, 1923
Orchis ochro-leuca (= Orchis incar-nata var. straminea)		40	Heusser, 1938		variable 16–24	variable 9–22	Fuchs & Zie-genspeck, 1924
						80	Sokolovskaja & Strelkova, 1960
Orchis pallens	20	40	Heusser, 1938	Orchis traun-steineri var. gigas (= Dactylorchis traunsteineri var. gigas)	20		Fuchs & Zie-genspeck, 1923
		40	Vermeulen, 1949				
Orchis palus-tris		42	Heusser, 1938				
		42	Vermeulen, 1949				
Orchis palus-tris ssp. ele-gans		42	Soo (in Löve & Löve, 1961)	Orchis triden-tata		42	Heusser, 1938
Orchis papilio-nacea	16	32	Heusser, 1938			42	Hagerup, 1938
Orchis patens ssp. spitzelii		42	Löve & Kjell-quist, 1973			42	Vermeulen, 1949
Orchis prae-tesmissa (= Dactylorchis praeter-missa)		80, 82	Maude, 1939			42	Susnik & Lovska, 1973
				Orchis ustulata	10		Fuchs & Zie-genspeck, 1923

Plant name	Chromosome number		Reference
	n	2n	
	10	20	Fuchs & Ziegenspeck, 1924
	21	42	Heusser, 1938
	21	42	Hagerup, 1938
		42	Vermeulen, 1947
		42	Diannelidis, 1948
		42	Vermeulen, 1949
		42	Diannelidis, 1955
	19, 20,	40 + (3 − 4B)	Schotsman, 1970b
	21 + (0 − 3B)	42 + (0 − 2B)	Schotsman, 1970b
		42	Löve & Kjellquist, 1973
Orchis unnamed (Orchis maculata × Gymnadenia odorata)	12	36	Fuchs & Ziegenspeck, 1923
Orchis unnamed (Orchis militaris × Aceras anthropophora)		42	Heusser, 1938
Orchis unnamed (Orchis morio × Orchis papilionacea)		34–36	Heusser, 1938
Orchis unnamed (Orchis pallens × Orchis mascula)		41	Heusser, 1938
Orchis unnamed (Orchis tridentata × Orchis ustulata)		42	Heusser, 1938
Oreorchis patens	24	48	Ohno et al., 1957
		48	Mutsuura & Nakahira, 1959
		50	Tanaka, 1965b
Ornithidium densum	24		Hoffmann, 1929
	24		Hoffmann, 1930
Ornithochilus fuscus		38 (36)	Sharma & Chatterji, 1966
		38	Mehra & Kashyap, 1976
Ornithophora radicans		56	Charanasri & Kamemoto, 1975
Otochilus alba	20		Mehra & Vij, 1970
O. fusca	20		Mehra & Vij, 1970
O. porrecta	20		Mehra & Vij, 1970
Pachystoma senile		40	Mehra & Kashyap, 1979
Paphiopedilum acmodontum		36	Karasawa, 1979
Paph. Actaeon		54	Duncan, 1947
Paph. Actaeus		26	Duncan, 1947
Paph. Actaeus 'Bianca'		26, 27	Mehlquist, 1947a
		27	Duncan, 1947

Plant name	Chromosome number		Reference
	n	2n	
Paph. Actaeus 'St. Alban'		28, 29	Mehlquist, 1947a
Paph. Actaeus 'Undine'		26	Duncan, 1947
Paph. Aladin		39	Duncan, 1947
Paph. Albion		39	Lenz, 1960
Paph. Alma Gevaert		36	Mehlquist, 1947a
Paph. Ambition		56	Duncan, 1947
Paph. angthong (natural hybrid)		26	Karasawa, 1979
Paph. appletonianum		38	Karasawa, 1979
Paph. argus		26	Pancho, 1965a
		26	Pancho, 1965b
		38	Tanaka & Aoyama, 1974
		38	Karasawa, 1979
Paph. Astarte		26 + 1B, 40 − 41 + 2B	Lenz, 1960
Paph. Ballet Girl		28	Duncan, 1947
Paph. barbatum (as Cypripedium barbatum)	16	32	Strasburger, 1888
	16		Francini, 1931
		38	Francini, 1934
		38	Mehlquist, 1947a
		38	Duncan, 1947
		38	Duncan & MacLeod, 1950a
	19		Chardard, 1963
		38	Karasawa, 1979
Paph. Baronial		40	Mehlquist, 1949
Paph. Bedfordiae		42	Duncan, 1947
Paph. bellatulum		26	Mehlquist, 1947a
		26	Duncan, 1947
	13	26	Duncan & MacLeod, 1950a
		26	Kamemoto et al., 1963
		26	Karasawa, 1979
Paph. Bellringer 'Chimes'		67	Lenz, 1960
Paph. Black Thorpe		52	Mehlquist, 1949
Paph. Blenheim		24	Hoffmann, 1929
		24	Hoffmann, 1930
Paph. bodegomii		26	Karasawa, 1979
Paph. Bodube 'Ean de Nil'		28	Duncan, 1947
Paph. Boltonii		26	Duncan & MacLeod, 1948b
		26 + (1 − 2B)	Lenz, 1960
Paph. bougainvilleanum		40	Karasawa, 1979
Paph. boxallii		26	Mehlquist, 1947a
		26	Duncan, 1947
	13	26	Duncan & MacLeod, 1948b

Plant name	n	2n	Reference
		26	Karasawa, 1979
Paph. Bruno		29	Duncan, 1947
Paph. bulleni-anum		40	Karasawa, 1979
Paph. callo-sum		32	Mehlquist, 1947a
		32	Duncan, 1947
	16	32	Duncan & MacLeod, 1950a
		32	Kamemoto et al., 1963
		32	Tanaka, 1965b
		32	Tanaka, 1971
		32	Karasawa, 1979
Paph. callo-sum var. sanderae		32	Mehlquist, 1947a
		32	Duncan, 1947
		32	McQuade, 1949
		32	Tanaka & Aoyama, 1974
Paph. Cardinal Mercier		39	Duncan, 1947
Paph. celebe-sense		42	Karasawa, 1979
Paph. cham-berlainianum	16	32	Hoffmann, 1929
	16	32	Hoffmann, 1930
		32	Duncan, 1947
	16	32	Duncan & MacLeod, 1949c
Paph. charles-worthii		26	Duncan, 1947
	13	26	Duncan & MacLeod, 1949a
		26	Karasawa, 1979
Paph. charles-worthii 'Bro-milowianum'	13	26	Duncan, 1947
		26	Duncan & MacLeod, 1949a
Paph. Chastity		39	Lenz, 1960
Paph. Christo-pher		27	Duncan, 1947
Paph. Christo-pher 'Grand Duke Nicho-las'		27	Duncan, 1947
Paph. ciliolare		32	Karasawa, 1979
Paph. Color-atum		56	Duncan, 1947
Paph. concolor	13	26	Duncan & MacLeod, 1948a
		26	Kamemoto et al., 1963
		26	Karasawa, 1979
Paph. Crastia		39 + (1 − 2B)	Lenz, 1960
Paph. curtisii		36	Mehlquist, 1947a
	18	36	Duncan & MacLeod, 1950a
		36	Karasawa, 1979
Paph. curtisii 'Exquisitum'		36	Duncan, 1947
Paph. curtisii 'Sanderae'		36	Mehlquist, 1947a
		36	Duncan, 1947
Paph. day-anum		34	Duncan, 1947
	17	34	Duncan & MacLeod, 1950a

Plant name	n	2n	Reference
		36	Karasawa, 1979
Paph. delenatii		26	Mehlquist, 1947a
		26	Duncan, 1947
	13	26	Duncan & MacLeod, 1948a
		26	Karasawa, 1979
Paph. Diana Broughton		26	Duncan, 1947
Paph. Doris Black		26	Duncan, 1947
Paph. Draco 'Atholl'		53	Duncan, 1947
Paph. druryi		26	Duncan, 1947
	13	26	Duncan & MacLeod, 1949a
		30	Karasawa, 1979
Paph. Earl of Tankerville		28	Duncan, 1947
Paph. Ellerlie		56	Duncan, 1947
Paph. esquiro-lei		26	Karasawa, 1979
Paph. exul		26	Duncan, 1947
	13	26	Duncan & MacLeod, 1949a
		26	Kamemoto et al., 1963
		26	Tanaka & Aoyama, 1974
		26	Karasawa, 1979
Paph. fairie-anum		26	Mehlquist, 1947a
		26	Duncan, 1947
	13	26	Duncan & MacLeod, 1949a
	13		Vij & Mehra, 1974
Paph. fairie-anum var. giganteum		26	Tanaka & Aoyama, 1974
		26	Karasawa, 1979
Paph. F. C. Puddle		ca. 41 + (1 − 2B)	Lenz, 1960
Paph. F. C. Puddle 'Superbum'		ca. 41 + (1 − 2B)	Lenz, 1960
Paph. glanduli-ferum		26	Karasawa, 1979
Paph. glauco-phyllum	18	36	Duncan, 1947
		36	Duncan & MacLeod, 1949c
Paph. gode-froyae		26	Kamemoto et al., 1963
		26	Tanaka & Aoyama, 1974
		26	Karasawa, 1979
Paph. Golden Fleece		26	Duncan, 1947
Paph. Golden Wren		26	Duncan, 1947
Paph. Goliath		39	Duncan, 1947
Paph. gratrixi-anum		26	Duncan, 1947
	13	26	Duncan & MacLeod, 1948b
Paph. Gwen Hannen 'Album'		27	Duncan, 1947

Plant name	Chromosome number n	Chromosome number 2n	Reference
Paph. Harrisianum		32	Francini, 1934
Paph. Harrisianum (Yellow Type)		45	Mehlquist, 1947a
Paph. Harrisianum 'Albescens'		32	Mehlquist, 1947a
Paph. Harrisianum 'G. S. Ball'		70	Duncan, 1959
Paph. Harrisianum 'Marginale'		51	Mehlquist, 1947a
Paph. Harrisianum 'Nigrum'		32	Mehlquist, 1947a
Paph. Harrisianum 'Superbum'		45	Mehlquist, 1947a
Paph. haynaldianum		26	Duncan, 1947
	13	26	Duncan & MacLeod, 1949b
		26	Pancho, 1965a
		26	Pancho, 1965b
		26	Tanaka & Aoyama, 1974
		26	Karasawa, 1979
Paph. hennisianum		36	Karasawa, 1979
Paph. hirsutissimum		26	Duncan, 1947
	13	26	Duncan & MacLeod, 1949a
		26	Tanaka & Aoyama, 1974
		26	Karasawa, 1979
Paph. insigne 'Royalty'		26	Mehlquist, 1947a
Paph. insigne var. sanderae		26	Mehlquist, 1947a
		26	Duncan, 1947
		26	Duncan & MacLeod, 1948b
		26	Tanaka, 1964a
		26	Tanaka, 1965b
		26, 28	Tanaka & Aoyama, 1974
	13		Terasaka & Tanaka, 1974
		26	Karasawa, 1978
Paph. insigne var. sanderae 'Super'		26	Karasawa, 1978
Paph. insigne var. sanderianum 'No. 1'		26	Karasawa, 1978
Paph. insigne var. sanderianum 'No. 2'		26	Karasawa, 1978
Paph. insigne 'Sylhetense'		26	Mehlquist, 1947a
		26, 28	Duncan, 1947
		26	Karasawa, 1978
Paph. insigne 'Tonbridgense'		26	Mehlquist, 1947a
Paph. javanicum		36	Duncan, 1947
	18	36	Duncan & MacLeod, 1950a
		38	Karasawa, 1979
Paph. J. M. Black 'Westpoint'		40	Duncan, 1947
Paph. Laddie		42	Duncan, 1947
Paph. Lady Dillon 'Magnificum'		27	Duncan, 1947
Paph. laevigatum		26	Karasawa, 1979
Paph. Lathamianum	13, 14	28	Francini, 1945
Paph. lawrenceanum		36	Mehlquist, 1947a
		36	McQuade, 1949
	18	36, 40	Duncan & MacLeod, 1950a
		36	Karasawa, 1979
Paph. Holdenii		34	Mehlquist, 1947a
Paph. hookerae		28	Karasawa, 1979
Paph. Ilium		27	Duncan, 1947
Paph. insigne (= Cypripedium insigne)	ca. 12		Afzelius, 1916
	8–9		Suessenguth, 1921
	12–13		Heitz, 1926
	16		Hoffmann, 1929
	16		Hoffmann, 1930
	16		Francini, 1931
		28	Eftimiu-Heim, 1941
		26	Mehlquist, 1947a
		26	Duncan, 1947
		26	Tanaka, 1964a
		26	Tanaka, 1965b
		26	Tanaka, 1971
		26	Tanaka, 1974
		26	Tanaka & Aoyama, 1974
	13		Vij & Mehra, 1974
		26	Karasawa, 1978
		26	Karasawa, 1979
Paph. insigne 'Chantinii'		26	Karasawa, 1978
Paph. insigne 'Ernesti'		26	Duncan, 1947
	13	26	Duncan & MacLeod, 1948a,b
Paph. insigne 'Forstermanni'		26	Karasawa, 1978
Paph. insigne 'Harefield Hall'		39	Mehlquist, 1947a
		39	Duncan & MacLeod, 1948b
		39	Karasawa, 1978
Paph. insigne 'Illustre'		26	Karasawa, 1978
Paph. insigne 'Laura Kimball'		26	Mehlquist, 1947a
Paph. insigne 'Maximum'		26	Karasawa, 1978
Paph. insigne 'Montanum'		26	Karasawa, 1978
Paph. insigne 'Mooreanum'		26	Karasawa, 1978

Plant name	Chromosome number		Reference	Plant name	Chromosome number		Reference
	n	2n			n	2n	
Paph. insigne 'Oddity'		26	Karasawa, 1978	Paph. Nitens-Leeanum 'Hannibal'		41	Duncan, 1947
Paph. lawrenceanum var. hyeanum		36	Duncan, 1947	Paph. niveum		26	Mehlquist, 1947a
		36	McQuade, 1949			26	Duncan, 1947
Paph. Leeanum	12		Hoffmann, 1929		13	26	Duncan & MacLeod, 1948a
	12		Hoffmann, 1930			26	Kamemoto et al., 1963
	16	32	Francini, 1930			26	Karasawa, 1979
	15, 16	31	Francini, 1931	Paph. parishii		26	Duncan, 1947
	15, 16	31	Francini, 1932		13	26	Duncan & MacLeod, 1949b
		27	Francini (from Duncan, 1959)			26	Kamemoto et al., 1963
Paph. Leeanum 'Aureum'		28	Mehlquist, 1947a			26	Karasawa, 1979
Paph. Leeanum 'Chinkaberryanum'		28	Mehlquist, 1947a	Paph. Perseus		42	Duncan, 1947
Paph. Leeanum 'Engelhartii'		28	Mehlquist, 1947a	Paph. philippinense		26	Duncan & MacLeod, 1949b
Paph. Leeanum 'Erectum'		28	Mehlquist, 1947a			26	Pancho, 1965a
Paph. Leeanum 'F₂'		16, 20, 26, 27, 28, 29, 30, 31, 32	Francini, 1931			26	Pancho, 1965b
Paph. Leeanum 'Giganteum'		28	Mehlquist, 1947a			26	Tanaka & Aoyama, 1974
Paph. Leeanum 'Prospero'		28	Mehlquist, 1947a			26	Karasawa, 1979
Paph. Lemanii 'Ducis'		42	Duncan, 1947	Paph. praestans		28	Duncan, 1947
Paph. leucochilum		26	Karasawa, 1979		14	28	Duncan & MacLeod, 1949b
Paph. Littlecot		56	Duncan, 1947			26	Karasawa, 1979
Paph. lowii		26	Duncan, 1947	Paph. Princess Mary		39	Lenz, 1960
	13	26	Duncan & MacLeod, 1949a	Paph. purpuratum	ca. 24	ca. 48	Hoffmann, 1930
		26	Tanaka & Aoyama, 1974			40	Karasawa, 1979
		26	Karasawa, 1979	Paph. Pyramus 'King Ferdinand'		42	Duncan, 1947
Paph. Madame Albert Fevrier		54	Duncan, 1947	Paph. randsii		26	Karasawa, 1979
Paph. Madelon		39	Duncan, 1947	Paph. Rainbow		40	Mehlquist, 1949
Paph. mastersianum		32	Duncan, 1947	Paph. roebbelenii		26	Karasawa, 1979
	16	32	Duncan & MacLeod, 1950a	Paph. Rossettii 'Goliath'		46, 47	Mehlquist, 1947a
		36	Karasawa, 1979	Paph. Rosettii 'Splendidissimum'		46, 47	Mehlquist, 1947a
Paph. Maudiae		34	Mehlquist, 1947a	Paph. Rosy Dawn		40 + 2B	Lenz, 1960
	ca. 17	34	McQuade, 1949	Paph. Rosy Dawn 'Sunbeam'		42	Lenz, 1960
Paph. Maudiae 'Coloratum'		34	Mehlquist, 1947a	Paph. Rosy Dawn 'Superbum'		39	Lenz, 1960
Paph. Maudiae 'Magnificum'		34	Mehlquist, 1947a	Paph. rothschildianum		26, 28	Duncan, 1947
Paph. Maudiae 'The Dell'		34	Mehlquist, 1947a			26, 28	Duncan & MacLeod, 1949b
Paph. Maudiae 'Westonbirt'		34	Mehlquist, 1947a			26	Karasawa, 1979
Paph. Memoria F. M. Ogilvie 'The Premier'		42	Duncan, 1947	Paph. Selma		55	Duncan, 1947
Paph. Mrs. O. W. Walker		28, 56	Duncan, 1947	Paph. Snow Bunting 'Muriel'		ca. 54	Lenz, 1960
Paph. Niobe-Leeanum		39	Duncan, 1947	Paph. speciosum (= Paph. villosum)		26	Francini, 1934
						26	Mulay & Panikkar, 1953
				Paph. spicerianum	15	30	Francini, 1930
					15	30	Francini, 1931

Plant name	n	2n	Reference
	15	30	Francini, 1932
	15	30	Francini, 1945
	14		Duncan, 1947
	14	28	Duncan & MacLeod, 1949a
		30	Tanaka & Aoyama, 1974
		30	Karasawa, 1979
Paph. stonei		26	Karasawa, 1979
Paph. stonei 'Mary Reginae'		26	Duncan, 1947
	13	26	Duncan & MacLeod, 1949b
Paph. sublaeve		57, 58	Duncan, 1947
	29	58	Duncan & MacLeod, 1950a
Paph. sukhakulii		40	Senghas & Schoser, 1965
		40	Tanaka & Aoyama, 1974
		40	Karasawa, 1979
Paph. Sumurun		39	Duncan, 1947
		39, 39 + 1B	Lenz, 1960
Paph. Sumurun 'Bolholt'		39	Lenz, 1960
Paph. Sumurun 'Boynton'		39 + 2B	Lenz, 1960
Paph. Sumurun 'Pearl'		39 + 1B	Lenz, 1960
Paph. Sumurun 'Snowball'		39	Lenz, 1960
Paph. superbiens		38	Duncan, 1947
	19	38	Duncan & MacLeod, 1950a
		38	Karasawa, 1979
Paph. Susan Tucker 'Morelia'		54	Lenz, 1960
Paph. Thebian		70	Duncan, 1947
Paph. Tom Worsley		39, 41	Duncan, 1947
Paph. tonsum		34	Duncan, 1947
	17	34	Duncan & MacLeod, 1950a
		32	Karasawa, 1979
Paph. venustum	18		Francini, 1931
		42	Duncan 1947
	21	42	Duncan & MacLeod, 1950a
	20 + 1B		Mehra & Vij, 1970
		40, 41	Tanaka & Aoyama, 1974
		40 + 2B	Vij & Mehra, 1974
		40, 41	Karasawa, 1979
Paph. victoria-regina subsp. *chamberlainianum*		34	Karasawa, 1979
Paph. victoria-regina subsp. *glaucophyllum*		36, 37	Karasawa, 1979
Paph. victoria-regina subsp. *glaucophyllum* var. *moquetteanum*		34	Karasawa, 1979
Paph. victoria-regina subsp. *liemianum*		32	Karasawa, 1979
Paph. victoria-regina subsp. *primulinum*		32	Karasawa, 1979
Paph. victoria-regina subsp. *primulinum* forma *purpurascens*		32	Karasawa, 1979
Paph. victoria-regina subsp. (unnamed hybrid)		33, 35, 36	Karasawa, 1979
Paph. villosum	14		Francini, 1931
		26	Francini, 1934
		19–28	Francini, 1945
		26	Mehlquist, 1947a
		26	Duncan, 1947
	13	26	Duncan & MacLeod, 1948b
		26	Kamemoto et al., 1963
	13		Vij & Mehra, 1974
		26	Karasawa, 1979
Paph. violascens		38	Karasawa, 1979
Paph. virens		40	Karasawa, 1979
Paph. wardii		40–45	Duncan, 1945
	20	40	Duncan & MacLeod, 1950a
		40	Senghas & Schoser, 1965
Paph. wentworthianum		40	Karasawa, 1979
Paph. Westminster		53	Duncan, 1947
Paph. Whitemoor 'Norriton'		53	Lenz, 1960
Paph. Whitemoor 'Snow Maiden'		54	Lenz, 1960
Paph. Worsleyi		40	Duncan, 1947
Paph. unnamed (*Paph.* Balbus × *Paph.* Balaclava)		27	Duncan, 1947
Paph. unnamed (*Paph.* Madame Albert Fevrier × *Paph.* Croesus)		54	Duncan, 1947
Pecteilis latilabris	21		Arora, 1971
P. radiata (= *Habenaria radiata*)		32	Miduno, 1939
P. radiata 'Triploid'		48	Miduno, 1940b

Plant name	Chromosome number n	Chromosome number 2n	Reference
P. unnamed (intergeneric hybrid) (P. radiata × Habenaria sagittifera)		30	Miduno, 1940b
Pelatantheria ctenoglossa		38	Kamemoto et al., 1964
		38	Tara & Kamemoto, 1970
Peristeria elata var. gatto-nensis		40	Daker & Jones, 1970
P. guttata		40	Daker & Jones, 1970
Peristylus cordatus		36	Larsen, 1960
P. goodyeroides	21	28, ca. 44	Larsen, 1966 Arora, 1968
		42	Mehra & Kashyap, 1978
P. goodyeroides var. affinis		42	Mehra & Kashyap, 1978
P. gracilis		42	Larsen, 1966
Perularia fuscescens		42	Sokolovskaya, 1966
Phaius albus		44	Sharma & Sarkar, 1967–1968
Phaius elatus		42	Setterfield (from Duncan, 1959)
Phaius flavus		42	Pancho, 1965a
		42	Pancho, 1965b
Phaius grandifolius (= Phaius tankervilliae)		50	Tanaka, 1965b
		38	Arora, 1968
Phaius longipes		ca. 42	Larsen, 1966
Phaius mindorensis		42	Pancho, 1965a
		42	Pancho, 1965b
Phaius minor		42	Mutsuura & Nakahira, 1958a
		44	Tanaka, 1965b
Phaius minor f. punctatus		44	Tanaka, 1965b
Phaius mishmensis	31		Sharma & Sarkar, 1967–1968
		42	Larsen, 1966
Phaius tankervilliae	23		Mehra & Sehgal, 1975
Phaius wallichii	21		Mehra & Vij, 1970
		48	Sharma & Sarkar, 1967–1968
Phaius wallichii var. assamica	21		Sharma & Sarkar, 1967–1968
Phalaenopsis Adm. Stump		74 ± 2	Kamemoto et al., 1961
Phal. Alice Bowen 'Deana'		81 ± 1	Kamemoto et al., 1961
Phal. Alice Bowen 'Diamond Head'		64 ± 2	Kamemoto et al., 1961
Phal. Alice Bowen 'Kaalawai'		62 ± 2	Kamemoto et al., 1961
Phal. Alice Bowen 'No. 1407'		71 ± 1	Kamemoto et al., 1961
Phal. amabilis		38, 114	Woodard, 1951
		38, 69 + 3f.	Sagawa, 1962b
		38	Pancho, 1965a

Plant name	Chromosome number n	Chromosome number 2n	Reference
Phal. amabilis 'Grandiflora'	19	38	Pancho, 1965b
		38	Arends, 1970
		38	Shoji, 1976
		38	Kamemoto et al., 1961
		38	Sagawa, 1962b
		38	Shindo & Kamemoto, 1963e
Phal. amabilis var. grandiflora		152 ± 2	Pancho, 1965a
		152 ± 2	Pancho, 1965b
		38	Shindo & Kamemoto, 1963e
Phal. amboinensis	19	38	Arends, 1970
		38	Shoji, 1976
Phal. amboinensis 'P'		38	Sagawa, 1962b
Phal. aphrodite		38	Woodard, 1951
	19	38	Arends, 1970
		38	Shoji, 1976
Phal. Aristocrat 'No. 1710'		76 ± 1	Kamemoto et al., 1967
Phal. Blanche Overman		87 ± 1	Kamemoto et al., 1961
Phal. Boulderi 'Flint Rock'		100	Sagawa, 1962b
Phal. boxallii		38	Shindo & Kamemoto, 1963a
Phal. buys-soniana (= Doritis buys-soniana)		76	Woodard (from Duncan, 1959)
Phal. Cast Iron Monarch		hexaploid	Sagawa, 1962b
Phal. Cast Iron Monarch 'King' (selfed)		114 ± 2	Kamemoto et al., 1967
Phal. Cathy Latham		71 ± 1	Kamemoto et al., 1967
Phal. Chief Awaho 'No. 1377A'		57	Kamemoto et al., 1961
Phal. Chieftain 'UF#1'		77	Sagawa, 1962b
Phal. Chieftain 'No. 1518A'		76 ± 1	Kamemoto et al., 1961
Phal. C. Knight 'Perfection'		56	Sagawa, 1962b
Phal. C. Knight 'Radiatum'		57	Sagawa, 1962b
Phal. C. Knight 'South Olive'		57	Sagawa, 1962b
Phal. C. Knight 'UF#1'		57	Sagawa, 1962b
Phal. cornu-cervi		38	Woodard, 1951
		38	Sagawa, 1962b
		38	Kamemoto et al., 1964
		38	Shoji, 1976
Phal. decumbens		38	Kamemoto et al., 1964
Phal. Doris		72 ± 1	Kamemoto et al., 1961
		76 ± 1	Kamemoto et al., 1961
Phal. Doris Selfed		74, 76	Sagawa, 1962b
Phal. Doris 'No. 1110J'		76 ± 1	Kamemoto et al., 1961
Phal. Dos Pueblos		76 ± 1	Kamemoto et al., 1967
Phal. Dr. Geo. N. MacDonell 'UF#1'		38	Sagawa, 1962b
Phal. Elisabethae		38, 114	Woodard, 1951

Plant name	Chromosome number n	Chromosome number 2n	Reference
Phal. Elisabethae 'UF#1'		76	Sagawa, 1962b
Phal. equestris (= Phal. rosea)		38	Woodard, 1951
		38	Sagawa, 1962b
		38	Shindo & Kamemoto, 1963e
	19	38	Arends, 1970
		38	Shoji, 1976
Phal. equestris 'New Type'		38	Sagawa, 1962b
Phal. equestris 'Three Lips'		38	Kamemoto et al., 1961
Phal. esmeralda (= Doritis pulcherrima)		38	Woodard, 1951
	19	38	Sagawa & Niimoto, 1961
	19	38	Sharma & Chatterji, 1966
Phal. Flamingo 'UF#1'		43	Sagawa, 1962b
Phal. fuscata		38	Shoji, 1976
Phal. gigantea		38	Shoji, 1976
Phal. Gilles Gratiot 'No. 206H'		76	Kamemoto et al., 1961
Phal. Grace Palm 'No. 115A'		78	Kamemoto et al., 1961
Phal. Grace Palm 'No. KS57'		73 ± 1	Kamemoto et al., 1961
Phal. Grace Palm 'No. 644'		76	Kamemoto et al., 1961
Phal. Harold Fisher		114 ± 1	Kamemoto et al., 1961
Phal. Helen Richards 'No. 1423'		78	Kamemoto et al., 1961
Phal. Hermione 'Trudy'		38	Sagawa & Niimoto, 1961
		38	Sagawa, 1962b
Phal. Hymen 'UF#1'		38	Sagawa, 1962b
Phal. Magale		92	Sagawa & Niimoto, 1961
		95	Sagawa, 1962b
Phal. J. Magale 'Varina'		95	Sagawa, 1962b
Phal. John Seden		38	Kamemoto et al., 1961
Phal. Juanita		76	Sagawa, 1962
		74, 77, 152	Kamemoto & Hashimoto, 1968
Phal. Karen 'UF#1'		63	Sagawa, 1962b
Phal. Karen 'UF#2'		65	Sagawa, 1962b
Phal. Katherine Siegwart 'UF#1'		76	Sagawa, 1962b
Phal. Lee Wilder 'Ruffles'		114	Kamemoto et al., 1961
Phal. lindenii		38	Sagawa, 1962b
		38	Shindo & Kamemoto, 1963e
Phal. L. Merkel		83, 87 + 1f.	Sagawa, 1962b
Phal. Lokelani		38	Kamemoto et al., 1961
Phal. Louise Dillingham 'No. 1493F'		76 ± 1	Kamemoto et al., 1961

Plant name	Chromosome number n	Chromosome number 2n	Reference
Phal. lueddemanniana		38	Woodard, 1951
		38	Shindo & Kamemoto, 1963e
	19	38	Arends, 1970
		38	Shoji, 1976
Phal. lueddemanniana var. boxalli		38	Sagawa, 1962b
		38	Shoji, 1976
Phal. lueddemanniana 'Division 1'		38	Sagawa, 1962b
Phal. lueddemanniana 'Division Plant A'		38	Sagawa, 1962b
Phal. lueddemanniana 'Fennell's'		38	Sagawa, 1962b
Phal. lueddemanniana var. hieroglyphica 'UF#1'		38	Sagawa, 1962b
Phal. lueddemanniana 'Jones'		38	Sagawa, 1962b
Phal. lueddemanniana 'Majus'		38	Sagawa, 1962b
Phal. lueddemanniana 'Ochracea'		38	Sagawa, 1962b
		38	Shindo & Kamemoto, 1963e
		38	Shoji, 1976
		38	Sagawa, 1962b
Phal. lueddemanniana 'Plant #2 pulchra (red)'		38	Sagawa, 1962b
Phal. lueddemanniana 'Pulchra'		38	Shoji, 1976
Phal. Luzon 'Crestwood'		38	Sagawa, 1962b
Phal. mannii		38	Woodard, 1951
		38	Sagawa, 1962b
		38	Shindo & Kamemoto, 1963e
	19	38	Sharma & Chatterji, 1966
	19	38	Arends, 1970
		38	Shoji, 1976
Phal. Mannipam	irregular	38	Duncan, 1959
Phal. Mariae 'UF#1'		38	Sagawa, 1962b
		38	Shoji, 1976
Phal. Martha		74	Kamemoto et al., 1967
Phal. Misty Clouds		77 ± 1	Kamemoto et al., 1967
Phal. Misty Clouds 'No. 1369E'		76 ± 1	Kamemoto et al., 1961
Phal. Monique 'No. 934F'		57	Kamemoto et al., 1961
Phal. Moonglow		55, 57	Sagawa & Niimoto, 1961
Phal. Palm Beach		92	Sagawa, 1962b
Phal. Pamela	19		Woodard (from Duncan, 1959)
Phal. parishii		38	Shoji, 1976
Phal. Pasadena 'No. 90'		76	Kamemoto et al., 1967

Plant name	Chromosome number n	Chromosome number 2n	Reference
Phal. Pink Chiffon 'UF#1'		57	Sagawa, 1962b
Phal. Pink Chiffon 'UF#2'		58	Sagawa, 1962b
Phal. Pink Cloud 'No. 192A'		60	Kamemoto et al., 1961
Phal. Pink Cloud 'No. 192C'		70	Kamemoto et al., 1961
Phal. Pink Glory 'UF#1'	19	38	Sagawa & Niimoto, 1961
Phal. Pink Pamela 'UF#1'		38	Sagawa, 1962b
Phal. Pink Pamela 'UF#2'		38	Sagawa, 1962b
Phal. Pink Star		38	Sagawa, 1962b
Phal. Pink Vision 'No. 1622c'		73	Kamemoto et al., 1961
Phal. Pinnochio		110 ± 2	Kamemoto et al., 1967
Phal. Princess Grace		95 ± 1	Kamemoto et al., 1967
Phal. pulcherrima (= Dorites pulcherrima)		38	Shindo & Kamemoto, 1963e
		38	Kamemoto et al., 1964
Phal. pulcherrima var. buyssoniana		76	Kamemoto et al., 1964
Phal. Ramona 'Jewel Box'		76	Kamemoto et al., 1961
Phal. Regnier 'No. 3-F'		38	Kamemoto et al., 1961
Phal. Rothomago 'UF#1'		38	Sagawa, 1962b
Phal. Ruby Lips 'UF#1'		73	Sagawa, 1962b
Phal. Sally Lowrey 'UF#1'		54	Sagawa, 1962b
Phal. sanderiana		38	Sagawa, 1962b
		38	Shindo & Kamemoto, 1963e
	19	38	Arends, 1970
		38	Shoji, 1976
Phal. schilleriana		40	Eftimiu-Heim, 1941
		38	Woodard, 1951
		38, 76	Kamemoto et al., 1961
		38	Sagawa, 1962b
		38	Shindo & Kamemoto, 1963e
		38	Tanaka, 1964a
		76	Kamemoto et al., 1967
		38	Shoji, 1976
Phal. schilleriana 'Malibu'		65	Sagawa, 1962b
Phal. schilleriana 'No. 1280A'		38	Kamemoto et al., 1961
Phal. Shocking Pink 'No. 1506G'		63 ± 1	Kamemoto et al., 1961
Phal. Snow Bird 'No. 1370H'		76 ± 2	Kamemoto et al., 1961
Phal. speciosa		38	Shoji, 1976
Phal. speciosa 'Orchidglade'		38	Sagawa, 1962b
Phal. Star of Sao Paulo		38	Sagawa, 1962b
Phal. stuartiana	19	38	Arends, 1970
		38	Shoji, 1976
Phal. Sunrise 'I'		72 ± 1	Kamemoto et al., 1961
Phal. Sunrise 'No. 1480A'		72 ± 1	Kamemoto et al., 1961
Phal. Sunrise 'Radiant K'		72	Kamemoto et al., 1961
Phal. Susie Darlin 'No. 1587B'		72 ± 1	Kamemoto et al., 1961
Phal. tetraspis		38	Shoji, 1976
Phal. T. Tucker		59	Sagawa, 1962b
Phal. violacea		38	Shindo & Kamemoto, 1963e
Phal. violacea 'Borneo B'		38	Shoji, 1976
Phal. White Goddess 'No. 1490'		77	Kamemoto et al., 1967
Phal. Winged Victory		92	Sagawa, 1962b
Phal. Zada		77	Sagawa, 1962b
Phal. unnamed (Phal. amabilis × Phal. stuartiana)		38	Sagawa, 1962b
Phal. unnamed (Phal. Ann Fisher × Phal. Clara Knight)		59 + 2f.	Sagawa, 1962b
Phal. unnamed (Phal. Boulderi × Phal. Palm Beach 'Gertrude')		76	Sagawa, 1962b
Phal. unnamed (Phal. Cast Iron Monarch × Phal. Star of Rio)		95	Sagawa, 1962b
Phal. unnamed (Phal. cornucervi × Phal. Lady Rothschild)		38	Sagawa, 1962b
Phal. unnamed (Phal. Doris × Phal. Harold Fisher)		88 ± 2	Kamemoto et al., 1961
Phal. unnamed (Phal. Doris 'Varina' × Phal. Boulderi 'Flint Rock')		87	Sagawa, 1962b
Phal. unnamed (Phal. Gladys Lovelace × Phal. Grandiflora)		55	Sagawa & Niimoto, 1961
Phal. unnamed (Phal. Gloriosa 'Tesselata' × Phal. Pink Pamela 'Tesselata')		38	Sagawa & Niimoto, 1961
		38	Sagawa, 1962b
Phal. unnamed (Phal. luedemanniana × Phal. equestris)		38	Sagawa, 1962b

Plant name	Chromosome number		Reference
	n	2n	
Phal. unnamed (Phal. Palm Beach × Phal. Serenity)		86	Sagawa, 1962b
Phal. unnamed (Phal. rimestadiana 'Helvetia' × Phal. Doris 'Superba')		76	Sagawa, 1962b
Phal. unnamed (Phal. Winged Victory × Phal. Margaret Bean)		76	Sagawa, 1962b
Pholidota articulata	20		Arora, 1968
	20		Mehra & Vij, 1970
		40	Mehra & Kashyap, 1979
P. caceata	21		Mehra & Sehgal, 1974
P. chinensis		40	Tanaka, 1962a
		40	Tanaka, 1971
P. conchoidea	20		Hoffmann, 1929
	20		Hoffmann, 1930
P. imbricata		40	Pancho, 1965a
		40	Pancho, 1965b
		40	Arora, 1968
	20		Mehra & Vij, 1970
P. protracta	20		Mehra & Vij, 1970
P. recurva	20		Mehra & Vij, 1970
Phragmipedium blenheimense		24	Hoffmann, 1929
P. boissierianum		18	Karasawa & Tanaka, 1976
P. caudatum		32	Hoffmann, 1929
P. longifolium var. hartwegii		20	Brown (from Duncan, 1959)
P. sedenii (= P. schlimii × P. longifolium)	12	24	Hoffmann, 1929
Phyllomphax obcordata var. major	21		Mehra & Sehgal, 1974
Physosiphon bifolia	21		Afzelius, 1922
		42	Richardson, 1935
	21	42	Heusser, 1938
P. carinatus	ca. 16		Hoffmann, 1929
	ca. 16		Hoffmann, 1930
P. loddigesii	ca. 16		Hoffmann, 1929
	16, 17, 18		Hoffmann, 1930
Platanthera bifolia	21		Afzelius, 1922
		42	Richardson, 1935
	21	42	Heusser, 1938
		42	Diannelidis, 1948
		42	Diannelidis, 1955
		42	Pogan & Wcislo (in Löve & Löve, 1961)

Plant name	Chromosome number		Reference
	n	2n	
	21	42	Kliphuis, 1963
		42	Gadilla & Kliphuis, 1963
		ca. 42	Sorsa, 1963
		42, ca. 42	Balaeva & Siplivinski, 1976
P. chlorantha	21		Afzelius, 1922
		42	Heusser, 1938
		42	Richardson, 1935
	12	42 (21)	Hagerup, 1947
		42	Mattison (in Löve & Löve, 1961)
		42	Pogan & Wcislo (in Löve & Löve, 1961)
		42	Gadella & Kliphuis, 1963
	21	42	Kliphuis, 1963
P. ciliaris (= Habenaria ciliaris)	16		Brown, 1909
	16		Richardson, 1935
P. cornu-bovis		42	Sokolovskaya, 1966
P. dilatata (= Habenaria dilatata)		42	Humphrey, 1933
		42	Löve & Löve, 1966
P. florenti		42	Mutsuura & Nakahira, 1958
P. hologlottis		42	Miduno, 1940b
		42	Tanaka, 1965b
		42	Tanaka, 1971
P. hyperborea (= Habenaria hyperborea)		42	Humphrey, 1933
	21	42	Richardson, 1935
	42	84	Harmsen, 1943
		84	Löve & Löve, 1956
		84	Löve & Ritchie, 1966
P. mandarinorum var. brachycentron		42	Tanaka, 1965b
P. mandarinorum var. maximowicziana		42	Mutsuura & Nakahira, 1958
P. metabifolia		21	Ohno & Hashimoto, 1956
		42	Tanaka, 1965b
P. minor		42	Mutsuura & Nakahira, 1958
		42	Tanaka, 1965b
P. obtusata		63	Afzelius, 1922
P. oligantha		126	Afzelius, 1922
		126	Löve & Löve, 1954
		ca. 126	Knaben & Engelskjön, 1967
P. ophrydioides		20	Ohno & Hashimoto, 1956
		42	Mutsuura & Nakahira, 1960
		40	Sinoto & Shoji, 1962
P. ophrydioides var. takedai		42	Mutsuura & Nakahira, 1958
P. rotundifolia		42	Löve & Ritchie, 1966
P. sachalinensis		42	Mutsuura & Nakahira, 1959
P. sussanae		42	Arora, 1968

Plant name	n	2n	Reference
P. typuloides		42	Mutsuura & Nakahira, 1959
P. typuloides var. nipponica		42	Mutsuura & Nakahira, 1960
		42	Tanaka, 1965b
Platyclinis glumaceum (=	20		Hoffmann, 1929
Dendrochilum glumanum)	20		Hoffmann, 1930
Pleione formosana		38	Tanaka, 1964a
		40	Miduno, 1940b
		40	Tanaka, 1962a
		40	Tanaka, 1965b
		40 + (1 - 2B)	Hunt & Vosa, 1971
Pln. formosana 'Alba'		40	Hunt & Vosa, 1971
Pln. forrestii		40	Hunt & Vosa, 1971
Pin. hookeriana		40 + (1 - 2B)	Hunt & Vosa, 1971
	20		Malla et al., 1979
Pln. humilis	20		Mehra & Vij, 1970
		40 + (1 - 3B)	Hunt & Vosa, 1971
Pin. humilis 'Tricolor'		40	Hunt & Vosa, 1971
Pln. limprichtii		40, 80	Hunt & Vosa, 1971
Pln. maculata		40	Hunt & Vosa, 1971
Pln. pogonioides		80	Hunt & Vosa, 1971
Pln. praecox		40	Sharma & Sarkar, 1967–1968
	20		Mehra & Vij, 1970
		40	Hunt & Vosa, 1971
Pln. praecox var. wallichiana		40	Hunt & Vosa, 1971
Pln. pricei		20 + 1B	La Cour, 1952
Pln. versailles		80	Hunt & Vosa, 1971
Pln. yunnanensis		120	Hunt & Vosa, 1971
Pleurothallis procumbens	16		Afzelius, 1966
P. vittata	21		Chardard, 1963
Plocoglottis javanica	19		Afzelius, 1943
Podochilus cultratus	19		Mehra & Vij, 1970
Pogonia japonica		19, 20, 21, 21, 23	Miduno, 1953
		24	Mutsuura & Nakahira, 1959
		20	Tanaka, 1962a
		19, 20	Miduno & Yamasaki, 1963
		20	Tanaka, 1965b
		19	Kondo, 1970
		20	Tanaka, 1971
		20	Tanaka, 1974
	10		Terasaka & Tanaka, 1974
	10		Taylor & Tanaka, 1977
P. minor		18, 20, 21	Miduno & Yamazaki, 1952
		18	Mutsuura & Nakahira, 1960
		18	Tanaka, 1962a
		18	Tanaka, 1965b
		18	Tanaka, 1971
P. ophioglossoides		18	Baldwin & Speese, 1957
		18	Löve & Löve, 1969
Polystachya adansoniae		40	Jones, 1966
		40	Ar-rushdi, 1971
Pol. affinis		40	Ar-rushdi, 1971
Pol. albescens		40	Jones, 1966
Pol. albescens ssp. albescens		40	Ar-rushdi, 1971
Pol. albescens ssp. imbricata		ca. 40	Jones, 1966
Pol. caloglossa		40	Jones, 1966
		40	Ar-rushdi, 1971
Pol. campyloglossa		ca. 80	Jones, 1966
Pol. clavata		ca. 80	Jones, 1966
Pol. cooperi		40	Jones, 1966
Pol. coriscens		40	Ar-rushdi, 1971
Pol. cultriformis		38, 39	Chardard, 1963
		40	Jones, 1966
Pol. dilichophylla		40	Ar-rushdi, 1971
Pol. doggettii		81	Jones, 1966
Pol. estrellensis		80	Blumenschein, 1960
		80	Jones, 1966
Pol. eurygnatha		40	Jones, 1966
Pol. extinctoria	40	80	Jones, 1966
Pol. fallax		40	Jones, 1966
Pol. fulvilabia		40	Jones, 1966
Pol. fusiformis		ca. 40	Jones, 1966
Pol. galeata		ca. 40	Jones, 1966
		40	Ar-rushdi, 1971
Pol. hislopii		80	Jones, 1966
Pol. hollandii		40	Jones, 1966
Pol. isochiloides		40	Jones, 1966
Pol. laxiflora		40	Jones, 1966
		40	Ar-rushdi, 1971
Pol. modesta		ca. 40	Jones, 1966
Pol. mukandaensis		40	Ar-rushdi, 1971
Pol. nyanzensis		40	Ar-rushdi, 1971
Pol. odorata		40	Jones, 1966
Pol. odorata var. odorata		40, 80	Ar-rushdi, 1971
Pol. polychaete	ca. 20		Hoffmann, 1930
		40	Jones, 1966
		40	Ar-rushdi, 1971
Pol. pubescens		ca. 120	Jones, 1966
Pol. ramulosa		40	Jones, 1966
		40	Ar-rushdi, 1971
Pol. rhodoptera	19		Chardard, 1963
		40, 41	Ar-rushdi, 1971
Pol. ruwenzoriensis		40	Jones, 1966
Pol. stauroglossa		40	Jones, 1966
Pol. stricta		40	Jones, 1966
Pol. stuhlmanii		40	Jones, 1966
Pol. subulata		40	Jones, 1966
Pol. supfiana		40	Ar-rushdi, 1971
Pol. tayloriana		40	Jones, 1966
Pol. tessellata		40	Jones, 1966
		40	Ar-rushdi, 1971
Pol. transvaalensis		40	Jones, 1966

Plant name	Chromosome number n	Chromosome number 2n	Reference	Plant name	Chromosome number n	Chromosome number 2n	Reference
Pol. species		40	Ar-rushdi, 1971	*Rntda.* unnamed (*V.* Tan Chay Yan × *Ren. storiei*)	irregular	76	Pancho, 1965b
Pomatocalpa spicatum		38	Kamemoto et al., 1964	*Renanthera coccinea*	57 + 1	38, 114, 115	Kamemoto & Shindo, 1962
Ponerorchis rotundifolia		42	Löve & Simon, 1968			38	Kamemoto et al., 1964
Porpax meriax	12		Mehra & Sehgal, 1974			38	Sharma & Chatterji, 1966
Potinara Dark Eyes 'Konan'		80	Tanaka, 1964a			ca. 114	Jones, 1967
Pot. Dark Eyes 'Perfecta'		84	Tanaka, 1964a	*Ren. elongata*	19	38	Kamemoto & Shindo, 1962
Pot. Dicksie Shortess 'Ann'		91 ± 1	Tanaka, 1966	*Ren. histrionica*	19	38	Kamemoto & Shindo, 1962
Pot. Vibrant Beauty 'Mitsuko'		78	Tanaka, 1966	*Ren. imschootiana*	19		Chardard, 1963
Pot. unnamed (*Pot.* Eleanor Dixon × *Pot.* Red Friar 'Saku')		80	Tanaka, 1966			38	Sharma & Chatterji, 1966
Pristiglottis tashiroi		26	Tanaka, 1965b	*Ren. matutina*	19	38	Kamemoto & Shindo, 1962
		26	Tanaka, 1971	*Ren. monachica*		38	Woodard (from Duncan, 1959)
Promenaea citrina		46	Tanaka, 1964a		19	38	Kamemoto & Shindo, 1962
Pseudorchis albida		42	Löve & Löve, 1969			38	Shindo & Kamemoto, 1963a
Rangaeris brachyceras		50	Jones, 1967	*Ren. storiei*	19	38	Kamemoto & Shindo, 1962
R. musicola		ca. 100	Jones, 1967			38	Kamemoto & Tara, 1969
R. rhipsalisocia	54	ca. 108	Ar-rushdi, 1971			38	Tara & Kamemoto, 1970
Renaglottis unnamed (*Renanthera storiei* × *Trichoglottis fasciata*)		38	Kamemoto & Tara, 1969	*Ren.* unnamed (*Ren. coccinea* × *Ren. monachica*)	38	76	Kamemoto & Shindo, 1962
Renades unnamed (*Aerides lawrenceae* × *Renanthera storiei*)	variable	38	Shindo & Kamemoto, 1963c	*Ren.* unnamed (*Ren. monachica* × *Ren. imschootiana*)	mostly unreduced (38)	38	Kamemoto & Shindo, 1962
Renanopsis Lena Rowold	variable	38	Kamemoto & Shindo, 1962	*Ren.* unnamed (*Ren. storiei* × *Ren. imschootiana*)	19	38	Kamemoto & Shindo, 1962
Rnps. Lena Rowold 'No. 1'		57	Kamemoto et al., 1967	*Ren.* unnamed (*Ren. storiei* × *Ren. monachica*)	18, 19, 20	38	Kamemoto & Shindo, 1962
Rnps. Lena Rowold 'No. 2'		57	Kamemoto et al., 1967	*Renanthopsis* Jan Goo	variable, 10–28, 38–76	38	Tanaka & Kamemoto, 1961
Renanstylis unnamed (*Ren. storiei* × *Rhy. gigantea*)	variable	38	Kamemoto & Shindo, 1962	*Rnthps.* Ulaula 'No. 30'		58 ± 1	Kamemoto et al., 1967
Renantanda Donald MacIntyre	variable	38	Tanaka & Kamemoto, 1961	*Rhynchostylis coelestis*		38	Kamemoto et al., 1964
Rntda. Mona Lisa	variable	38	Tanaka & Kamemoto, 1961			38	Tara & Kamemoto, 1970
Rntda. unnamed (*Ren. storiei* × *V. coerulea*)	variable (14–24)	38	Kamemoto & Shindo, 1962	*Rhy. gigantea*		38	Kamemoto et al., 1964
Rntda. unnamed (*Ren. storiei* × *V. merrillii*)	variable (1–38)	38	Kamemoto & Shindo, 1962	*Rhy. gigantea* var. *illustre*		38	Kamemoto et al., 1964
Rntda. unnamed (*Ren. storiei* × *V. spathulata*)	variable	76	Storey et al., 1963	*Rhy. retusa*		38	Kamemoto et al., 1964
Rntda. unnamed (*Ren. storiei* × *V. teres*)	variable (1–25)	38	Kamemoto & Shindo, 1962		19	38	Sharma & Chatterji, 1966
					19		Arora, 1968

Plant name	Chromosome number n	Chromosome number 2n	Reference
		38	Tara & Kamemoto, 1970
		38	Kulkarni & Jorapur, 1979
Robiquetia paniculata		38	Kamemoto et al., 1964
		38	Tara & Kamemoto, 1970
R. spathulata		38	Kamemoto et al., 1964
Rodrettia Hawaii		42	Sinoto, 1962
Rodricidium Joy		42	Sinoto, 1962
Rdcm. Tahiti		49	Sinoto, 1962
Rdcm.		49	Sinoto, 1962
Rdcm. unnamed (Oncidium gardneri × Rodriguezia secunda)		42	Sinoto, 1962
Rdcm. unnamed (Onc. harrisonianum × Rdza. venusta)		40, 42, 58, 80, 84	Sinoto, 1962
Rdcm. unnamed (Onc. pulchellum × Rdza. venusta)		42	Sinoto, 1962
Rodriguezia batemani		42	Sinoto, 1962
Rdza. decora		42	Sinoto, 1962
Rdza. fragrans		42	Sinoto, 1962
Rdza. secunda		42	Sinoto, 1962
		42	Charanasri & Kamemoto, 1975
Rdza. strobelii		42	Sinoto, 1962
Rdza. teuscheri		28, 29	Sinoto, 1962
Rdza. venusta		42	Sinoto, 1962
		42	Charanasri et al., 1973
Rdza. unnamed (Rdza. decora × Rdza. candida)		42	Sinoto, 1962
Rodritonia Freckles		49	Sinoto, 1962
Saccolabium albo-lineatum	19–20		Chardard, 1963
Saccm. calceolare	19–20		Chardard, 1963
	38		Mehra & Vij, 1970
Saccm. dasypogon		38	Sharma & Chatterji, 1966
Saccm. distichum	19		Mehra & Vij, 1970
Saccm. eberhardtii	19–20		Chardard, 1963
Saccm. kotoense		30	Hsu, 1972
Saccm. longifolium	19		Mehra & Vij, 1970
Saccm. obtussifolium	19		Mehra & Vij, 1970
Saccm. papillosum	38		Mehra & Vij, 1970
Saccm. pseudodistichum	19		Mehra & Vij, 1970
Saccm. rubescens	19–20		Chardard, 1963
Saccm. tenerum		ca. 38	Jones, 1967
Saccm. triflorum	19–20		Chardard, 1963
Sarcanthus appendiculatus		38	Kamemoto et al., 1964
		38	Chatterji, 1968
S. carinatus		38	Kamemoto et al., 1964
		38	Tara & Kamemoto, 1970
S. dealbatus	19		Chardard, 1963
S. erinaceous		38	Tara & Kamemoto, 1970
S. filiformis	19		Mehra & Vij, 1970
S. flagelliformis		38	Kamemoto et al., 1964
		38	Tara & Kamemoto, 1970
S. kunstleri		38	Kamemoto et al., 1964
S. micranthus		36	Hsu, 1972
S. pallidus		38	Chatterji, 1970
S. rostratus		36	Hoffmann, 1930
	18		Sugiura, 1939
S. scolopendrifolius		38	Mutsuura & Nakahira, 1959
S. strongyloides		38	Jones, 1967
S. subulatus		38	Kamemoto et al., 1964
		38	Tara & Kamemoto, 1970
		38	Jones, 1967
S. termissus		38	Kamemoto et al., 1964
		38	Tara & Kamemoto, 1970
S. williamsonii	19		Mehra & Vij, 1974
S. species		38	Sharma & Chatterji, 1966
Sarcochilus japonicus		38	Mutsuura & Nakahira, 1959
		36	Shoji, 1963
		38	Tanaka, 1965b
Sarco. longicalcarus		38	Pancho, 1965a
		38	Pancho, 1965b
Sarco. luniferus	19		Mehra & Vij, 1970
Sarco. palawanensis		38	Pancho, 1965a
		38	Pancho, 1965b
Sarco. purpureus		38	Mehra & Sehgal, 1974
Sarcorhynchus bilobatus		50	Jones, 1967
Satyrium nepalense		41	Swamy, 1944
		41, 82	Mehra & Vij, 1972b
	82		Vij & Gupta, 1975
Sauroglossum nitidum		44	Blumenschein, 1960
Schomburgkia crispa		40	Blumenschein, 1960
Serapias longipetala	12		Baranow, 1915
S. vomeracea		36	Heusser, 1938
		36	Lovka et al., 1972
		36	Susnik & Lovka, 1973

Plant name	Chromosome number		Reference
	n	2n	
Sigmatostalix radicans		60	Sinoto, 1962
		60	Sinoto, 1969b
Sophrolaeliocattleya Anzac 'Orchidhurst'		ca. 80	Kamemoto, 1959b
Slc. Brandywine 'Kyoko'		77	Tanaka, 1966
Slc. Brandywine '7'		82	Tanaka, 1964a
Slc. Canzac 'Burma Ruby'		80	Tanaka, 1964a
Slc. Canzac 'Sunset'		80 ± 1	Tanaka, 1966
Slc. Carna		44	Tanaka, 1964a
Slc. Dizac 'Dark'		80	Tanaka, 1964a
Slc. Dizac 'Kako'		84	Tanaka, 1966
Slc. Dizac 'Sumiyoshi'		82	Tanaka, 1966
Slc. East Mona 'Aiko Yamamoto'		ca. 60	Kamemoto, 1959b
Slc. East Mona 'Golden Queen'		ca. 60	Kamemoto, 1959b
Slc. East Mona 'Mikage'		ca. 60	Kamemoto, 1959b
Slc. East Mona 'Sumiyoshi'		60 ± 1f.	Tanaka, 1964a
Slc. Golden Star '0-1'		81 ± 1	Tanaka, 1966
Slc. Lancingmona 'Golden Princess'		60 ± 1	Tanaka, 1964a
Slc. Lancingmona 'Mikage'		ca. 60	Kamemoto, 1959b
Slc. Lindores		83 ± 1	Kamemoto *et al.,* 1967
Slc. Lindores 'Peerless'		80 ± 1	Kamemoto *et al.,* 1967
Slc. Lindores 'Queen of Heart'		80	Tanaka, 1964a
Slc. Meulange		ca. 100	Kamemoto, 1959b
Slc. Monartte 'Mikage'		60	Tanaka, 1964a
Slc. Ormona 'Coral Crest'		80 ± 1	Tanaka, 1964a
Slc. Ormona 'Kako'		80	Tanaka, 1966
Slc. Ormona 'Pigeon Blood'		80	Tanaka, 1964a
Slc. Phena 'Saturn'		60	Tanaka, 1966
Slc. Prince Hirohito		61 ± 1	Tanaka, 1966
Slc. Radians 'Bonnycrest'		triploid	de Tomasi, 1954
Slc. Rainbow Hill 'Bantan'		82	Tanaka, 1966
Slc. Red Austin		80 ± 1	Tanaka, 1964a
Slc. Tropic Dawn 'Elsa'		80	Tanaka, 1966
Slc. Tropic Dawn 'SD#2'		86	Tanaka, 1966
Slc. Valemona 'Redwing'		85	Tanaka, 1964a
Sophronitis cernua		40	Blumenschein, 1960
Spathoglottis plicata		40	Tanaka, 1965b
		18	Hsu, 1972
Spa. pubescencs	19		Mehra & Sehgal, 1974

Plant name	Chromosome number		Reference
	n	2n	
Spiranthes australis (= *S. sinensis*)	12		Baranow, 1915
	12		Takamine, 1916
	15, 16		Mehra & Vij, 1970
S. autumnalis		35	Tischler, 1934
	20, 28, 30, 30 + 2B		Vij & Vohra, 1974a
S. cernua (= *Gyrostachys cernua*)		30	Pace, 1914
		30	Tanaka, 1965b
		30	Tanaka, 1968
S. gracilis (= *Gyrostachys gracilis*)	15	30	Pace, 1914
	15		Cave, 1966
S. lacera		30	Kapoor, 1972
S. lancea		30	Mehra & Kashyap, 1979
S. romanzoffiana		60	Heslop-Harrison (in Löve & Löve, 1961)
	15		Taylor & Mulligan, 1968
S. sinensis (= *S. australis*)		30	Miduno, 1939
	15	30	Hagerup, 1944a
	12		
		24	Ohno *et al.,* 1957
		30	Mutsuura & Nakahira, 1958
		30	Mutsuura, 1959
		30	Mutsuura & Nakahira, 1959
		26, 30	Sinoto & Shoji, 1962
		30	Tanaka, 1962b
		30	Tanaka, 1965b
		30	Tanaka, 1965c
		30	Tanaka, 1969a
	15	30	Tanaka, 1969b
	15	30	Tanaka, 1969c
		30	Tanaka, 1971
	15, 16	30	Mehra & Vij, 1972a
	15, 30		Vij & Vohra, 1974a
		30	Tanaka & Taniguchi, 1975
		30	Taniguchi *et al.,* 1975
	30		Vij & Gupta, 1975
		30	Terasaka *et al.,* 1979
S. spiralis	15	30	Hagerup, 1944a
Stanhopea bucephalus		40	Daker & Jones, 1970
Stan. candida		40	Daker & Jones, 1970
Stan. costaricensis		40	Daker & Jones, 1970
Stan. devoniensis		40	Daker & Jones, 1970
Stan. ecornuta		ca. 40	Daker & Jones, 1970
Stan. gibbosa		40	Daker & Jones, 1970
Stan. grandiflora		40	Daker & Jones, 1970
Stan. grandiflora 'Alba'		42	Daker & Jones, 1970
Stan. graveolens		40	Daker & Jones, 1970
Stan. inodora		40	Daker & Jones, 1970
Stan. inodora 'Amona'		42	Daker & Jones, 1970

Plant name	Chromosome number n	2n	Reference	Plant name	Chromosome number n	2n	Reference
Stan. insignis	20		Hoffmann, 1929			(mode 2B)	Tanaka & Matsuda, 1972
	20		Hoffmann, 1930			36 + (1 − 4B)	Matsuda & Tanaka, 1977
Stan. oculata	20		Afzelius, 1943			36 + 8B	Matsuda & Tanaka, 1977
		40	Chardard, 1963	*T. minor*	20	40 (36)	Sharma & Chatterji, 1966
		ca. 40, 42	Daker & Jones, 1970	*T. penangiana*		ca. 72	Larsen, 1966
		40	Arp, 1973	*T. viridofusca*		40	Larsen, 1966
Stan. peruviana		42	Daker & Jones, 1970	*Thelymitra longifolia*		26	Hair, 1942
Stan. ruckeri		40	Daker & Jones, 1970	*Thrixspermum acuminatissimum*		38	Kamemoto et al., 1964
Stan. saccata		ca. 40	Daker & Jones, 1970			38	Tara & Kamemoto, 1970
Stan. tigrina (= *Stan. hernandezii*)	20		Hoffmann, 1929	*T. arachnites*		38	Kamemoto et al., 1964
	20		Hoffmann, 1930	*T. centripeda*		38	Chardard, 1963
		42	Tanaka, 1962a	*Thunia alba*		42	Tanaka, 1964a
		40	Chardard, 1963		20		Mehra & Vij, 1970
		40	Daker & Jones, 1970			42	Tanaka, 1971
		80	Arp, 1973		20		Mehra & Kashyap, 1978
Stan. tigrina 'Superba'		40	Daker & Jones, 1970		ca. 40		Mehra & Sehgal, 1978
Stan. wardii		41, 42	Daker & Jones, 1970	*Thu. marshalliana*	20		Mehra & Vij, 1970
Staurochilus dawsonianus (= *Trichoglottis dawsonianus*)		38	Kamemoto et al., 1964	*Thu. venosa*	20		Malla et al., 1976
S. fasciatus (= *Trichoglottis fasciata*)		38	Kamemoto et al., 1964	*Traunsteinera globosa* (= *Orchis globosa*)	21	42	Heusser, 1938
S. luchuensis		38	Tanaka, 1965b			42	Diannelidis, 1948
		38	Nakasone & Moromizato, 1964			42	Diannelidis, 1955
Stauropsis undulatus	19		Mehra & Vij, 1970			42	Pogan & Wcislo (in Löve & Löve, 1961)
Stelis atropurpurea (= *S. ciliaris*)	16		Hoffmann, 1929	*Trias stocksii*		38	Kulkarni & Jorapur, 1979
	16		Hoffmann, 1930	*Trichocentrum albo-purpureum*		28	Dodson, 1957c
S. concaviflora		32	Favarger & Huynh, 1965			24	Sinoto, 1962
S. miersii		32	Hoffmann, 1929			24	Charanasri & Kamemoto, 1975
		32	Hoffmann, 1930	*Trctm. capistratum*		28	Charanasri & Kamemoto, 1975
S. pygmaea	16		Chardard, 1963	*Trctm. maculata*		24	Sinoto, 1962
Stenoglottis longifolia		36	Tanaka, 1964a	*Trctm. panamense*		28	Dodson, 1958
		36	Tanaka, 1965b			28	Sinoto, 1962
Taeniophyllum aphyllum		38?	Mutsuura & Nakahira, 1958	*Trctm. tigrinum*		24	Sinoto, 1962
		38?	Mutsuura, 1959	*Trichocidium* unnamed (*Trichocentrum tigrinum* × *Oncidium splendidum*)		30	Sinoto, 1962
		24	Mutsuura, 1963				
		38	Tanaka, 1965b	*Trichoglottis cirrhifera*		38	Tara & Kamemoto, 1970
		38	Tanaka, 1971	*Trgl. fasciata* (= *Staurochilus fasciatus*)		38	Kamemoto & Tara, 1969
T. crepidiforme	19		Mehra & Vij, 1970			38	Tara & Kamemoto, 1970
T. elmeri		40	Pancho, 1965a	*Trgl. philippinensis*		38	Shindo & Kamemoto, 1963a
		40	Pancho, 1965b	*Trgl. rosea*		38	Tara & Kamemoto, 1970
T. philippinensis		40	Pancho, 1965a	*Trichopilia marginata*		56	Charanasri & Kamemoto, 1975
		40	Pancho, 1965b	*Trpla. suavis*		56	Sinoto, 1962
Tainia laxiflora		36	Miduno, 1940b				
		36 + 1B, 36 + 2B, 36 + 3B, 36 + 4B	Tanaka, 1965b				
		36 + (1 − 4B)	Tanaka, 1971				
		36 + (0 − 9B)	Tanaka & Matsuda, 1972				

Plant name	Chromosome number n	2n	Reference
Trichovanda Ulaula	38, variable (19–76)	38	Tanaka & Kamemoto, 1961
Tridactyle anthomaniaca		ca. 100	Jones, 1967
T. tridactylites		ca. 100	Jones, 1967
T. species		ca. 50	Jones, 1967
Triphora trianthophora		44	Baldwin & Speese, 1957
Tropidia curculigoides		60	Larsen, 1966
T. nipponica		56	Tanaka & Kamemoto, 1972
Uncifera species		38	Tanaka, 1964a
Vanda Akala	irregular	38	Storey, 1952
V. Alice Fukunaga		38	Kamemoto et al., 1961
V. alpina		38	Kamemoto, 1959a
	19		Mehra & Vij, 1970
V. amesiana		38	Storey, 1952
		38	Woodard, 1952
		38	Kamemoto, 1959a
		38	Sharma & Chatterji, 1966
V. amoena		38	Kamemoto et al., 1961
V. Amy	irregular	38	Storey, 1952
V. Andes Segovia	irregular	57	Storey, 1952
V. Ann Kirsch	irregular	38	Storey, 1952
V. Betsy Sumner		38 ± 1	Kamemoto et al., 1961
V. Betty Goto		57	Kamemoto et al., 1961
V. Bill Sutton	38	76	Tanaka & Kamemoto, 1960
		38, 76	Kamemoto et al., 1961
		57	Kamemoto et al., 1967
V. Brenden D. Loui		57	Kamemoto et al., 1961
V. Burgeffii		38	Sagawa & Niimoto, 1961
V. Chimey Walker		76 ± 1	Kamemoto et al., 1961
V. Clara Shipman Fisher	19	38	Storey, 1952
		38	Kamemoto et al., 1961
V. Clara Shipman Fisher 'No. 1'		57	Kamemoto et al., 1961
V. Clara Shipman Fisher 'No. 2'		57 ± 1	Kamemoto et al., 1961
V. Clara Shipman Fisher 'No. 4'		57 ± 1	Kamemoto et al., 1961
V. Clara Shipman Fisher 'No. 7'		57 ± 1	Kamemoto et al., 1961
V. Clara Shipman Fisher 'Karen'		38 ± 2	Kamemoto et al., 1961
V. Cobber Kain	irregular	57	Storey, 1952
		76	Kamemoto et al., 1967
V. coerulea		38	Storey, 1952
		38	Woodard, 1952
		38	Kamemoto et al., 1961
		38	Kamemoto et al., 1964

Plant name	Chromosome number n	2n	Reference
		38 (36)	Sharma & Chatterji, 1966
V. coerulescens		38	Kamemoto et al., 1964
		38 (36)	Sharma & Chatterji, 1966
		ca. 38	Jones, 1967
V. Colorful		57, 95	Kamemoto et al., 1961
V. Colorsan		62, 63, 65, 66, 68	Kamemoto & Tanaka, 1960
	variable (19–76)	57	Tanaka & Kamemoto, 1960
V. concolor		76	Storey, 1952
V. Cooperi		38, 57	Storey, 1952
V. cristata	19	38	Sharma & Chatterji, 1966
	19		Arora, 1971
		38	Mehra & Kashyap, 1976
V. dearei		38	Storey, 1952
		38	Kamemoto et al., 1961
V. denisoniana (brown)		38, 76	Kamemoto et al., 1964
V. denisoniana (green to yellow)		38	Kamemoto et al., 1964
V. densiflora		36 (42)	Sharma & Chatterji, 1966
		38	Sharma & Chatterji, 1966
V. Dorothy Ficklin	25–57	57	Tanaka & Kamemoto, 1960
V. Eisenhower		38	Kamemoto et al., 1961
V. Elizabeth McNeil		38	Kamemoto et al., 1961
V. Ellen Noa		38, 76 ± 1	Kamemoto et al., 1961
V. Ellen Noa 'Saito'		38 ± 1	Kamemoto et al., 1961
V. Emma van Deventer	irregular	38	Kamemoto, 1956
	38	76	Kamemoto, 1956
	11–76	38	Tanaka & Kamemoto, 1960
	38	76	Tanaka & Kamemoto, 1960
		38, 76	Kamemoto & Tanaka, 1961
		76	Kamemoto et al., 1961
V. Emma van Deventer 'Kondo'		76	Kamemoto et al., 1961
V. Emma van Deventer 'No. 310-1'		76	Kamemoto et al., 1961
V. Emma van Deventer 'No. 310-2'		76	Kamemoto et al., 1961
V. Faye		38	Kamemoto et al., 1961
V. Fennell		38	Sagawa & Niimoto, 1961
V. Flammerolle		38	Storey, 1952
V. Gam Ho		57	Kamemoto et al., 1961
V. Helen Paoa		76 ± 1	Kamemoto et al., 1961

Plant name	n	2n	Reference
		Chromosome number	
V. Herbert Beaumont		95	Kamemoto et al., 1961
V. Herziana		38	Storey, 1952
V. Hilo Blue		38	Kamemoto et al., 1967
V. Hilo Blue 'No. 1'		38	Kamemoto et al., 1967
V. Hilo Blue 'No. 2'		38	Kamemoto et al., 1967
V. hookeriana	19	38	Storey, 1952
V. Irma C. Bryan		57	Kamemoto et al., 1961
V. Janet Kanealii	71, 73, 75, 76		Kamemoto & Tanaka, 1960
		variable (71–76)	Kamemoto et al., 1961
V. Jennie Hashimoto		38	Kamemoto et al., 1961
V. Jill Walker	19	38	Storey, 1952
V. Josephine Van Brero		76	Kamemoto et al., 1961
V. Judith Choo	11–76	38	Tanaka & Kamemoto, 1960
V. kimballiana		38	Storey, 1952
V. Kinau		76 ± 2	Kamemoto et al., 1961
V. Kona		57	Kamemoto et al., 1961
V. lamellata		38	Shindo & Kamemoto, 1963a
V. lamellata var. boxallii	19	38	Storey, 1952
V. laotica		38	Kamemoto et al., 1964
V. Leilani		59, 60, 63–68, 76	Kamemoto & Tanaka, 1960
		variable (59–76)	Kamemoto et al., 1961
V. Lester McCoy		38	Storey, 1952
V. luzonica	19	38	Storey, 1952
		38	Woodard, 1952
		38–42	Chardard, 1963
V. Mabelmae Kamahele		38	Kamemoto et al., 1961
V. Mabelmae Kamahele 'Lois'		38	Kamemoto et al., 1967
V. Mabelmae Kamahele 'No. 1'		38	Kamemoto et al., 1961
V. Mabelmae Kamahele 'No. 2'		38	Kamemoto et al., 1961
V. Manila	19	38	Tanaka & Kamemoto, 1960
V. Manila 'No. 1'		95	Kamemoto et al., 1961
V. Manila 'No. 2'		95 ± 1	Kamemoto et al., 1961
V. Manila 'No. 3'		57 ± 1	Kamemoto et al., 1961
V. Manila 'No. 4'		57 ± 2	Kamemoto et al., 1961
V. Manila 'No. 6'		76 ± 2	Kamemoto et al., 1961
V. Manila 'No. 29'		57 ± 1	Kamemoto et al., 1961
V. Manila 'No. 46'		57 ± 1	Kamemoto et al., 1961
V. Manila 'No. 50'		38	Kamemoto et al., 1961
V. Manila 'No. 51'		76	Kamemoto et al., 1961
V. Manila 'No. 94'		76 ± 2	Kamemoto et al., 1961
V. Maurice Restrepo		76	Kamemoto et al., 1961
V. Mevr. L.		38	Storey, 1953
V. Mevr. L. Velthuis	11–76	38	Tanaka & Kamemoto, 1960
		76	Kamemoto et al., 1961
V. Miss Joaquim		38	Woodard, 1952
	19	38	Storey, 1952
	19	38	Tanaka & Kamemoto, 1960
	38	76	Tanaka & Kamemoto, 1960
		38	Nakasone & Kamemoto, 1961
		76 (colchiploid)	Nakasone & Kamemoto, 1961
V. Miss Joaquim 'Douglas'		76	Kamemoto et al., 1961
V. Miss Joaquim 'Juliet'		76	Kamemoto et al., 1961
V. Miss Joaquim 'Snowdrift'		76	Kamemoto et al., 1961
V. Miss van Deun	19	38	Storey, 1952
V. Moana		57	Kamemoto et al., 1961
V. Monacensis		76	Kamemoto et al., 1961
V. Nellie Morley		57, 95	Kamemoto, 1956
	variable	38	Kamemoto & Tanaka, 1960
	(19–38, 57)	57	Kamemoto & Tanaka, 1960
	38–57	95	Kamemoto & Tanaka, 1960
	19–76	57	Tanaka & Kamemoto, 1960
	38–57	95	Tanaka & Kamemoto, 1960
		57, 95	Kamemoto & Tanaka, 1961
		57, 95	Kamemoto et al., 1961
V. Nellie Morley 'No. 1'		57	Kamemoto et al., 1967
V. Nellie Morley 'No. 310'		76	Kamemoto et al., 1967
V. Noboru	irregular	38	Storey, 1952
V. Noel	19–76	57	Tanaka & Kamemoto, 1960
		57	Kamemoto et al., 1961
V. Nora Potter	irregular	95	Storey, 1952
		95	Kamemoto et al., 1961
V. Ohuohu		38	Storey, 1952
		38, 38 ± 1	Kamemoto et al., 1961
V. Ohuohu '010-7'		38	Kamemoto et al., 1961
V. Onomea		57	Kamemoto et al., 1967
V. Onomea 'Hilo'		38	Kamemoto et al., 1961
V. Onomea 'Ogawa'		38 ± 1	Kamemoto et al., 1961

Plant name	Chromosome number n	Chromosome number 2n	Reference
V. Oscar Kirsch		57	Kamemoto et al., 1961
		57	Kamemoto et al., 1967
V. parishii (= Vandopsis parishii)		38	Storey, 1952
		38	Chardard, 1963
		38	Kamemoto et al., 1964
	19		Mehra & Vij, 1970
V. parviflora		ca. 40	Jones, 1967
	19		Mehra & Kashyap, 1976
V. Piihonua		76 ± 1	Kamemoto et al., 1961
V. Poepoe 'No. 3'		76	Kamemoto et al., 1961
V. Poepoe 'No. 9'		76	Kamemoto et al., 1961
V. Pojo	21–57	57	Tanaka & Kamemoto, 1960
V. Prince Kan		57	Kamemoto et al., 1961
V. Princess Elizabeth	11–76	38	Tanaka & Kamemoto, 1960
V. Quinn		96	Kamemoto et al., 1967
V. Roberta Chun		57, 95	Kamemoto et al., 1961
V. roeblingiana		38	Storey, 1952
V. Rose Marie		76	Kamemoto et al., 1961
V. Rothschildiana	19	38	Storey, 1952
	38	76	Tanaka & Kamemoto, 1960
		76, 76 ± 1	Kamemoto et al., 1961
		75, 76	Kamemoto et al., 1967
V. Rothschildiana 'A'		38	Kamemoto et al., 1967
V. Rothschildiana 'No. 300-1'		76 ± 2	Kamemoto et al., 1961
V. roxburghii	19	38 (42)	Sharma & Chatterji, 1966
		38	Sarkar et al., 1977
V. sanderiana	19	38	Storey, 1952
		38	Kamemoto et al., 1961
V. sanderiana 'No. 1'		38	Kamemoto et al., 1961
V. sanderiana 'No. 2'		38	Kamemoto et al., 1961
V. sanderiana 'No. 3'		38	Kamemoto et al., 1961
V. sanderiana 'O'		38	Kamemoto et al., 1961
V. spathulata	38	76	Storey, 1952
		114	Kamemoto et al., 1961
		114, 115	Storey et al., 1963
V. stangeana	19		Mehra & Vij, 1970
V. suavis		38–39	Chardard, 1963
V. Sunset	irregular	57	Storey, 1952
		76	Kamemoto et al., 1961
V. Tan Chay Yan		57	Kamemoto et al., 1961
		57	Kamemoto et al., 1967
V. Tan Lok Tek 'No. 610-1'		38	Kamemoto et al., 1961
V. Tan Lok Tek 'No. 610-2'		38	Kamemoto et al., 1961
V. Tatzeri		38	Storey, 1952
		76 ± 1	Kamemoto et al., 1961
V. teres	19	38	Storey, 1952
		38	Shindo & Kamemoto, 1963a
		38	Kamemoto et al., 1964
	19	38 (36)	Sharma & Chatterji, 1966
V. teres 'Alba'		38	Kamemoto et al., 1961
V. teres 'Alba-candida'		38	Kamemoto et al., 1961
V. tessellata		38	Kulkarni & Jorapur, 1979
V. testacea	19		Arora, 1971
		38	Kulkarni & Jorapur, 1979
V. Thelma Beaumont		57	Storey, 1952
V. Towers		57	Kamemoto et al., 1967
V. tricolor		ca. 16	Hoffmann, 1929
		ca. 18, ca. 20	Hoffmann, 1930
		28	Eftimiu-Heim, 1941
		38	Woodard, 1952
	19	38	Storey, 1952
V. tricolor var. suavis	ca. 16		Hoffmann, 1929
	ca. 18		Hoffmann, 1930
	19	38	Storey, 1952
		38	Chardard, 1963
V. tricuspidata		76	Storey, 1952
		76	Kamemoto et al., 1967
V. Trikimbal		38	Storey, 1952
V. Trisher		38	Kamemoto et al., 1967
V. Waikiki		76	Kamemoto et al., 1967
V. Waimea 'No. 1'		57 ± 1	Kamemoto et al., 1961
V. Waimea 'No. 2'		57 ± 1	Kamemoto et al., 1961
V. Waimea 'No. 3'		57	Kamemoto et al., 1961
V. Waipuna		38	Kamemoto et al., 1961
V. Walter Oumae		57, 95	Kamemoto et al., 1961
V. Yuet Yeng Lim		57	Kamemoto et al., 1961
V. species		38, (37, 77)	Sharma & Chatterji, 1966
V. unnamed (V. Mary Foster × V. Clara Shipman Fisher)		57	Kamemoto et al., 1961
V. unnamed (V. Nellie Morley × V. coerulea)		57	Kamemoto & Tanaka, 1960
V. unnamed (V. Nellie Morley × V. Rothschildiana)		38, 39, 52, 70, 76, 95	Kamemoto & Tanaka, 1960

Plant name	Chromosome number		Reference	Plant name	Chromosome number		Reference
	n	2n			n	2n	
V. unnamed (V. Roberta Chun × V. sanderiana)		63, 66	Kamemoto & Tanaka, 1960		16	28–32 32	Hurel-Py, 1938 Eftimiu-Heim, 1950
V. unnamed (V. spathula-ta × V. Miss Joaquim)	variable	76	Storey et al., 1963		16, 14	32	Martin, 1963 Ravindran, 1979
V. unnamed (V. spathu-lata × V. sanderiana)	variable	76	Storey et al., 1963	V. pompona V. siamensis V. thaitii	16	32 32 32 32	Eftimiu-Heim, 1950 Martin, 1963 Larsen, 1966 Eftimiu-Heim, 1950
Vandachnis Premier	16–22, 38	38	Tanaka & Kamemoto, 1961	Vermeulenia papilionacea		32	Löve & Löve, 1972
Vandaenopsis unnamed (Vanda tri-color var. purpurea × Phalaenop-sis denevei)	13–25, 38	38	Tanaka & Kamemoto, 1961	Vexillabium fissum V. nakaianum V. yakushi-mense		32 40 26 26	Löve & Kjell-quist, 1973 Tanaka, 1965b Tanaka, 1965b Tanaka, 1965b
Vandofinetia Premier	variable (19 ± 4)	38	Shindo & Kamemoto, 1962	Yoania amagi-ensis Y. japonica	12 12	24	Aoyama et al., 1978 Aoyama et al., 1978
Vandopsis gigantea		38	Kamemoto et al., 1964	Zeuxine affinis	10		Mehra & Seh-gal, 1974
		38	Jones, 1967	Z. strateuma-tica		42	Tanaka, 1965b
Vdps. lissochil-oides		38	Kamemoto et al., 1964		10, 11, 20, 50	50	Mehra & Vij, 1970
Vdps. parishii (= Vanda parishii)		38 38 38	Woodard, 1952 Storey, 1952 Chardard, 1963		10 10	20–100	Mehra & Vij, 1972a Vij & Vohra, 1974b
		38	Kamemoto et al., 1964	Z. sulcata (= Zeuxine strateuma-tica)	22 22	44 44	Seshagiriah, 1934 Seshagiriah, 1941
	19		Mehra & Vij, 1970			44–48	Swamy, 1944
Vanilla aromatica		32	Eftimiu-Heim, 1950		10		Mehra & Bawa, 1970
V. barbellata		32	Martin, 1963	Zygopetalum B. G. White		47	Tanaka, 1964a
V. dilloniana		32	Martin, 1963	Z. crinitum		96	Tanaka, 1964a
V. fragrans		30–32	Chardard, 1963	Z. discolor (= Warczewicz-ella discolor)		ca. 48	Chardard, 1963
V. hartii		32	Eftimiu-Heim, 1950	Z. mackayi	ca. 24		Sussenguth, 1923
V. imperialis	16		Eftimiu-Heim, 1950			48(?)	Hoffmann, 1930
V. moonii		32	Eftimiu-Heim, 1950			96	Tanaka, 1964a
V. papeno		32	Eftimiu-Heim, 1950	Z. maxillare		48	Blumenschein, 1960
V. plaeantha		32	Martin, 1963	Z. odoratissi-mum		48–50	Chardard, 1963
V. planifolia		32	Hoffmann, 1929				
		32	Hoffmann, 1930				

Literature Cited

Adair, V. L., and Y. Sagawa, 1969. Cytological and morphological studies of *Caularthron bicornutum*. Caryologia 22:369–373.

Afzelius, K. 1916. Zur Embryosackentwicklung der Orchideen. Sv. Bot. Tidskr. 10:183–227.

——. 1922. Embryosackentwicklung und Chromosomenzahl bei einigen *Platanthera*-Arten. Sv. Bot. Tidskr. 16:371–382.

——. 1928. Die Embryobildung bei *Nigritella nigra*. Sv. Bot. Tidskr. 22:82–91.

——. 1932. Zur Kenntnis der Fortpflanzungsverhältnisse und Chromosomenzahlen bei *Nigritella nigra*. Sv. Bot. Tidskr. 26:365–369.

——. 1943. Zytologische Beobachtungen an einigen Orchidaceen. Sv. Bot. Tidskr. 37:266–276.

——. 1954. Embryo-sac development in *Epigogium aphyllum*. Sv. Bot. Tidskr. 48:513–520.

——. 1958. En egendomlig form av *Orchis maculata* L. sens. lat. Sv. Bot. Tidskr. 52:18–22.

——. 1966. Cleistogamy in *Pleurothallus procumbens* Lindl. Act. Hort. Berg. 20:313–317.

Aoyama, M., R. Tanaka, and K. Karasawa. 1978. Karyomorphological studies on two species *Yoania*. Japan Orchid Soc. Bull. 24:3–5.

Arends, J. C. 1970. Cytological observations on genome homology in eight interspecific hybrids of *Phalaenopsis*. Genetica 41:88–100.

Arora, C. M. 1968. *In* IOPB chromosome number reports, 16. Taxon 17:199–204.

——. 1971. *In* IOPB chromosome number reports, 34. Taxon 20:785–797.

Arp, G. K. 1973. *In* IOPB chromosome number reports, 40. Taxon 22:285–291.

Ar-rushdi, A. H. 1971. Chromosomes of some West African orchids. Cytologia 36:487–492.

Avanzi, S., P. G. Cionini, and F. D'amato. 1970. Cytochemical and autoradiographic analyses on the embryo suspensor cells of *Phaseolus coccineus*. Caryologia 23:605–638.

Balaeva, V. A., and V. N. Siplivinski. 1975. Chromosome numbers and taxonomy of some species of Baikal flora. Botanitsheskii Djurnal 60:864–872.

——. 1976. Chromosome numbers and taxonomy of some species of Baikal flora, II. Botanitsheskii Djurnal 61:873–880.

Baldwin, J. T., and B. M. Speese. 1957. Chromosomes of *Pogonia* and of its allies in the range of Gray's manual. Am. J. Bot. 44:651–653.

Banerji, M., and M. Chaudhuri. 1972. Further studies on chromosomes of some Orchidaceae and Iridaceae from the temperate Himalayas. Proc. Indian Sci. Cong. Assoc. 59:347.

Baranow, P. 1915. Recherches sur le développement du sac embryonnaire chez les *Spiranthes australis* Lindl. et *Serapias pseudocordigera* Mor. Bull. Soc. Imp. Nat. Moscow 29:74–92.

——. 1925. Über die Reduktion des weiblichen Gametophyten in der Familie Orchidaceae. Bull. Univ. Centralasiens 10:181–195.

Barber, H. N. 1942. The pollen grain division in the Orchidaceae. J. Genet. 43:97–103.

Barganur, B. M. 1972. Cyto-embryological studies in the orchid *Acampe wightiana* Lindl. Proc. Indian Sci. Cong. Assoc. 59:352.

Belling, J. 1924. Detachment (elimination) of chromosomes in *Cypripedium acaule*. Bot. Gaz. 78:458–460.

——. 1926a. Iron-acetocarmine method of staining chromosomes. Biol. Bull. 50:160–162.

——. 1926b. Structure of chromosomes. Brit. J. Exp. Biol. 3:145–147.

Bent, F. C. 1969. Chromosome studies in *Habenaria*. Rhodora 71:541–543.

Blumenschein, A. 1960. Número de chromossomas de algumas espécies de orquideas. Publ. Cien. Univ. São Paulo, Inst. Genet. 1:45–50.

——. 1961. Uma nova espécie do gênero *Cattleya* Lindle. Publ. Cien. Univ. São Paulo, Inst. Genet. 2:23–33.

Borgen, L. 1969. Chromosome numbers of vascular plants from the Canary Islands, with special reference to the occurrence of polyploidy. Nytt Magasin Botanik 16:18–121.

Bostick, P. E. 1965. Documented chromosome numbers of plants. Index to Plant Chromosome Numbers for 1965. Sida 2:165–168.

Brown, W. H. 1909. The embryo sac of *Habenaria*. Bot. Gaz. 48:241–258.

Carlson, M. C. 1945. Megasporogenesis and development of the embryo sac of *Cypripedium parviflorum*. Bot. Gaz. 107:107–113.

Cave, M. S. 1966. Documented chromosome numbers of Plants. Madroño 18:245–246.

Charanasri, U., and H. Kamemoto. 1975. Additional chromosome numbers in *Oncidium* and allied genera. Am. Orchid Soc. Bull. 44:686–691.

——. 1978. Interspecific hybridization involving Miltoniastrum and Cebolletae sections in the genus *Oncidium*. Am. Orchid Soc. Bull. 47:701–705.

Charanasri, U., H. Kamemoto, and M. Takeshita. 1973. Chromosome numbers in the genus *Oncidium* and some allied genera. Am. Orchid Soc. Bull. 42:518–524.

Chardard, R. 1963. Contribution à l'étude cyto-taxinomique des orchidées. Rev. Cyt. et Biol. Vég. 26:1–58.

Chatterji, A. K. 1965. Chromosomes of *Eulophia*. Chromosome Inf. Serv. 6:8–9.

——. 1968. Chromosome numbers and karyotypes of some orchids. Am. Orchid Soc. Bull. 37:202–205.

Chennaveeraiah, M. S., and S. M. Jorapur. 1966. Chromosome number and morphology in five species of *Nervilia* Gaud. Nucleus 9:39–44.

Chiarugi, A. 1929. Diploidismo con anfimissa e tetraploidismo con apomissa in una medesina specie:*Nigritella nigra*, Rehb. Boll. Soc. Ital. Biol. Sper. 4:659–661.

Chodat, R. 1924. La caryocinèse et la réduction chromatique observées sur le vivant. Comp. Rend. Soc. Phys. et Hist. Nat. Genève (Series 2) 41:96–99.

Corrias, B., and R. Villa. 1973. Ad floram italicam notulae taxonomicae et geobotanicae, X. *Orchis purpurea* Huds. nuovo reperto per la flora sarda. Webbia 28:49–51.

Coutinho, L. de A. 1957. Noda sobre a constitução chromosomica do *Limodorum trabutianum* Batt. e do *Limodorum abortivum* (L.) Sw. Agron. Lusitana 19:219–231.

Dahlgren, R., Th. Karlsson, and P. Lassen. 1971. Studies on the flora of the Balearic Islands, I. Chromosome numbers in Balearic angiosperms. Bot. Notiser 124:249–269.

Daker, M. G. 1970. The chromosomes of orchids, IV. Bulbophyllinae Schltr. Kew Bull. 24:179–184.

Daker, M. G., and K. Jones. 1970. The chromosomes of orchids, V. Stanhopeinae Benth. (Gongorinae Auct.). Kew Bull. 24:457–459.

Darlington, C. D. 1937. Recent advances in cytology, 2d ed. Churchill, London.

Déliot, M. 1955. Étude structurale du chromosome somatique chez le *Loroglossum hircinum* (L.) Richard. Botaniste 39:315–337.

Diannelidis, T. 1948. A study of chromosomes of the Orchidaceae. Proktika Acad. Athenon 23:352–359.

——. 1955. Chromosomenzahlen einiger Orchidaceen. Ann. Fac. Sci. Univ. Thessaloniki 7:99–105.

Dillon, G. W. 1969. Handbook on orchid nomenclature and registration. Intern. Orchid Comm. Classif. Nomencl. and Registr., Cambridge, Mass.

Dodson, C. H. 1957a. Studies in *Oncidium*, I. *Oncidium pusillum* and its allies. Am. Orchid Soc. Bull. 26:170–172.

——. 1957b. Studies in *Oncidium*, II. *Oncidium papilio* and its allies. Am. Orchid Soc. Bull. 26:240–244.

——. 1957c. Studies in *Oncidium*, III. Chromosome numbers in *Oncidium* and allied genera. Am. Orchid. Soc. Bull. 26:323–330.

——. 1958. Cytogenetics in *Oncidium*. Proc. 2nd World Orchid Conf. (Honolulu). Harvard University Press, Cambridge, Mass., pp. 135–139.

Dorn, E. C., and H. Kamemoto. 1962. Chromosome transmission of *Dendrobium phalaenopsis* 'Lyons Light No. 1.' Am. Orchid Soc. Bull. 31:997–1006.

Dressler, R. L., and C. H. Dodson. 1960. Classification and phylogeny in the Orchidaceae. Annals of the Missouri Bot. Gardens, 47:25–68.

Duncan, R. E. 1945. Production of variable aneuploid numbers of chromosomes within the root tips of *Paphiopedilum wardii*. Am. J. Bot. 32:506–509.

——. 1947. The hybrid lady slipper. Orchid Digest 11:199–207.

——. 1959a. Orchids and cytology, pp. 189–260. *In* The orchids: A scientific survey, C. L. Withner (ed.). Ronald Press, New York.

——. 1959b. List of chromosome numbers in orchids, pp. 529–587. *In* The orchids: A scientific survey, C. L. Withner (ed.). Ronald Press, New York.

Duncan, R. E., and R. A. MacLeod. 1948a. Chromosomes of the Brachypetalums. Am. Orchid Soc. Bull. 17:170–174.

——. 1948b. Chromosomes of the *insigne* complex of lady-slippers. Am. Orchid. Soc. Bull. 17:424–429.

——. 1949a. The chromosomes of the continental species of *Paphiopedilum* with solid green leaves. Am. Orchid Soc. Bull. 18:84–89.

——. 1949b. The chromosomes of some of the Polyantha. Am. Orchid Soc. Bull. 18:159–163.

——. 1949c. The chromosomes of the species of Cochlopetalum Hallier. Am. Orchid Soc. Bull. 18:573–576.

——. 1950a. The chromosomes of Eremantha Tesselata. Am. Orchid Soc. Bull. 19:137–142.

——. 1950b. The chromosomes of *Paphiopedilum sublaeve*. Am. Orchid Soc. Bull. 19:489–492.

Eftimiu-Heim, P. 1941. Recherches sur les noyaux des Orchidées. Le Botaniste 31:65–111.

——. 1950. Le noyau dans le genre *Vanilla*. Encyclopédie Mycologique.

Engelskjoen, T., and G. Knaben. 1971. Chromosome numbers of Scandinavian arctic-alpine plant species, III. Acta Boreal., A. Scientia No. 28:1–30.

Favarger, C., and K. L. Huynh. 1965. *In* IOPB chromosome number reports, 4. Taxon 14:86–87.

Fernandes, A. 1950. Sobre a cariológia de algumas plantas da Serra do Gerês. Agron. Lusit 12:551–600.

Frahm-Leliveld, J. A. 1941. Some remarks on the formation of the pollinia of *Gymnadaenia conopea* (L.) R. Br. Natuurkundig Tijdschr. 101:242–244.

Francini, E. 1930. Primi dati di una revisione critica della sviluppo del gametofito gemmineo del genere *Cypripedium*. Nuovo Giornale Bot. Ital. 37:277–278.

——. 1931. Ricerche embriologiche e cariologiche sul genere *Cypripedium*. Nuovo Giornale Bot. Ital. 38:155–212.

——. 1932. Un reperto cariologico nella F_2 di *Paphiopedilum leeanum* × (*P. Spicerianum* × *P. insigne*). Nuovo Giornale Bot. Ital. 39:251–253.

——. 1934. Ibridazione interspecifica nel genera *Paphiopedilum*. Nuovo Giornale Bot. Ital. 41:189–237.

——. 1945. Ibridazione interspecifica nel genera *Paphiopedilum*. Nuovo Giornale Bot. Ital. 52:21–29.

Freytag, A. H. 1966. Use of a mitotic increment for orchid chromosome counting. Am. Orchid Soc. Bull. 35:111–114.

Friemann, W. 1910. Über die Entwicklung der generativen Zelle in Pollenkorn der monokotylen Pflanzen. Diss., U. of Bonn.

Fuchs, A., and H. Ziegenspeck. 1923. Aus der Monographie des *Orchis traunsteineri* Saut. IV. Chromosomen einiger Orchideen. Bot. Arch. 5:457–470.

——. 1924. Naturw. Verein f. Schwaben u. Neuburg 43, Ber.

Gadella, T. W. J., and K. Kliphuis. 1963. Chromosome numbers of flowering plants in the Netherlands. Acta Bot. Neerl. 12:195–230.

Garay, L. A. 1960. On the origin of the Orchidaceae. Bot. Mus. Leaflets, Harvard Univ. 19:57–96.

——. 1963. *Oliveriana* and its position in the Oncidieae. Am. Orchid Soc. Bull., 32:18–24.

Garabari, F. 1971. B chromosomes in *Listera ovata* (L.) R. Br. (Orchidaceae). Preliminary observations in Italian populations. Inf. Bot. Italiano 3:216–221.

Geitler, L. 1940. Die Polyploidie der Dünergewebe höherer Pflanzen. Ber. Deutsch. Bot. Ges. 58:131–142.

Groll, M. 1965. Fruchtansatz, Bestäubung und Merkmalsanalyse bei diploiden und polyploiden Sippen von *Dactylorchis* (*Orchis*) *maculata* und *Gymnadenia conopsea*. Oesterr. Bot. Zeits. 112:657–700.

Guignard, L. 1884. Structure et division du noyau cellulaire. Ann. Sci. Nat. Bot. (Series 6) 17:5–59.

——. 1886. Sur la pollinisation et ses effets chez des orchidées. Ann. Sci. Nat. Bot. (Series 7) 4:202–240.

——. 1891. Nouvelles études sur la fécondation. Comparison des phénomènes morphologiques observés chez les plantes et chez les animaux. Ann. Sci. Nat. Bot., Ser. 7, 14:163–296.

Hagerup, O. 1938. Studies on the significance of polyploidy, II. *Orchis*. Hereditas 24:258–264.

——. 1941. Nordiske kromosom Tal, I. Bot. Tidsskr. 45:385–395.

——. 1944a. Notes on some boreal polyploids. Hereditas 30:152–160.

——. 1944b. On fertilisation, polyploidy and haploidy in *Orchis maculatus*. L. sens lat. Dansk. Bot. Ark. 11:1–26.

——. 1945. Facultative parthenogenesis and haploidy in *Epipactis latifolia*. K. Dansk. Videnskab. Selskab. Biol. Meddelel. 19:1–13.

——. 1947. The spontaneous formation of haploid, polyploid, and aneuploid embryos in some orchids. K. Dansk. Videnskab. Selskab. Biol. Meddelel. 20:1–22.

Hair, J. B. 1942. The chromosome complements of some New Zealand plants, I. Trans. Roy. Soc. N. Z. 71:271–276.

Hall, A. V. 1965. Studies in the genus *Eulophia*. J. S. African Bot. Suppl. 5:1–248.

Harmsen, L. 1943. Studies on the cytology of Arctic plants, II. *Habenaria*. Meddelelser om Grønland 131:3–15.

Hedge, S. N., and G. Boraiah. 1973. Cytotaxonomical studies in the genus *Dendrobium* Sw. Proc. Indian Sci. Cong. Assoc. 60:309.

Heitz, E. 1926. Der Nachweis der Chromosomen vergleichende Studien über ihre Zahl, Grosse und Form im Pflanzenreich. Zeits. f. Bot. 18:625–681.

——. 1932. Die Herkunft der Chromocentren. Planta 18:571–636.

Heslop-Harrison, J. 1948. Field studies in *Orchis* L., I. The structure of dactylorchid populations on certain islands in the Inner and Outer Hebrides. Transact. and Proc. Bot. Soc. Edinb. 35:26–66.

——. 1950. *Orchis cruenta* Mull. in the British Isles. Watsonia 1:366–375.

——. 1951. A comparison of some Swedish and British forms of *Orchis maculata* L. sens. lat. Sv. Bot. Tidskr. 45:608–635.

——. 1953. Microsporogenesis in some triploid dactylorchid hybrids. Ann. Bot. N. S. 17:539–549.

Heusser, K. 1915. Die Entwicklung der generativen Organe von *Himantoglossum hircinum* Spr. Beih. Bot. Centralbl. 32:218–277.

——. 1938. Chromosomenverhältnisse bei schweizerischen basitonen Orchideen. Ber. schweisz. Bot. Gesell. 48:562–605.

Hoffmann, K. M. 1929. Zytologische Studien der Orchidaceen. (Vorläufige Mitteilung.) Ber. deutschen Bot. Gesell. 47:321–326.

——. 1930. Beiträge zur Cytologie der Orchidaceen. Planta 10:523–595.

Holmen, K., and P. Kaad, 1956. Uber *Dactylorchis traunsteineri* auf der Insel Läsö. Bot. Tidssk. 53:35–48.

Holttum, R. E. 1953. Flora of Malaya, Vol. 1. Orchids. Government Printing Office, Singapore.

——. 1958. Evolutionary trends in the sarcanthine orchids. Proc. 2nd World Orchid Conf. (Honolulu), pp. 40–48.

Hsu, C. C. 1971. Preliminary chromosome studies on the vascular plants of Taiwan, IV. Counts and some systematic notes on some monocotyledons. Taiwania 16:123–136.

——. 1972. Preliminary chromosome studies on the vascular plants of Taiwan, V. Taiwania 17:48–65.

Hsu, T. C., W. Schmid, and E. Stubblefield. 1964. DNA replication sequences in higher animals. The role of chromosomes in development. Academic Press, New York and London, pp. 83–112.

Humphrey, L. M. 1932a. Somatic chromosomes in certain Minnesota orchids. Am. Nat. 66:471–474.

——. 1932b. The somatic chromosomes of eight species of Orchidaceae. Proc. Iowa Acad. Sci. 39:137.

——. 1933 and 1934. Somatic chromosomes of *Cyp. hirsutum* and six species of genus *Habenaria*. Proc. Iowa Acad. Sci. 40:75; Am. Nat. 68:184–186.

Hunt, P. F., and C. G. Vosa. 1971. The cytology and taxonomy of the genus *Pleione* D. Don (Orchidaceae). Kew Bull. 25:423–432.

Hurel-Py, G. 1938. Etude des noyaux végétatifs de *Vanilla planifolia*. Rev. de Cytologie et de Cytophysiologie Végétates 3:129–133.

Huynh, K. L. 1965. Contribution à l'étude caryologique et embryologique des phanerogames du Pérou. Denkschr. Schweiz. Nat. Ges. 85:1–178.

Ito, I. 1956. Germination of immature seeds. Japan Orchid Soc. Bull. 2:4–5.

——. 1959. Fertility of crossed seeds of "Ebine." Japan Orchid Soc. Bull. 5:2–4.

Ito, I., and O. Mutsuura. 1957. Chromosome numbers in *Dendrobium* species and hybrids. Japan Orchid Soc. Bull. 3:1–3.

——. 1958. "Ebine" groups and their chromosome numbers. Japan Orchid Soc. Bull. 4:4–6.

——. 1959. Chromosome numbers of "Ebine" and its allies (*Calanthe* species) native to Japan, II. Japan Orchid Soc. Bull. 5:1–2.

Johnson, N. G. 1951. Comparative effects of sodium nucleate and sodium barbital on mitosis. Master's thesis, Univ. of Wisconsin.

Jones, K. 1963. The chromosomes of *Dendrobium*. Am. Orchid Soc. Bull. 32:634–640.

——. 1966. Chromosomes of orchids, I. Polystachya Hook. Kew Bull. 20:357–359.

——. 1967. The chromosomes of orchids, II. Vandeae Lindl. Kew Bull. 21:151–156.

Jones, K., and M. G. Daker. 1968. The chromosomes of orchids, III. Catasetinae Schltr. Kew Bull. 22:421–427.

Jorapur, S. M., and S. N. Hedge. 1974. Karyomorphological studies in *Bulbophytum neilgherrense* Wt. Orchidaceae. Curr. Sci. 43:460–461.

——. 1975. Karyomorphological studies in five species of *Oberonia* Lindl. Cytologia 40:517–524.

Jorapur, S. M., S. N. Hedge, and A. L. Kulkarni. 1979. Cytotaxonomical studies in five species of the genus *Eria* Lindl. Cytologia 44:479–485.

Jørgensen, C. A., Th. Sørensen, and W. Westergaad. 1958. The flowering plants of Greenland. A taxonomical and cytological survey. Biol. Skr. Dansk. Vidensk. Selsk. 9:1–172.

Kamemoto, H. 1950. Polyploidy in cattleyas. Am. Orchid Soc. Bull. 19:366–373.

——. 1952. Further studies on polyploid cattleyas. Bull. Pacific Orchid Soc. Hawaii 10:141–148.

——. 1955. Cytology of *V.* Nellie Morley and *V.* Emma van Deventer. Na Pua Okika o Hawaii Nei. 5:146–158.

——. 1956. Cytology of *Vanda* Nellie Morley and *Vanda* Emma van Deventer. Am. Orchid Soc. Bull. 25:234–243.

——. 1958a. The significance of polyploidy in orchid breeding. Japan Orchid Soc. Bull. 4:1–6.

——. 1958b. Polyploidy in *Vanda*. Proc. 2nd World Orchid Conf., Honolulu. Harvard University Press, Cambridge, Mass., pp. 51–55.

——. 1959a. The origin and significance of polyploidy in *Vanda*. Pacific Orchid Soc. Bull. 16:77–95.

——. 1959b. Studies on chromosome numbers of orchids in Japan. Japan Orchid Soc. Bull. 5:1–4.

Kamemoto, H., and K. Hashimoto. 1968. An octoploid Phalaenopsis. Bull. Pacific Orchid Soc. Hawaii. 26:6–8.

Kamemoto, H., K. Kosaki, and K. Shindo. 1967. Chromosome counts of orchids in Hawaii, 1960–64. Na Pua Okika o Hawaii Nei 17:79–82.

Kamemoto, H., and L. F. Randolph. 1949. Chromosomes of the *Cattleya* tribe. Am. Orchid Soc. Bull. 18:366–369.

Kamemoto, H., and R. Sagarik. 1967. Chromosome numbers of *Dendrobium* species of Thailand. Am. Orchid Soc. Bull. 36:889–894.

Kamemoto, H., R. Sagarik, and S. Dieutrakul. 1963. Karyotypes of *Paphiopedilum* species of Thailand. Kasetsart J. 3:69–78.

Kamemoto, H., R. Sagarik, and S. Kasemsap. 1964. Chromosome numbers of sarcanthine orchid species of Thailand. Nat. Hist. Bull. Siam Soc. 20:235–241.

Kamemoto, H., and K. Shindo. 1962. Genome relationships in interspecific and intergeneric hybrids of *Renanthera*. Am. J. Bot. 49:737–748.

Kamemoto, H., and R. Tanaka. 1960. Chromosome transmission of triploid and pentaploid *Vanda* hybrids. Am. Orchid Soc. Bull. 29:667–675.

——. 1961. Reversal of ploidy in *Vanda* Emma van Deventer. Proc. Am. Soc. Hort. Sci. 77:594–599.

Kamemoto, H., R. Tanaka, and K. Kosaki. 1961. Chromosome numbers of orchids in Hawaii. Univ. Hawaii Agr. Exp. Sta. Bull. 127:1–28.

Kamemoto, H., and Tara, M. 1968. Chromosome inheritance in reciprocal crosses of *Dendrobium phalaenopsis* 'Lyon's Light No. 1.' Proc. Am. Soc. Hort. Sci. 92:665–671.

——. 1969. The relationship of *Renanthera storiei* and *Trichoglottis fasciata*. Brittonia 21:126–129.

Kapoor, B. M. 1972. *In* IOPB chromosome number reports, 35. Taxon 21:161–166.

Karasawa, K. 1978. Karyomorphological studies on the intraspecific variation of *Paphiopedilum insigne*. La Kromosomo 11:233–255.

——. 1979. Karyomorphological studies in *Paphiopedilum*, Orchidaceae. Bull. Hiroshima Bot. Gar. 2:1–149.

Karasawa, K., and R. Tanaka. 1976. 2n = 18 in *Phragmipedium boissierianum*. Chromosome Inf. Serv. 20:13–14.

Kliphuis, E. 1963. Cytological observations in relation to the taxonomy of the orchids of the Netherlands. Acta Bot. Neerl. 12:172–194.

Knaben, G. 1950. Chromosome numbers of Scandinavian arctic-alpine plant species, I. Blyttia 8:129–155.

Knaben, G., and T. Engelskjön. 1967. Chromosome numbers of Scandinavian arctic-alpine plant species, II. Act. Boreal. A. Sci. 21:1–57.

Kondo, K. 1970. Notes on a spontaneous haploid individual of *Pogonia japonica* Reichenb. F. (Orchidaceae) in natural populations. Caryologia 23:515–518.

——. 1972. The chromosome number of *Listera smallii*. Chromosome Inf. Serv. 13:7–9.

Kosaki, K. 1958. Preliminary investigations on the cytogenetics of *Dendrobium*. Proc. 2nd World Orchid Conf., Honolulu. Harvard University Press, Cambridge, Mass., pp. 25–29.

Kosaki, K., and H. Kamemoto. 1961. Chromosomes of some *Dendrobium* species and hybrids. Na Pua Okika o Hawaii Nei 11:75–86.

Kugust, K. 1966. Hybridizing with *Oncidium*. Proc. 5th World Orchid Conf., Long Beach, Calif. Harvard University Press, Cambridge, Mass., pp. 45–52.

Kulkarni, H., and S. M. Jorapur. 1979. *In* IOPB chromosome number reports, 64. Taxon 28:391–408.

Kusano, S. 1915. Experimental studies on the embryonal development in an Angiosperm. J. Coll. Agr. Imp. Univ. Tokyo. 6:7–120.

Laane, M. M. 1965. Kromosomundersökelser hos noen norske plantearter. Blyttia 23:169–189.

——. 1967. Kromosomundersökelser i Öst-Finnmarks flora, II. Chromosome numbers in the flora of eastern Finnmark Blyttia 25:45–54.

——. 1969. Further chromosome studies in Norwegian vascular plants. Blyttia 27:5–17.

La Cour, L. F. 1952. Chromosome counts of species and varieties of garden plants. Ann. Rpt. John Innes Hort. Inst. (1951), 42:47–50.

Larsen, K. 1960. Cytological and experimental studies on the flowering plants of the Canary Islands. Biol. Skrift. K. Dansk. Vidensk. Selsk. 11:1–60.

——. 1966. Studies in the flora of Thailand. 40. Cytology of vascular plants, II. Dansk. Bot. Ark. 23:375–399.

——. 1968. Brief notes on *Neuwiedia singapureana*. Thailand Nat. Hist. Bull. Siam Soc. 22:330–331.

Lee, Y. N. 1967. Chromosome numbers of flowering plants in Korea (1). J. Korean Cult. Res. Inst. 11:455–478.

Lenz, L. W. 1960. The cytology of the white Cypripediums. Am. Orchid Soc. Bull. 29:187–191.

Leveque, M., and R. Gorenflot. 1969. Prospections caryologiques dans la flore littorale du Boulonnais. Bull. Soc. Bot. Nord France 22:27–58.

Lindley, J. 1830–1840. The genera and species of orchidaceous plants. Ridgways, London.

Löve, A. 1951. Tofragros (*Dactylorchis Fuchsii*) a Islandi. Natuurufraedingurinn 21:91–93.

Löve, A., and E. Kjellquist. 1973. Cytotaxonomy of Spanish plants, II. Monocotyledons. Lagascalia 3:147–182.

Löve, A., and D. Löve. 1944. Cyto-taxonomical studies on boreal plants, III. Some new chromosome numbers of Scandinavian plants. Arkiv. für Bot. 31A:1–22.

——. 1948. Chromosome numbers of northern plant species. University Inst. of Applied Sci., Department of Agriculture Reports, Reykjavik, Iceland, Series B, No. 3, pp. 9–131.

——. 1954. Cytotaxonomical evaluation of corresponding taxa. Vegetatio Acta Geobotanica 5–6: 212–224.

——. 1956. Cytotaxonomical conspectus of Icelandic flora. Acta Hort. Gotab. 20:65–290.

——. 1961. Chromosome numbers of central and northwest European plant species. Opera Botanica. Suppl. Ser. Botaniska Notiiser 5:1–581.

——. 1965. *In* IOPB chromosome number reports, 3. Taxon 14:50–57.

——. 1965. *In* IOPB chromosome number reports, 4. Taxon 14:86–92.

——. 1966. Cytotaxonomy of the alpine vascular plants of Mount Washington. Univ. of Colorado Studies, Series Biol., No. 24, pp. 1–74.

——. 1969. *In* IOPB chromosome number reports, 21. Taxon 18:310–315.

——. 1972. *Vermeulenia*—a new genus of Orchids. Acta Bot. Neerl. 21:553–554.

Löve, A., and J. C. Ritchie. 1966. Chromosome numbers from central Canada. Can. J. Bot. 44:429–439.

Löve, A., and W. Simon. 1968. Cytotaxonomical notes on some American orchids. Southwestern Naturalist 13:335–342.

Lovka, M., F. Susnik, A. Löve, and D. Löve. 1971. *In* IOPB chromosome number reports, 34. Taxon 20:785–797.

——. 1972. *In* IOPB chromosome number reports, 36. Taxon 21:333–346.

MacMahon, B. 1936. Meiosis in the pollen mother-cells of *Listera ovata*. Cellule 45:209–262.

Maekawa, F. 1963. Reduction in chromosomes and major polyploidy: Their bearing on plant evolution. J. Fac. Sci., Univ. Tokyo, Sec. 3, Bot. 8:377–398.

——. 1965. On the differentiation of the genus *Cypripedium* sensu lato. J. Japan. Bot. 40:321–326.

Majovsky, J., *et al.* 1974. Index of chromosome numbers of Slovakian flora, IV. Acta Fac. Rerum Nat. Univ. Comenianae Bot. 23:1–23.

Malla, S. B., S. Bhattarai, M. Gorkhali, H. Saiju, and M. Kayastha. 1978. *In* IOPB chromosome number reports, 59. Taxon 27:53–61.

Malla, S. B., S. Bhattarai, M. Gorkhali, H. Saiju, M. Kayastha, and M. P. Singh. 1976. *In* IOPB chromosome number reports, 53. Taxon 25:483–500.

——. 1977a. *In* IOPB chromosome number reports, 58. Taxon 26:443–452.

——. 1977b. *In* IOPB chromosome number reports, 58. Taxon 26:557–565.

——. 1979. *In* IOPB chromosome number reports, 65. Taxon 28:627–637.

Malvesin-Fabre, G., and J. Eyme. 1949. Le noyau et la mitose chez *Limodorum abortivum*. C. R. Acad. Sci. 228:2050–2057.

Martin, F. W. 1963. Chromosome number and behavior in a *Vanilla* hybrid and several *Vanilla* species. Bull. Torrey Bot. Club 90:416.

Matsuda, T., and R. Tanaka. 1977. The behavior of B-chromosomes of *Tainia laxiflora* in male gametogenesis. Japan J. Genet. 52:239–246.

Matsuura, H., and T. Suto. 1935. Contributions to the idiogram study in phanerogamous plants. I. Fac. Sci. J. Hokkaido Imp. Univ., Series 5, 5:32–75.

Maude, R. F. 1939. The Merton catalogue. A list of the chromosome numerals of species of British flowering plants. New Phytol. 38:7–31.

Maxwell, M. K. 1967. The *Dendrobium kingianum* Bidw. ex Lindl. complex. Austral. Orchid Rev. 32:25–30.

——. 1971. The *Dendrobium kingianum* Bidw. ex. Lindl. complex. Proc. 6th World Orchid Conf., Harvard University Press, Cambridge, Mass., pp. 47–50., Sydney.

McQuade, H. A. 1949. The cytology of *Paphiopedilum* Maudiae. Ann. Missouri Bot. Gardens 36:433–474.

Mehlquist, G. A. L. 1947a. Polyploidy in the genus *Paphiopedilum* Pfitz (*Cypripedium* Hort.) and its implications. Mo. Bot. Gar. Bull. 35:211–228.

——. 1947b. Some smear techniques for counting chromosomes in orchids. Mo. Bot. Gar. Bull. 35:229–231.

——. 1949. The importance of chromosome numbers in orchid breeding. Am. Orchid Soc. Bull. 18:284–293.

——. 1952. Chromosome numbers in the genus *Cymbidium*. Cymbidium Soc. News 7.

Mehlquist, G. A. L., and J. Clovis. 1957. Counting chromosomes in orchids. Am. Orchid Soc. Bull. 26:389–393.

Mehra, P. N., and K. S. Bawa. 1962. Chromosome studies in Orchidaceae. Proc. Ind. Sci. Cong., pp. 326–327.

——. 1970. Cytological observations on some northwest Himalayan orchids. Caryologia 23:273–282.

Mehra, P. N., and S. K. Kashyap. 1976. *In* IOPB chromosome number reports, 53. Taxon 25:483–500.

——. 1978. *In* IOPB chromosome number reports, 60. Taxon 27:223–231.

——. 1979. *In* IOPB chromosome number reports, 64. Taxon 28:391–408.

Mehra, P. N., and T. K. Pandita. 1978. *In* IOPB chromosome number reports, 61. Taxon 27:375–392.

——. 1979. *In* IOPB chromosome number reports, 64. Taxon 28:391–408.

Mehra, P. N., and R. N. Sehgal. 1974. *In* IOPB chromosome number reports, 46. Taxon 23:801–812.

——. 1975. *In* IOPB chromosome number reports, 49. Taxon 24:501–516.

——. 1978. *In* IOPB chromosome number reports, 61. Taxon 27:375–392.

Mehra, P. N., K. S. Bawa, K. K. Kashyap, and S. P. Vij. 1970. *In* IOPB chromosome number reports, 25. Taxon 19:102–113.

——. 1972a. Cytological studies in the East Himalayan Orchidaceae, 1. Neottieae. Caryologia 25:237–251.

——. 1972b. Cytological studies in the East Himalayan Orchidaceae, 2. Orchideae. Caryologia 25:335–351.

Menninger, E. D. 1954. Tetraploid Cymbidiums. Am. Orchid. Soc. Bull. 23:158–161.

——. 1963. Diary of a colchicine-induced tetraploid *Cymbidium*. Am. Orchid Soc. Bull. 32:885–887.

Miduno, T. 1937. Chromosomenstudien von Orchidazeen (Vorläufige Mitteilung). Japan. J. Genet. 13:259.

——. 1938. Chromosomenstudien an Orchidazeen, I. Karyotype und Mixoploidie bei *Cephalanthera* und *Epipactis*. Cytologia 8:505–514.

——. 1939. Chromosomenstudien an Orchidazeen, II. Somatischen Chromosomenzahlen einiger Orchideen. Cytologia 9:447–451.

——. 1940a. Chromosomenstudien an Orchidazeen, III. Über das Vorkommen von haploiden Pflanzen bei *Bletilla striata* Reichb. f. var. *gebina* Reichb. f. Cytologia 11:156–177.

——. 1940b. Chromosomenstudien an Orchidazeen, IV. Chromosomenzahlen einiger Arten und Bastarde bei Orchideen. Cytologia 11:179–185.

——. 1953. Die Meiose und die erste Teilung in Pollen Korn bei *Pogonia japonica*. Japan. J. Genet. 28:175.

——. 1954. Chromosomenstudien an Orchidazeen, V. Über das zytologischen Verhalten des Artbastardes zwischen *Bletilla striata* (n = 16) und *Bl. formosana* (n = 18). Cytologia 19:239–248.

——. 1955. Karyotypanalyse und differentielle Färbung der Chromosomen von *Cypripedium debile*. Japan. J. Genet. (abstract) 30:176.

Miduno, T., and N. Yamazaki. 1952. Über die verschiedenen Karyotypen und Kinetochorpaarung, beobachtet an den Kerntielung der jeden Wurzelspitze der an die Gattung *Pogonia* gehörenden Pflanzen. Japan. J. Genet. 27:210.

——. 1963. Chromosome number and meiosis of *Pogonia*. 28th Ann. Meeting Bot. Soc. Japan.

Mitsukuri, Y., and K. Hayashi. 1967. An electron microscopic study of *Prasiola japonica* Yatabe. La Kromosomo 69–70:2281–2288.

Modilewski, J. 1918. Cytological and embryological studies on *Neottia nidus-avis* (L.) Rich. Verh. Kiewer Ges. Naturf. 26:1–55.

——. 1936. Zur Frage über die Entstehung von diploiden Gameten. J. Inst. Bot. Acad. Sci. Ukraine 9:87–90.

Morinaga, T., and E. Fukushima. 1931. Chromosome numbers of cultivated plants, III. Bot. Mag. Tokyo 45:140–145.

Mulay, B. N., and T. K. B. Panikkar. 1953. The chromosome number and morphology in *Cypripedium speciosum* L. Porc. Rajasthan Acad. Sci. 4:29–31.

Müller, H. A. C. 1912. Kernstudien an Pflanzen. Arch. Zellfor. 8:1–52.

Murín, A., and J. Majovsky. 1976. *In* IOPB chromosome number reports, 53. Taxon 25:483–500.

Mutsuura, O. 1959. On chromosome counts in orchids native to Japan. Japan Orchid Soc. Bull. 5:5–7.

———. 1963. Chromosome numbers of orchid species in Japan. Kyoto Shigaku Kenkyu Ronbun Shu 1:123–132.

Mutsuura, O., and R. Nakahira. 1958. Chromosome numbers of the family Orchidaceae in Japan (1). Scientific Reps. Saikyo Univ. 2:25–30.

———. 1959. Chromosome numbers of the family Orchidaceae in Japan, (2). Scientific Reps. Kyoto Prefectural Univ. 3:27–31.

———. 1960. Chromosome numbers of the family Orchidaceae in Japan (3). Scientific Reps. Kyoto Prefectural Univ. 3:11–16.

Nakasone, H. Y., and H. Kamemoto. 1961. Artificial induction of polyploidy in orchids by the use of colchicine. Hawaii Agr. Exp. Sta. Tech. Bull. 42–27 pp.

Nakasone, H. Y., and S. Moromizato. 1964. Chromosome determinations of some Ryukyuan orchid species. Sci. Bull. Div. Agr. Home Economics and Engineering Univ. Ryukyus 11:13–18.

Natarajan, G. 1978. *In* IOPB chromosome number reports, 62. Taxon 27:519–535.

———. 1979. *In* IOPB chromosome number reports, 65. Taxon 28:627–637.

Nevling, L. I. 1969. Ecology of an elfin forest in Puerto Rico. Pt. 3. Chromosome numbers of some flowering plants. J. Arnold Arboretum 50:99–103.

Niehaus, T., and L. Wong, Jr. 1971. *In* IOPB chromosome reports, 32. Taxon 20:349–356.

Niimoto, D. H., and L. F. Randolph. 1958. Chromosome inheritance in *Cattleya*. Am. Orchid Soc. Bull. 27:157–162; 240–247.

Ohno, R. 1954. Notes on the chromosomes in some species of the phanerogamous plants. J. Hokkaido Gakugei Univ. 5:33–36.

———. 1971. Chromosome studies in some species of the phanerogamous plants. Seibutsu Kyozai Kikonai Marine Biol. Lab. Hokkaido Univ. Educ. 8:69–71.

Ohno, R., and A. Hashimoto. 1956. Chromosome studies in Orchidaceae, I. Chromosome numbers in four species of Orchidaceae. Bot. Mag. Tokyo. 69:286–288.

Ohno, R., T. Fujiya, and Y. Okamoto. 1957. Chromosome studies in Orchidaceae, II. Chromosome numbers of *Oreorchis patens* Lindl. and *Spiranthes sinensis* Ames. J. Hokkaido Gakugei Univ. 8:32–34.

Ono, M. 1977. Cytotaxonomical studies on the flowering plants endemic to the Bonin Islands. Memoirs of the Natl. Science Mus. 10:63–80.

Pace, L. 1907. Fertilization in *Cypripedium*. Bot. Gaz. 44:353–374.

———. 1909. The gametophytes of *Calopogon*. Bot. Gaz. 48:126–139.

———. 1914. Two species of *Gyrostachys*. Baylor Univ. Bull. 17:1–16.

Pancho, J. V. 1965a. *In* IOPB chromosome number reports, 3. Taxon 14:50–57.

———. 1965b. *In* IOPB chromosome number reports, 4. Taxon 14:86–87.

Phang, V. P. E., U. Charanasri, and H. Kamemoto. 1978. *Oncidium triquetrum* × *Oncidium splendidum* an intersectional species hybrid. Orch. Digest 42:228–229.

———. 1979. Genome relationships of intra- and intersectional species hybrids of *Oncidium triquetrum*. Am. J. Bot. 66:805–809.

Pojar, J. 1973. Levels of polyploidy in four vegetation types of southwestern British Columbia. Can. J. Bot. 51:621–628.

Raven, P. H., D. W. Kyhos, and A. J. Hill. 1965. Chromosome numbers of spermatophytes, mostly Californian. Aliso 6:105–113.

Ravindran, P. N. 1979. Nuclear behaviour in the sterile pollen of *Vanilla planifolia* (Andrews). Cytologia 44:391–396.

Raynaud, C. 1971. *In* IOPB chromosome number reports, 34. Taxon 20:785–797.

Richards, A. J. 1972. *In* IOPB chromosome number reports, 35. Taxon 21:161–166.

Richardson, M. M. 1933. Chromosome variation in *Listera ovata* R. Br. Univ. Calif. Publ. Bot. 17:51–60.

———. 1935. The chromosomes of some British orchids. Durham Univ. Phil. Soc. Proc. 9:135–140.

Rolfe, R. A. 1911. *Phaiocymbidium chardwarense*. Orchid Rev. 19:295–296.

Rosenberg, O. 1905. Zur Kenntnis der Reduktionsteilung in Pflanzen. Bot. Notiser 1–25.

Sagawa, Y. 1962a. Chromosome numbers of some species and hybrids of the *Cattleya* group in Florida. Florida Orchidist 5:201–203.

———. 1962b. Cytological studies of the genus *Phalaenopsis*. Am. Orchid Soc. Bull. 31:459–465.

Sagawa, Y., and D. H. Niimoto. 1961. Cytological studies in the Orchidaceae. Am. Orchid. Soc. Bull. 30:628–632.

Sampathkumaran, M., and K. N. Rangaswamy. 1931. Cytology of the embryo sac in orchids. Proc. Indian Sci. Congress 18:277–278.

Sarkar, A. K., N. Datta, and U. Chatterjee. 1978. *In* IOPB chromosome number reports, 62. Taxon 27:519–535.

Sarkar, A. K., R. Mallick, N. Datta, and U. Chatterjee. 1977. *In* IOPB chromosome number reports, 67. Taxon 26:443–452.

Schlechter, R. 1926. Das System der Orchidaceen. Notizbl. Bot. Gart. u. Mus. Berlin-Dahlem 9:563–591.

——. 1927. Die Orchideen, 2d. ed. Parey, Berlin.

Schotsman, H. D. 1970a. Contribution à la caryologie des angiospermes de la Sologne et du Val de Loire, I. Bull. Centr. Etudes Rech. Sci. 8:21–63.

——. 1970b. Contribution à la caryologie des angiospermes de la Sologne et du Val de Loire, II. Bull. Centr. Etudes Rech. Sci. 8:199–255.

Schweinfurth, C. 1959. Key to the orchids, pp. 511–518. *In* The orchids: A scientific survey, C. L. Withner (ed.). Ronald Press, New York.

Senghas, K., and G. Schoser. 1965. *Paphiopedilum sukhakulii*. Die Orchidee 16:224–236.

Senianinova, M. 1925. Etude embryologique de l'*Ophrys myodes*. Zeit. Russ. Bot. Ges. 9:10–14.

Seshagiriah, K. N. 1934. Pollen sterility in *Zeuxine sulcata* Lindley. Curr. Sci. 3:205–206.

——. 1941. Morphological studies in Orchidaceae, I. *Zeuxine sulcata* Lindley. J. Indian Bot. Soc. 20:357–365.

Sharma, A. K., and A. K. Chatterji. 1966. Cytological studies on orchids with respect to their evolution and affinities. Nucleus 9:177–203.

Sharma, A. K., and A. K. Sarkar. 1967–1968. Chromosome number reports of plants. Annual Report, Cytogenetics Laboratory, Department of Botany, Univ. of Calcutta. Research Bull. 2:38–48.

Shimoya, C., and L. Ferlan. 1952. Estudos orquideologicos, III. Determinacoes cromosomicas em *Ophrys*. Brotéria 21:171–176.

Shindo, K., and H. Kamemoto. 1962. Genome relationships of *Neofinetia* Hu and some allied genera of Orchidaceae. Cytologia 27:402–409.

——. 1963a. Karyotype analysis of some Sarcanthine orchids. Am. J. Bot. 50:73–79.

——. 1963b. Chromosomes of *Dendrophylax funalis* and *Aerangis biloba*. Am. Orchid Soc. Bull. 32:821–823.

——. 1963c. Chromosome relationships of *Aerides* and allied genera. Am. Orchid Soc. Bull. 32:922–926.

——. 1963d. Chromosome numbers and genome relationships of some species in the Nigrohirsutae section of *Dendrobium*. Cytologia 28:68–75.

——. 1963e. Karyotype analysis of some species of *Phalaenopsis*. Cytologia 28:390–398.

Shoji, T. 1963. Cytological studies on Orchidaceae, II. Chromosome numbers and karyotypes of six Japanese species. La Kromosomo 55–56:1823–1828.

——. 1976. Cytological studies on Orchidaceae, III. Chromosome numbers and karyotypes in *Phalaenopsis*. La Kromosomo 2:91–98.

Simon, W. 1968. Chromosome numbers and b-chromosomes in *Listera*. Caryologia 21:181–189.

Sinoto, Y. 1962. Chromosome numbers in *Oncidium* alliance. Cytologia 27:306–313.

——. 1964. A karyotype of *Oncidium nanum* Lindl. Chromosome Inf. Serv. 5:15–16.

——. 1966. *Brassidium* Supreme clearly showing its parental karyotypes. Chromosome Inf. Serv. 7:30–31.

——. 1969a. Chromosomes in *Oncidium* and allied genera, I. Genus *Ondidium*. La Kromosomo 76:2459–2473.

——. 1969b. Chromosomes in *Oncidium* and allied genera, II. Genera *Erycina, Gomesa, Odontoglossum, Miltonia, Brassia* and *Sigmatostalix*. La Kromosomo 77–78:2532–2538.

Sinoto, Y., and T. Shoji. 1962. Cytological studies on Orchidaceae, I. Chromosome numbers and karyotypes of some native orchids in Japan. International Christian Univ. Publ. 1:20–27.

Skalinska, M., M. Piotrowicz, A. Sokolowska-Kulczycka, *et al.* 1961. Further additions to chromosome numbers of Polish Angiosperms. Acta Polsk. Towarz. Bot. 30:463–489.

Skalinska, M., M. Piotrowicz, A. Sokolowska-Kulczycka, and E. Pogan, *et al.* 1966. Further studies in chromosome numbers of Polish angiosperms. Acta Biol. Cracov. Ser. Bot. 9:31–58.

Sokolovskaya, A. P. 1963. Geographical distribution of polyploidy in plants. Vest. Leningrad Univ., Series Biol., 15:38–52.

——. 1966. Geograficheskoe rasprostranenie poliploidnykh vidov rasteniy. (Issledovanie flory Primorskogo kraya). Vest. Leningrad Univ., Series Biol. 3:92–106.

Sokolovskaya, A. P., and O. S. Strelkova. 1940. Karyological investigations of the alpine flora on the main Caucasus range and the problem of geographical distribution of polyploids. Comp. Rend. Acad. Sci. U.S.S.R. 29:415–418.

——. 1960. Geographical distribution of the polyploid species of plants in the Eurasiatic Arctic. Bot. Zhur. U.S.S.R. 45:369–381.

Sorsa, V. 1962. Chromosomenzahlen finnischer Kormophyten, I. Ann. Acad. Sci. Fennicae, Series No. 34 A, Biologica 58:1–14.

——. 1963. Chromosomenzahlen finnischer Kormophyten, II. Ann. Acad. Sci. Fennicae Series No. 4 A. Biologica 68:1–14.

Speta, F., and W. Voeth. 1972. X *Dactyloglossum dominianum* (Camus) Soo. Die Orchidee 23:117–120.

Staner, P. 1929. Préréduction ou postréduction dans *Listera ovata* R. Br. Cellule 39:219–235.

Stebbins, G. L., Jr. 1938. Cytological characteristics associated with the different growth habits in the dicotyledons. Am. J. Bot. 25:189–198.

Stenar, H. 1937. Om *Acroanthes monophyllos* (L.). Greene dessgeogrophiska utbrenning ach embryologi. Heimbygdas Tidskr. (1). Fornvardaren Uppsala (Festskrift till Erik Modin) 6:177–231.

Storey, W. B. 1952. Chromosome numbers of some *Vanda* species and hybrids. Am. Orchid Soc. Bull. 21:801–806.

——. 1953. The pentaploidal origin of *Vanda* Nora Potter. Bull. Pacif. Orchid Soc. Hawaii 11:17–25.

Storey, W. B., Kamemoto, H., and K. Shindo. 1963. Chromosomes of *Vanda spathulata* and its hybrids. Am. Orchid Soc. Bull. 32:703–709.

Strasburger, E. 1888. Über Kern- und Zellteilung im Pflanzenreich, nebst einem Anhang über Befruchtung. Histol. Beiträge, I. Fischer, Jena.

Suessenguth, K. 1921. Beiträge zur Frage des systematischen Anschlusses der Monokotylen. Bot. Centbl. Beihefte 38:1–80.

——. 1923. Über die Pseudogamie bei *Zygopetalum Mackayi* Hook. Ber. deut. Bot. Gesell. 41:16–23.

Sugiura, T. 1928. Chromosome numbers in some higher plants, I. Bot. Mag. Tokyo 42:504–506.

——. 1939. Studies on the chromosome numbers in higher plants, III. Cytologia 10:205–212.

Susnik, F., and M. Lovka. 1973. *In* IOPB chromosome number reports, 41. Taxon 22:459–464.

Swamy, B. G. L. 1941. The development of the male gamete in *Cymbidium bicolor* Lindl. Proc. Ind. Acad. Sci. B 14:454–460.

——. 1944. The embryo sac and embryo of *Satyrium nepalense*. Indian Bot. Soc. J. 23:66–70.

——. 1949a. Embryological studies in the Orchidaceae, I. Gametophytes. Am. Midland Naturalist 41:184–201.

——. 1949b. Embryological studies in the Orchidaceae, II. Embryogeny. Am. Midland Naturalist 41:202–232.

Tahara, M. 1977. Studies on artificial hybrid of *Calanthe discolor*. Japan Orchid Soc. Bull. 23:3–7.

Takamine, N. 1916. Über die ruhenden und die präsynaptischen Phasen der Reduktionsteilung. Bot. Mag. Tokyo 30:293–303.

Tan, K. W. 1969. The systematic status of the genus *Bletilla* (Orchidaceae). Brittonia 21:202–214.

Tanaka, R. 1960. Cytogenetics and the breeding of orchids. Japan Orchid Soc. Bull. 6:8–15.

——. 1962a. Chromosome count of orchids in Japan, I. Japan Orchid Soc. Bull. 8:1–4.

——. 1962b. Cytological studies on the speciation in *Spiranthes sinensis*. Proc. 27th Ann. Meeting Bot. Soc. Japan, p. 131.

——. 1962c. Differentiation in karyotypes between *Pogonia minor* and *P. japonica*. Japan. J. Genet. 37:414.

——. 1963. Differentiation and polyploidy in garden orchids. Japan. J. Genet. 38:221–222.

——. 1964a. Chromosome count of orchids in Japan, II. Japan Orchid Soc. Bull. 10:1–5.

——. 1964b. Differentiation and chromosomes in garden orchids. Heredity 18:20–24.

——. 1965a. Intraspecific polyploidy in *Goodyera maximowicziana* Makino. La Kromosomo 60:1945–1950.

——. 1965b. Chromosome numbers of some species of Orchidaceae from Japan and its neighbouring areas. J. Japan. Bot. 40:65–77.

——. 1965c. H³-thymidine autoradiographic studies on the heteropycnosis, heterochromatin and euchromatin in *Spiranthes sinensis*. Bot. Mag. Tokyo 78:50–62.

——. 1966. Chromosome count of orchids in Japan, III. Japan Orchid Soc. Bull. 12:2–4.

——. 1968. Cytology of the Orchidaceae, pp. 1–62. *In* H. Torigata (ed.), Seed formation and sterile culture of the orchids. Seibundo-Shinko-Sha, Tokyo.

——. 1969a. Deheterochromatinization of chromosomes and gigantic form in *Spiranthes sinensis*. Proc. 6th World Orchid Conf., Sydney. Harvard University Press, Cambridge, Mass., p. 131.

——. 1969b. Deheterochromatinization of the chromosomes in *Spiranthes sinensis*. Japan. J. Genet. 44:291–296.

——. 1969c. Speciation and karyotypes in *Spiranthes sinensis*. J. Sci. Hiroshima Univ., Series B, Div. 2, 12:165–197.

——. 1971. Types of resting nuclei in Orchidaceae. Bot. Mag. Tokyo 84:118–122.

——. 1974. Organizational system of meiotic division and the development of reproductive cells in higher plants. Cell 6:22–25.

——. 1975. Chromosome study in *Galeola septentrionalis*, a saprophyte. Japan Orchid Soc. Bull. 21:3–5.

Tanaka, R., and M. Aoyama. 1974. Karyological studies on some species of *Paphiopedilum*. Japan Orchid Soc. Bull. 20:3–8.

Tanaka, R., and H. Kamemoto. 1960. Meiotic chromosome behavior in diploid and polyploid *Vanda* orchid hybrids. Cytologia 25:405–418.

——. 1961. Meiotic chromosome behavior in some intergeneric hybrids of the *Vanda* alliance. Am. J. Bot. 48:573–582.

——. 1963. Tabulation of chromosome numbers of orchids, I. Japan Orchid Soc., Kobe.

——. 1964. Tabulation of chromosome numbers of orchids, II. Japan Orchid Soc. Bull. 10:21–31.

——. 1972. A complete tabulation of chromosome numbers in Orchidaceae. *In* Japan Orchid Soc. (ed.), The orchids, culture and breeding, Seibundo-Shindosha, Tokyo, pp. 667–773.

——. 1974. List of chromosome numbers in species of the Orchidaceae. *In* C. L. Withner (ed.), The orchids: Scientific studies. John Wiley & Sons, New York, pp. 411–483.

Tanaka, R., and T. Matsuda. 1972. A high occurrence of accessory chromosomal type in *Tainia laxiflora*. Orchidaceae. Bot. Mag. Tokyo 85:43–49.

Tanaka, R., and K. Taniguchi. 1975. A banding method for plant chromosomes. Japan. J. Genet. 50:163–167.

Taniguchi, K., R. Tanaka, Y. Yonezawa, and H. Komatsu. 1975. Types of banding patterns of plant chromosomes by modified BSG method. La Kromosomo 100:3123–3135.

Tara, M. and H. Kamemoto. 1970. Karyotype relationships in the Sarcanthinae (Orchidaceae). Am. J. Bot. 57:176–182.

Taylor, J. A., and R. Tanaka. 1977. Nuclear behavior in the megagametogenesis and embryogenesis of *Pogonia japonica*. Chromosome Inf. Serv. 23:11–12.

Taylor, R. L. 1967. *In* IOPB chromosome number reports, 13. Taxon 16:445–461.

Taylor, R. L., and R. P. Brockman. 1966. Chromosome numbers of some western Canadian plants. Can. J. Bot. 44:1093–1103.

Taylor, R. L., and G. A. Mulligan. 1968. Flora of the Queen Charlotte Islands, Pt. 2. Cytological aspects of the vascular plants. Queen's Printer, Ottawa, p. 148.

Terasaka, O., T. Niitsu, and R. Tanaka. 1979. Single fertilization in *Spiranthes sinensis*. Bot. Mag. Tokyo 92:59–67.

Terasaka, O., and R. Tanaka. 1974. Cytological studies on the nuclear differentiation in microspore division of some angiosperms. Bot. Mag. Tokyo 87:209–217.

Thien, L. B. 1973. Isolating mechanisms in the genus *Calopogon*. Am. Orchid Soc. Bull. 42:794–797.

Thulin, M. 1970. Chromosome numbers of some vascular plants from East Africa. Bot. Notiser 123:488–494.

Tischler, G. 1934. Die Bedeutung der Polyploidie für die Verbreitung der Angiospermen. Bot. Jahrb. 67:1–36.

——. 1935–1936. Pflanzliche Chromosomen-Zahlen. Tabulae Biologicae Periodicae 11–12:1–83; 109–226.

Titz, W. 1965. Vergleichende Untersuchungen über den Grad der somatischen Polyploidie an nahe verwandten diploiden und polyploiden Sippen einschliesslich der Cytologie von Antipoden. Oest. Bot. Zeits. 112:101–172.

———. 1966. Chromosomenzahlen dreier Angiospermenarten aus Oesterreich. Oest. Bot. Zeits. 113:187–190.

Tomasi, J. A. de. 1954. An introductory note. Kiesewetter orchid gardens 1954 catalogue.

Tuschnjakova, M. 1929. Embryologische und zytologische Beobachtungen über *Listera ovata* (Orchidaceae). Planta 7:29–44.

Uhriková, A., and V. Feráková. 1978. *In* IOPB chromosome number reports, 61. Taxon 27:375–392.

Uhriková, A., and T. Schwarzová. 1976. *In* IOPB chromosome number reports, 53. Taxon 25:483–500.

———. 1978. *In* IOPB chromosome number reports, 61. Taxon 27:375–392.

Vajrabhaya, T., and L. F. Randolph. 1960. Chromosome studies in *Dendrobium*. Am. Orchid Soc. Bull. 29:507–517.

———. 1961. Chromosome inheritance in pentaploid and aneuploid Cattleyas. Am. Orchid Soc. Bull. 30:209–213.

van Loon, J., and H. de Jong. 1978. *In* IOPB chromosome number reports, 69. Taxon 27:53–61.

Vaucher, C. 1966. Contribution à l'étude cytologique du genre *Dactylorchis* (Klinge) Vermeulen. Bull. Soc. Neuchât. Sci. Nat. 89:75–85.

Vermeuien, P. 1938. Chromosomes in *Orchis*. Chrom. Bot. 4:107–108.

———. 1947. Studies on Dactylorchids. F. Schoturius and Jens, Utrecht.

———. 1949. Varieties and forms of Dutch orchids. Nederlandsche Botanische Vereenegeng, Leylen 56:204–242.

Vij, S. P., and G. C. Gupta. 1975. Cytological investigations into W. Himalayan Orchidaceae, I. Chromosome numbers and karyotypes of taxa from Kashmir. Cytologia 40:613–621.

Vij, S. P., and P. N. Mehra. 1974. Cytological studies in the East Himalayan Orchidaceae, III. Cypripedieae. Caryologia 27:293–300.

Vij, S. P., and N. Vohra. 1974a. Cytomorphological studies in the genus *Spiranthes* Rich. Cytologia 39:139–143.

———. 1974b. Cytomorphological studies in *Zeuxine strateumatica* (L.). Cytologia 39:411–417.

Vis, J. D. 1933. Iets over de Cytologie der Orchideen. Verh. 24 Neerl. Natuur en Geneesk Congress, pp. 186–189.

Vosa, C. G., and P. W. Barlow. 1972. Meiosis and B-chromosomes in *Listera ovata* (Orchidaceae). Caryologia 25:1–8.

Wegener, K. A. 1966. Ein Beitrag zur Zytologie von Orchideen aus dem Gebiet der DDR. Wiss. Zschr. Ernst-Mortiz-Arndt-Univ. Greifswald, Mat.-nat. Reihe 15:1–7.

Weijer, J. 1952. The colour-differences in *Epipactis helleboriae* (Cr. Wats.) Coult. and the selection of the genetical varieties by environment. Genetica 26:1–32.

Wells, E. W. 1956a. The elusive tetraploid, I. Counting chromosomes in Cymbidiums. Am. Orchid Soc. Bull. 25:84–88.

———. 1956b. The elusive tetraploid, II. A tabulation of 110 chromosome counts of award and other choice Cymbidiums. Am. Orchid Soc. Bull. 25:175–178.

Wilfret, G. J., and H. Kamemoto. 1969. Genome and karyotype relationships in the genus *Dendrobium* (Orchidaceae), I. Crossability. Am. J. Bot. 56:521–526.

———. 1971. Genome and karyotype relationships in the genus *Dendrobium* (Orchidaceae), II. Karyotype relationships. Cytologia 36:604–613.

Wilfret, G. T., T. Takeshita, and H. Kamemoto. 1979. Genome and karyotype relationships in *Dendrobium* (Orchidaceae), III. Meiotic behavior. J. Am. Orchid Soc. Hort. Sci. 104:43–46.

Wimber, D. E. 1954. Note on *Cymbidium* Flamingo 'Nobilior.' Cymbidium Soc. News 9:16–17.

———. 1957a. Cytogenetic studies in the genus *Cymbidium*, I. Chromosome numbers within the genus and related genera. Am. Orchid Soc. Bull. 26:636–639.

———. 1957b. Cytogenetic studies in the genus *Cymbidium*, II. Pollen formation in the species. Am. Orchid Soc. Bull. 26:700–703.

———. 1957c. Cytogenetic studies in the genus *Cymbidium*, III. Pollen formation in the hybrids. Am. Orchid Soc. Bull. 26:771–777.

———. 1957d. Cytology of Cymbidiums. Dos Pueblos Catalog, Goleta, Calif., pp. 4–5.

Wimber, D. E., and K. Hernlund. 1955. Aneuploid chromosome numbers in Cymbidiums. Am. Orchid Soc. Bull. 24:743–745.

Wirth, M., and C. L. Withner. 1959. Embryology and development in the Orchidaceae, pp. 155–188. *In* The Orchids: A scientific survey. Ronald Press, New York.

Withner, C. L. 1959. The orchids: A scientific survey. Chronica Botanica, No. 32. Ronald Press, New York.

Woodard, J. W. 1951. Some chromosome numbers in *Phalaenopsis*. Am. Orchid Soc. Bull. 20:356–358.

——. 1952. Some chromosome numbers in *Vanda*. Am. Orchid Soc. Bull. 21:247–249.

Yamasaki, N. 1959. Differentielle Färbung der Chromosomen der ersten meiotischen Metaphase von *Cypripedium debile*. Chromosoma 10:454–460.

Yeh, J. C. C. 1962. A cytological study of selected *Cymbidium pumilum* hybrids. Am. Orchid Soc. Bull. 31:904–915.

Yuasa, A. 1936. Nagoran no Sensyokutaisu (Chromosomenzahl von *Aerides japonicum*). Bot. and Zool., Tokyo 4:953.

Zhukova, P. G. 1967. Karyology of some plants, cultivated in the Arctic-Alpine Botanical Garden (in Russian), pp. 139–149. *In* N. A. Avrorin (ed.), Plantarum in Zonam Polarem Transportatio, Vol. 2. Leningrad.

Zhukova, P. G., and A. D. Tikkonova. 1971. Chromosome numbers of certain plant species indigenous to the Chukotsky province (in Russian). Bot. Zurn. 56:868–875.

Zuck, T. T. 1957. Pentaploid *Cattleya* hybrids and their successful breeding. Am. Orchid Soc. Bull. 26:477–479; 503–504.

INDEX OF PERSONS

Where only one name is given in the text or in footnotes or literature cited, initials or last names have been added by the indexer and editor for identification. Initials were not added for individuals usually referred to in the botanical, historical, or other literature by their last names only (i.e., Fuchs, Kircher, Linnaeus, Theophrastus, Confucius, etc.), or when none could be found.

INDEX OF PLANT NAMES

This index includes common, scientific, and regional names as well as other taxonomic designations. Scientific names (*Cattleya labiata*, for example) are italicized. All others appear in Roman type. Taxonomic groupings above the generic level are in capital letters. Boldface numerals denote illustrations. The names in the list of species and synonyms of *Cymbidium* and the names listed in the Appendix are not included here because they are already arranged alphabetically.

SUBJECT INDEX

Boldface numerals indicate plates, figures, and chemical formulas shown in graphic form.